L

SBVMWD

Louis Fletcher
SBVMWD

FLUID MECHANICS

WITH ENGINEERING APPLICATIONS

FLUID MECHANICS

WITH ENGINEERING APPLICATIONS

ROBERT L. DAUGHERTY, A.B., M.E.

Professor Emeritus of Mechanical and Hydraulic Engineering
California Institute of Technology

JOSEPH B. FRANZINI, Ph.D.

Professor of Civil Engineering
Stanford University

SIXTH EDITION
A revision of the fifth edition
by R. L. Daugherty and A. C. Ingersoll

McGRAW-HILL BOOK COMPANY
New York, St. Louis, San Francisco, Toronto, London, Sydney

FLUID MECHANICS

PREFACE

This sixth edition of "Fluid Mechanics: With Engineering Applications" has been written to serve as a textbook for a first course in fluid mechanics for engineering students. In most curricula this course comes in the junior year and the student will already have had courses in differential and integral calculus and engineering mechanics. He may also have had a course in differential equations. The coverage in this book is broad, so that it can also be used for a second course in fluid mechanics if desired.

In accordance with current educational trends, the basic principles of fluid mechanics have been developed in a more rigorous fashion than in the previous editions. However, the authors have always felt it most important that the engineering student clearly visualize the physical situation under consideration. Hence there is considerable emphasis on physical phenomena throughout.

The book is essentially "self-contained." The treatment is such that an instructor generally need not resort to another reference to answer any question that a student might normally be expected to ask. This has required more detailed discussion than would have been necessary if the presentation of certain topics had been more superficial. A list of selected references is provided at the end of the book to serve as a guide for those students who wish to probe deeper into the various fields of fluid mechanics. The Appendix contains information on dimensions and units, conversion factors, physical properties of fluids, and other useful tables.

For a brief course it is possible to omit certain chapters of the book without loss of continuity. For example, an excellent first course in fluid mechanics can be achieved by covering Chapters 1 to 10; however, Chapter 10 and the last half of Chapter 8 could be omitted if desired. One might wish to include Chapter 13 in a first course. If so, Chapters 10 to 12 could be omitted without harm. The book can be used in a variety of ways. Schools having stringent requirements in fluid mechanics might wish to cover the entire text in their course or courses required of all engineers. At other schools only partial coverage of the text might suffice for the course required of all engineers, and other portions of the text might be covered in a second course for students in a particular branch of engineering.

Illustrative examples are given to indicate to the student how the basic principles of fluid mechanics can be applied to particular engineering problems. These examples also serve to clarify the text. Numerous problems are presented for assignment purposes. The authors feel that the subject matter is best learned by placing heavy emphasis on the development of basic principles, the assumptions made in the develop ment of these principles, and their limits of applicability. Only through working numerous problems will the student experience the evolution so necessary to the learning process.

The coauthor of this edition, Professor Franzini, received his first exposure to the subject of fluid mechanics some twenty-four years ago as an undergraduate student, from the fourth edition of this book. Even at that time, the book "Hydraulics: A Text on Practical Fluid Mechanics" by Daugherty was a leader in its field. This same fourth edition was the textbook used by Professor Franzini in his first teaching experience. In 1954 the fifth edition of the book was published and the title was changed to "Fluid Mechanics with Engineering Applications." The coauthors of the fifth edition were Professors Robert L. Daugherty and Alfred C. Ingersoll. When time for revision of the fifth edition arrived, Professor Ingersoll was unavailable because of his very time-consuming administrative duties as Dean of Engineering at the University of Southern California. Hence Professor Franzini was called in to work on the sixth edition of the book.

The authors wish to acknowledge the valuable contributions that were made by Professor Ingersoll in the fifth edition. The suggestions and criticisms from the numerous users of the book throughout the years and from the various reviewers of the manuscript are hereby gratefully acknowledged. Professor Kenneth J. Schneider of California State Polytechnic College (Kellogg-Voorhis Campus) carefully reviewed this edition of the text. His comments and suggestions are greatly appreciated.

Robert L. Daugherty

Joseph B. Franzini

CONTENTS

NOTATION

The following table lists the letter symbols generally used throughout the text. Because there are so many more concepts than there are English and suitable Greek letters, certain conflicts are unavoidable. However, where the same letter has been used for different concepts, the topics are so far removed from each other that no confusion should result. Occasionally a particular letter will be used in one special case only, but this local deviation from the table will be clearly indicated, and the usage will not be employed elsewhere.

The equations given in the text may, for the most part, be used with any consistent system of units. There are exceptions where an equation contains a numerical factor that is not an abstract number, in which case certain specific units must be employed, but these will then be indicated.

In this book the engineers' foot-pound(force)-second (ft-lb-sec) system of units is employed, except where special convenience or general custom renders an exception desirable. For the convenience of the reader, therefore, most of the concepts which have dimensions are given in these units. However, an application of the most elementary principles of dimensional analysis will enable one to determine what units are allowable in any equation. A more comprehensive discussion of the basic systems of engineering units is presented in Appendix 1.

With respect to symbols, the authors have for the most part attempted to adhere to generally accepted ones, but not always.

A = any area, ft^2
= cross-sectional area of a stream normal to the velocity
= area in turbines or pumps normal to the direction of absolute velocity of the fluid
A_s = area of a liquid surface, as for a reservoir
a = area in turbines or pumps normal to the relative velocity of the fluid, ft^2
= linear acceleration, fps/sec
B = any width, ft
= length of weir crest, ft
= width of turbine runner or pump impeller at periphery
= bed width of open channel, ft
C = any coefficient

$\quad\quad = $ Chézy's coefficient

$C_c = $ coefficient of contraction $\left.\vphantom{\begin{matrix}a\\b\\c\end{matrix}}\right\}$ for orifices, tubes, and nozzles

$C_d = $ coefficient of discharge

$C_v = $ coefficient of velocity

$C_D = $ drag coefficient

$C_f = $ average skin coefficient for total surface

$C_L = $ lift coefficient

$\quad c = $ wave or acoustic velocity (celerity), fps

$\quad\quad = $ specific heat, Btu/(lb)(°F)

$c_f = $ local skin-friction coefficient

$D = $ diameter of pipe, turbine runner, or pump impeller, ft

$E = $ enthalpy $= I + pv/J$, Btu/lb[1]

$\quad\quad = $ specific energy in open channels $= y + V^2/2g$

$\quad\quad = $ linear modulus of elasticity, psi

$E_v = $ volume modulus of elasticity, psi

$\quad e = $ efficiency ($= e_h \times e_m \times e_v$) for turbine or pump

$e_h = $ hydraulic efficiency

$e_m = $ mechanical efficiency

$e_v = $ volumetric efficiency

$F = $ any force, lb

$\quad f = $ friction factor for pipe flow

$G = $ weight rate of discharge, lb/sec $= \gamma Q$

$\quad g = $ acceleration of gravity $= 32.174$ fps/sec (standard)

$\quad\quad = 32.2$ fps/sec for usual slide-rule computation

$H = $ total head $= p/\gamma + z + V^2/2g$

$\quad h = $ any head, ft

$h_a = $ atmospheric pressure in equivalent height of fluid

$h_L = $ head lost in friction

$\quad I = $ plane moment of inertia, ft^4

$\quad\quad = $ internal thermal energy, Btu/lb

$\quad J = 778$ ft-lb in 1 Btu

$K = $ any constant

$\quad\quad = $ equivalent volume modulus for fluid in elastic pipe

$\quad k = $ any coefficient of loss

$\quad\quad = c_p/c_v$ for gases

$L = $ length, ft

$\quad l = $ Prandtl mixing length

$M = $ constant for venturi or orifice meter

$MR = $ manometer reading

$m = $ mass, slugs $= W/g$

$\quad\quad = $ molecular weight

$N_F = $ Froude number $= V/\sqrt{gL}$

$N_M = $ Mach number $= V/c$

$N_R = $ Reynolds number $= LV\rho/\mu = LV/\nu$

$N_W = $ Weber number $= V/\sqrt{\sigma/\rho L}$

$\quad n = $ an exponent or any number in general

$\quad\quad = $ Kutter or Manning coefficient of roughness

$\quad\quad = $ revolutions per minute

[1] In thermodynamics texts this is usually written $h = u + pv/J$.

n_s = specific speed = $n\sqrt{\mathrm{bhp}}/h^{5/4}$ for turbines
$\qquad$ = $n\sqrt{Q}/h^{3/4}$ for pumps and fans
N_s = $n\sqrt{\mathrm{gpm}}/h^{3/4}$ for pumps
P = power, ft-lb/sec
$\qquad$ = height of weir crest above channel bottom
$\qquad$ = wetted perimeter, ft
p = fluid pressure, psf or psi
p_a = atmospheric pressure
p_v = vapor pressure
Q = volume rate of flow, cfs
q = volume rate of flow per unit width of rectangular channel, cfs/ft
$\qquad$ = heat flow, Btu/lb of fluid
R = hydraulic radius, ft = A/P
$\qquad$ = gas constant
r = any radius
r_0 = radius of pipe
S = slope of energy grade line = h_L/L
S_0 = slope of channel bed
S_w = slope of stream surface
s = specific gravity of a fluid = ratio of its density to that of some standard fluid
T = absolute temperature (in Fahrenheit scale = °F + 460°)
$\qquad$ = period of time for travel of a pressure wave, sec
$\qquad$ = torque, ft-lb
t = time, sec
$\qquad$ = thickness
U, U_0 = uniform velocity of fluid, fps
u = velocity of a solid, fps
$\qquad$ = linear velocity of a point on a rotating body = $r\omega$
$\qquad$ = local velocity of fluid
u' = turbulent velocity fluctuation in the direction of flow
V = mean velocity of fluid, fps
$\qquad$ = absolute velocity of fluid in hydraulic machines
V_r = radial component of velocity = $V\sin\alpha = v\sin\beta$
V_u = tangential component of velocity = $V\cos\alpha = u + v\cos\beta$
V_L = total volume, ft³
v = relative velocity in hydraulic machines
$\qquad$ = specific volume, ft³/lb = $1/\gamma$
v' = turbulent velocity fluctuation normal to the direction of flow
u, v, w = components of velocity in general x, y, z directions
W = total weight, lb
$\qquad$ = work, ft-lb
x = a distance, usually parallel to flow
Y = expansion factor for compressible flow
y = a distance along a plane in hydrostatics, ft
$\qquad$ = total depth of open stream, ft
y_c = critical depth of open stream
y_0 = depth for uniform flow in open stream
z = elevation above any arbitrary datum plane, ft
α (alpha) = angle between V and u in rotating machinery, measured between their positive directions

$\quad\quad\quad\quad$ = kinetic energy correction factor

β (beta) = angle between v and u in rotating machinery, measured between $+v$
$\quad\quad\quad\quad$ and $+u$

$\quad\quad\quad\quad$ = momentum correction factor

Γ (gamma) = circulation, ft³/sec

γ (gamma) = specific weight, pcf = $1/v$

δ (delta) = thickness of boundary layer

$\quad\quad\quad\quad$ = thickness of laminar sublayer in turbulent flow

ϵ (epsilon) = height of surface roughness

η (eta) = mechanical or eddy viscosity

θ (theta) = any angle

μ (mu) = absolute or dynamic viscosity, lb-sec/ft²

ν (nu) = kinematic viscosity, ft²/sec = μ/ρ

ρ (rho) = density, mass per unit volume = γ/g

σ (sigma) = surface tension, lb/ft

$\quad\quad\quad\quad$ = cavitation factor in machines

τ (tau) = shear stress, psf

ϕ (phi) = ratio $u_1/\sqrt{2gh}$ for turbines and $u_2/\sqrt{2gh}$ for centrifugal pumps

$\quad\phi_e$ = value of ϕ at point of maximum efficiency

$\quad\phi$ = velocity potential

ψ (psi) = stream function

ω (omega) = angular velocity, rad/sec

$\quad\quad\quad\quad$ = $u/r = 2\pi n/60$

Values at specific points will be indicated by suitable subscripts. In the use of subscripts 1 and 2, the fluid is always assumed to flow from 1 to 2.

ABBREVIATIONS

atm = atmosphere
avg = average
bhp = brake horsepower
cfm = cubic feet per minute
cfs = cubic feet per second
fpm = feet per minute
fps = feet per second
gpm = gallons per minute
ln = $\log_e$
pcf = pounds per cubic foot
psf = pounds per square foot
psfa = pounds per square foot absolute
psi = pounds per square inch
psia = pounds per square inch absolute
psig = pounds per square inch gage
rpm = revolutions per minute
rps = revolutions per second
whp = water horsepower

ONE

PROPERTIES OF FLUIDS

Fluid mechanics is the science of the mechanics of liquids and gases and is based on the same fundamental principles that are employed in the mechanics of solids. Fluid mechanics is a more difficult subject, however, because with solids one deals with separate and tangible elements, while with fluids there are no separate elements to be distinguished.

1.1. DEVELOPMENT OF FLUID MECHANICS

Fluid mechanics may be divided into three branches: *fluid statics* is the study of the mechanics of fluids at rest; *kinematics* deals with velocities and streamlines without considering forces or energy; and *hydrodynamics* is concerned with the relations between velocities and accelerations and the forces exerted by or upon fluids in motion.

Classical hydrodynamics is largely a subject in mathematics, since it deals with an imaginary ideal fluid that is completely frictionless. The results of such studies, without consideration of all the properties of real fluids, are of limited practical value. Consequently, in the past, engineers turned to experiments, and from these developed empirical formulas which supplied answers to practical problems. This subject was called *hydraulics.*

Empirical hydraulics was confined largely to water and was limited in scope. With developments in aeronautics, chemical engineering, and the petroleum industry, the need arose for a broader treatment. This has led to the combining of classical hydrodynamics with the study of real fluids, and this new science is called *fluid mechanics.* In modern fluid mechanics the basic principles of hydrodynamics are combined with the experimental techniques of hydraulics. The experimental data can be used to verify theory or to provide information supplementary to mathematical analysis. The end product is a unified body of basic principles of fluid mechanics that can be applied to the solution of fluid-flow problems of engineering significance.

1.2. DISTINCTION BETWEEN A SOLID AND A FLUID

The molecules of a solid are closer together than those of a fluid. The attractive forces between the molecules of a solid are so large that a solid tends to retain its shape. This is not the case for a fluid, where the attractive forces between the molecules are smaller. There are plastic solids which flow under the proper circumstances, and even metals may flow under high pressures. On the other hand, there are certain very viscous liquids which do not flow readily, and it is easy to confuse them with the plastic solids. The distinction is that any fluid, no matter how viscous, will yield in time to the slightest stress. But a solid, no matter how plastic, requires a certain magnitude of stress to be exerted before it will flow.

Also, when the shape of a solid is altered by external forces, the tangential stresses between adjacent particles tend to restore the body to its original figure. With a fluid, these tangential stresses are proportional to the velocity of deformation and vanish as the velocity approaches zero. When motion ceases, the tangential stresses disappear and the fluid does not tend to regain its original shape.

1.3. DISTINCTION BETWEEN A GAS AND A LIQUID

A fluid may be either a gas or a liquid. The molecules of a gas are much farther apart than those of a liquid. Hence a gas is very compressible, and when all external pressure is removed, it tends to expand indefinitely. A gas is therefore in equilibrium only when it is completely enclosed. A liquid is relatively incompressible, and if all pressure, except that of its own vapor pressure, is removed, the cohesion between molecules holds them together, so that the liquid does not expand indefinitely. Therefore a liquid may have a free surface, i.e., a surface from which all pressure is removed, except that of its own vapor.

A *vapor* is a gas whose temperature and pressure are such that it is very near the liquid phase. Thus steam is considered a vapor because its state is normally not far from that of water. A gas may be defined as a highly superheated vapor; that is, its state is far removed from the liquid phase. Thus air is considered a gas because its state is normally very far from that of liquid air.

The volume of a gas or a vapor is greatly affected by changes in pressure or temperature or both. It is usually necessary, therefore, to take account of changes in volume and temperature in dealing with gases or vapors. Whenever significant temperature or phase changes are involved in dealing with vapors and gases, the subject is largely dependent on heat phenomena (*thermodynamics*). Thus fluid mechanics and thermodynamics are interrelated.

1.4. DENSITY, SPECIFIC WEIGHT, SPECIFIC VOLUME, AND SPECIFIC GRAVITY

The *density* of a fluid is its *mass* per unit volume, while the *specific weight* is its *weight* per unit volume. In the English engineers', or gravitational, system density ρ will be in slugs per cubic foot, which may also be expressed as units of lb-sec^2/ft^4 (Appendix 1).

Specific weight γ represents the force exerted by gravity on a unit volume of fluid and therefore must have the units of force per unit volume, such as pounds per cubic foot.

Density and specific weight of a fluid are related as follows:

$$\rho = \frac{\gamma}{g} \qquad \text{or} \qquad \gamma = \rho g \qquad (1.1)$$

Since the physical equations are dimensionally homogeneous, the dimensions of density are

$$\text{Dimensions of } \rho = \frac{\text{dimensions of } \gamma}{\text{dimensions of } g} = \frac{\text{pcf}}{\text{ft/sec}^2} = \frac{\text{lb-sec}^2}{\text{ft}^4}$$

Specific volume v is the volume occupied by a unit weight of fluid. It is commonly applied to gases and is usually expressed in cubic feet per pound.   Specific volume is the reciprocal of specific weight.   Thus

$$v = \frac{1}{\gamma} \tag{1.2}$$

Specific gravity s of a liquid is the ratio of its density to that of pure water at a standard temperature.   Physicists use 39.2°F (4°C) as the standard, but engineers ordinarily use 60°F.   In the metric system the density of water at 4°C is 1.00 g/cm³, and hence the specific gravity (which is dimensionless) has the same numerical value for a liquid as its density in that system.

The specific gravity of a gas is the ratio of its density to that of either hydrogen or air at some specified temperature and pressure, but there is no general agreement on these standards, and so they must be stated in any given case.

Since the density of a fluid varies with temperature, specific gravities must be determined and specified at particular temperatures.

Illustrative example 1.1:   The specific weight of water at ordinary pressure and temperature is 62.4 pcf.   The specific gravity of mercury is 13.55.   Compute the density of water and the specific weight and density of mercury.

$$\rho_{water} = \frac{\gamma_{water}}{g} = \frac{62.4}{32.2} = 1.94 \text{ slugs/ft}^3$$

$$\gamma_{mercury} = s_{mercury}\gamma_{water} = 13.55(62.4) = 846 \text{ pcf}$$

$$\rho_{mercury} = s_{mercury}\rho_{water} = 13.55(1.94) = 26.3 \text{ slugs/ft}^3$$

1.5. COMPRESSIBLE AND INCOMPRESSIBLE FLUIDS

Fluid mechanics deals with both incompressible and compressible fluids, that is, with fluids of either constant or variable density.   Although there is no such thing in reality as an incompressible fluid, this term is applied where the change in density with pressure is so small as to be negligible. This is usually the case with all liquids.   Gases, too, may be considered incompressible when the pressure variation is small compared with the absolute pressure.

Liquids are ordinarily considered incompressible fluids, yet sound waves, which are really pressure waves, travel through them.   This is evidence of the elasticity of liquids.   In problems involving *water hammer*, it is necessary to consider the compressibility of the liquid.

The flow of air in a ventilating system is a case where a gas may be treated as incompressible, for the pressure variation is so small that the change in density is of no importance.   But for a gas or steam flowing at high velocity through a long pipeline, the drop in pressure may be so great that change of density cannot be ignored. For an airplane flying at speeds below 250 mph, the air may be considered to be of constant density. But as an object moving through the air approaches the velocity of sound, which is of the order of 700 mph, the pressure and density of the air adjacent to the body become materially different from those of the air at some distance away, and the air must then be treated as a compressible fluid (Chap. 9).

1.6. COMPRESSIBILITY OF LIQUIDS

The compressibility of a liquid is inversely proportional to its volume modulus of elasticity, also known as the *bulk modulus*. This modulus is defined as $E_v = -v\, dp/dv = -(v/dv)\, dp$, where v = specific volume and p = unit pressure. As v/dv is a dimensionless ratio, the units of E_v and p are the same. The bulk modulus is analogous to the modulus of elasticity for solids; however, for fluids it is defined on a volume basis rather than in terms of the familiar one-dimensional stress-strain relation for solid bodies.

In most engineering problems the bulk modulus at or near atmospheric pressure is the one of interest. The bulk modulus is a property of the fluid and is a function of temperature and pressure. In Table 1.1 are shown a few values of the bulk modulus for water. At any temperature it can be noted that the value of E_v increases continuously with pressure, but at any one pressure the value of E_v is a maximum at about 120°F. Thus water has a minimum compressibility at about 120°F.

The volume modulus of mild steel is about 25,000,000 psi. Taking a typical value for the volume modulus of cold water to be 300,000 psi, it is seen that water is about 80 times as compressible as steel. The com-

Table 1.1   Bulk modulus of water, psi*

Pressure, psi	Temperature, °F				
	32°	68°	120°	200°	300°
15	292,000	320,000	332,000	308,000	
1,500	300,000	330,000	342,000	319,000	248,000
4,500	317,000	348,000	362,000	338,000	271,000
15,000	380,000	410,000	426,000	405,000	350,000

* R. L. Daugherty, Some Physical Properties of Water and Other Fluids, *Trans. ASME*, vol. 57, no. 5, July, 1935.

pressibility of liquids covers a wide range.   Mercury,[1] for example, is approximately 8 per cent as compressible as water, while the compressibility of nitric acid is nearly six times greater than that of water.

Table 1.1 shows that at any one temperature the bulk modulus does not vary a great deal for a moderate range in pressure, and thus as an approximation one may use

$$\frac{v_1 - v_2}{v_1} = \frac{p_2 - p_1}{E_{vm}}$$

or

$$\frac{\Delta v}{v_1} = -\frac{\Delta p}{E_{vm}} \tag{1.3}$$

where E_{vm} is the mean value of the modulus for the pressure range.

Assuming E_v to have a value of $300,000 \times 144$ psf, it may be seen that increasing the pressure of water by 1,000 psi will compress it only $\frac{1}{300}$, or 0.3 per cent, of its original volume.   Therefore it is seen that the usual assumption regarding water as incompressible is justified.

1.7. EQUATIONS OF STATE FOR GASES

There is no such thing as a perfect gas, but air and other real gases that are far removed from the liquid phase may be so considered.   For a perfect gas the equation of state per unit weight is

$$pv = RT \tag{1.4}$$

where p = absolute pressure
v = specific volume
R = a gas constant, the value of which depends upon the particular gas
T = absolute temperature[2]

For air the value of R is 53.3 ft/°F in our system of units.   Since $v = 1/\gamma$, Eq. (1.4) may also be written

$$\gamma = \frac{p}{RT} \tag{1.5}$$

from which the specific weight of any gas at any temperature can be computed if R is known.

Avogadro's law states that all gases at the same temperature and

---

[1] "Handbook of Chemistry and Physics," Chemical Rubber Publishing Company, Cleveland, Ohio.

[2] Absolute temperature is measured above absolute zero.   It may be recalled that absolute zero on the centigrade scale occurs at $-273°C$.   On the Fahrenheit scale absolute zero is approximately $-460°F$.

pressure have the same number of molecules per unit of volume, from which it follows that the specific weight of a gas is proportional to its molecular weight. Thus, if m denotes molecular weight, $\gamma_2/\gamma_1 = m_2/m_1$ and from Eq. (1.5) $\gamma_2/\gamma_1 = R_1/R_2$ for the same temperature and pressure. Hence

$$m_1 R_1 = m_2 R_2 = \text{constant}$$

But this is strictly true for perfect gases only. The exact equation for any real gas is more complicated than Eq. (1.4), and hence mR is not strictly constant. For the perfect gas $mR = 1{,}544$, while for actual gases the values of mR range between 1,512 and 1,546, which is a variation of less than 3 per cent.

Values of mR and R may be found in texts on thermodynamics and in handbooks, but a value of R may always be estimated by dividing an assumed value of mR by molecular weight. Thus water vapor in the air, because of its low partial pressure, may be treated as a perfect gas with $R = 1{,}540/18 = 85.6$ ft/°F. For steam at higher pressures this value is not applicable.

As the pressure is increased and the temperature simultaneously lowered, a gas becomes a vapor, and as gases depart more and more from the gas phase and approach the liquid phase, the equation of state becomes much more complicated than Eq. (1.4) and specific weight and other properties must then be obtained from vapor tables or charts. Such tables and charts exist for steam, ammonia, sulfur dioxide, freon, and other vapors in common engineering use.

Another fundamental equation for a perfect gas is

$$pv^n = p_1 v_1^{\,n} = p_2 v_2^{\,n} = \text{constant} \tag{1.6}$$

where p is absolute pressure, $v \ (= 1/\gamma)$ is specific volume, and n may have any value from zero to infinity, depending upon the process to which the gas is subjected. If the process is at constant temperature (*isothermal*), $n = 1$. If there is no heat transfer to or from the gas, the process is known as *adiabatic*, it is accompanied by a decided change in temperature, and the value of n is then denoted by k, where $k = c_p/c_v$, that is, the ratio of the specific heat at constant pressure to that at constant volume. Values for k may be found in Appendix 3, Table A.4, and in thermodynamics texts and in handbooks. For air and diatomic gases at usual temperatures, k may be taken as 1.4.

By combining Eqs. (1.4) and (1.6) it is possible to obtain other useful relations such as

$$\frac{T_2}{T_1} = \left(\frac{v_1}{v_2}\right)^{n-1} = \left(\frac{p_2}{p_1}\right)^{(n-1)/n} \tag{1.7}$$

1.8. COMPRESSIBILITY OF GASES

Differentiating Eq. (1.6) gives $npv^{n-1} dv + v^n dp = 0$. Inserting this value of dp in $E_v = -(v/dv) dp$ from Sec. 1.6 yields

$$E_v = np$$

so that for an isothermal process of a gas $E_v = p$ and for an adiabatic process $E_v = kp$.

Thus, at a pressure of 15 psia, the isothermal modulus of elasticity for a gas is 144×15 psf, and for air in an adiabatic process it is $1.4 \times 144 \times 15$ psf. Assuming from Table 1.1 a typical value of the modulus of elasticity of cold water to be $144 \times 300{,}000$ psf, it is seen that air at 15 psia is $300{,}000/15 = 20{,}000$ times as compressible as cold water isothermally, or $14{,}140$ times as compressible adiabatically. This emphasizes the great difference between the compressibility of normal atmospheric air and that of water.

Illustrative example 1.2   One cubic foot of oxygen at 100°F and 15 psia is compressed adiabatically to 0.4 ft³. What, then, are the temperature and pressure of the gas? If the process had been isothermal, what would the temperature and pressure have been?

$$R \approx 1{,}540/32 = 48.1 \text{ ft/°F}$$

$$pv = RT \qquad (15 \times 144)v_1 = 48.1(460 + 100)$$

$$v_1 = 12.5 \text{ ft}^3/\text{lb} \qquad \gamma_1 = \frac{1}{v_1} = 0.08 \text{ pcf}$$

$$pv^k = (15 \times 144)(12.5)^{1.4} = (p_2 \times 144)\left(\frac{12.5}{1/0.4}\right)^{1.4}$$

$$p_2 = 54.0 \text{ psia}$$

$$(54 \times 144)\frac{12.5}{1/0.4} = 48.1(460 + T_2) \qquad T_2 = 350\text{°F}$$

If isothermal, that is, $T_2 = 100$°F,

$$pv = \text{constant} \qquad p_2 = \frac{15}{0.4} = 37.5 \text{ psia}$$

1.9. IDEAL FLUID

An *ideal* fluid may be defined as one in which there is *no friction;* that is, its viscosity is zero. Thus the internal forces at any internal section are always normal to the section, even during motion. Hence the forces are purely pressure forces. Such a fluid does not exist in reality.

In a *real* fluid, either liquid or gas, tangential or shearing forces always come into being whenever motion takes place, thus giving rise to fluid friction, because these forces oppose the movement of one particle

past another.   These friction forces are due to a property of the fluid
called *viscosity*.

1.10. VISCOSITY

The viscosity of a fluid is a measure of its resistance to shear or angular
deformation.   The friction forces in fluid flow result from the cohesion
and momentum interchange between molecules in the fluid.   The viscosities of typical fluids are shown in Figs. 1.1 and 1.2.   As the temperature
increases, the viscosities of all liquids decrease, while the viscosities of all
gases increase.   This is because the force of cohesion, which diminishes
with temperature, predominates with liquids, while with gases the predominating factor is the interchange of molecules between the layers of
different velocities.   Thus a rapidly moving molecule shifting into a
slower-moving layer tends to speed up the latter.   And a slow-moving
molecule entering a faster-moving layer tends to slow it down.   This
molecular interchange sets up a shear, or produces a friction force between
adjacent layers.   Increased molecular activity at higher temperatures
causes the viscosity of gases to increase with temperature.

Consider two parallel plates (Fig. 1.3), sufficiently large so that edge
conditions may be neglected, placed a small distance Y apart, the space
between being filled with the fluid.   The lower surface is assumed to be
stationary, while the upper one is moved parallel to it with a velocity U
by the application of a force F corresponding to some area A of the moving
plate.   Such a condition is approximated, for instance, in the clearance
space of a flooded journal bearing (any radial load being neglected).

Particles of the fluid in contact with each plate will adhere to it, and
if the distance Y is not too great or the velocity U too high, the velocity
gradient will be a straight line.   The action is much as if the fluid were
made up of a series of thin sheets, each of which would slip a little relative
to the next.   Experiment has shown that for a large class of fluids

$$F \sim \frac{AU}{Y}$$

It may be seen from similar triangles in Fig. 1.3 that U/Y can be replaced
by the velocity gradient du/dy.   If a constant of proportionality μ is now
introduced, the shearing stress τ between any two thin sheets of fluid may
be expressed by

$$\tau = \frac{F}{A} = \mu \frac{U}{Y} = \mu \frac{du}{dy} \tag{1.8}$$

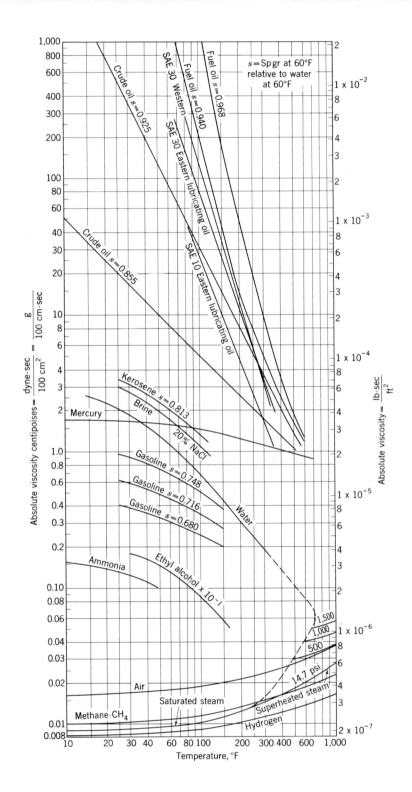

Fig. 1.1. Absolute viscosity of fluids.

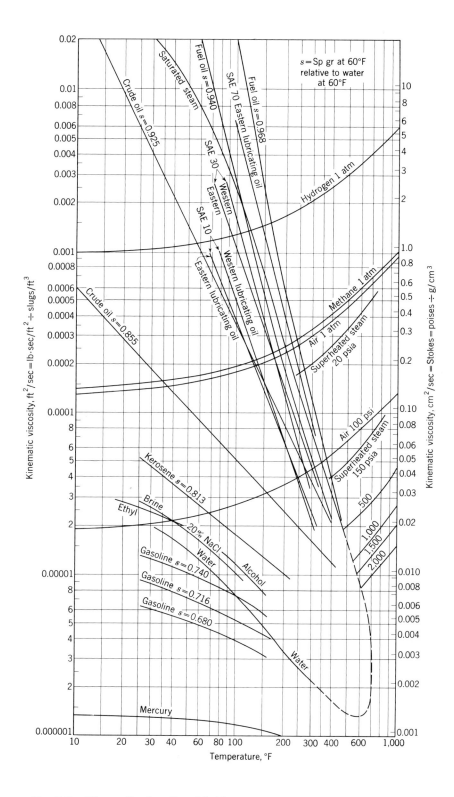

Fig. 1.2. Kinematic viscosity of fluids.

11

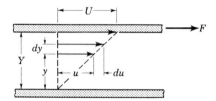

Fig. 1.3

Equation (1.8) is called *Newton's equation of viscosity*, and in transposed form it serves to define the proportionality constant

$$\mu = \frac{\tau}{du/dy} \tag{1.9}$$

which is called the *coefficient of viscosity*, the *absolute viscosity*, the *dynamic viscosity* (since it involves force), or simply the *viscosity* of the fluid.

It has been explained in Sec. 1.2 that the distinction between a solid and a fluid lies in the manner in which each can resist shearing stresses. A further distinction among various kinds of fluids and solids will be clarified by reference to Fig. 1.4. In the case of a solid, shear stress is proportional to the *magnitude* of the deformation; but Eq. (1.8) shows that in a fluid the shear stress is proportional to the *time rate* of (angular) deformation.

A fluid for which the constant of proportionality (i.e., the viscosity) does not change with rate of deformation is said to be a *Newtonian fluid* and can be represented by a straight line in Fig. 1.4. The slope of this line is determined by the viscosity. The ideal fluid, with no viscosity, is represented by the horizontal axis, while the true elastic solid is represented by the vertical axis. A plastic which sustains a certain amount of stress before suffering a plastic flow can be shown by a straight line intersecting the vertical axis at the yield stress. Although there are certain

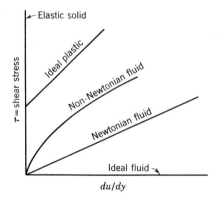

Fig. 1.4

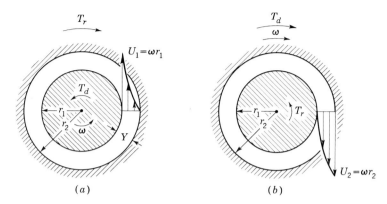

$$T_r \qquad\qquad T_d$$

Fig. 1.5. Velocity profile, rotating coaxial cylinders with gap completely filled with fluid. (a) Inner cylinder rotating. (b) Outer cylinder rotating.

Resisting torque = driving torque

$$\tau_1(2\pi r_1)Z(r_1) = \tau_2(2\pi r_2)Z(r_2)$$

$$\left(\frac{du}{dy}\right)_1 = \left(\frac{du}{dy}\right)_2 \left(\frac{r_2{}^2}{r_1{}^2}\right)$$

non-Newtonian fluids[1] in which μ varies with the rate of deformation, these are not generally of engineering importance, and the remainder of this text will be restricted to the common fluids which obey Newton's law.

In the case of two parallel plates (Fig. 1.3), if U is constant, the shear stress on both plates is the same if end conditions are neglected. And since $\tau \propto (du/dy)$, the velocity gradient is constant throughout the fluid. However, for coaxial cylinders (Fig. 1.5) with rotative speed ω constant, the shear stress on the inner cylinder will be larger than that on the outer because of the different radii, and thus the velocity gradient will not be constant across the gap. By equating the resisting torque T_r to the driving torque T_d, the relationship between du/dy at r_1 and r_2 can be determined. As gap distance $Y \to 0$, $du/dy \to U/Y$ = constant, so when the gap distance is very small, the velocity profile can be assumed to be a straight line.

The dimensions of absolute viscosity are force per unit area divided by velocity gradient. In the English gravitational, or engineers', system the dimensions of absolute viscosity are as follows:

$$\text{Dimensions of } \mu = \frac{\text{dimensions of } \tau}{\text{dimensions of } du/dy} = \frac{\text{psf}}{\text{fps/ft}} = \text{lb-sec/ft}^2$$

[1] Typical non-Newtonian fluids include paints, sludges, and certain plastics. An excellent treatment of the subject may be found in W. L. Wilkinson, "Non-Newtonian Fluids," Pergamon Press, New York, 1960.

In the metric system, absolute viscosity is expressed in force-length-time units (Appendix 1) as dyne-sec/cm², or equivalently, in mass-length-time units as g/cm-sec.   This unit is named the *poise*, after Poiseuille, who was one of the first investigators of viscosity.   The *centipoise* (= 0.01 poise) is frequently a more convenient unit.   It has a further advantage in that the viscosity of water at 68.4°F is 1 centipoise.   Thus the value of the viscosity in centipoises is an indication of the viscosity of the fluid relative to that of water at 68.4°F.

In many problems involving viscosity there frequently appears the value of viscosity divided by density.   This is defined as *kinematic viscosity* ν, so called because force is not involved, the only dimensions being length and time, as in kinematics.   Thus

$$\nu = \frac{\mu}{\rho} \tag{1.10}$$

In the English system, kinematic viscosity is usually measured in ft²/sec while in the metric system the common units are cm²/sec, also called the *stoke*, after G. G. Stokes.   The *centistoke* (0.01 stoke) is often a more convenient unit.

The absolute viscosity of all fluids is practically independent of pressure for the range that is ordinarily encountered in engineering work. For extremely high pressures the values are somewhat higher than those shown in Fig. 1.1.   The kinematic viscosity of gases varies with pressure because of changes in density.

1.11. SURFACE TENSION

Capillarity.   Liquids have cohesion and adhesion, both of which are forms of molecular attraction.   *Cohesion* enables a liquid to resist tensile stress, while *adhesion* enables it to adhere to another body.[1]   The attraction between molecules forms an imaginary film capable of resisting tension at the interface between two immiscible liquids or at the interface between a liquid and a gas.   The liquid property that creates this capability is known as *surface tension*.   The surface tension of liquids covers a wide range.   Typical values of the surface tension of water are presented in Table 1.3.   *Capillarity* is due to both cohesion and adhesion.   When

---

[1] In 1877 Osborne Reynolds demonstrated that a column of mercury ¼ in. in diameter could withstand a tensile stress of 3 atm for a time but that it would separate upon external jarring of the tube.   Liquid tension (said to be as high as 400 atm) accounts for the rise of water in the minute channels of xylem tissue in tall trees.   For practical engineering purposes, however, liquids are assumed to be incapable of resisting any direct tensile stress.

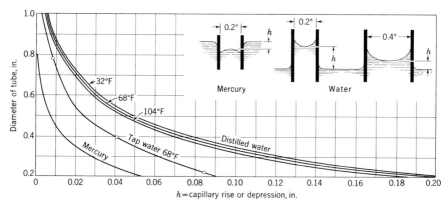

Fig. 1.6. Capillarity in circular glass tubes.

the former is of less effect than the latter, the liquid will wet a solid surface with which it is in contact and rise at the point of contact; if cohesion predominates, the liquid surface will be depressed at the point of contact. For example, capillarity makes water rise in a glass tube, while mercury is depressed below the true level, as is shown by the insert in Fig. 1.6, which is drawn to scale and reproduced actual size.

Capillary rise (or depression) in a tube is depicted in Fig. 1.7. From free-body considerations, assuming the meniscus is spherical and equating the lifting force created by surface tension to the gravity force,

$$2\pi r\sigma \cos\theta = \pi r^2 h\gamma$$

$$h = \frac{2\sigma \cos\theta}{\gamma r} \tag{1.11}$$

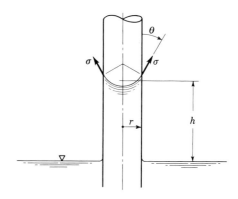

Fig. 1.7

where σ = surface tension in units of force per unit length
γ = specific weight of liquid
r = radius of tube
h = capillary rise

This expression can be used to compute the approximate capillary rise or depression in a tube. If the tube is clean, $\theta = 0°$ for water and about 140° for mercury. For tube diameters larger than ½ in., capillary effects are negligible. The curves[1] of Fig. 1.6 are for water or mercury in contact with air. If mercury is in contact with water, the surface-tension effect is slightly less than when in contact with air.

Surface tension decreases slightly with increasing temperature. Surface-tension effects are generally negligible in most engineering situations; however, they may be important in problems involving capillary rise, the formation of drops and bubbles, the breakup of liquid jets, and in hydraulic model studies where the model is small.

1.12. VAPOR PRESSURE OF LIQUIDS

All liquids tend to evaporate or vaporize, which they do by projecting molecules into the space above their surfaces. If this is a confined space, the partial pressure exerted by the molecules increases until the rate at which molecules reenter the liquid is equal to the rate at which they leave. For this equilibrium condition the vapor pressure is known as the *saturation pressure*.

Molecular activity increases with temperature, and hence saturation pressure increases with temperature. At any one temperature the pressure on the liquid surface may be higher than this value, but it cannot be any lower, as any slight reduction induces a rapid rate of evaporation

Table 1.2   Vapor pressure of selected liquids at 70°F

	psia
Mercury	0.000,025
Water	0.363
Kerosene	0.492
Methyl alcohol	1.965
Gasoline	4.42

[1] The curve for tap water in Fig. 1.6 was determined experimentally at the California Institute of Technology by R. G. Folsom. He found dirty water to give even slightly lower values. The curves for pure water and for mercury were computed by the author by methods suggested by N. K. Adam in "The Physics and Chemistry of Surfaces," based upon the analysis of Lord Rayleigh in his "Scientific Papers," vol. VI, p. 350.

Table 1.3   Saturation vapor pressure and surface tension of water

Temp, °F	Saturation pressure, psia	Surface tension, lb/ft	Temp, °F	Saturation pressure, psia	Surface tension, lb/ft
32	0.089	0.00518	100	0.949	0.00480
40	0.122	0.00514	120	1.692	0.00467
50	0.178	0.00509	140	2.887	0.00454
60	0.256	0.00504	160	4.739	0.00440
70	0.363	0.00498	180	7.510	0.00427
80	0.507	0.00492	200	11.525	0.00413
90	0.698	0.00486	212	14.696	0.00404

known as *boiling*. Thus the saturation pressure may be known as the *boiling pressure* for a given temperature.

The value of saturation vapor pressure is of practical interest in the case of liquids, for if the confining pressure on the liquid becomes less than this value, the liquid will vaporize.[1] The wide variation in vapor pressure of various liquids is shown in Table 1.2. The very low vapor pressure of mercury makes it particularly suitable for use in barometers. Some values for the vapor pressure of water are presented in Table 1.3.

1.13. SPECIFIC WEIGHT OF FLUIDS

As indicated in Secs. 1.7 and 1.8, the specific weight of a *gas* varies considerably with changes in temperature and pressure. The specific weight of a *liquid* varies only slightly with pressure, depending on the bulk modulus of the liquid (Sec. 1.6); it also depends on temperature, and the variation may be considerable. Since specific weight γ is equal to ρg, the specific weight of a *fluid* depends on the local value of the acceleration of gravity in addition to the variations with temperature and pressure. The variation of the specific weight of water with temperature under normal conditions, where $g = 32.2$ fps/sec, is shown in Fig. 1.8. The presence of dissolved air, salts in solution, and suspended matter will increase these values a very slight amount. Ocean water may ordinarily

---

[1] Values of the saturation pressure for water for temperatures from 32 to 705.4°F may be found in J. H. Keenan and F. G. Keyes, "Thermodynamic Properties of Steam," John Wiley & Sons, Inc., New York, 1936, and in other steam tables. There are similar vapor tables published for ammonia, carbon dioxide, sulfur dioxide, and other vapors of engineering interest.

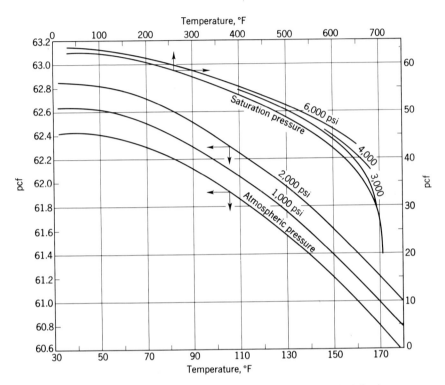

Fig. 1.8. Specific weight of pure water for condition where $g = 32.2$ fps/sec.

be assumed to weigh 64.0 pcf. Unless otherwise specified or implied by some specific temperature being given, the value to use for water in the problems in the text is $\gamma = 62.4$ pcf.

The specific weight of some common fluids at 68°F and standard sea level atmospheric pressure with $g = 32.2$ fps/sec is given in Table 1.4.

Table 1.4 Specific weights, pcf, of common fluids at 68°F, 14.7 psia, with $g = 32$ fps/sec

Gases		Liquids	
Air.....................	0.076	Carbon tetrachloride.......	99.4
Carbon dioxide.........	0.115	Ethyl alcohol.............	49.3
Hydrogen.............	0.0052	Gasolene.................	42
Methane.............	0.0415	Glycerin.................	78.7
Nitrogen.............	0.073	Motor oil................	54
Oxygen..............	0.083	Water...................	62.4

More detailed properties of water, air (including the standard atmosphere), and other fluids may be found in Appendix 3.

PROBLEMS

1.1. If a certain gasoline weighs 45 pcf, what are the values of its density, specific volume, and specific gravity relative to water at 60°F (Appendix 3)?

1.2. A certain gas weighs 0.10 pcf at a certain temperature and pressure. What are the values of its density, specific volume, and specific gravity relative to air weighing 0.075 pcf?

1.3. The specific weight of glycerin is 78.7 pcf. Compute its density and specific gravity.

1.4. Water in a hydraulic press is subjected to a pressure of 15,000 psi at 68°F. If the initial pressure is 15 psi, what will be the percentage decrease in specific volume (Table 1.1)?

1.5. At a depth of 5 miles in the ocean the pressure is 11,930 psi. Assume specific weight at the surface is 64 pcf and that the average volume modulus is 340,000 psi for that pressure range. (*a*) What will be the change in specific volume between that at the surface and at that depth? (*b*) What will be the specific volume at that depth? (*c*) What will be the specific weight at that depth?

1.6. (*a*) What is the percentage change in the specific volume in Prob. 1.5? (*b*) What is the percentage change in the specific weight in Prob. 1.5?

1.7. The legal definition of explosion is the term *violent expansion*, which in turn depends upon the sudden release of energy. Assuming an inexpandable container completely filled with water at 68°F, compute the energy stored per pound relative to atmospheric pressure if its pressure is 1,000 psig. (*Note:* The equation of state for water is very complicated, but at a constant temperature the relation between pressure and volume is approximately a straight line. This is not strictly true, since the volume modulus is not a constant, but the curvature of the line is small. Hence the energy is given approximately by the area of a triangle the sides of which are Δp and Δv. A result such as this is applicable only for cold water. If the temperature of the water were above 212°F, then upon its release to the air, the water would flash into steam with a volume 1,600 or more times that of the liquid.)

1.8. Approximately what pressure must be applied to water to reduce its volume 2 per cent?

1.9. A hydrogen-filled cellophane balloon, of the type used in cosmic-ray studies, is to be expanded to its full size, which is a 100-ft-diameter sphere, without stress in the wall at an altitude of 150,000 ft. If the pressure and temperature at this altitude are 0.14 psia and −67°F, respectively, find the volume of hydrogen at 14.7 psia and 68°F which should be added on the ground.

1.10. If natural gas has a specific gravity of 0.6 relative to air at 14.7 psia and 60°F, what are its specific weight and specific volume at that same pressure and temperature. What is the value of R for the gas?

1.11. If water vapor in the atmosphere has a partial pressure of 0.50 psia and the temperature is 90°F, what is its specific weight? [*Note:* By Dalton's law of partial pressures, the water vapor and the air both occupy the same space at the same temperature, but each exerts its own pressure as if the other were not present, and it is the partial pressure that is to be used in Eq. (1.4). The pressure read by a barometer is the sum of the partial pressures of the water vapor and of the air.]

1.12. If the barometer reads 14.5 psia in Prob. 1.11, what is the partial pressure of the air, and what is its specific weight? What is the specific weight of the atmosphere? (*Note:* Atmosphere here means the air plus the water vapor present.)

1.13. Calculate the specific weight and specific volume of air at 100°F and 70 psia.

1.14. Ten cubic feet of carbon dioxide at 80°F and 20 psia is compressed iso-thermally to 2 ft³. What is the resulting pressure? What would the pressure and temperature have been if the process had been adiabatic? The adiabatic exponent k for carbon dioxide is 1.28.

1.15. What is the ratio of the dynamic viscosity of water at a temperature of 70°F to that of water at 200°F? What is the ratio of the viscosity of the crude oil in Fig. 1.1 ($s = 0.925$) to that of the gasoline ($s = 0.680$), both being at a temperature of 60°F? In cooling from 300 to 80°F, what is the ratio of the change of the dynamic viscosity of the SAE 30 western oil to that of the SAE 30 eastern oil?

1.16. At 60°F what is the kinematic viscosity of the gasoline in Fig. 1.1 whose specific gravity is 0.680? Give answer in both metric and English units.

1.17. To what temperature must the fuel oil with the highest specific gravity in Fig. 1.1 be heated in order that its viscosity may be reduced to three times that of water at 40°F?

1.18. The absolute viscosity of a certain diatomic gas is 0.0206 centipoise, while its kinematic viscosity is 22 centistokes, both measured at 14.7 psia and 200°F. Calculate its approximate molecular weight, and suggest what gas it may be. (*Note: mR* for the perfect gas is theoretically 1,544. Actual gases have values which depart slightly from this, but monatomic and diatomic gases are very close to it.)

1.19. Compare the ratio of the absolute viscosities of air and water at 70°F with that of their kinematic viscosities under the same temperature and at 14.7 psia.

1.20. A hydraulic lift, of the type commonly used for greasing automobiles, consists of a 10.000-in.-diameter ram which slides in a 10.006-in.-diameter cylinder, the annular space being filled with oil having a kinematic viscosity of 0.004 ft²/sec and specific gravity of 0.85. If the rate of travel of the ram is 30 fpm, find the frictional resistance when 10 ft of the ram is engaged in the cylinder.

1.21. A journal bearing consists of a 6.00-in. shaft in a 6.01-in. sleeve 8 in. long, the clearance space (assumed to be uniform) being filled with SAE 30 eastern lubricating oil at 100°F. Calculate the rate at which heat is gener-ated at the bearing when the shaft turns at 100 rpm. Express answer in Btu per hour.

1.22. Repeat Prob. 1.21 for the case where the sleeve has a diameter of 6.48 in. Compute as accurately as possible the velocity gradient in the fluid at the shaft and sleeve.

1.23. A space of 1-in. width between two large plane surfaces is filled with SAE 30 western lubricating oil at 80°F. What force is required to drag a very thin plate of 4-ft² area between the surfaces at a speed of 20 fpm if this plate is equally spaced between the two surfaces? If it is at a distance of 0.33 in. from one surface?

1.24. In using a rotating-cylinder viscometer, a bottom correction must be applied to account for the drag on the flat bottom of the inner cylinder. Calculate the theoretical amount of this torque correction, neglecting centrifugal effects, for a cylinder of diameter d, rotated at a constant angular velocity ω, in a liquid of viscosity μ, with a clearance Δh between the bottom of the inner cylinder and the floor of the outer one.

1.25. Assuming a velocity distribution as shown in the diagram, which is a parabola having its vertex 4 in. from the boundary, calculate the velocity gradients for $y = 0, 1, 2, 3,$ and 4 in. Also calculate the shear stresses at these points if the fluid viscosity is 400 centipoises.

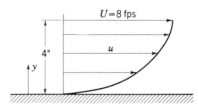

Fig. Prob. 1.25

1.26. In the figure, oil of viscosity μ fills the gap of thickness Y. Calculate the torque T required to rotate the truncated cone at constant speed ω. Neglect fluid stress exerted on the circular bottom.

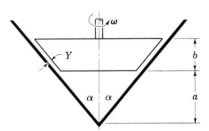

Fig. Prob. 1.26

1.27. Tap water at 68°F stands in a glass tube of 0.32-in. diameter at a height of 4.50 in. What is the true static height?

1.28. Use Eq. (1.11) to compute the capillary rise of water to be expected in a 0.20-in.-diameter tube. Assume pure water at 68°F. Compare result with Fig. 1.6.

1.29. Use Eq. (1.11) to compute the capillary depression of mercury to be expected in a 0.20-in.-diameter tube. At 68°F the surface tension of mercury is 0.0318 lb/ft. Compare result with Fig. 1.6.

1.30. The height of a mercury column at 68°F is observed in a glass tube of 0.30-in. diameter. If this reading is converted into an equivalent height of water, what is the error in inches (Sec. 2.3)? Will the error be plus or minus?

1.31. Derive an expression for capillary rise (or depression) between two vertical parallel plates.

1.32. At approximately what temperature will water boil in Mexico City (elevation 7,400 ft)? (See Appendix 3, Table A.2.)

1.33. Water at 100°F is placed in a beaker within an airtight container. Air is gradually pumped out of the container. What reduction below standard atmospheric pressure of 14.7 psia must be achieved before the water boils?

1.34. A vessel contains 3 ft³ of water at 50°F and atmospheric pressure. If it is heated to 160°F, what will be the percentage change in its volume? What weight of water must be removed to maintain the volume at the original value?

TWO

FLUID STATICS

There are no shear stresses in fluids at rest; hence only normal pressure forces are present. The *average pressure intensity* is defined as the force exerted on a unit area. If F represents the total force on some finite area A, while dF represents the force on an infinitesimal area dA, the pressure is

$$p = \frac{dF}{dA} \tag{2.1}$$

If the pressure is uniform over the total area, then $p = F/A$. In engineering units, pressure is generally expressed in pounds per square inch (psi) or pounds per square foot (psf).

2.1. PRESSURE THE SAME IN ALL DIRECTIONS

In a solid, because of the possibility of tangential stresses between adjacent particles, the stresses at a given point may be different

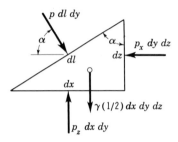

Fig. 2.1

in different directions.   But in a fluid at rest, no tangential stresses can exist, and the only forces between adjacent surfaces are pressure forces normal to the surfaces.   Therefore the pressure at any point in a fluid at rest is the same in every direction.

This can be proved by reference to Fig. 2.1, a small wedge-shaped element of fluid at rest whose thickness perpendicular to the plane of the paper is constant and equal to dy.   Let α be any angle, p the average pressure in any direction, and p_x and p_z the average pressures in the horizontal and vertical directions.   The forces acting on the element of fluid, with the exception of those in the y direction on the two faces parallel to the plane of the paper, are shown in the diagram.   For our purpose, forces in the y direction need not be considered.   Since the fluid is at rest, no tangential forces are involved.   As this is a condition of equilibrium, the sum of the force components on the element in any direction must be equal to zero.   Writing such an equation for the components in the x direction, $p\ dl\ dy\ \cos\alpha - p_x\ dy\ dz = 0$.   Since $dz = dl \cos\alpha$, it follows that $p = p_x$. Similarly, summing up forces in the z direction gives $p_z\ dx\ dy - p\ dl\ dy$ $\sin\alpha - \frac{1}{2}\gamma\ dx\ dy\ dz = 0$.   The third term is of higher order than the other two terms and may be neglected.   From this it follows that $p = p_z$. The results are independent of α; hence the pressure at any point in a fluid at rest is the same in all directions.

2.2. VARIATION OF PRESSURE IN A STATIC FLUID

Consider the differential element of fluid shown in Fig. 2.2.   Since the element is very small, we can assume that the density of the fluid within the element is constant.   Assume the pressure at O is p.   Then the pressures at various corners of the element are generally expressible as follows:

$$p_A = p + \frac{\partial p}{\partial x}\ dx$$

$$p_B = p + \frac{\partial p}{\partial x}\ dx + \frac{\partial p}{\partial y}\ dy$$

$$p_C = p + \frac{\partial p}{\partial y} dy$$

$$\cdots\cdots\cdots\cdots\cdots\cdots\cdots$$

$$p_G = p + \frac{\partial p}{\partial x} dx + \frac{\partial p}{\partial y} dy + \frac{\partial p}{\partial z} dz$$

Since the element is in equilibrium, the summation of the force components acting on the element in any direction must be zero. If forces are summed up in the horizontal direction, that is, x or y, the only forces acting are the pressure forces on the vertical faces of the element. To satisfy $\Sigma F_x = 0$ and $\Sigma F_y = 0$, the pressure on the opposite vertical faces must be equal. Thus $\partial p/\partial x = \partial p/\partial y = 0$ for the case of the fluid at rest.

Summing up forces acting in the vertical direction gives

$$p \, dx \, dy - \left(p + \frac{\partial p}{\partial z} dz\right) dx \, dy - \gamma \, dx \, dy \, dz = 0$$

This results in $\partial p/\partial z = -\gamma$, which, since p is independent of x and y, can be written as

$$\frac{dp}{dz} = -\gamma \qquad (2.2)$$

This is the general expression that relates variation of pressure in a static fluid to vertical position. The minus sign indicates that as z gets larger (increasing elevation), the pressure gets smaller.

To evaluate pressure variation in a fluid at rest one must integrate Eq. (2.2) between appropriately chosen limits. For incompressible fluids (γ = constant), Eq. (2.2) can be integrated directly. For compressible fluids, however, γ must be expressed algebraically as a function of z or p if one is to determine pressure accurately as a function of elevation. The variation of pressure in the earth's atmosphere is an important problem, and several approaches are illustrated in the following example.

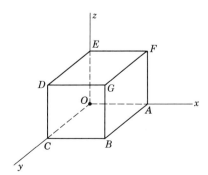

Fig. 2.2

Illustrative example 2.1: Compute the atmospheric pressure at elevation 10,000 ft, considering the atmosphere as a static fluid. Assume standard atmosphere at sea level. Use four methods: (*a*) air of constant density; (*b*) constant temperature between sea level and 10,000 ft; (*c*) adiabatic conditions; and (*d*) air temperature decreasing linearly with elevation at the rate of 0.00356°F/ft.

From Appendix 3, Table A.2, the conditions of the standard atmosphere at sea level are $T = 59°F$, $p = 14.7$ psia, $\gamma = 0.076$ pcf.

(*a*) Constant density:

$$\frac{dp}{dz} = -\gamma \qquad dp = -\gamma \, dz \qquad \int_{p_1}^{p} dp = -\gamma \int_{z_1}^{z} dz$$

$$p - p_1 = -\gamma(z - z_1)$$

$$p = 14.7 \times 144 - 0.076(10{,}000) = 1{,}360 \text{ psf} = 9.4 \text{ psi}$$

(*b*) Isothermal:

$$pv = \text{constant} = \frac{p}{\gamma} = \frac{p_1}{\gamma_1}$$

$$\frac{dp}{dz} = -\gamma \qquad \text{where} \qquad \gamma = \frac{p\gamma_1}{p_1}.$$

$$\frac{dp}{p} = -\frac{\gamma_1}{p_1} \, dz$$

$$\int_{p_1}^{p} \frac{dp}{p} = \ln \frac{p}{p_1} = -\frac{\gamma_1}{p_1} \int_{z_1}^{z} dz = -\frac{\gamma_1}{p_1}(z - z_1)$$

$$\frac{p}{p_1} = \exp\left[-\left(\frac{\gamma_1}{p_1}\right)(z - z_1)\right]$$

$$p = 14.7 \exp\left[-\frac{0.076}{14.7 \times 144}(10{,}000)\right] = 10.3 \text{ psi}$$

(*c*) Adiabatic:

$$pv^{1.4} = \frac{p}{\gamma^{1.4}} = \text{constant} = \frac{p_1}{\gamma_1^{1.4}}$$

$$\frac{dp}{dz} = -\gamma \qquad \text{where } \gamma = \gamma_1 \left(\frac{p}{p_1}\right)^{0.715}$$

$$\int_{p_1}^{p} p^{-0.715} \, dp = -\gamma_1 p_1^{-0.715} \int_{z_1}^{z} dz$$

$$p^{0.285} - p_1^{0.285} = -0.285\gamma_1 p_1^{-0.715}(z - z_1)$$

$$p^{0.285} = (14.7 \times 144)^{0.285} - 0.285(0.076)(14.7 \times 144)^{-0.715}(10{,}000)$$

$$p = 1{,}490 \text{ psf} = 10.35 \text{ psi}$$

(*d*) Temperature decreasing linearly with elevation:

$$T = (460 + 59) + Kz \qquad \text{where } K = -0.00356°F/ft$$

$$dT = K \, dz \qquad \text{hence} \qquad dz = \frac{dT}{K}$$

$$\frac{pv}{T} = R = \frac{p}{\gamma T} = \frac{p_1}{\gamma_1 T_1}$$

$$\frac{dp}{dz} = -\gamma \quad \text{where} \quad \gamma = \frac{\gamma_1 T_1 p}{T p_1}$$

$$\frac{dp}{p} = -\frac{\gamma_1 T_1}{p_1 T} dz = -\frac{\gamma_1 T_1}{p_1 K} \frac{dT}{T}$$

$$\int_{p_1}^{p} \frac{dp}{p} = -\frac{\gamma_1 T_1}{p_1 K} \int_{T_1}^{T} \frac{dT}{T}$$

$$\ln \frac{p}{p_1} = -\frac{\gamma_1 T_1}{p_1 K} \ln \frac{T}{T_1} = \ln \left(\frac{T_1}{T}\right)^{\gamma_1 T_1 / p_1 K}$$

$$p = p_1 \left(\frac{T_1}{T_1 + Kz}\right)^{\gamma_1 T_1 / p_1 K}$$

$$p = 14.7 \left(\frac{519}{483.4}\right)^{\frac{(0.076)(519)}{14.7(144)(-0.00356)}} = 10.2 \text{ psi}$$

The latter approach corresponds to the standard atmosphere, where it is assumed the temperature varies linearly from 59°F at sea level to −69.7°F at elevation 36,150 ft. This region of the atmosphere is known as the troposphere. Beyond elevation 36,150 ft and up to 80,000 ft (stratosphere) the temperature has been observed to be approximately constant at −69.7°F. This standard atmosphere is generally used in design calculations where the performance of high-altitude aircraft is of interest; it serves a good approximation of conditions to be expected in the atmosphere.

In Illustrative Example 2.1a it was shown that, for the case of an incompressible fluid,

$$p - p_1 = -\gamma(z - z_1) \tag{2.3}$$

where p is the pressure at any elevation z. This expression is generally applicable to liquids since they are only slightly compressible. Only where there are large changes in elevation, as in the ocean, need the compressibility of the liquid be considered, to arrive at an accurate determination of pressure variation.

For the case of a liquid at rest, it is convenient to measure distances vertically downward from the free liquid surface. If h is the distance below the free liquid surface and if the pressure of air and vapor on the surface is arbitrarily taken to be zero, Eq. (2.3) can be written as

$$p = \gamma h \tag{2.4}$$

As there must always be some pressure on the surface of any liquid, the total pressure at any depth h is given by Eq. (2.4) plus the pressure on the surface.   In many situations this surface pressure may be disregarded, as pointed out in Sec. 2.4.

From Eqs. (2.3) and (2.4) it may be seen that all points in a connected body of fluid at rest are under the same pressure if they are at the same depth below the liquid surface (Pascal's law).   This indicates that a surface of equal pressure for a liquid at rest is a horizontal plane.   Strictly speaking, it is a surface everywhere normal to the direction of gravity and is approximately a spherical surface concentric with the earth.   For practical purposes a limited portion of this surface may be considered a plane area.

2.3. PRESSURE EXPRESSED IN HEIGHT OF FLUID

In Fig. 2.3 imagine an open tank of liquid upon whose surface there is no pressure, though in reality the minimum pressure upon any liquid surface is the pressure of its own vapor.   Disregarding this for the moment, by Eq. (2.4) the pressure at any depth h is $p = \gamma h$.   If γ is assumed constant, there is a definite relation between p and h.   That is, pressure (force per unit area) is equivalent to a height h of some fluid of constant specific weight γ.   It is often more convenient to express pressure in terms of a height of a column of fluid rather than in pressure per unit area.

Even if the surface of the liquid is under some pressure, it is necessary only to convert this pressure into an equivalent height of the fluid in question and add this to the value of h, as shown in Fig. 2.3, to obtain the total pressure.

The preceding discussion has been applied to a liquid, but it is equally possible to use it for a gas or vapor by specifying some *constant* specific weight γ for the gas or vapor in question.   Thus pressure p may be expressed in the height of a column of *any* fluid by the relation

$$h = \frac{p}{\gamma} \qquad (2.5)$$

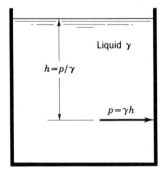

Fig. 2.3

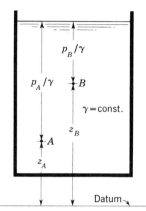

Fig. 2.4

This relationship is true for any consistent system of units. If p is in pounds per square foot, γ must be in pounds per cubic foot, and then h will be in feet. When pressure is expressed in this fashion, it is commonly referred to as *pressure head*. Because pressure is commonly expressed in pounds per square inch and as the value of γ for water is usually assumed to be 62.4 pcf (Fig. 1.8), a convenient relationship is

$$h \text{ (ft of H}_2\text{O)} = \frac{144 \times \text{psi}}{62.4} = 2.308 \times \text{psi}$$

It is convenient to express pressures occurring in one fluid in terms of height of another fluid, e.g., barometric pressure in millimeters of mercury.

Equation (2.3) may be expressed as follows:

$$z + \frac{p}{\gamma} = z_1 + \frac{p_1}{\gamma} = \text{constant} \tag{2.6}$$

This shows that for incompressible fluid at rest the summation of the elevation z at any point in a fluid plus the pressure head p/γ at that point is equal to the sum of these two quantities at any other point. The significance of this statement is that, in a fluid at rest with an increase in elevation, there is a decrease in pressure head, and vice versa. This concept is depicted in Fig. 2.4.

2.4. ABSOLUTE AND GAGE PRESSURES

If pressure is measured relative to absolute zero, it is called *absolute* pressure; when measured relative to atmospheric pressure as a base, it is called *gage* pressure. This is because practically all pressure gages register zero when open to the atmosphere and hence measure the difference between the pressure of the fluid to which they are connected and that of the surrounding air.

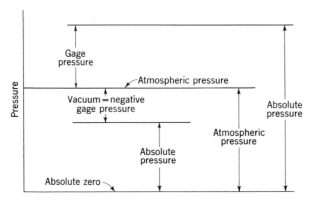

Fig. 2.5

If the pressure is below that of the atmosphere, it is designated as a *vacuum* and its gage value is the amount by which it is *below* that of the atmosphere. What is called a "high vacuum" is really a low absolute pressure. A perfect vacuum would correspond to absolute zero pressure.

All values of absolute pressure are positive, since a negative value would indicate tension, which is normally considered impossible in any fluid. Gage pressures are positive if they are above that of the atmosphere and negative if they are vacuum (Fig. 2.5).

From the foregoing discussion it can be seen that the following relation holds:

$$p_{abs} = p_{atm} + p_{gage} \qquad (2.7)$$

where p_{gage} may be positive or negative (vacuum).

The atmospheric pressure is also called the *barometric* pressure and varies with the altitude. Also, at a given place it varies slightly from time to time because of changes in meteorological conditions.

In thermodynamics it is essential to use absolute pressure, because most thermal properties are functions of the actual pressure of the fluid, regardless of the atmospheric pressure. For example, the equation of state of gas [Eq. (1.4)] is one in which absolute pressure must be used. In fact, absolute pressures must be employed in most problems involving gases and vapors.

The properties of liquids are usually not much affected by pressure, and hence gage pressures are commonly employed in problems dealing with liquids. Also, it will usually be found that the atmospheric pressure appears on both sides of an equation and hence cancels. Thus the value of atmospheric pressure is usually of no significance, and for this reason

as well, gage pressures are almost universally used with liquids.   About
the only case where the absolute pressure of a liquid needs to be considered
is where conditions are such that the pressure may approach or equal the
saturated vapor pressure.   Throughout this text all numerical pressures
will be understood to be gage pressures unless specifically given as absolute
values.

2.5. BAROMETER

The absolute pressure of the atmosphere is measured by the barometer.
If a tube such as that in Fig. 2.6 has its lower end immersed in a liquid
which is exposed to the atmospheric pressure, and if air is exhausted from
the tube, the liquid will rise in it.   If the air were completely exhausted,
the only pressure on the surface of the liquid in the tube would then be
that of its own vapor pressure and the liquid would have reached its
maximum height.

In Sec. 2.2 it was seen that the pressure at O within the tube and at
a at the surface of the liquid outside is the same; that is, $p_0 = p_a$.   From
the conditions of statical equilibrium of the liquid above O in the tube
(Fig. 2.6),

$$p_{atm}A - p_{vapor}A - \gamma Ay = 0$$

$$p_{atm} = \gamma y + p_{vapor} \tag{2.8}$$

If the vapor pressure on the surface of the liquid in the tube were negligible, then we should have

$$p_{atm} = \gamma y$$

The liquid employed for barometers is usually mercury, because its
density is sufficiently great to enable a reasonably short tube to be used,
and also because its vapor pressure is negligibly small at ordinary temperatures.   If some other liquid were used, the tube necessarily would be

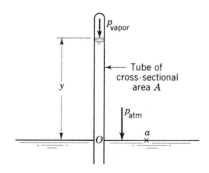

Fig. 2.6

so high as to be inconvenient and its vapor pressure at ordinary temperatures would be appreciable; hence a nearly perfect vacuum at the top of the column would not be attainable. The height attained by the liquid would consequently be less than the true barometric height and would necessitate applying a correction to the reading. When using a mercury barometer, to get as accurate a measurement of atmospheric pressure as possible, corrections for capillarity and vapor pressure should be applied to the reading.

Since atmospheric pressure at sea level is so widely used, it is well to have in mind equivalent forms of expression. Application of Eq. (2.5) shows that sea-level atmospheric pressure may be expressed as follows:

14.7 psia, 29.9 in. Hg, 33.9 ft of water

These are approximate equivalents and within the limits of slide-rule accuracy.

2.6. MEASUREMENT OF PRESSURE

There are many ways by which pressure in a fluid may be measured. Some are discussed below.

Bourdon gage. Pressures or vacuums are commonly measured by the bourdon gage of Fig. 2.7. In this gage a curved tube of elliptical cross section will change its curvature with changes in pressure within the tube. The moving end of the tube rotates a hand on a dial through a linkage system. A pressure and vacuum gage combined into one is known as a *compound gage* and is shown in Fig. 2.8. The pressure indicated by the gage is assumed to be that at its center. If the connecting piping is filled completely with fluid of the same density as that in A of Fig. 2.7 and if the pressure gage is graduated to read in pounds per square

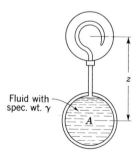

Fluid with spec. wt. γ

A

z

Fig. 2.7.   Bourdon gage.

Fig. 2.8. Compound pressure and vacuum gage. Pressures in pounds per square inch, vacuums in inches of mercury. (*Courtesy of Crosby-Ashton Steam Gage and Valve Co.*)

inch, as is customary, then

$$p_A \text{ (psi)} = \text{gage reading (psi)} + \frac{\gamma z}{144}$$

A vacuum gage, or the negative-pressure portion of a compound gage, is traditionally graduated to read in inches of mercury. For vacuums,

$$\text{In. Hg vacuum at } A = \text{gage reading (in. Hg vacuum)} - \frac{\gamma z (29.9)}{144 \times 14.7}$$

where γ is the specific weight of the fluid in A. Here, once again, it is assumed that this fluid completely fills the connecting tube of Fig. 2.7. The elevation-correction terms, i.e., those containing z, may be positive or negative, depending on whether the gage is above or below the point at which the pressure determination is desired. The expressions given are for the situation depicted in Fig. 2.7. When measuring gas pressures, the elevation correction terms are generally negligible.

Piezometer column. A piezometer column is a simple device for measuring moderate pressures of liquids. It consists of a tube (Fig. 2.9) in which the liquid can freely rise without overflowing. The height of the liquid in the tube will give the value of the pressure head directly. To reduce capillary error the tube diameter should be at least 0.5 in.

If the pressure of a *flowing* fluid is to be measured, special precautions should be taken in making the connection. The hole must be drilled absolutely normal to the interior surface of the wall, and the piezometer tube or the connection for any other pressure-measuring device must not project beyond the surface. All burrs and surface roughness near the hole must be removed, and it is well to round the edge of the hole slightly. Also, the hole should be small, preferably not larger than ⅛ in.

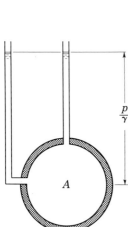

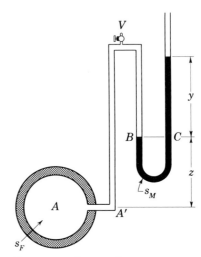

Fig. 2.9. Piezometer.   **Fig. 2.10.** Open-end manometer.

Simple manometer.   For high pressures the open piezometer tube is cumbersome, and some modification must be adopted.   The simple manometer or mercury U tube of Fig. 2.10 may then be used.   To determine the pressure at A, one may write a *gage equation* based on the fundamental relations of hydrostatic pressures [Eq. (2.3)].   Although any units of pressure or head may be used in the gage equation, it is generally advantageous to express all terms in *feet of the fluid whose pressure is to be measured.*   Thus, if s is defined as s_M/s_F, the ratio of the specific gravity[1] of the manometer or gage fluid to that of the fluid whose pressure is being measured, the pressure head at point C is sy.   This is also the head at B, while the head at A is greater than this by z, assuming the fluid in the connecting tube $A'B$ is of the same specific weight as that of the fluid at A. For this simple case the head at A can be written down directly, but for more complicated gages it is helpful to commence the equation at the open end of the manometer with the pressure head there, then proceed through the tube to A, adding terms when descending and subtracting when ascending, equating the result to the head at A.   Thus, for this example (Fig. 2.10),

$$0 + sy + z = \frac{p_A}{\gamma} \tag{2.9}$$

---

[1] It is customary for specific gravity to denote the ratio of the specific weight of the fluid to that of water in the case of liquids or to that of air in the case of gases, but it is not so restricted here.

If the absolute head at A is desired, then the zero of the first term will be replaced by the atmospheric-pressure head expressed in feet of the fluid whose pressure is to be measured.   If the fluid in A is a gas, the numerical values of pressure head will be quite high, and the equation may prove more workable if the terms are given in units of pressure rather than pressure head.

It should be noted that due account must be taken of the specific weight of the fluid in the connecting tube if it is different from that at A. If vessel A contained water, for example, and the connecting tube $A'B$ were filled with air, the contribution from the distance z would be negligible compared with the other quantities because of the relatively small specific weight of air.   But it would be difficult to ensure that the tube would be completely filled with air, and if it were partially filled with air and partially with water, an accurate computation would require the elevation of the water surface in the tube to be known.   It is therefore desirable to provide some means by which all the air may be permitted to escape and its place taken by the liquid in A.   The air-relief valve V (Fig. 2.10) serves this purpose.

In measuring a vacuum, for which the arrangement in Fig. 2.11 might be used, the resulting gage equation, subject to the same conditions as in the preceding case, is

$$0 - sy + z = \frac{p_A}{\gamma} \tag{2.10}$$

Again, it would simplify the equation to have the connecting tube $A'B$ filled with air.   As before, however, it is difficult to ensure this condition, and the arrangement in Fig. 2.12 is much better, since this permits

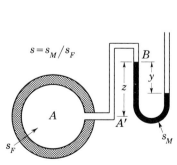

Fig. 2.11

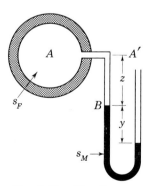

Fig. 2.12.   Negative-pressure manometer.

no air or vapor to collect.   For this case

$$\frac{p_A}{\gamma} = -(z + sy) \tag{2.11}$$

Of course, other liquids besides mercury might be used.   As the specific gravity of the measuring fluid approaches that of the fluid whose pressure is being measured, the reading becomes larger for a given pressure, thus increasing the accuracy of the instrument.

Differential manometers.   In many cases only the difference between two pressures is desired, and for this purpose differential manometers, such as shown in Fig. 2.13, may be used.   In Fig. 2.13a the measuring fluid is of greater density than that of the fluid whose pressure difference is involved.   If the fluids in A and B (Fig. 2.13a) are of the same density,

$$\frac{p_A}{\gamma} - z_A - sy + z_B = \frac{p_B}{\gamma}$$

and

$$\frac{p_A}{\gamma} - \frac{p_B}{\gamma} = z_A - z_B + sy$$

Hence

$$\frac{p_A}{\gamma} - \frac{p_B}{\gamma} = -y + sy = (s - 1)y \tag{2.12}$$

where $s = s_M/s_F$ as before.

Equation (2.12) is applicable only if A and B are at the same elevation.   If their elevations are different, an elevation-difference term must

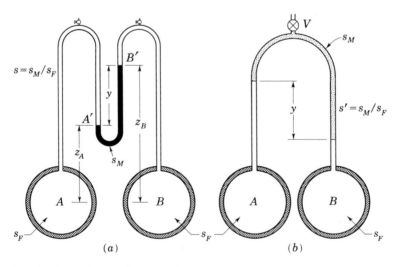

Fig. 2.13.   Differential manometers.

be added to the equation. It should be emphasized that by far the most common mistake made in working differential-manometer problems is to omit the $s - 1$ multiplier for the gage difference y. The reason for this term is that the effect of the column of fluid of specific gravity s_M between the levels of A' and B' (distance y) is offset by the effect of a column of fluid of specific gravity s_F of the same length in the other leg of the tube.

The differential manometer, when used with a heavy liquid such as mercury, is suitable for measuring large pressure differences. For a small pressure difference a light fluid, such as oil, or even air, may be used, and in this case the manometer is arranged as in Fig. 2.13b. Naturally, the fluid must be one that will not mix with the fluid in A or B. By the same method of analysis as the preceding, it may be shown that for the simple case with identical liquids in A and B,

$$\frac{p_A}{\gamma} - \frac{p_B}{\gamma} = (1 - s')y \tag{2.13}$$

where $s' = s_M/s_F$, the ratio of the specific gravities, and has a value less than 1. As the density of the measuring fluid approaches that of the fluid being measured, $1 - s'$ approaches zero and larger values of y are obtained for small pressure differences, thus increasing the sensitivity of the gage. Once again, the equation must be modified if A and B are not at the same elevation.

It is often satisfactory to use air or some other gas as the measuring fluid (Fig. 2.13b). Air can then be pumped through valve V until the pressure is such as to bring the two liquid columns to a suitable level. Any change in air pressure raises or lowers both liquid columns by the same amount so that the difference between them is constant. In this case the value of s' may be considered to be zero, since the density of air is so much less than that of a liquid, and the difference in pressure head between A and B is given by y directly. But for high pressures in A and B, with correspondingly high gas pressure and small pressure differences, the value of s' may not be negligible.

Another scheme for obtaining increased sensitivity is simply to incline the gage tube so that a vertical gage difference y is transposed into a reading which is magnified by $1/\sin \alpha$, where α is the angle of inclination with the horizontal.

2.7. FORCE ON PLANE AREA

When a fluid is at rest, no tangential force can exist within the fluid. All forces are then normal to the surfaces in question. If the pressure is uniformly distributed over an area, the force is equal to the pressure times the area, and the point of application of the force is at the centroid of the area. In the case of compressible fluids (gases), the pressure variation with vertical distance is very small because of the low specific weight; hence, when computing the static fluid force exerted by a gas, p may usually be considered constant. Thus, for this case,

$$F = \int p \, dA = p\int dA = pA \qquad (2.14)$$

In the case of liquids the distribution of pressure is not uniform; hence further analysis is necessary. In Fig. 2.14 consider a vertical plane whose upper edge lies in the free surface of a liquid. Let this plane be perpendicular to the plane of the paper, so that MN is merely its trace. The pressure will vary from zero at M to NK at N. Thus the total force on one side is the summation of the products of the elementary areas and the pressure upon them. It is apparent that the resultant of this system of parallel forces must be applied at a point *below* the centroid of the area, because the centroid of an area is the point of application of the resultant of a system of *uniform* parallel forces.

If the plane is lowered to $M'N'$, the proportionate change of pressure from M' to N' is less than that from M to N. Hence the center of pressure will be nearer to the centroid of the plane surface, and the deeper the plane is submerged, the more uniform the pressure becomes and the closer these two points will be together.

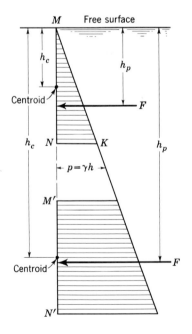

Fig. 2.14

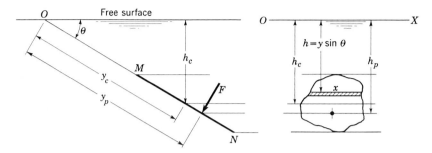

Fig. 2.15

In Fig. 2.15 let MN be the trace of a plane area making an angle θ with the horizontal. To the right is the projection of this area upon a vertical plane. Let h be the variable depth to any point and y be the corresponding distance from OX, the intersection of the plane produced and the free surface.

Consider an element of area so chosen that the pressure is uniform over it. Such an element is a horizontal strip. If x denotes the width of the area at any depth, then $dA = x\,dy$. As $p = \gamma h$ and $h = y \sin \theta$,

$$dF = p\,dA = \gamma h\,dA = \gamma y \sin \theta\,dA$$

Hence $$F = \gamma \sin \theta \int y\,dA = \gamma \sin \theta y_c A \qquad (2.15)$$

where y_c is the distance to the centroid of the area A. If the vertical depth of the centroid is denoted by h_c, then $h_c = y_c \sin \theta$ and

$$F = \gamma h_c A \qquad (2.16)$$

Thus the total force on any plane area submerged in a liquid is found by multiplying the specific weight of the liquid by the product of the area and the depth of its centroid. The value of F is independent of the angle of inclination of the plane so long as the depth of its centroid is unchanged.[1]

Since γh_c is the pressure at the centroid, another statement is that the total force on any plane area submerged in a liquid is the product of the area and the pressure at its centroid.

2.8. CENTER OF PRESSURE

The point of application of the resultant force on an area is called the *center of pressure*. Taking OX in Fig. 2.15 as an axis of moments, the

---

[1] For a plane submerged as in Fig. 2.15, it is obvious that Eq. (2.16) applies to one side only. As the pressures are there identical on the two sides, the net force is zero. In most practical cases where the thickness of the plane is not negligible, the pressures on the two sides are not the same.

moment of an elementary force $\gamma y \sin \theta \, dA$ is

$$y \, dF = \gamma \sin \theta y^2 \, dA$$

and if y_p denotes the distance to the center of pressure,

$$y_p F = \gamma \sin \theta \int y^2 \, dA = \gamma \sin \theta I_O$$

where I_O is the moment of inertia of the plane area about an axis through O.

If the preceding expression is divided by the value of F as given in Eq. (2.16), the result is

$$y_p = \frac{\gamma \sin \theta I_O}{\gamma \sin \theta y_c A} = \frac{I_O}{y_c A} \tag{2.17}$$

That is, the distance of the center of pressure from the axis where the plane or plane produced intersects the liquid surface is obtained by dividing the moment of inertia of the area A about the surface axis by its static moment about the same axis.

This may also be expressed in another form, by noting that

$$I_O = y_c^2 A + I_c$$

where I_c is the moment of inertia of an area about its centroidal axis. Thus

$$y_p = \frac{A y_c^2 + I_c}{y_c A} = y_c + \frac{I_c}{y_c A} \tag{2.18}$$

From this equation it may be seen that the location of the center of pressure is independent of the angle θ; that is, the plane area may be rotated about axis OX without affecting the location of the center of pressure. Also, it may be seen that the center of pressure is always below the centroid and that, as the depth of immersion is increased, the center of pressure approaches the centroid.

The lateral location of the center of pressure may be determined by considering the area to be made up of a series of elemental horizontal strips. The center of pressure for each strip would be at the midpoint of the strip. Since the moment of the resultant force, F, must be equal to the moment of the distributed force system about any axis, say, the y axis,

$$X_p F = \int x_p p \, dA$$

where X_p is the lateral distance from the selected y axis to the center of pressure of the resultant force F, and x_p is the lateral distance to the center of any elemental horizontal strip of area dA on which the pressure is p.

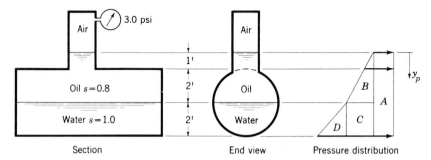

Section   End view   Pressure distribution

Illustrative Example 2.2

Illustrative example 2.2: Find the force exerted by the fluids on the end of the cylindrical tank in the accompanying figure, and determine the location of the center of pressure.

The confined gas exerts a pressure of 3.0 psi that is transmitted through the other fluids to the end of the tank.

$$F_A = 3.0 \times 144(\pi 2^2) = 5,450 \text{ lb}$$

The force F_B on the upper half of the end of the tank due to the presence of oil is

$$F_B = \gamma h_c A = (0.8 \times 62.4)\left(3 - \frac{4 \times 2}{3\pi}\right)\left(\frac{1}{2}\pi 2^2\right) = 675 \text{ lb}$$

The force F_C on the lower half of the end of the tank due to the presence of oil is

$$F_C = pA = (0.8 \times 62.4)3(\tfrac{1}{2}\pi 2^2) = 942 \text{ lb}$$

The force F_D on the lower half of the end of the tank due to the water is

$$F_D = \gamma h_c A = 62.4\left(\frac{4 \times 2}{3\pi}\right)\left(\frac{1}{2}\pi 2^2\right) = 334 \text{ lb}$$

The total force F on the end of the tank is therefore

$$F = F_A + F_B + F_C + F_D = 7,401 \text{ lb}$$

The locations of the centers of pressure of the component forces are

$$(y_p)_A = 3.0 \text{ ft}$$

$$(y_p)_B = 3 - \frac{4 \times 2}{3\pi} + \frac{I_c}{y_c A}$$

where

$$(I_c)_B = \frac{\pi 4^4}{128} - \frac{1}{2}\pi 2^2 \left(\frac{4 \times 2}{3\pi}\right)^2 = 1.72 \text{ ft}^4$$

$$(y_c)_B = 3 - \frac{4 \times 2}{3\pi} = 2.15 \text{ ft}$$

Thus

$$(y_p)_B = 2.15 + \frac{1.72}{2.15(\tfrac{1}{2}\pi 2^2)} = 2.28 \text{ ft}$$

$$(y_p)_C = 3 + \frac{4 \times 2}{3\pi} = 3.85 \text{ ft}$$

$$(y_p)_D = 3 + \frac{4 \times 2}{3\pi} + \frac{I_c}{y_c A}$$

where
$$(I_c)_D = (I_c)_B = 1.72 \text{ ft}^4$$
$$(y_c)_D = \frac{4 \times 2}{3\pi} = 0.85 \text{ ft}$$

Thus
$$(y_p)_D = 3.85 + \frac{1.72}{0.85(\frac{1}{2}\pi 2^2)} = 4.17 \text{ ft}$$

Finally,
$$F(y_p) = F_A(y_p)_A + F_B(y_p)_B + \cdots$$
$$y_p = 3.08 \text{ ft}$$

2.9. FORCE ON CURVED SURFACE

On any curved or warped area such as MN in Fig. 2.16a, the forces upon the various elements are different in direction and magnitude, and an algebraic summation is impossible. Hence Eq. (2.16) can be applied only to a plane area. But for any nonplanar area the resultant forces in certain directions can be found.

Horizontal force on curved surface. Any irregular curved area (Fig. 2.16) may be projected upon a vertical plane whose trace is $M'N'$. The projecting elements, which are all horizontal, enclose a volume whose ends are the vertical plane $M'N'$ and the irregular area MN. This volume of liquid is in static equilibrium. Upon the vertical plane is a force F', and the horizontal force upon the irregular area is F_x. Gravity W' is vertical, and the lateral forces on all the projecting elements are normal to these elements and hence normal to F'. Thus the only horizontal forces are F' and F_x, and therefore

$$F_x = F' \tag{2.19}$$

Hence the horizontal force in any given direction upon any area is equal to the force upon the projection of that area upon a vertical plane normal to the given direction. The line of action of F_x must be the same as that of F'.

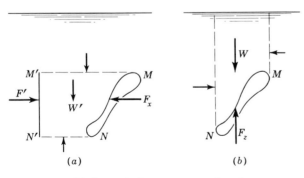

Fig. 2.16. Hydrostatic forces on curved surfaces.

Vertical force on curved surface. The vertical force on a curved or warped area, such as MN in Fig. 2.16b, can be found by considering the volume of liquid enclosed by the area and vertical elements extending to the free surface. This volume of liquid is in static equilibrium. Disregarding the pressure on the free surface, the only vertical forces are gravity W and F_z, the vertical force on the irregular area. The forces on the vertical elements are normal to these and hence are horizontal. Therefore

$$F_z = W \qquad (2.20)$$

Hence the vertical force upon any area is equal to the weight of the volume of fluid extending above that area to the free surface. The line of action of F_z must be the same as that of W; that is, it must pass through the center of gravity of the volume. The vertical force exerted by a gas on a curved surface or from pressure acting on the free liquid surface of Fig. 2.16b is equal to the pressure multiplied by the area of the horizontal projection of the curved surface.

In case the lower side of the surface is subjected to a force while the upper side is not, the vertical force is equal to the weight of the imaginary volume of liquid above the area up to the free-surface level. That is, the result is the same numerically as that given by Eq. (2.20). Once again, if a gas is involved, the vertical force is computed by multiplying the pressure by the area of the horizontal projection of the curved surface.

Resultant force on curved surface. In general, there is no single resultant force on an irregular area, for the horizontal and vertical forces, as found in the foregoing discussion, may not be in the same plane. But in certain cases these two forces will lie in the same plane and then can be combined into a single force.

Illustrative example 2.3: Find the horizontal and vertical components of the force exerted by the fluids on the horizontal cylinder in the accompanying figure if (*a*) the fluid to the left of the cylinder is a gas confined in a closed tank at a pressure

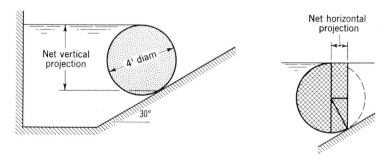

Illustrative Example 2.3

of 5.0 psi; (*b*) the fluid to the left of the cylinder is water with a free surface at an elevation coincident with the uppermost part of the cylinder.   Assume in both instances that atmospheric pressure occurs to the right of the cylinder.

(*a*) The net vertical projection of the portion of the cylindrical surface under consideration is $4 - 2(1 - \cos 30°)$.   Hence

$$F_x = 5 \times 144[4 - 2(1 - \cos 30°)] = 5 \times 144 \times 3.73 = 2,680 \text{ lb/ft}$$

The net horizontal projection of the portion of the cylindrical surface under consideration is $2 \sin 30°$.   Hence

$$F_z = 5 \times 144(2 \sin 30°) = 720 \text{ lb/ft}$$

(*b*) $\quad F_x = 62.4(\tfrac{1}{2} \times 3.73)(3.73) = 434 \text{ lb/ft}$

$\quad\quad F_z = \text{weight of crosshatched volume of liquid}$

$\quad\quad F_z = 62.4(^{210}\!\!/_{360}\pi 2^2 + \tfrac{1}{2}1 \times 1.732 + 1 \times 2) = 639 \text{ lb/ft}$

2.10. BUOYANCY AND STABILITY OF SUBMERGED AND FLOATING BODIES

The body $DHCK$ immersed in the fluid in Fig. 2.17 is acted upon by gravity and the pressures of the surrounding fluid.   On its upper surface the vertical component of the force is F_z and is equal to the weight of the volume of fluid $ABCHD$.   In similar manner the vertical component of force on the undersurface is F_z' and is equal to the weight of the volume of fluid $ABCKD$.   The difference between these two volumes is the volume of the body $DHCK$.

The buoyant force of a fluid is denoted by F_B, and it is vertically upward and equal to $F_z' - F_z$, which is equal to the weight of the volume of fluid $DHCK$.   That is, the buoyant force on any body is equal to the weight of fluid displaced.   If the body in Fig. 2.17 is in equilibrium, $W = F_B$, which means that the densities of body and fluid are equal.   If

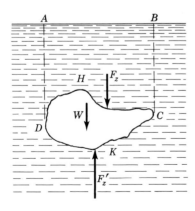

Fig. 2.17

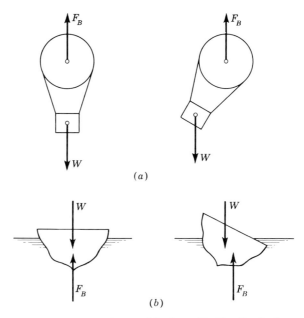

Fig. 2.18. (*a*) Submerged body. (*b*) Floating body.

W is greater than F_B, the body will sink.   If W is less than F_B, the body will rise until its density and that of the fluid are equal, as in the case of a balloon in the air.   If the body is less compressible than the fluid, there is a definite level at which it will reach equilibrium.   If it is more compressible than the fluid, it will rise indefinitely, provided the fluid has no definite limit of height, as in the case of the earth's atmosphere.

For a body in a liquid with a free surface, if its weight W is less than that of the same volume of liquid, it will rise and float on the surface so that $W = F_B$.   Hence a floating body displaces a volume of liquid equivalent to its weight.

When a body in equilibrium is given a slight displacement, if the forces thereby created tend to restore the body to its original position, the body is said to be in stable equilibrium.   The stability of submerged or floating bodies depends on the relative position of the buoyant force and the weight of the body.   The buoyant force acts through the *center of buoyancy*, which is coincident with the center of mass of the displaced fluid.   The criterion for stability of a submerged body (balloon or submarine) is that the center of buoyancy must be above the center of mass of the body.   The validity of this statement may be confirmed by inspecting Fig. 2.18*a*.

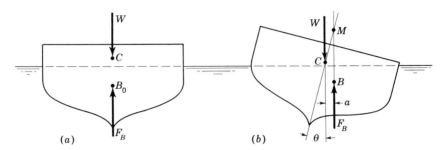

Fig. 2.19

In order for a floating body (surface vessel) to be stable (Fig. 2.18b), the center of buoyancy may be either above or below the center of mass. So long as a righting moment is developed when the floating body *lists*, the body will be stable.   It is of interest to examine in detail the stability of a floating body (Fig. 2.19).   For equilibrium the two forces W and F_B must lie in the same vertical line.   Suppose the body is rolled through the angle θ.   The center of gravity C of the body is usually fixed in position, but B will generally change as shown.   Thus W and F_B constitute a couple. For the case under consideration this is a righting couple since it tends to restore the body to the upright position.   The line of action of F_B in Fig. 2.19b cuts the axis at point M.   In proper ship design M lies above C so that there is a righting couple to restore the body to the upright position for all angles of heel that may be encountered.   As θ approaches zero, M approaches a limiting position called the *metacenter*, and the limiting distance of CM is called the *metacentric height*.   To find the metacentric height consider the hull to be rotated through an infinitesimal angle $\Delta\theta$ as in Fig. 2.20.   The resulting shift of the center of buoyancy from B_0 to B can be found by geometry.   The list of the hull causes a wedge-shaped volume to emerge on one side and a similar wedge to submerge on the other.   Let the total volume of water displaced by the hull be V, and let A represent the *waterline area*, the horizontal area of the hull in the plane of the water surface.

An element of volume at a distance x from the axis is the product of the length $x\,\Delta\theta$ (shown in section) and the element of area dA, which is normal to the section; i.e., it is an element in the waterline area.   For an infinitesimal angle $\Delta\theta$, the moments of volumes about point B_0 give

$$V \cdot \overline{B_0 B} = V \cdot 0 + \int_A x \, \Delta\theta \, dA \cdot x = \Delta\theta \int_A x^2 \, dA$$

But $\int_A x^2 \, dA$ is I, the moment of inertia of the waterline area of the ship about its longitudinal axis through O (perpendicular to the plane of the

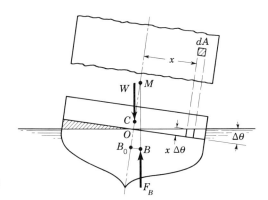

Fig. 2.20

section). Thus

$$\overline{B_0 B} = \Delta\theta \frac{I}{V}$$

and from Fig. 2.20, $\overline{B_0 B} = \overline{MB_0} \, \Delta\theta$. Equating the two expressions for $\overline{B_0 B}$ gives $\overline{MB_0} = I/V$, and since $\overline{CM} = \overline{MB_0} - \overline{CB_0}$,

$$\overline{CM} = \frac{I}{V} - \overline{CB_0} \tag{2.21}$$

If C falls below B_0, as might occur in a heavily loaded barge, the term $\overline{CB_0}$ in Eq. (2.21) would be added rather than subtracted.

If M were below B, the floating body would be unstable and it would roll over as shown in Fig. 2.21. Free ballast water in the hull of a floating body will displace the center of mass toward the center of buoyancy, thus decreasing the righting couple. For this reason liquid ballast of fuel oil on floating vessels should be stored in tanks or bulkheaded compartments.

2.11. FLUID MASSES SUBJECTED TO ACCELERATION

Under certain conditions there may be no relative motion between the particles of a fluid mass yet the mass itself may be in motion. If a body

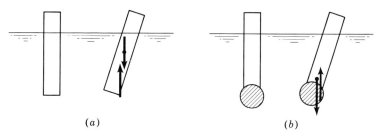

(*a*)   (*b*)

Fig. 2.21. (*a*) Unstable. (*b*) Stable.

of fluid in a tank is transported at a uniform velocity, the conditions are those of ordinary fluid statics.   But if it is subjected to acceleration, special treatment is required.   Consider the case of a liquid mass moving horizontally with a linear acceleration a_x, as shown in Fig. 2.22a.   A particle at the surface is acted upon by gravity; so $F_z = W = mg$.   The horizontal force of acceleration to the right is $F_x = ma_x$.   By D'Alembert's principle, the problem may be transformed into one of static equilibrium if the actual accelerating force is replaced by a fictitious inertia force of the same magnitude but opposite direction.   The resultant of F_z and $-F_x$ is F, and the surface must be normal to the direction of F.   Therefore $\tan \theta = a_x/g$.   Hence the surface and all planes of equal hydrostatic pressure must be inclined at this angle θ with the horizontal.

Taking a free-body diagram of an elemental cube of the liquid (Fig. 2.22b) and applying D'Alembert's principle and the conditions of statical equilibrium give:

For $\Sigma F_z = 0$:

$$p\,dx\,dy - \gamma\,dx\,dy\,dz - \left(p + \frac{\partial p}{\partial z}\,dz\right)dx\,dy = 0$$

$$\frac{\partial p}{\partial z} = -\gamma = -\rho g \tag{2.22}$$

For $\Sigma F_x = 0$:

$$p\,dy\,dz - \frac{\gamma}{g}\,a_x\,dx\,dy\,dz - \left(p + \frac{\partial p}{\partial x}\,dx\right)dy\,dz = 0$$

$$\frac{\partial p}{\partial x} = -\frac{\gamma}{g}\,a_x = -\rho a_x \tag{2.23}$$

Thus $\qquad\qquad \dfrac{\partial p}{\partial n} = -\rho(a_x{}^2 + g^2)^{1/2} \tag{2.24}$

where n is the direction at right angles to the planes of equal pressure.

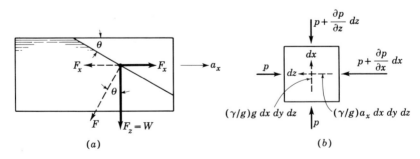

(a)   (b)

Fig. 2.22

In the foregoing discussion the acceleration of the fluid mass was at right angles to the direction of the gravitational acceleration. When the acceleration of the fluid mass is in some other direction, the same general approach can be used.

PROBLEMS

2.1. Neglecting the pressure upon the surface and the compressibility of water, what is the pressure in pounds per square inch at a depth of 15,000 ft below the surface of the ocean? The specific weight of ocean water under ordinary conditions is 64.0 pcf.

2.2. Repeat Prob. 2.1, but consider the effects of compressibility ($E_v = 300,000$ psi). Neglect changes in density caused by temperature variations.

2.3. A pressure gage at elevation 20.0 ft on the side of a tank containing a liquid reads 12.8 psi. Another gage at elevation 13.0 ft reads 15.5 psi. Compute the specific weight, density, and specific gravity of the liquid.

2.4. An open tank contains 10 ft of water covered with 2 ft of oil ($s = 0.86$). Find the pressure at the interface between the liquids and at the bottom of the tank.

2.5. On a certain day the barometric pressure at sea level is 30.1 in. Hg and the temperature is 70°F. The pressure gage on an airplane flying overhead indicates that the atmospheric pressure at that point is 10.6 psia and that the air temperature is 46°F. Calculate as accurately as you can the height of the airplane above sea level.

2.6. If the specific weight of a sludge can be expressed as $\gamma = 65.0 + 0.2h$, determine the pressure in pounds per square inch at a depth of 15 ft below the surface. γ is in pounds per cubic foot, and h in feet below surface.

2.7. If air had a constant specific weight of 0.076 pcf and were incompressible, what would be the height of air surrounding the earth to produce a pressure at the surface of 14.7 psia?

2.8. If the atmospheric pressure is 13.70 psia and a gage attached to a tank reads 8.0 in. Hg vacuum, what is the absolute pressure within the tank?

2.9. A gage is connected to a tank in which the pressure of the fluid is 40 psi above atmospheric. If the absolute pressure of the fluid remains unchanged but the gage is in a chamber where the air pressure is reduced to a vacuum of 25 in. Hg, what reading in pounds per square inch will then be observed?

2.10. If the atmospheric pressure is 29.9 in. Hg, what will be the height of water in a water barometer if the temperature of the water is 90°F; 140°F? Be as precise as possible.

2.11. The tire of an airplane is inflated at sea level to 60 psi. Assuming the tire does not expand, what is the pressure within the tire at elevation 30,000 ft? Assume standard atmosphere. Express the answer in pounds per square inch and pounds per square inch absolute.

2.12. If the atmospheric pressure were equivalent to 32.8 ft of water, what would be the reading on a barometer containing an alcohol ($s = 0.84$) if the vapor pressure of the alcohol at the temperature of observation were 2.4 psia?

2.13. In the figure, originally there is a 4-in. manometer reading. Atmospheric pressure is 14.7 psia. If the absolute pressure at A is doubled, what then would be the manometer reading?

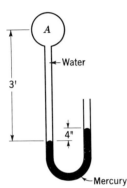

Fig. Prob. 2.13

2.14. A mercury manometer (Fig. 2.10) is connected to a pipeline carrying water at 150°F and located in a room where the temperature is also 150°F. If the elevation of point B is 10 ft above A and the mercury reading is 48 in., what is the pressure in the pipe in pounds per square inch? Repeat, assuming all temperatures are 68°F. Be as precise as possible, and note the effect of temperature.

2.15. Two vessels are connected to a differential manometer using mercury ($s = 13.6$), the connecting tubing being filled with water. The higher-pressure vessel is 5 ft lower in elevation than the other. Room temperature prevails. If the mercury reading is 4.0 in., what is the pressure difference in feet of water, in pounds per square inch? If carbon tetrachloride ($s = 1.59$) were used instead of mercury, what would be the manometer reading for the same pressure difference?

2.16. Refer to the manometer of Fig. 2.13b. A and B are at the same elevation. Water is contained in A and rises in the tube to a level 76 in. above A. Glycerin is contained in B. The inverted U tube is filled with air at 20 psi and 70°F. Atmospheric pressure is 14.7 psia. Determine the difference in pressure between A and B if y is 14 in. Express the answer in pounds per square inch. What is the absolute pressure in B in inches of mercury, feet of glycerin?

2.17. Gas confined in a rigid container exerts a pressure of 20 psi when its temperature is 40°F. What pressure would the gas exert if the temperature were raised to 140°F? Barometric pressure remains constant at 28.0 in. Hg.

2.18. The diameter of tube C in Fig. 2.10 is d_1, and that of tube B is d_2. Let z_0 be the elevation of the mercury when both mercury columns are at the same level. R is the reading of column C above this same zero point when the fluid in A is under some pressure, but it is not the same as y. Let γ' be the specific weight of the mercury (or any other measuring fluid), while γ is the specific weight of the fluid in A and the connecting tubing. Prove that

$$p_A = \gamma z_0 + \left[\gamma' + (\gamma' - \gamma)\left(\frac{d_1}{d_2}\right)^2\right] R = M + NR$$

where M and N are constants. It is seen that this equation involves only one variable, which is a reading on the scale for column C. It also shows the significance of having d_2 large compared with d_1.

2.19. In the figure, atmospheric pressure is 14.7 psia; the gage reading is 5.0 psi; the vapor pressure of the alcohol is 1.7 psia. Compute x and y.

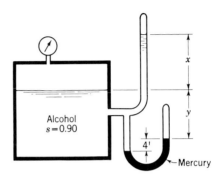

Fig. Prob. 2.19

2.20. At a certain point the pressure in a pipeline containing gas ($\gamma = 0.05$ pcf) is 4.5 in. of water. The gas is not flowing. What is the pressure in inches of water at another point in the line whose elevation is 500 ft greater than the first point? Make and state clearly any necessary assumptions.

2.21. If a triangle of height d and base b is vertical and submerged in liquid with its vertex at the liquid surface, derive an expression for the depth to its center of pressure.

2.22. Repeat Prob. 2.21 for the same triangle but with its vertex a distance a below the liquid surface.

2.23. If a triangle of height d and base b is vertical and submerged in a liquid with its base at the liquid surface, derive an expression for the depth to its center of pressure.

2.24. A circular area of diameter d is vertical and submerged in a liquid. Its upper edge is coincident with the liquid surface. Derive an expression for the depth to its center of pressure.

2.25. A vertical semicircular area has its diameter in a liquid surface. Derive an expression for the depth to its center of pressure.

2.26. Refer to Illustrative Example 2.1. If the air pressure were 5 psi rather than 3 psi, compute the total force and determine the location of the center of pressure.

2.27. A rectangular plate submerged in water is 5 by 6 ft, the 5-ft side being horizontal and the 6-ft side being vertical. Determine the magnitude of the force on one side of the plate and the depth to its center of pressure if the top edge is (a) at the water surface; (b) 1 ft below the water surface; (c) 100 ft below the water surface.

2.28. A rectangular plate 5 by 6 ft is at an angle of 30° with the horizontal, and the 5-ft side is horizontal. Find the magnitude of the force on one side of the plate and the location of its center of pressure when the top edge is (a) at the water surface; (b) 1 ft below the water surface.

2.29. A rectangular area is 5 by 6 ft, with the 5-ft side horizontal. It is placed with its centroid 4 ft below a water surface and rotated about an axis through its centroid. Find the magnitude of the force on one side and the distance between the center of pressure and the centroid of the plane when the angle θ = 90, 60, 30, 0°.

2.30. Repeat Prob. 2.27 for the case where the liquids consist of a 2-ft layer of oil (s = 0.8) resting above water.

2.31. A plane surface is circular and 4 ft in diameter. If it is vertical and the top edge is 1 ft below the water surface, find the magnitude of the force on one side and the depth to the center of pressure.

2.32. A triangle with a height of 6 ft and a base of 4 ft is placed vertically with its base horizontal and 1 ft below a liquid surface. Determine the depth and horizontal position of the center of pressure.

2.33. Prove that for a plane area such that a straight line can be drawn through the midpoints of all horizontal elements, the center of pressure must lie on this line.

2.34. A vertical right triangle of height d and base b submerged in liquid has its vertex at the liquid surface. Find the distance from the vertical side to the center of pressure by (a) inspection; (b) calculus.

2.35. A common type of irrigation head gate is a plate which slides over the opening to a culvert. The coefficient of friction between the gate and its sliding ways is 0.6. If the top edge of a 60-in.-square gate weighing 900 lb is 15 ft below the water surface in a closed position, find the force required to open the gate if it is set (a) vertically; (b) on a 2:1 slope, as is frequently the case. (*Note:* As used here, *slope* means the ratio of the horizontal distance to the vertical distance, or the horizontal distance for a 1-ft rise.)

2.36. In the drainage of irrigated lands it is frequently desirable to install automatic flap gates to prevent a flood from backing up into the lateral drains from a river. Suppose a 60-in.-square flap gate, weighing 2,555 lb, is hinged 40 in. above the center, as shown in the figure, and the face is sloped 4° from the vertical. Find the depth to which water will rise behind the gate before it will open.

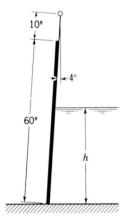

Fig. Prob. 2.36

2.37. The figure shows a cylindrical tank. What is the force on the bottom? What is the force on the annular surface MM? Find the longitudinal tensile stress in the sidewalls BB if (a) the tank is suspended from the top; (b) it is supported on the bottom.

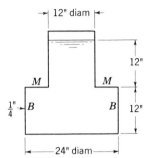

Fig. Prob. 2.37

2.38. Find the magnitude and point of application of the force on the circular gate shown in the figure.

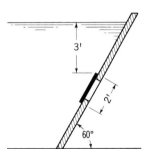

Fig. Prob. 2.38

2.39. The gate MN in the figure rotates about an axis through N. If the width perpendicular to the plane of the figure is 4 ft, what torque applied to that shaft through N is required to hold the gate closed?

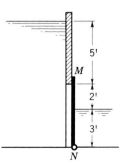

Fig. Prob. 2.39

2.40. Find the minimum value of z for which the gate in the figure will rotate counterclockwise if the gate is (*a*) rectangular, 4 by 4 ft; (*b*) triangular, 4-ft base as axis, height 4 ft.   Neglect friction in bearings.

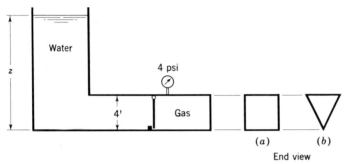

Water

4 psi

4'

Gas

(*a*)   (*b*)

End view

Fig. Prob. 2.40

2.41. Referring to the figure, what value of b is necessary to keep the rectangular masonry wall from sliding if it weighs 150 pcf and the coefficient of friction is 0.4?   Will it also be safe against overturning?   Assume that water does not get underneath the block.

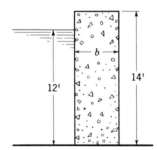

b

12'

14'

Fig. Prob. 2.41

2.42. In the figure, the rectangular flashboard MN, 6 ft high, is pivoted at B. (*a*) What must be the maximum height of B above N if the flashboard is on the verge of tipping when the water surface rises to M?   (*b*) If the flashboard is pivoted at the location determined in (*a*) and the water surface is 1 ft below M, what are the reactions at B and N per foot of length of crest?

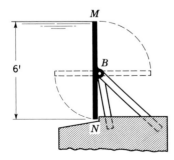

M

B

6'

N

Fig. Prob. 2.42

2.43. Find horizontal and vertical forces per foot of width on the Tainter gate shown in the figure. Locate the horizontal force, and indicate the line of action of the vertical force, without actually computing its location.

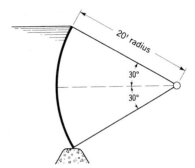

Fig. Prob. 2.43

2.44. A tank with vertical ends contains water and is 8 ft long normal to the plane of the figure shown. The sketch shows a portion of its cross section where MN is one-quarter of an ellipse with semiaxes b and d. If $b = 4$ ft, $d = 6$ ft, and $a = 1.5$ ft, find for the surface represented by MN the magnitude and position of the line of action of (a) the horizontal component of force; (b) the vertical component of force; (c) the resultant force and its direction with the horizontal.

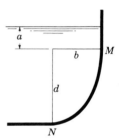

Fig. Prob. 2.44

2.45. Find the answers called for in Prob. 2.44 if MN represents a parabola with vertex at N.

2.46. A vertical thrust bearing for a large hydraulic gate is composed of an 11-in.-radius bronze hemisphere mating into a steel hemispherical shell in the gate bottom. At what pressure must lubricant be supplied to the bearing so that a complete oil film is present if the vertical thrust on the bearing is 800,000 lb?

2.47. The cross section of a tank is as shown in the figure. BC is a cylindrical surface. If the tank contains water to a depth of 7 ft, determine the

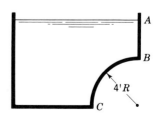

Fig. Prob. 2.47

magnitude and location of the horizontal and vertical force components on the wall ABC.

2.48. Repeat Prob. 2.47 for the case where the tank contains 3 ft of water overlain with 4 ft of oil ($s = 0.8$).

2.49. Repeat Prob. 2.47 where the tank is closed and contains gas at a pressure of 8 psi.

2.50. Repeat Prob. 2.47 where the tank is closed and contains 3 ft of water overlain with a gas that is under a pressure of 2.0 psi.

2.51. The hemispherical body shown in the figure projects into a tank. Find the horizontal and vertical forces acting on the hemispherical projection for the following cases: (a) tank is full of water with free surface 5 ft above A; (b) tank contains CCl_4 ($s = 1.59$) to the level of A overlain with water having free surface 5 ft above A; (c) tank is closed and contains gas at a pressure of 6 psi; (d) tank is closed and contains water to level of A overlain with gas at a pressure of 2 psi.

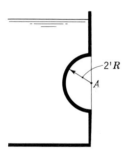

Fig. Prob. 2.51

2.52. Determine the force required to hold the cone shown in the figure in position.

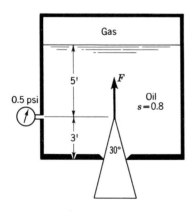

Fig. Prob. 2.52

2.53. The cross section of a gate is shown in the figure. Its dimension normal to the plane of the paper is 10 ft, and its shape is such that $x = 0.2y^2$. The gate is pivoted about O. Develop analytic expressions in terms of the water depth y upstream of the gate for the following: (a) horizontal force; (b) vertical force; (c) clockwise moment acting on the gate.

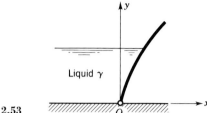

Fig. Prob. 2.53

2.54. An iceberg in the ocean floats with one-seventh of its volume above the surface. What is its specific gravity relative to ocean water? What portion of its volume would be above the surface if ice were floating in pure water?

2.55. A balloon weighs 250 lb and has a volume of 14,000 ft³. It is filled with helium, which weighs 0.0112 pcf at the temperature and pressure of the air, which weighs 0.0807 pcf. What load will the balloon support, or what force in a cable would be required to keep it from rising?

2.56. For the conditions shown in the figure, find the force F required to lift the concrete-block gate if the concrete weighs 150 pcf.

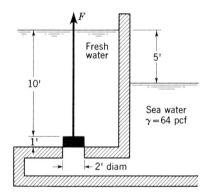

Fig. Prob. 2.56

2.57. A rectangular iron caisson is to be sunk in 20 ft of water. It is a box 50 by 20 by 23 ft high and weighs 75 tons. How deep will it sink when launched? What weight must be added to cause it to sink to the bottom?

2.58. A metal block 1 ft square and 10 in. deep is floated on a body of liquid which consists of an 8-in. layer of water above a layer of mercury. The block weighs 120 pcf. What is the position of the upper level of the block? If a downward vertical force of 250 lb is applied to this block, what is the new position of the upper level of the block? Assume that the tank containing the fluid is of infinite dimensions.

2.59. A large rectangular block of timber, 8 by 4 by 2 ft, weighing 2,300 lb, is used as a float. Its 2-ft dimension is vertical. At what level does the block float in freshwater?   If a 200-lb man stood at the center of the block, at what level would it then float?   How far from center could the man stand on the longitudinal axis of the float without upsetting it?

2.60. A wooden pole weighing 2 lb/ft has a cross-sectional area of 7 in.² and is supported as shown in the figure.   The hinge is frictionless.   Find θ.

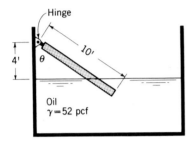

Fig. Prob. 2.60

2.61. The metacentric height of a body of weight W can be determined experimentally by moving a weight W_0 a distance b from the center line of the body, at approximately the elevation of the metacenter, and observing the resulting small angle θ of list.   Prove that, for this case, the metacentric height is given by

$$\overline{CM} = \frac{W_0 b}{W \tan \theta}$$

2.62. A ship displaces 6,000 tons when floating in seawater with its axis vertical and a weight of 600 tons on the center line.   Moving the weight 4 ft toward one side of the deck causes a plumb bob, suspended on a 10-ft string, to move 15 in.   Find the metacentric height of unloaded ship.

2.63. A cube of homogeneous material floats in freshwater.   Within what limits of specific weight will the cube be stable with (a) one face uppermost and horizontal; (b) one edge uppermost and horizontal; (c) one corner uppermost?

2.64. A cylindrical caisson having an outside diameter of 30 ft floats in seawater with its axis vertical and its lower end submerged 30 ft below the water surface.   Its center of gravity is on the vertical axis and is 12 ft above the bottom.   Find (a) true metacentric height; (b) righting couple when the caisson is tipped through an angle of 8°.

2.65. A block of wood weighing 40 pcf is in the shape of a rectangular parallelepiped having a 4-in.-square base.   If the block floats in freshwater with the square base horizontal, what is its maximum height for stable equilibrium in the upright position?

2.66. Suppose the tank shown in Fig. 2.22 is rectangular and open at the top. It is 20 ft long and 4 ft wide.   If it is initially filled to the top, how much liquid will be spilled if it is given a horizontal acceleration $a_x = 0.3g$?

2.67. If the tank of Fig. 2.22 is closed at the top and is completely filled, what will be the pressure difference between the left-hand end at the top and the right-hand end at the top if the liquid has a specific weight of 50 pcf and the horizontal acceleration is $a_x = 0.3g$?   Sketch planes of equal pressure, indicating their magnitude, assuming zero pressure in upper right-hand corner.

2.68. A tank containing water to a depth of 6 ft is accelerated upward at 10 ft/sec². Calculate the pressure on the bottom of the tank.

2.69. At a particular instant an airplane is traveling upward at a velocity of 150 mph in a direction that makes an angle of 30° with the horizontal. At this instant the airplane is losing speed at the rate of 3 mph/sec. Also, it is moving on a concave downward circular path having a radius of 4,000 ft. Determine for the given conditions the position of the free liquid surface in the fuel tank of this vehicle.

THREE

KINEMATICS OF FLUID FLOW

When speaking of fluid flow, one often refers to the flow of an *ideal fluid*. Such a fluid is presumed to have no viscosity. This is an idealized situation which does not exist; however, there are instances in engineering problems where the assumption of an ideal fluid is helpful. When referring to the flow of a *real fluid*, the effects of viscosity are introduced into the problem. This results in the development of shear stresses between neighboring fluid particles when they are moving at different velocities.

Flow may also be classified as that of an *incompressible* or *compressible* fluid. Since liquids are relatively incompressible, they are generally treated as wholly incompressible fluids. Under particular conditions where there is little pressure variation, the flow of gases may also be considered incompressible, though generally the effects of the compressibility of the gas should be considered. Some of the basic concepts governing the flow of compressible fluids are discussed in Chap. 9.

In addition to the flow of different types of fluids, i.e., real, ideal, incompressible, and compressible, there are various classifications of flow. Flow may be *steady* or *unsteady* with respect to time. It may be *laminar* or *turbulent*, as discussed in the following section. Other classifications of flow include *rotational* or *irrotational* (Chap. 5), *supercritical* or *subcritical* (Chap. 10), etc.

3.1. LAMINAR AND TURBULENT FLOW

In this chapter we deal only with velocities and accelerations and their distribution in space without consideration of any forces involved. That there are two distinctly different types of fluid flow was demonstrated by Osborne Reynolds in 1883. He injected a fine, threadlike stream of colored liquid at the entrance to a large glass tube through which water was flowing from a tank. A valve at the discharge end permitted him to vary the flow. When the velocity in the tube was small, this colored liquid was visible as a straight line throughout the length of the tube, thus showing that the particles of water moved in parallel straight lines. As the velocity of the water was gradually increased by opening the valve further, there was a point at which the flow changed. The line would first become wavy, and then at a short distance from the entrance it would break into numerous vortices beyond which the color would be uniformly diffused so that no streamlines could be distinguished. Later observations have shown that in this latter type of flow the velocities are continuously subject to irregular fluctuations.

The first type is known as *laminar, streamline,* or *viscous* flow. The significance of these terms is that the fluid appears to move by the sliding of laminations of infinitesimal thickness relative to adjacent layers; that the particles move in definite and observable paths or streamlines, as in Fig. 3.1; and also that the flow is characteristic of a viscous fluid or is one in which viscosity plays a significant part (Fig. 1.3 and Sec. 1.10).

The second type is known as *turbulent* flow and is illustrated in Fig. 3.2, where (*a*) represents the irregular motion of a large number of particles during a very brief time interval, while (*b*) shows the erratic path followed

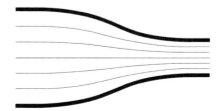

Fig. 3.1

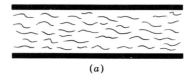
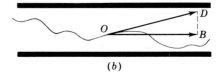

(a)   (b)

Fig. 3.2. Turbulent flow.

by a single particle during a longer time interval. A distinguishing characteristic of turbulence is its irregularity, there being no definite frequency, as in wave action, and no observable pattern, as in the case of eddies.

Large eddies and swirls and irregular movements of large bodies of fluid, which can be traced to obvious sources of disturbance, do not constitute turbulence, but may be described as *disturbed flow*. By contrast, turbulence may be found in what appears to be a very smoothly flowing stream and one in which there is no apparent source of disturbance. The fluctuations of velocity are comparatively small and can often be detected only by special instrumentation.

At a certain instant a particle at O in Fig. 3.2b may be moving with the velocity OD, but in turbulent flow OD will vary continuously both in direction and in magnitude. Fluctuations of velocity are accompanied by fluctuations in pressure, which is the reason why manometers or pressure gages attached to a pipe in which fluid is flowing usually show pulsations. In this type of flow an individual particle will follow a very irregular and erratic path, and no two particles may have identical or even similar motions. Thus a rigid mathematical treatment of turbulent flow is impossible, and instead statistical means of evaluation must be employed.

Criteria governing the conditions under which the flow will be laminar and those under which it will be turbulent are discussed in Sec. 8.2.

3.2. STEADY FLOW AND UNIFORM FLOW

A *steady flow* is one in which all conditions at any point in a stream remain constant with respect to *time*, but the conditions may be different at different points. A truly *uniform flow* is one in which the velocity is the same in both magnitude and direction at a given instant at every point in *space*. Both of these definitions must be modified somewhat, for true steady flow is found only in laminar flow. In turbulent flow there are continual fluctuations in velocity and pressure at every point, as has been explained. But if the values fluctuate equally on both sides of a constant average

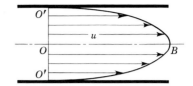

Fig. 3.3.   Velocity profile for real fluid in a
pipe.

value, the flow is called steady flow.   However, a more exact definition
for this case would be *mean steady flow*.

Likewise, this strict definition of uniform flow can have little meaning
for the flow of a real fluid where the velocity varies across a section, as in
Fig. 3.3.   But when the size and shape of cross section are constant along
the length of channel under consideration, the flow is said to be *uniform*.

Steady (or unsteady) and uniform (or nonuniform) flow can exist
independently of each other, so that any of four combinations is possible.
Thus the flow of liquid at a constant rate in a long straight pipe of constant diameter is *steady uniform* flow, the flow of liquid at a constant
rate through a conical pipe is *steady nonuniform* flow, while at a changing
rate of flow these cases become *unsteady uniform* and *unsteady nonuniform
flow*, respectively.

Unsteady flow may be a transient phenomenon which in time becomes
either steady flow or zero flow.   An example may be seen in Fig. 3.4,
where (*a*) denotes the surface of a stream that has just been admitted to
the bed of a canal by the sudden opening of a gate.   After a time the
water surface will be at (*b*), later at (*c*), and finally reaches equilibrium at
(*d*).   The unsteady flow has then become mean steady flow.   Another
example of transient phenomenon is when a valve is closed at the discharge end of a pipeline, thus causing the velocity in the pipe to decrease
to zero.   In the meantime there will be fluctuations in both velocity and
pressure within the pipe.

Unsteady flow may also include periodic motion such as that of waves

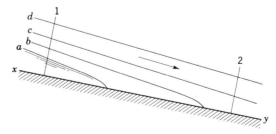

Fig. 3.4.   Unsteady flow in a canal.

on beaches, tidal motion in estuaries, and other oscillations.   The difference between such cases and that of mean steady flow is that the deviations from the mean are very much greater and the time scale is also much longer.

3.3. RATE OF DISCHARGE AND MEAN VELOCITY

The quantity of fluid flowing per unit time across any section is called the *rate of discharge* (commonly shortened to *discharge*, or *flow*).   It may be expressed in any suitable units, such as cubic feet per minute, pounds per hour, million gallons per day, depending upon the specific application. In consistent ft-lb-sec units it would be in cubic feet per second, or for a compressible fluid it might preferably be in pounds per second.

In the case of an ideal (nonviscous) fluid flowing in a straight channel, all particles move in parallel lines with equal velocities.   In Fig. 3.5 the magnitude of the velocity is OB and the *velocity profile* is MBN.   The rate of discharge would be obtained by multiplying this uniform velocity OB by the area of the stream normal to OB.

In the flow of a real fluid the velocity adjacent to the wall will be zero; it will increase very rapidly within a short distance from the wall and produce a velocity profile such as shown in Fig. 3.3.   If the flow is laminar, there is merely the velocity profile to consider; if the flow is turbulent, not only will the velocity vary across the section, but at any one point it will fluctuate with time.   In Fig. 3.2*b* it is shown that the velocity OD will continuously change, and consequently its axial component OB will also fluctuate.   It is the axial component in which we are interested. The instantaneous component parallel to the channel at a given point is represented by u'' in Fig. 3.6.   The average ordinate to the graph of u'' over a period of time determines the temporal mean local velocity u at this point.   It is this value of u which is represented in Fig. 3.3.

The difference between u'' and u, which may be designated as u', is called the *turbulent fluctuation* of this component.   The temporal mean value of u' must be zero, as must the temporal means of all components

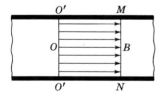

Fig. 3.5

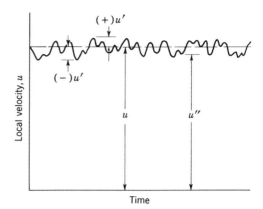

Fig. 3.6. Fluctuating velocity at a point.

transverse to the channel, such as BD in Fig. 3.2. Thus at any instant

$$u'' = u + u' \tag{3.1}$$

and u may be evaluated for any finite time t as $u = (1/t) \int_0^t u'' \, dt$.

The value of u will vary across the section in some manner, such as that shown in Fig. 3.3, and hence the rate of discharge may be expressed as

$$Q = \int_A u \, dA = AV \tag{3.2}$$

where u is the temporal mean velocity through an infinitesimal area dA, while V is the *mean*, or average, velocity over the entire sectional area A. If u is known as a function of A, the foregoing may be integrated. If only average values of V are known for different finite areas into which the total area may be divided, then

$$Q = A_a V_a + A_b V_b + \cdots + A_n V_n = AV \tag{3.3}$$

On the other hand, if the rate of discharge has been determined directly by some method, the mean velocity may be found by

$$V = \frac{Q}{A} = \frac{G}{\gamma A} \tag{3.4}$$

where Q and G are the volume and weight rates of discharge, respectively.

3.4. EQUATION OF CONTINUITY

Referring to Fig. 3.4, it is seen that when the water surface is at (a), there is a rate of discharge Q_1 past section (1) but Q_2 is zero. And when the water surface is at (c), Q_1 must be greater than Q_2 in order to supply the increasing quantity of fluid which is accumulating between (1) and (2). But when equilibrium is reached and the flow is thus steady, the volume between (1) and (2) becomes constant. Even if the fluid is compressible, the total weight between (1) and (2) must then remain constant. Thus the rate at which fluid flows past section (1) must equal the rate at which it flows past section (2). That is, for steady flow only,

$$G = \gamma_1 A_1 V_1 = \gamma_2 A_2 V_2 = \cdots = \gamma A V = \text{constant} \qquad (3.5)$$

This equation is applicable to any fluid; if the fluid is incompressible ($\gamma = \text{constant}$), the above equation reduces to

$$Q = A_1 V_1 = A_2 V_2 = \cdots = A V = \text{constant} \qquad (3.6)$$

In order to use Eq. (3.5), it is necessary to know the way in which the specific weight varies with pressure and temperature. But for an incompressible fluid, Eq. (3.6) shows that the velocity varies inversely as the cross-sectional area of the stream. If the latter is known, the variation in velocity along the length of the stream is determined (Fig. 3.8). The equation of continuity applies both to an ideal fluid and to a real fluid, provided the mean velocity is employed in the case of the latter.

It should be noted that in Eq. (3.2) the element of area dA is at right angles to the direction of the velocity u. Thus in vector notation $dQ = \mathbf{V} \cdot d\mathbf{A}$, which in turn means that in Eq. (3.6), where it is stated that $Q = A V$, the area A is defined by a surface that is everywhere at right angles to the velocity vectors. Equations (3.5) and (3.6) are generally adequate for the analysis of flows in conduits with solid boundaries, but for the consideration of flow in space, as that of air around an airplane, for example, it is desirable to express the continuity equation in another form, as indicated in Sec. 5.1.

3.5. PATH LINES, STREAMLINES, AND STREAK LINES

A *path line* is the trace made by a *single* particle over a *period* of time. If a camera were to take a time exposure of a flow in which there were a few particles so colored that they would register on the negative, the picture would show the course followed by each particle, which would be its path line. Thus the path line shows the direction of the velocity of the *same* particle at *successive* instants of time.

Streamlines show the mean direction of a *number* of particles at the *same* instant of time. If a camera were to take a very short time exposure of a flow in which there were a large number of particles, each particle

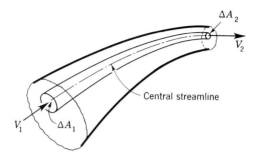

Fig. 3.7. Stream tube.

would trace a short path, which would indicate its velocity during that brief interval. A series of curves drawn tangent to the means of the velocity vectors are streamlines.

Path lines and streamlines are identical in the steady flow of a fluid in which there are no fluctuating velocity components, in other words, for truly steady flow. This is because particles always move *along* streamlines, since these lines show the direction of motion of every particle. Truly steady flow may be either that of an ideal frictionless fluid or that of one so viscous and moving so slowly that no eddies are formed. This latter is the *laminar* type of flow, wherein the layers of fluid slide smoothly, one upon another. In turbulent flow, however, path lines and streamlines are not coincident, the path lines being very irregular while the streamlines are everywhere tangent to the local mean temporal velocity.

Of importance in theoretical considerations is the *stream tube*, which may be assumed, for practical purposes, as a bundle of streamlines (Fig. 3.7). As it is bounded on all sides by streamlines and as there can be no velocity normal to a streamline, no fluid can enter or leave the stream tube, except at the ends. The equation of continuity is then seen to apply to the case of the stream tube, even though it has no solid boundaries.

In experimental fluid mechanics, a dye or other tracer is frequently injected into the flow to trace the motion of the fluid particles. If the flow is laminar, a ribbon of color results. This is called a *streak line*, or *filament line*. It is an instantaneous picture of the positions of all particles in the flow which have passed through a given point (namely, the point of injection). In utilizing fluid-tracer techniques it is important to choose a tracer with physical characteristics (especially density) the same as those of the fluid being observed. Thus the smoke rising from a cigarette, while giving the appearance of a streak line, does not properly represent the movement of the ambient air in the room because it is less dense than the air and therefore rises more rapidly.

3.6. ONE-, TWO-, AND THREE-DIMENSIONAL FLOW

In true one-dimensional flow the velocity has at all points the same direction and (for an incompressible fluid) the same magnitude.   Such a case is rarely of practical interest.   However, the term *one-dimensional method of analysis* is applied to the flow between boundaries which are really three-dimensional, with the understanding that the "one dimension" is taken *along the central streamline* of the flow.   Average values of velocity, pressure, and elevation across a section normal to this streamline are considered typical of the flow as a whole.   Thus the equation of continuity in Sec. 3.4 is called the one-dimensional equation of continuity, even though it may be applied to flow in conduits which curve in space and in which the velocity varies across any section normal to the flow.   It will be of increasing importance in the following chapters to recognize that, when high accuracy is desired, the equations derived by the one-dimensional method of analysis require refinement to account for the variation in conditions across the section.

If the flow is such that all streamlines are plane curves and are identical in a series of parallel planes, it is said to be two-dimensional.   In Fig. 3.8a the channel has a constant dimension perpendicular to the plane of the figure.   Thus every cross section normal to the flow must be a rectangle of this constant width.   If the total rate of discharge is to be divided by streamlines into equal parts, the streamlines must be equally spaced, provided that the velocity is uniform over the cross section (which will be true in ideal flow except at the sections where the boundary changes alignment).

Three-dimensional flow is illustrated in Fig. 3.8b, which differs from Fig. 3.8a in that the cross sections are not rectangles but, in this particular case, circles.   The longitudinal section is taken through the diameter MN, and every streamline in such a section is a plane curve with no velocity component perpendicular to the plane of the paper.   Clearly, any streamline not in this longitudinal section will have such velocity components in

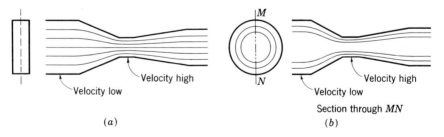

Fig. 3.8.   Two- and three-dimensional flow of an ideal fluid.

the conical part of the tube.   If the total flow is divided into equal parts by stream surfaces, the streamlines which are the traces of these surfaces on diametral sections will not be equally spaced.

Two-dimensional flow offers the advantage that it is usually easier to draw diagrams describing the flow, but the same principles apply to three-dimensional flow.

3.7. THE FLOW NET

The streamlines and velocity distribution in the case of steady flow of an *ideal* fluid within any boundary configuration may be determined by a *flow net*, such as is shown in Fig. 3.9.   This is a network of streamlines and lines normal to them so spaced that the distances between both sets of lines are inversely proportional to the local velocities.   The streamlines show the direction of flow at any point.   A fundamental property of the flow net is that it provides the one and only representation of the ideal flow within the given boundaries.   It is also independent of the actual magnitude of the flow and, for the *ideal* fluid, is the same whether the flow is in one direction or the reverse.

In a few simple cases it is possible to obtain mathematical expressions, known as *potential functions* (Sec. 5.4), from which one can plot stream-

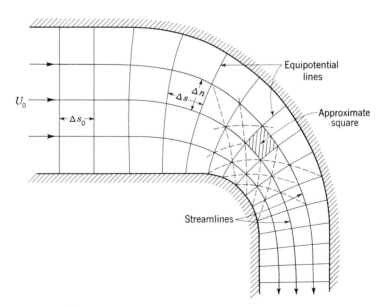

Fig. 3.9.   Flow net.

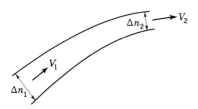

Fig. 3.10

lines.   But even the most complex cases can be solved by plotting a flow
net by a trial-and-error method.   Although it is possible to construct nets
for three-dimensional flow, treatment here will be restricted to the simpler
two-dimensional net, which will more clearly illustrate the method.
Consider the two-dimensional stream tube of Fig. 3.10.   Assuming a
constant unit thickness perpendicular to the paper, the continuity equation gives $V_1 \Delta n_1 = V_2 \Delta n_2$.

Consider next a region of uniform flow divided into a number of strips
of equal width, separated by streamlines, as in Fig. 3.8a.   Each strip
represents a stream tube, and the flow is equally divided among the tubes.
As the flow approaches a bend or obstruction, the streamlines must deviate
so as to conform to the boundaries, but each stream tube still carries the
same flow.   Thus the spacing between all streamlines in the entire field is
everywhere inversely proportional to the local velocities, so that, for any
section normal to the velocity,

$$V \Delta n = \text{constant} \tag{3.7}$$

To draw the streamlines, it is necessary to start by estimating not
only the spacing between them but also their directions at all points.   As
an aid in the latter we make use of normal, or *equipotential*, lines.   As an
analogy consider the flow of heat through a homogeneous material
enclosed between perfectly insulated boundaries.   The heat might be
considered to flow along the equivalent of streamlines.   As there can be
no flow of heat along a line of constant temperature, it follows that the
heat flow must be everywhere perpendicular to isothermal lines.   In like
manner streamlines must be everywhere perpendicular to equipotential
lines.   As solid boundaries, across which there can be no flow, also represent streamlines, it follows that equipotential lines must meet the boundaries everywhere at right angles.

If the equipotential lines are spaced the same distance apart as the
streamlines in the region of uniform flow, the net for that region is composed of perfect squares.   In a region of deformed flow the quadrilaterals
cannot remain square, but they will approach squares as the number of
streamlines and equipotential lines increase indefinitely.   It is frequently

helpful, in regions where the deformation is marked, to introduce extra streamlines and equipotential lines spaced midway between the original ones.

In drawing a flow net the beginner will make considerable use of the eraser, but with some practice a net can be sketched with fair facility to represent any boundary configuration. It is even possible to construct a flow net for cases where one solid boundary does not exist and the fluid extends laterally indefinitely, as in the flow around an immersed object. Such a case reveals an advantage of the flow net that is not evident from Fig. 3.9. In the flow between any confining solid boundaries it is at least always possible to determine the mean velocity across any section by dividing the total flow by the section area. For flow around an immersed object, as in Fig. 3.11, there is no fixed area by which to divide a definite flow, but the flow net affords a means of determining the velocity in the region of such an object.

It is even possible to draw a flow net for a free stream without any solid boundaries, as in the case of the jet from an orifice. For this purpose it is necessary first to determine the profile of the jet as it is influenced by gravity.

Where a channel is curved, the equipotential lines must diverge inasmuch as they radiate from centers of curvature. The distance between the associated streamlines must vary in the same way as that between the equipotential lines. Therefore, as in Fig. 3.9, the areas are smallest along the inner radius of the bend and increase toward the outside.

The accuracy of the final flow net can be checked by drawing diagonals, as indicated by a few dashed lines in Fig. 3.9. If the net is correct, these

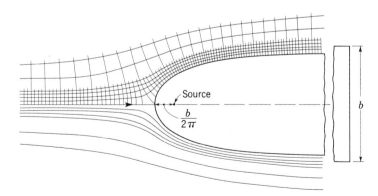

Fig. 3.11. Two-dimensional flow of a frictionless fluid past a solid whose surface is perpendicular to the plane of the paper. Streamlines or path lines for steady flow.

dashed lines also form a network of lines that cross each other at right angles and produce areas that approach squares in shape.

3.8. USE AND LIMITATIONS OF FLOW NET

Although the flow net is based on an ideal frictionless fluid, it may be applied to the flow of a real fluid within certain limits. Such limits are dictated by the extent to which the real fluid is affected by factors which the ideal-fluid theory neglects, the principal one of which is fluid friction.

The viscosity effects of a real fluid are most pronounced at or near a solid boundary and diminish rapidly with distance from the boundary. Hence, for an airplane or a submerged submarine, the fluid may be considered as frictionless, except when very close to the object.   The flow net always indicates a velocity next to a solid boundary, whereas a real fluid must have zero velocity adjacent to a wall.   The region in which the velocity is so distorted, however, is confined to a relatively thin layer called the *boundary* layer, outside of which the real fluid behaves very much like the ideal fluid.

The effect of the boundary friction is at a minimum when the streamlines are converging, but in a diverging flow there is a tendency for the streamlines not to follow the boundaries if the rate of divergence is too great.   In a sharply diverging flow, such as is shown schematically in Fig. 3.12, there may be a *separation* of the boundary layer from the wall, resulting in eddies and even reverse flow in that region.   The flow is badly disturbed in such a case, and the flow net is of little value.

A practical application of the flow net may be seen in the flow around a body, as shown in Fig. 3.11, which may represent, for example, the upstream portion of a bridge pier at a distance below the surface where

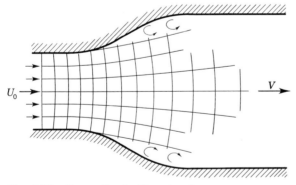

Fig. 3.12.   Separation in diverging flow.

surface wave action is not a factor.   Except for a thin layer adjacent to the body, this diagram does represent the flow in front of and around the sides of the body.   The central streamline is seen to branch at the forward tip to form two streamlines along the walls.   As the flow net indicates zero velocity at this forward tip, this is called the forward *stagnation point.*

Considering the limitations of the flow net in diverging flow, it may be seen that, while the flow net gives a fairly accurate picture of the velocity distribution for the upstream part of any solid body, it can give little information concerning the flow conditions at the rear because of separation and eddies.   The disturbed flow in the rear of a body is known as a *turbulent wake.*   The space occupied by it may be greatly diminished by streamlining the body, i.e., giving the body a long slender tail, which tapers to a sharp edge for two-dimensional flow or to a point for three-dimensional flow.

3.9. FRAME OF REFERENCE IN FLOW PROBLEMS

In flow problems we are really concerned only with the *relative* velocity between the fluid and the body.   It makes no difference whether the body is at rest and the fluid flows past it or whether the fluid is at rest and the body moves through it.   There are thus two frames of reference.   In one the observer (or the camera) is at rest with respect to the solid body. If the observer at rest with respect to a bridge pier views a steady flow past it or is on a ship moving at constant velocity through still water, the streamlines appear to him to be unchanging and therefore the flow is steady.   But if he floats with the current past the pier or views a ship going by while he stands on the bank, the flow pattern which he observes is changing with time.   Thus the flow is unsteady.

The same flow may then be either steady or unsteady according to the frame of reference.   The case that is usually of more practical importance is the one of steady flow, and for this case streamlines and path lines are identical.   In unsteady flow streamlines and path lines are entirely different from each other and also bear no resemblance to those of steady flow.

Illustrative example 3.1:   An incompressible ideal fluid flows at 0.5 cfs through a circular pipe into a conically converging nozzle.   Determine the average velocity of flow at sections A and B of the accompanying figure.

As a first step an approximate flow net is constructed to provide a general picture of the flow.   At section A the streamlines are parallel and hence the area at right angles to the velocity vectors is a plane circle.   Thus

$$V_A = \frac{Q}{A_A} = \frac{0.5}{(\pi/4)(\frac{8}{12})^2} = 1.42 \text{ fps}$$

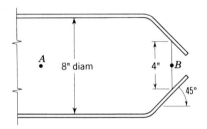

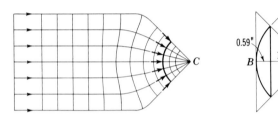

Illustrative Example 3.1

At section B, however, the area at right angles to the streamlines is not clearly defined; it is a curved, dish-shaped section. As a rough approximation it might be assumed to be the portion of the surface of a sphere of radius 2.0 in. that is intersected by a circle of diameter 2.82 in. Thus

$$V_B = \frac{Q}{A_B} = \frac{Q}{2\pi Rh} = \frac{0.5}{[2\pi(2)(0.59)]/144} = 9.75 \text{ fps}$$

3.10. VELOCITY AND ACCELERATION IN STEADY FLOW

In a typical three-dimensional flow field the velocities are everywhere different in magnitude and direction. Also, the velocity at any point in the field may change with time. Let us first consider the case where the flow is steady and thus independent of time. If the velocity of a fluid particle has components u, v, and w parallel to the x, y, and z axes, then for steady flow,

$$u_{st} = u(x,y,z) \tag{3.8a}$$

$$v_{st} = v(x,y,z) \tag{3.8b}$$

$$w_{st} = w(x,y,z) \tag{3.8c}$$

The acceleration of the fluid particle for steady flow can be expressed as

$$\mathbf{a}_{st} = \frac{d}{dt}\mathbf{V}(x,y,z) = \frac{\partial \mathbf{V}}{\partial x}\frac{dx}{dt} + \frac{\partial \mathbf{V}}{\partial y}\frac{dy}{dt} + \frac{\partial \mathbf{V}}{\partial z}\frac{dz}{dt} \tag{3.9}$$

where

$$|\mathbf{V}| = (u^2 + v^2 + w^2)^{1/2}$$

Noting that $dx/dt = u$, $dy/dt = v$, and $dz/dt = w$,

$$\mathbf{a}_{st} = u \frac{\partial \mathbf{V}}{\partial x} + v \frac{\partial \mathbf{V}}{\partial y} + w \frac{\partial \mathbf{V}}{\partial z} \qquad (3.10)$$

This equation can be written as three scalar equations:

$$(a_x)_{st} = u \frac{\partial u}{\partial x} + v \frac{\partial u}{\partial y} + w \frac{\partial u}{\partial z} \qquad (3.11a)$$

$$(a_y)_{st} = u \frac{\partial v}{\partial x} + v \frac{\partial v}{\partial y} + w \frac{\partial v}{\partial z} \qquad (3.11b)$$

$$(a_z)_{st} = u \frac{\partial w}{\partial x} + v \frac{\partial w}{\partial y} + w \frac{\partial w}{\partial z} \qquad (3.11c)$$

These equations show that even though the flow is steady, the fluid may possess an acceleration by virtue of a change in velocity with change in position. This type of acceleration is commonly referred to as *acceleration of transport*, or *convective acceleration*.

3.11. VELOCITY AND ACCELERATION IN UNSTEADY FLOW

If the flow is unsteady, then Eqs. (3.8a) to (3.8c) take the form

$$u = u(x,y,z,t) \; \cdots \qquad (3.12a)$$

Following a similar procedure to that of the preceding section results in the following set of scalar equations:

$$a_x = \left(u \frac{\partial u}{\partial x} + v \frac{\partial u}{\partial y} + w \frac{\partial u}{\partial z} \right) + \frac{\partial u}{\partial t} \qquad (3.13a)$$

$$a_y = \left(u \frac{\partial v}{\partial x} + v \frac{\partial v}{\partial y} + w \frac{\partial v}{\partial z} \right) + \frac{\partial v}{\partial t} \qquad (3.13b)$$

$$a_z = \left(u \frac{\partial w}{\partial x} + v \frac{\partial w}{\partial y} + w \frac{\partial w}{\partial z} \right) + \frac{\partial w}{\partial t} \qquad (3.13c)$$

In the above set of equations the three terms in parentheses are recognized as the convective accelerations, while the $\partial u/\partial t$, $\partial v/\partial t$, and $\partial w/\partial t$ terms represent the acceleration caused by the unsteadiness of the flow. This type of acceleration is commonly referred to as the *local acceleration*.

In the case of uniform flow (streamlines parallel to one another) the convective acceleration is zero and

$$\mathbf{a} = \frac{\partial \mathbf{V}}{\partial t} \qquad (3.14)$$

At times it is helpful to superimpose the coordinate system on the streamline pattern in such a fashion that the x axis is coincident with the streamline at a particular point of concern. In such a case the position s will indicate location along the streamline. Thus, generally, $\mathbf{V} = \mathbf{V}(s,t)$ and the acceleration of the particle can be conveniently expressed as

$$\mathbf{a} = V\frac{\partial \mathbf{V}}{\partial s} + \frac{\partial \mathbf{V}}{\partial t} \tag{3.15}$$

In uniform flow the first term of the above expression is zero, while in steady flow the second term becomes zero. In Eq. (3.15) $\mathbf{a}$ represents the acceleration of the fluid particle along the streamline. In the terminology of curvilinear motion this is referred to as the *tangential acceleration*. At this point in our discussion we should recall that a particle moving steadily along a curved path has a *normal acceleration* a_n toward the center of the path. From mechanics,

$$a_n = \frac{V^2}{r} \tag{3.16}$$

where r is the radius of the path. A particle moving on a curved path will always have a normal acceleration, though its tangential acceleration may be zero.

Illustrative example 3.2: Refer to the figure of Illustrative Example 3.1. The flow is steady at 0.5 cfs. Find the acceleration in the flow at sections A and B.

$$\mathbf{a}_A = 0 \qquad \text{(because the flow is uniform at section A and also steady)}$$

At section B the flow is really three-dimensional but may be considered as an axisymmetric two-dimensional flow. For any point in section B,

$$\mathbf{a}_B = u\frac{\partial \mathbf{V}}{\partial x} + v\frac{\partial \mathbf{V}}{\partial y}$$

For the point B on the axis of the pipe at section B,

$$\mathbf{a}_B = u\frac{\partial \mathbf{V}}{\partial x}$$

The effective area through which the flow is occurring in the vicinity of the nozzle may be expressed approximately as $A = 2\pi hr$, where $h = r(1 - \cos 45°) = 0.293r$ and r is the distance from point C.

Thus $A = 2\pi(0.293r^2) = 1.84r^2$, and the velocity in the converging nozzle (assuming the streamlines flow radially toward C) may be expressed approximately as

$$V = \frac{Q}{A} = \frac{0.5}{1.84r^2}$$

At point B ($r = 2$ in.),

$$V = \frac{0.5}{1.84r^2} = 9.75 \text{ fps}$$

and

$$\frac{\partial V}{\partial x} = -\frac{\partial V}{\partial r} = \frac{0.54}{r^3} = 118 \text{ fps/ft}$$

Thus

$$a_B = u\frac{\partial V}{\partial x} = 9.75(118) = 1{,}150 \text{ ft/sec}^2$$

Illustrative example 3.3: A two-dimensional flow field is given by $u = 2y$, $v = x$. Sketch the flow field. Derive a general expression for the velocity and acceleration.

Velocity components u and v are plotted to scale, and streamlines are sketched tangentially to the resultant velocity vectors. This gives a general picture of the flow field.

$$V = (u^2 + v^2)^{1/2} = (4y^2 + x^2)^{1/2}$$

$$a_x = u\frac{\partial u}{\partial x} + v\frac{\partial u}{\partial y} = 2y(0) + x(2) = 2x$$

$$a_y = u\frac{\partial v}{\partial x} + v\frac{\partial v}{\partial y} = 2y(1) + x(0) = 2y$$

$$\mathbf{a} = (a_x{}^2 + a_y{}^2)^{1/2} = (4x^2 + 4y^2)^{1/2}$$

To get a rough check on the acceleration imagine a velocity vector at point A in the accompanying figure. This vector would have a magnitude approximately midway

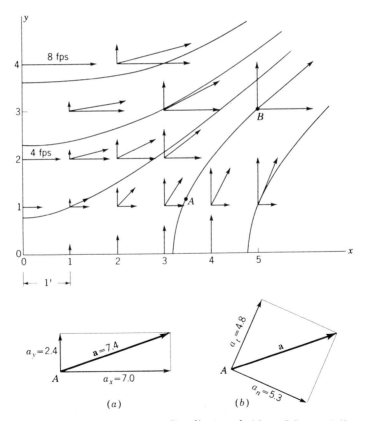

Illustrative Example 3.3. Coordinates of $A(x = 3.5, y = 1.2)$; $a_x = 2x = 7.0$ fps/sec; $a_y = 2y = 2.4$ fps/sec; $\mathbf{a} = [(7.0)^2 + (2.4)^2]^{1/2} = 7.4$ fps/sec. (a) True vector diagram of acceleration at A. (b) Approximate vector diagram of acceleration at A.

between that of the adjoining vectors, or $V_A \approx 4$ fps. The radius of curvature of the sketched streamline at A is roughly 3 ft. Thus $a_n \approx 4^2/3 = 5.3$ fps. The tangential acceleration of the particle at A may be approximated by noting that the velocity along the streamline increases from about 3.2 fps, where it crosses the x axis, to about 8 fps at B. The distance along the streamline between these two points is roughly 4 ft. Hence a very approximate value of the tangential acceleration at A is

$$a_t = V \frac{\partial V}{\partial s} = 4 \left(\frac{8 - 3.2}{4} \right) = 4.8 \text{ fps/sec}$$

Vector diagrams of these roughly computed normal and tangential acceleration components are plotted for comparison with the true acceleration as given by the analytic expressions.

PROBLEMS

3.1. Classify the following cases of flow as to whether they are steady or unsteady, uniform or nonuniform: (*a*) water flowing from a tilted pail; (*b*) flow from a rotating lawn sprinkler; (*c*) flow through the hose leading to the sprinkler; (*d*) natural stream during dry-weather flow; (*e*) natural stream during flood; (*f*) flow in a city water-distribution main in a straight section of constant diameter and no side connections. (*Note:* There is room for legitimate argument in some of the above cases, which should stimulate independent thought.)

3.2. It is sometimes assumed, though there is no theoretical reason for it, that the velocity profile for turbulent flow in a circular pipe is the semiellipse MBN shown in the figure and that the center velocity OB is twice that near the wall. The rate of discharge $\int u \, dA$ is represented by the volume of the solid $O'MBNO'$. Therefore the mean velocity is represented by the length of a cylinder of the same volume and base. The volume of an ellipsoid is two-thirds that of the circumscribing cylinder. Prove that for this assumption the ratio of mean velocity to maximum velocity is 0.833.

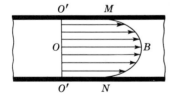

Fig. Prob. 3.2

3.3. In the laminar flow of a fluid in a circular pipe the velocity profile is exactly a true parabola. The rate of discharge is then represented by the volume of a paraboloid. Prove that for this case the ratio of the mean velocity to the maximum velocity is 0.5.

3.4. The velocities in a circular conduit 20 in. in diameter were measured at radii 0, 3.16, 4.45, 5.48, 6.33, 7.07, 7.75, 8.37, 8.94, 9.49, and 10 in. and were found to be 7.50, 7.10, 6.75, 6.42, 6.15, 5.81, 5.47, 5.10, 4.50, 3.82, and 2.40 fps, respectively. Find the rate of discharge and mean velocity.

This may be solved graphically. Since $Q = \int u \, dA = \int_0^{r_0} u \, d(\pi r^2)$, it follows that Q is π times the area under a curve of u plotted against simultaneous values of r^2, such as those shown in the figure, where r_0 is the radius to the wall. In cases where the difference between the maximum and minimum velocities is small compared with the actual values, greater accuracy may be obtained by plotting and measuring only the area above the line xy in the figure and adding to the result the area of the rectangle below xy. In this particular problem, since the radii were so chosen as to secure equal steps in the values of r^2, the answer may be obtained without actually plotting the curve. As the ordinates are all spaced at *equal* intervals of 10 in.^{2}, Simpson's rule or some other method may be used. In applying Simpson's rule the area is obtained by multiplying even-numbered ordinates by 4 and odd ones by 2, except the first and the last, and adding. This sum should then be multiplied by one-third of the interval between ordinates ($= 0.02315$ ft^2).

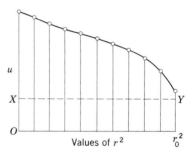

Fig. Prob. 3.4

Values of r^2

3.5. A gas ($\gamma = 0.04$ pcf) flows at the rate of 1.0 lb/sec past section A through a long rectangular duct of uniform cross section 2 by 2 ft. At section B some distance along the duct the gas weighs 0.065 pcf. What is the average velocity of flow at sections A and B?

3.6. Make an approximate plot of the frictionless velocity along both the inner and the outer boundaries of Fig. 3.9. By what per cent is the ideal maximum inner velocity greater than the ideal minimum outer velocity?

3.7. Consider the two-dimensional flow about a cylinder 2 in. in diameter. Sketch the flow net for the ideal flow around one-quarter of the cylinder. Start with a uniform net of $\frac{1}{2}$-in. squares, and fill in with $\frac{1}{4}$-in. squares where desirable. (*Note:* The velocity at the stagnation point is zero, and it can be proved by classical hydrodynamics that the velocity tangent to the cylinder at a point 90° from the stagnation point is twice the uniform velocity.) Make a plot of the velocity along the center streamline from a distance upstream where the velocity is uniform up to the stagnation point, and then along the boundary of the cylinder from the stagnation point to the 90° point. Compare the result thus obtained with the value given by the equation $V = 2U_0 \sin \theta$, where U_0 is the undisturbed stream velocity and θ is the angle from the stagnation point to any point on the cylinder where V is desired.

3.8. The figure shows the flow net for two-dimensional flow from a rounded, long-slotted exit from a tank. If a is 3 in. and U_0 is 10 fps, find how long

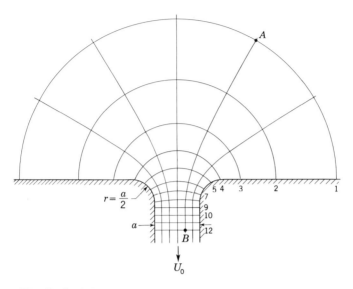

Fig. Prob. 3.8

it will take a particle to move from point A to point B on the same stream-line. (*Note:* Between each pair of equipotential lines, measure Δs, and then compute the average velocity and time increment.)

3.9. Assume that the streamlines for a two-dimensional flow of a frictionless incompressible fluid against a flat plate normal to the initial velocity may be represented by the equation $xy = $ constant and that the flow is symmetrical about the plane through $y = 0$. A different streamline may be plotted for each value of the constant. Using a scale 1 in. = 6 units of distance, plot streamlines for values of the constant of 16, 64, and 128.

3.10. For the case in Prob. 3.9, it can be shown that the velocity components at any point are $u = ax$ and $v = -ay$, where a is a constant. Thus the actual velocity is $\mathbf{V} = a\sqrt{x^2 + y^2} = ar$, where r is the radius to the origin. Let $a = \frac{1}{3}$; then if 1 in. = 6 ft for the streamlines, 1 in. = 2 fps for the velocity scale. Draw curves of equal velocity for values of 2, 4, 6, 8, and 10 fps. How does the velocity vary along the surface of the plate?

3.11. For three-dimensional flow with the x axis as the axis of symmetry the streamline equations are $xy^2 = $ constant and the velocity is given by

$$\mathbf{V} = a\sqrt{4x^2 + y^2}$$

Plot streamlines and lines of constant velocity. How does the velocity vary along the plate?

3.12. In Fig. 3.11 assume that $b = 5$ ft and the uniform velocity is 10 fps. Make a plot of the velocity along the boundary of the solid. By what per cent does the maximum velocity along the boundary exceed the uniform velocity?

3.13. The velocity along a streamline lying on the x axis is given by $u = 10 + x^{\frac{1}{2}}$. What is the convective acceleration at $x = 3$? Is the flow converging or diverging? Sketch to approximate scale the adjoining streamlines.

3.14. Sketch the flow field defined by $u = 3y$, $v = 2$, and derive expressions for the x and y components of acceleration. Find the magnitude of the velocity and acceleration for the point having the coordinates (3,4).

3.15. Sketch the flow field defined by $u = 0$, $v = 3xy$, and derive expressions for the x and y components of acceleration. Find the acceleration at the point (2,2).

3.16. Sketch the flow field defined by $u = -2y$, $v = 3x$, and derive expressions for the x and y components of acceleration. As in Illustrative Example 3.3, find approximate values of the normal and tangential accelerations of the particle at the point (2,3). Compare the value of $(a_n{}^2 + a_t{}^2)^{1/2}$ with the computed value $(a_x{}^2 + a_y{}^2)^{1/2}$.

3.17. The velocity along a circular streamline of radius 5 ft is 3 fps. Find the normal and tangential components of the acceleration if the flow is steady.

3.18. A large tank contains an ideal liquid which flows out of the bottom of the tank through a 6-in.-diameter hole. The rate of steady outflow is 10 cfs. Assume that the liquid approaches the center of the hole radially. Find the velocities and convective accelerations at points that are 2 and 3 ft from the center of the hole.

3.19. Refer to Prob. 3.18. Suppose the flow is unsteady and $Q = 10 - 0.5t$, where Q is in cubic feet per second and t is in seconds. Find the local acceleration at a point 2 ft from the center of the hole at time $t = 10$ sec. What is the local acceleration at this point at $t = 20$ sec? Find the total acceleration at a point 3 ft from the center of the hole at $t = 30$ sec.

3.20. A flow field is defined by $u = 2$, $v = 3$, $w = 4$. What is the velocity of flow?

3.21. A flow is defined by $u = 2(1 + t)$, $v = 3(1 + t)$, $w = 4(1 + t)$. What is the velocity of flow at the point (3,1,4) at $t = 2$ sec? What is the acceleration at that point at $t = 2$ sec?

3.22. A two-dimensional flow field is given by $u = 3 + 2xy + 4t^2$, $v = xy^2 + 3t$. Find the velocity and acceleration of a particle of fluid at point (2,1) at $t = 5$.

3.23. The figure shows to scale a two-dimensional stream tube. The flow rate is 40 cfs/ft perpendicular to the plane of the sketch. Determine approximate values of the normal and tangential accelerations of a fluid particle at A. What is the resultant acceleration of a particle at A?

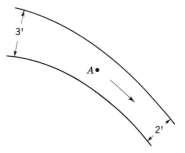

Fig. Prob. 3.23

FOUR

ENERGY CONSIDERATIONS
IN STEADY FLOW

In this chapter fluid flow is approached from the viewpoint of energy considerations. The first law of thermodynamics tells us that energy can neither be created nor destroyed. Moreover, all forms of energy are equivalent. In the following sections the various forms of energy present in fluid flow are briefly discussed.

4.1. KINETIC ENERGY OF A FLOWING FLUID

A body of mass m and velocity V possesses kinetic energy $= mV^2/2$, or $V^2/2$ per unit of mass. As there are g units of weight per unit of mass, the kinetic energy per unit of weight is $V^2/2g$.

In the flow of a real fluid the velocities of different particles will usually not be the same, so it is necessary to integrate the kinetic energies of all portions of the stream to obtain the total value. Consider the case where the axial components of velocity vary across a section. If u is the local axial velocity component at a point, the mass flow per unit time through an elementary area dA is $\rho\,dQ = \rho u\,dA = (\gamma/g)u\,dA$. Thus the flow of kinetic energy per unit time across the area dA is $(\rho u\,dA)u^2/2 = (\gamma/2g)u^3\,dA$; so the total kinetic energy possessed by the fluid and physically carried across the entire section per unit time is

$$\frac{\rho}{2}\int_A u^3\,dA = \frac{\gamma}{2g}\int_A u^3\,dA \tag{4.1}$$

If the exact velocity profile is known, the true kinetic energy of a flowing stream can be determined by integration of this equation.

It is convenient to use the mean velocity V and a factor α such that, for the entire section, the true average value is

$$\text{Kinetic energy per unit weight} = \alpha\,\frac{V^2}{2g} \tag{4.2}$$

The flow across the entire section is $G = g\rho Q = \gamma Q = \gamma A V$, so the total kinetic energy transmitted is

$$G\alpha\,\frac{V^2}{2g} = \gamma A V\alpha\,\frac{V^2}{2g} = \alpha\,\frac{\gamma}{2g}\,A V^3 \tag{4.3}$$

Equating (4.3) to (4.1), we obtain

$$\alpha = \frac{1}{A V^3}\int_A u^3\,dA \tag{4.4}$$

As the average of cubes is greater than the cube of the average, the value of α will always be more than 1. The greater the variation in velocity across the section, the larger will be the value of α. For laminar flow in a circular pipe, $\alpha = 2$; for turbulent flow in pipes, α ranges from 1.01 to 1.15, but it is usually between 1.03 and 1.06.

In some instances it is very desirable to use the proper value of α, but in most cases the error in neglecting its divergence from 1.0 is negligible. As precise values of α are seldom known, it is customary to assume that the kinetic energy is $V^2/2g$ per unit weight of fluid.

4.2. POTENTIAL ENERGY

The potential energy of a particle of fluid depends on its elevation above any arbitrary datum plane. We are usually interested only in differences of elevation, and therefore the location of the datum plane is determined solely by considerations of convenience. A fluid particle of weight W situated a distance z above datum possesses a potential energy of Wz. Thus its potential energy per unit weight is z.

4.3. INTERNAL ENERGY

Internal energy I is more fully presented in texts on thermodynamics since it is thermal energy, but in brief, it is the energy due to molecular activity, which is a function of temperature. Internal potential energy is due to the forces of attraction between molecules. A perfect gas is one for which these forces are assumed to be zero, and hence, by Joule's law, the internal energy of a perfect gas is a function of its temperature only and is independent of pressure and volume. For gases at usual temperatures and pressures, the distance between molecules is so great that these forces are negligible, and hence in most cases real gases can be treated as ideal, or perfect, gases.

The zero of internal energy may be taken at any arbitrary temperature, since we are usually concerned only with differences. For a unit weight, $\Delta I = c_v \, \Delta T$, where c_v is specific heat at constant volume, and in this text is taken as Btu per pound per degree Fahrenheit. Thus I is in Btu per pound.[1]

4.4. GENERAL EQUATION FOR STEADY FLOW OF ANY FLUID

In Fig. 4.1 is shown a stream of fluid for which an equation will be derived by using the first law of thermodynamics, which states that the external work done upon any system is equal to the change of energy of the system. At section (1) the total force is $p_1 A_1$. Assume that, in a brief time dt, this section moves a short distance ds_1; then the force will do work $(p_1 A_1) \, ds_1$ on the body of fluid between (1) and (2). In similar manner, at (2) the external work due to the pressure and the motion is $-(p_2 A_2) \, ds_2$, the minus sign indicating that the force and the displacement are in opposite directions.

Also between (1) and (2) there might be a machine which does work *on* the fluid and puts mechanical energy *into* it, which will be denoted by M ft-lb/lb of fluid flowing. If the machine were a turbine, the fluid would do work upon it and then M would be minus. Heat q in Btu per pound of fluid flowing may be transferred to the fluid from the surroundings, but if the heat flow is out of the fluid, the value of q will be negative.

During the time dt the weight of fluid entering at (1) is $\gamma_1 A_1 \, ds_1$, and

---

[1] The definition given is for *sensible* internal energy and applies to liquids as well as to gases. For a change of state, as when water is evaporated into steam, there may be a great change in volume. For example, a pint of water when transformed into steam may occupy a volume of several cubic feet and even as much as 1,000 ft³ or more, depending upon the pressure. The change in potential energy at constant temperature due to the separation of the molecules against the forces of attraction between them is called the *internal latent heat*.

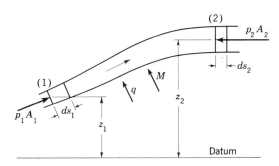

Fig. 4.1

for steady flow an equal weight must leave at (2) during the same time interval. Hence the energy which enters at (1) during the time dt is $\gamma_1 A_1\, ds_1\, (z_1 + \alpha_1 V_1{}^2/2g + JI_1)$, while that which leaves at (2) is represented by a similar expression. (In the ft-lb-sec system of units, $J = 778$ ft-lb/Btu.)

Equating the work done and the transfer of thermal energy to the change in the energy of the fluid, and at the same time factoring out $\gamma_1 A_1\, ds_1 = \gamma_2 A_2\, ds_2$,

$$\left(\frac{p_1}{\gamma_1} - \frac{p_2}{\gamma_2}\right) + M + Jq$$
$$= (z_2 - z_1) + \left(\alpha_2 \frac{V_2{}^2}{2g} - \alpha_1 \frac{V_1{}^2}{2g}\right) + J(I_2 - I_1) \quad (4.5)$$

This equation applies to liquids, gases, and vapors and to ideal fluids as well as to real fluids with friction. The only restriction is that it is for steady flow.

In turbulent flow there are other forms of kinetic energy besides that of translation described in Sec. 4.1. These are the rotational kinetic energy of eddies initiated by fluid friction and the kinetic energy of the turbulent fluctuations of velocity. They are not represented by any specific terms in Eq. (4.5) because their effect appears indirectly. The kinetic energy of translation can be converted into increases in p/γ or z, but these other forms of kinetic energy can never be transformed into anything but thermal energy. Thus they appear as an increase in the numerical value of I_2 over the value it would have if there were no friction, or else they produce an equivalent change in the numerical values of some other terms.

The general energy equation (4.5) and the continuity equation are two important keys to the solution of many problems in fluid mechanics. For compressible fluids it is necessary to have a third equation, which is the equation of state, i.e., the relation between pressure, temperature, and specific volume (or specific weight or density).

In many cases Eq. (4.5) is greatly shortened because certain quantities are equal and thus cancel each other, or are zero. Thus, if two points are at the same elevation, $z_1 - z_2 = 0$. If the conduit is well insulated or if the temperature of the fluid and that of its surroundings are practically the same, q may be taken as zero. On the other hand, q may be very large, as in the case of flow of water through a boiler tube. If there is no machine between (1) and (2), then the term M drops out. If there is a machine present, the work done by or upon it may be determined by solving Eq. (4.5) for M.

4.5. ENERGY EQUATION FOR STEADY FLOW OF INCOMPRESSIBLE FLUIDS

For liquids, and even for gases and vapors when the change in pressure is small, the fluid may be considered as incompressible for all practical purposes, and thus we may take $\gamma_1 = \gamma_2 = \gamma = $ constant. In turbulent flow the value of α is only a little more than unity, and as a simplifying assumption, it will now be omitted. Then Eq. (4.5) becomes

$$\left(\frac{p_1}{\gamma} + z_1 + \frac{V_1{}^2}{2g}\right) + M + Jq = \left(\frac{p_2}{\gamma} + z_2 + \frac{V_2{}^2}{2g}\right) + J(I_2 - I_1)$$

Fluid friction produces eddies and turbulence, and these forms of kinetic energy are eventually transformed into thermal energy. If there is no heat transfer, the effect of friction is to produce an increase in temperature so that I_2 becomes greater than I_1.

Suppose there is a loss of heat q at such a rate as to maintain the temperature constant so that $I_2 = I_1$. In this event there is an actual loss of energy from the system equal to the mechanical energy which has been converted into thermal energy by friction.

The transfer of heat may be of any value and may be in either direction; i.e., it may be either plus or minus. But whatever may be the value of q, the fluid friction is the same. Thus the loss of useful energy per pound of liquid caused by friction may be represented by

$$h_L = J(I_2 - I_1) - Jq = Jc(T_2 - T_1) - Jq \qquad (4.6)$$

where c is specific heat. If the loss of heat is greater than h_L, then T_2 will be less than T_1. If there is any absorption of heat, T_2 will be greater than the value which would have resulted from friction alone. Regardless of the value of q, however, the value of h_L is unaffected.[1]

[1] Because of the magnitude of J, which is 778 in our usual units, a large value of h_L produces only a very small rise in temperature if there is no heat transfer, or only a very few Btu of heat transfer if the flow is isothermal.

If there is no machine between (1) and (2), the energy equation becomes

$$\frac{p_1}{\gamma} + z_1 + \frac{V_1^2}{2g} = \frac{p_2}{\gamma} + z_2 + \frac{V_2^2}{2g} + h_L \qquad (4.7)$$

where h_L represents the energy loss per pound of fluid. In some cases the value of h_L may be very large, and although for any real fluid it can never be zero, there are cases when it is so small that it may be neglected with small error. In such special cases

$$\frac{p_1}{\gamma} + z_1 + \frac{V_1^2}{2g} = \frac{p_2}{\gamma} + z_2 + \frac{V_2^2}{2g} \qquad (4.8)$$

and from this it follows that

$$\frac{p}{\gamma} + z + \frac{V^2}{2g} = \text{constant} \qquad (4.9)$$

The equation in either of these last two forms is known as Bernoulli's theorem, in honor of Daniel Bernoulli, who presented it in 1738. Note that Bernoulli's theorem is for a *frictionless incompressible* fluid only.

Illustrative example 4.1: A liquid ($\gamma = 78.5$ pcf) flows in a pipe at a rate of 25 cfs. At one point where the pipe diameter is 24 in., the pressure is 45 psi. Find the pressure at a second point where the pipe diameter is 12 in. if the second point is 3 ft lower than the first point. Neglect head loss.

$$V_1 = \frac{25}{\pi} = 7.95 \text{ fps} \qquad V_2 = \frac{25}{\pi/4} = 31.8 \text{ fps}$$

$$0 + \frac{45(144)}{78.5} + \frac{(7.95)^2}{64.4} = -3 + \frac{p_2(144)}{78.5} + \frac{(31.8)^2}{64.4}$$

$$p_2 = 38.4 \text{ psi}$$

4.6. HEAD

In Eq. (4.7) every term has the dimensions of *length*. Thus p/γ, called *pressure* head, is an equivalent height of liquid representing a pressure p in a fluid of specific weight γ, z is *elevation* head, and $V^2/2g$ is *velocity* head. It is obvious that h_L must have the dimensions of length also; it is called *friction* head, or *lost* head. The sum of the first three is called *total* head and is denoted by H, where

$$H = \frac{p}{\gamma} + z + \frac{V^2}{2g} \qquad (4.10)$$

Each term in this equation, though ordinarily expressed in *feet*, represents *foot-pounds of energy per pound of fluid flowing.*

For a frictionless incompressible fluid, $H_1 = H_2$, but for any real fluid,

$$H_1 = H_2 + h_L \tag{4.11}$$

which is merely a brief way of writing Eq. (4.7). For a real fluid it is obvious that if there is no input of energy head M by a machine between sections (1) and (2), the total head must *decrease* in the direction of flow.

If there is a pump between (1) and (2), then

$$M = h_p = H_2 - H_1 + h_L \tag{4.12}$$

where h_p is the energy head put into the flow by the pump. If there is a turbine between (1) and (2), then

$$M = -h_t = H_1 - H_2 - h_L \tag{4.13}$$

where $-h_t$ is the energy head removed from the flow by the turbine.

4.7. POWER CONSIDERATIONS IN FLUID FLOW

In deriving Eq. (4.5), the term $\gamma A\, ds$ representing the weight of fluid was factored out; thus every term of the equation represents energy in foot-pounds per pound. If energy head is multiplied by the weight rate of flow, the resulting product represents power since the dimensions are feet times pounds per second. Thus

$$P = GH = \gamma QH \tag{4.14}$$

where P = power, ft-lb/sec,
   G = weight rate of flow, lb/sec
   H = energy head, ft

In the application of this expression H may be any head for which the corresponding power is desired.[1] For example, suppose the surface of water in a reservoir is 500 ft above the level of the site of a power plant and that there is available a flow of 200 cfs. In this case, $H = z = 500$ ft and $P = 62.4 \times 200 \times 500 = 6{,}240{,}000$ ft-lb/sec, or 11,340 hp, which is the total power available. If in the pipeline the friction loss is $h_L = 25$ ft, the power lost by friction is Gh_L and is seen to be 567 hp. Again, suppose a nozzle discharges 50 lb/sec of water in a jet with a velocity of 120 fps. $H = V^2/2g = 224$ ft. Then the available power in the jet is

$$50 \times 224/550 = 20.3 \text{ hp}$$

With respect to power, it may be recalled from mechanics that the

---

[1] Since one horsepower is equivalent to 550 ft-lb/sec, a convenient way of expressing Eq. (4.14) is HP $= \gamma QH/550$.

horsepower developed when a force F acts on a moving body, or when a torque T acts on a rotating body, is given by

$$\text{HP} = \frac{Fu}{550} = \frac{T\omega}{550} \qquad (4.15)$$

where F and T are expressed in pounds and foot-pounds, respectively. The force F represents the component force in the direction of u. The velocity u is in feet per second, and ω represents the rotative speed in radians per second. These equations will be referred to in Chap. 6, where the dynamic forces exerted by moving fluids are discussed, and again in Chaps. 14 through 18, in the discussion of turbomachinery.

Illustrative example 4.2: Consider a situation identical with Illustrative Example 4.1 except that a pump is in the line. When the pressure at the first point is 45 psi and the pressure at the second point is 50 psi, find the flow rate if the pump puts 22 hp into the flow. Once again neglect head loss.

$$\text{HP} = 22 = \frac{78.5 Q h_p}{550}$$

so
$$h_p = \frac{154}{Q}$$

$$0 + \frac{45(144)}{78.5} + \frac{(Q/\pi)^2}{64.4} + \frac{154}{Q} = -3 + \frac{50(144)}{78.5} + \frac{[Q/(\pi/4)]^2}{64.4}$$

By trial
$$Q = 14.5 \text{ cfs}$$

4.8. CAVITATION

In liquid flow problems the possibility of cavitation must be investigated. According to the Bernoulli theorem [Eq. (4.9)], if at any point the velocity head increases, there must be a corresponding decrease in the pressure head. For any liquid there is a minimum absolute pressure possible, namely, the vapor pressure of the liquid. The vapor pressure depends upon the liquid and its temperature. If the conditions are such that a calculation results in a lower absolute pressure than the vapor pressure, this simply means that the assumptions upon which the calculations are based no longer apply. Expressed in equation form, the criterion with respect to cavitation is as follows:

$$\left(\frac{p_{\text{crit}}}{\gamma}\right)_{\text{abs}} = \frac{p_v}{\gamma}$$

But
$$\left(\frac{p_{\text{crit}}}{\gamma}\right)_{\text{abs}} = \frac{p_a}{\gamma} + \left(\frac{p_{\text{crit}}}{\gamma}\right)_{\text{gage}}$$

Thus,
$$\left(\frac{p_{\text{crit}}}{\gamma}\right)_{\text{gage}} = -\left(\frac{p_a}{\gamma} - \frac{p_v}{\gamma}\right) \qquad (4.16)$$

where p_a, p_v, and p_{crit} represent the atmospheric pressure, the vapor pressure, and the critical (or minimum) possible pressure, respectively, in liquid flow. Equation (4.16) shows that the gage pressure head in a flowing liquid can be negative, but no more negative than $p_a/\gamma - p_v/\gamma$.

If at any point the local velocity is so high that the pressure in a liquid is reduced to its vapor pressure, the liquid will then vaporize (or boil) at that point and bubbles of vapor will form. As the fluid flows into a region of higher pressure, the bubbles of vapor will suddenly condense; in other words, they may be said to *collapse*. This action may produce very high dynamic pressure upon the adjacent solid walls, and since this action is continuous and has a high frequency, the material in that zone may be damaged. Turbine runners, pump impellers, and ship screw propellers are often severely and quickly damaged by such

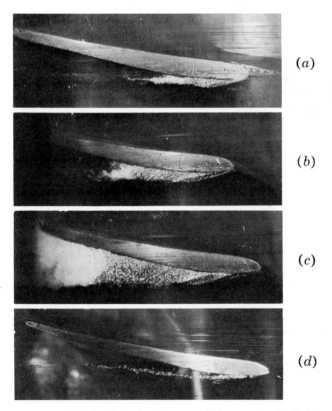

(a)

(b)

(c)

(d)

Fig. 4.2. Cavitation phenomena. (*Photographs by California Institute of Technology, Hydrodynamics Laboratory.*)

action, because holes are rapidly produced in the metal. Spillways and other types of hydraulic structures are also subject to damage from cavitation. The damaging action is commonly referred to as *pitting*. Not only is cavitation destructive, but it may produce a drop in efficiency of the machine or propeller or other device.

In order to avoid cavitation, it is necessary that the absolute pressure at every point be above the vapor pressure. To ensure this, it is necessary to raise the general pressure level, either by placing the device below the intake level so that the liquid flows to it by gravity rather than being drawn up by suction or by designing the machine so that there are no local velocities high enough to produce such a low pressure.

Figure 4.2 shows photographs of blades for an axial-flow pump set up in a transparent-lucite working section where the pressure level can be varied. For *a*, *b*, and *c* there was the same water velocity on the same vane but with decreasing absolute pressures. This resulted in the formation of a vapor pocket of increasing size. The stream flow and the pressure for *d* were the same as for *b*, but the nose of the blade was slightly different in shape, which gave a different type of bubble formation. This shows the effect of a slight change in design.

Illustrative example 4.3:   A liquid ($s = 0.86$) with a vapor pressure of 3.8 psia flows through the horizontal constriction in the accompanying figure. Atmospheric

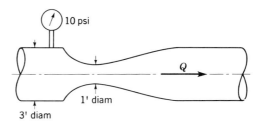

Illustrative Example 4.3

pressure is 26.7 in. Hg.   Find the maximum theoretical flow rate (i.e., at what Q does cavitation occur?).   Neglect head loss.

$$p_a = \frac{26.7}{29.9} (14.7) = 13.2 \text{ psia}$$

$$0 + \frac{10(144)}{0.86(62.4)} + \frac{(Q/2.25\pi)^2}{64.4} = 0 - 25.2 + \frac{(Q/4\pi)^2}{64.4}$$

$$Q = 45.8 \text{ cfs}$$

4.9. ENERGY EQUATION FOR STEADY FLOW OF COMPRESSIBLE FLUIDS

If sections (1) and (2) are so chosen that there is no machine between them, and if α is assumed as unity as in the preceding section, Eq. (4.5) becomes

$$\left(\frac{p_1}{\gamma_1} + JI_1 + z_1 + \frac{V_1{}^2}{2g}\right) + Jq = \left(\frac{p_2}{\gamma_2} + JI_2 + z_2 + \frac{V_2{}^2}{2g}\right) \quad (4.17)$$

For most compressible fluids, i.e., gases or vapors, the quantity p/γ is usually very large compared with $z_1 - z_2$ because of the small value of γ, and therefore the z terms are usually omitted. But $z_1 - z_2$ should not be ignored unless it is known to be negligible compared with the other quantities.

The $p/\gamma(=pv)$ and the I terms are usually combined for gases and vapors into a single term called *enthalpy*, indicated by a single symbol such as $E = I + pv/J$, where E is in Btu per pound.[1] With these changes Eq. (4.17) becomes

$$JE_1 + \frac{V_1{}^2}{2g} + Jq = JE_2 + \frac{V_2{}^2}{2g} \quad (4.18)$$

This equation may be used for any gas or vapor and for any process. Some knowledge of thermodynamics is required to evaluate the E terms, and in the case of vapors it is necessary to use vapor tables or charts, because their properties cannot be expressed by any simple equations.

Isothermal flow of a gas. For constant temperature, $I_1 = I_2$ and $pv = $ constant, or $p_1/\gamma_1 = p_2/\gamma_2$. Consequently, $E_1 = E_2$, and hence for this case Eq. (4.17) becomes

$$\frac{V_2{}^2 - V_1{}^2}{2g} = +Jq \quad (4.19)$$

which shows that an isothermal flow is accompanied by an *absorption* of heat when there is an *increase* in kinetic energy. This equation applies either with or without friction. If there is friction, less heat is absorbed from the surroundings. Since q is numerically less, there is then less increase in kinetic energy.

---

[1] In thermodynamics h is used instead of E, but the letter h has so many uses in fluid mechanics that it seems desirable to use a different letter here. Values of E for vapors commonly used in engineering, such as steam, ammonia, sulfur dioxide, freon, and others, may be obtained by the use of vapor tables or charts. For a perfect gas and practically for real gases $\Delta E = c_p \, \Delta T$, where c_p is specific heat at constant pressure. For air at usual temperatures its value is 0.24 Btu/(lb)(°F), but it increases with increasing temperature. Values for this and for other gases may be found in thermodynamics texts and in handbooks.

Adiabatic flow. If heat transfer q is zero and the same assumptions regarding the z and α terms are made as before, the energy equation for any compressible fluid becomes

$$JE_1 + \frac{V_1^2}{2g} = JE_2 + \frac{V_2^2}{2g} \qquad (4.20)$$

and since $778 \times 2g$ is practically $50,000$, this may be written

$$V_2^2 - V_1^2 = 50,000(E_1 - E_2) \qquad (4\text{-}21)$$

For a gas, $\Delta E = c_p \, \Delta T$, and therefore for gases

$$V_2^2 - V_1^2 = 2gJc_p(T_1 - T_2) = 50,000c_p(T_1 - T_2) \qquad (4.22)$$

For vapors Eq. (4.21) is convenient, but for gases a different expression from Eq. (4.22) is often useful. From thermodynamics

$$c_p = \frac{kR}{(k-1)J}$$

and for a perfect gas $pv = RT$. Therefore, for a perfect gas,

$$\frac{V_2^2 - V_1^2}{2g} = \frac{k}{k-1}(p_1v_1 - p_2v_2) \qquad (4.23)$$

The preceding equations are valid for flow either with or without friction. For ideal flow without friction the values of E_2, T_2, and v_2 are all determined as the result of a frictionless (or isentropic) expansion from p_1 to p_2. Fluid friction increases the numerical value of all these quantities, and it is sometimes desirable to designate these larger values as E_2', T_2', and v_2'.

Sometimes it is feasible to calculate these terminal values with friction, but more often it is convenient to use the ideal frictionless values in the equations and then multiply the ideal result, such as V_2, for example, by an experimental factor to obtain the correct value with friction. Further discussion of the flow of compressible fluids is presented in Chap. 9.

4.10. EQUATION OF STEADY MOTION ALONG A STREAMLINE FOR IDEAL FLUID

Referring to Fig. 4.3, let us consider frictionless steady flow of an incompressible fluid along the streamline. We shall consider the forces acting on the fluid element in the direction of the streamline and apply Newton's second law, that is, $F = ma$. The forces tending to accelerate the fluid

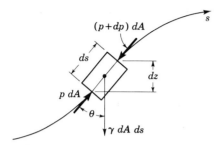

Fig. 4.3. Element on stream tube (ideal fluid).

mass are pressure forces on the two ends of the element

$$p \, dA - (p + dp) \, dA = -dp \, dA$$

where dA is the cross section of the element at right angles to the streamline, and the weight component in the direction of motion

$$-\rho g \, ds \, dA \, (dz/ds) = -\rho g \, dA \, dz$$

The mass of the element is $\rho \, dA \, ds$, while its acceleration for steady flow can be expressed by Eq. (3.15) as $V \, (dV/ds)$.   Thus

$$-dp \, dA - \rho g \, dA \, dz = \rho \, ds \, dA \, V \frac{dV}{ds}$$

Dividing by $-\rho \, dA$,

$$\frac{dp}{\rho} + V \, dV + g \, dz = 0 \tag{4.24}$$

This equation is commonly referred to as the one-dimensional Euler equation, because it was first derived by Leonhard Euler in about 1750.

Equation (4.24) can also be expressed as

$$\frac{dp}{\gamma} + d \frac{V^2}{2g} + dz = 0 \tag{4.25}$$

Now integrating,

$$\int \frac{dp}{\gamma} + \int d \frac{V^2}{2g} + \int dz = \text{constant} \tag{4.26}$$

Thus $$\frac{p}{\gamma} + \frac{V^2}{2g} + z = \text{constant} = \text{total head} \tag{4.27}$$

This is Bernoulli's equation [Eq. (4.9)] for steady flow of a frictionless incompressible fluid along a streamline.   Thus we have developed the Bernoulli equation from two viewpoints, first from energy considerations and now from Newton's second law.

If there is no flow,

$$z + \frac{p}{\gamma} = \text{constant} \tag{4.28}$$

This equation is identical with Eq. (2.6); it shows that for an incompressible fluid at rest, the summation of the elevation z at any point in the fluid plus the pressure head p/γ at that point is equal to the sum of these two quantities at any other point.

4.11. EQUATION OF STEADY MOTION ALONG A STREAMLINE FOR REAL FLUID

Let us now follow the same procedure as in the last section, except that now we shall consider a real incompressible fluid. The fluid element (Fig. 4.4) is similar to the one of Fig. 4.3, except that with a real fluid there is an additional force acting because of fluid friction, namely, $\tau(2\pi r)\,ds$, where τ is the shear stress at the boundary of the element and $2\pi r\,ds$ is the area over which the shear stress acts, r being the radius of the stream tube under consideration. Writing $F = ma$, we get for steady flow

$$-dp\,dA - \rho g\,dA\,dz - \tau(2\pi r)\,ds = \rho\,ds\,dA\;V\frac{dV}{ds}$$

In this case $dA = \pi r^2$. Making this substitution for dA and dividing through by $-\rho\pi r^2$ gives

$$\frac{dp}{\rho} + V\,dV + g\,dz = -\frac{2\tau\,ds}{\rho r} \tag{4.29}$$

This equation is similar to Eq. (4.24), except that it has an extra term. The extra term $-(2\tau\,ds)/\rho r$ accounts for fluid friction.

Equation (4.29) may also be expressed as

$$\frac{dp}{\gamma} + d\frac{V^2}{2g} + dz = -\frac{2\tau\,ds}{\gamma r} \tag{4.30}$$

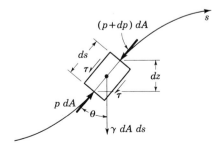

Fig. 4.4. Element on stream tube (real fluid).

Now integrating from some section (1) to another section (2), where the distance between them is L, we get

$$\frac{p_2}{\gamma} - \frac{p_1}{\gamma} + \frac{V_2^2}{2g} - \frac{V_1^2}{2g} + z_2 - z_1 = -\frac{2\tau L}{\gamma r}$$

or $$\left(\frac{p_1}{\gamma} + \frac{V_1^2}{2g} + z_1\right) - \frac{2\tau L}{\gamma r} = \frac{p_2}{\gamma} + \frac{V_2^2}{2g} + z_2 \tag{4.31}$$

Comparing Eq. (4.31) with Eq. (4.7), we see that

$$h_L = \frac{2\tau L}{\gamma r} \tag{4.32}$$

This expression will be referred to in Chap. 8.   Reference to Eq. (4.6) indicates that fluid friction is dissipated as heat.   In an adiabatic flow with an incompressible fluid Eq. (4.6) shows that $h_L = Jc(T_2 - T_1)$.

4.12. HYDRAULIC GRADE LINE AND ENERGY LINE

The term $z + p/\gamma$ is referred to as the *static head*, or *piezometric head*, because it represents the level to which liquid will rise in a piezometer tube (Sec. 2.6).   The *piezometric head line*, or *hydraulic grade line* (HGL), is a line drawn through the tops of the piezometer columns.   A pitot tube (Sec. 11.3), a small open tube with its open end pointing upstream, will intercept the kinetic energy of the flow and hence indicate the *total energy head*, $z + p/\gamma + u^2/2g$.   Referring to Fig. 4.5, which depicts the

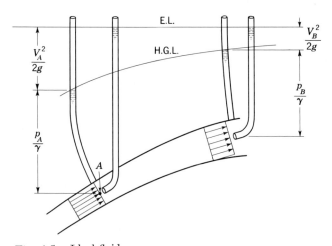

Fig. 4.5.   Ideal fluid.

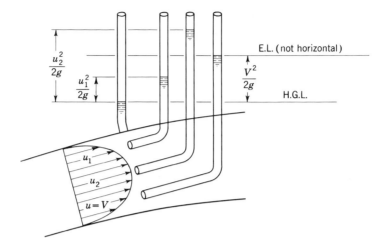

Fig. 4.6.   Real fluid.

flow of an ideal fluid, the vertical distance from point A on the stream tube to the level of the piezometric head at that point represents the pressure head in the flow at point A. The vertical distance from the liquid level in the piezometer tube to that in the pitot tube is $V^2/2g$. In Fig. 4.5, the horizontal line sketched through the pitot-tube liquid levels is known as the energy line (EL). For flow of an ideal fluid, the energy line is horizontal since there is no head loss.

A pitot tube intercepts the total energy in the flow field at the point at which it is located (Fig. 4.6). Hence the level above datum to which liquid will rise in a pitot tube is $z + p/\gamma + u^2/2g$, where u is the local velocity. For a pitot tube to indicate the true level of the energy line, it must be placed in the flow at a point where $u^2/2g = \alpha\,(V^2/2g)$, or where $u = \sqrt{\alpha}\,V$. If α (Sec. 4.1) is assumed to have a value of 1.0, then to indicate the energy line, the tube must be placed in the flow at a point where $u = V$. One rarely knows ahead of time where in the flow $u = V$; hence the correct positioning of a pitot tube, in order that it may indicate the true position of the energy line, is generally unknown.

Illustrative example 4.4:   Water flows in a wide open channel as shown in the accompanying figure. Two pitot tubes are connected to a differential manometer containing a liquid ($s = 0.82$). Find u_A and u_B.

$$\frac{u_A{}^2}{2g} = 3 \text{ ft}$$

$$u_A = 13.9 \text{ fps}$$

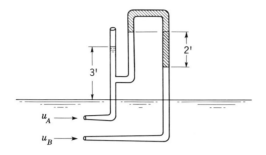

Illustrative Example 4.4

Applying Eq. (2.13), noting that a pitot tube intercepts $z + p/\gamma + u^2/2g$,

$$\frac{u_A{}^2}{2g} - \frac{u_B{}^2}{2g} = \frac{24}{12}(1 - 0.82)$$

from which $u_B = 13.0$ fps

Familiarity with the concept of the energy line and hydraulic grade line is useful in the solution of flow problems involving incompressible fluids. If a piezometer tube is erected at B in Fig. 4.7, the liquid will rise in it to a height BB' equal to the pressure head existing at that point. If the end of the pipe at E were closed so that no flow would take place, the height of this column would then be BM. The drop from M to B' when flow occurs is due to two factors, one of these being that a portion of the pressure head has been converted into the velocity head which

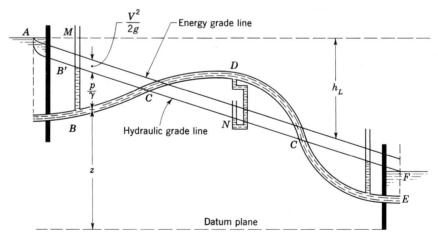

Fig. 4.7. Hydraulic and energy grade lines.

the liquid has at B, and the other that there has been a loss of head due to fluid friction between A and B.

If a series of piezometers were erected along the pipe, the liquid would rise in them to various levels.   The line drawn through the summits of such an imaginary series of liquid columns is called the *hydraulic grade line*.   It may be observed that the hydraulic grade line represents what would be the free surface if one could exist and maintain the same conditions of flow.

The hydraulic grade line indicates the pressure along the pipe, as at any point the vertical distance from the pipe to the hydraulic grade line is the pressure head at that point, assuming the profile to be drawn to scale.   At C this distance is zero, thus indicating that the absolute pressure within the pipe at that point is atmospheric.   At D the pipe is above the hydraulic grade line, indicating that there the pressure head is $-DN$, or a vacuum of DN ft of liquid.

If the profile of a pipeline is drawn to scale, then not only does the hydraulic grade line enable the pressure head to be determined at any point by measurement on the diagram, but it shows by mere inspection the variation of the pressure in the entire length of the pipe.   The grade line is a straight line only if the pipe is straight and of uniform diameter. But for the gradual curvatures that are often found in long pipelines, the deviation from a straight line will be small.   Of course, if there are local losses of head, aside from those due to normal pipe friction, there may be abrupt drops in the grade line, and also any changes in diameter with resultant changes in velocity will make marked changes in it.

If the velocity head is constant, as in Fig. 4.7, the drop in the hydraulic grade line between any two points is the value of the loss of

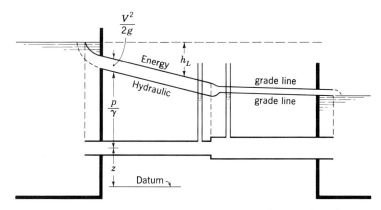

Fig. 4.8   (*Plotted to scale from measurements made by Daugherty.*)

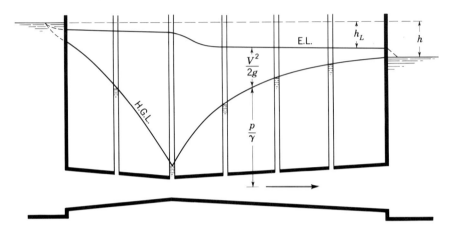

Fig. 4.9.   *(Plotted to scale from measurements made by Daugherty.)*

head between those two points, and the slope of the hydraulic grade line is then a measure of the rate of loss.   Thus in Fig. 4.8 the rate of loss in the larger pipe is much less than in the smaller pipe.   If the velocity changes, the hydraulic grade line might actually rise in the direction of flow, as shown in Figs. 4.8 and 4.9.

The vertical distance from the level of the surface at A in Fig. 4.7 down to the hydraulic grade line represents $V^2/2g + h_L$ from A to any point in question.   Hence the position of the grade line is independent of the position of the pipe.   Thus it is not necessary to compute pressure heads at various points in the pipe to plot the hydraulic grade line. Instead, values of $V^2/2g + h_L$ from A to various points can be laid off below the horizontal line through A, and this procedure is often more convenient.   If the pipe is of uniform diameter, it is necessary to locate only a few points, and often only two are required.

If Fig. 4.7 represents to scale the profile of a pipe of uniform diameter, the hydraulic grade line can be drawn as follows.   At the intake to the pipe there will be a drop below the surface at A, which should be laid off equal to $V^2/2g$ plus a local entrance loss.   (This latter is explained in Chap. 8.)   At E the pressure is EF, and hence the grade line must end at F.   If the pipe discharged freely into the air at E, the line would pass through E.   The location of other points, such as B' and N, may be computed if desired.   In the case of a long pipe of uniform diameter the error is very small if the hydraulic grade line is drawn as a straight line from the surface directly above the intake to a surface directly above the discharge end if the latter is submerged or to the end of the pipe if there is a free discharge into the atmosphere.

If values of h_L are laid off below the horizontal line through A, the resulting line represents values of the total energy head H measured above any arbitrary datum plane inasmuch as this line is above the hydraulic grade line a distance equal to $V^2/2g$.   This line is the *energy grade line*. It shows the rate at which the energy decreases, and it must always drop downward in the direction of flow unless there is an energy input from a pump.   The energy grade line is also independent of the position of the pipeline.

Energy grade lines are shown in Figs. 4.7 to 4.9.   The last one, plotted to scale from measurements made by Daughtery, shows that the chief loss of head is in the diverging portion and just beyond the section of minimum diameter.

4.13. METHOD OF SOLUTION OF FLOW PROBLEMS

For the solutions of problems of liquid flow there are two fundamental equations, the equation of continuity and the energy equation in one of the forms from Eqs. (4.5) to (4.9).   The following procedure may be employed:

1. Choose a datum plane through any convenient point.
2. Note at what sections the velocity is known or is to be assumed. If at any point the section area is great as compared with its value elsewhere, the velocity head is so small that it may be disregarded.
3. Note at what points the pressure is known or is to be assumed. In a body of liquid at rest with a free surface the pressure is known at every point within the body.   The pressure in a jet is the same as that of the medium surrounding the jet.
4. Note whether or not there is any point where all three terms, pressure, elevation, and velocity, are known.
5. Note whether or not there is any point where there is only one unknown quantity.

It is generally possible to write an energy equation that will fulfill conditions 4 and 5.   If there are two unknowns in the equation, then the continuity equation must be used also.   The application of these principles is shown in the following illustrative examples.

Illustrative example 4.5:   A pipeline with a pump leads to a nozzle as shown in the accompanying figure.   Find the flow rate when the pump develops a head of 80 ft.   Assume that the head loss in the 6-in.-diameter pipe may be expressed by $h_L = 5V_6^2/2g$, while the head loss in the 4-in.-diameter pipe is $h_L = 12V_4^2/2g$.

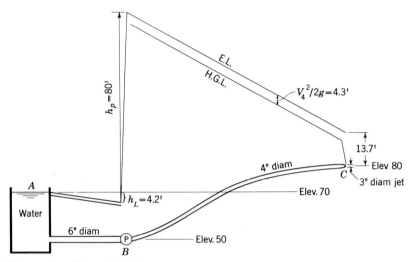

Illustrative Example 4.5

Sketch the energy line and hydraulic grade line, and find the pressure head at the suction side of the pump. Select the datum as the elevation of the water surface in the reservoir. Note from continuity that

$$V_6 = (\tfrac{3}{6})^2 V_3 = 0.25 V_3 \quad \text{and} \quad V_4 = (\tfrac{3}{4})^2 V_3 = 0.563 V_3$$

where V_3 is the jet velocity. Writing an energy equation from the surface of the reservoir to the jet,

$$\left(z_1 + \frac{p_1}{\gamma} + \frac{V_1{}^2}{2g}\right) - h_L + h_p - h_L = z_3 + \frac{p_3}{\gamma} + \frac{V_3{}^2}{2g}$$

$$0 + 0 + 0 - 5\frac{V_6{}^2}{2g} + 80 - 12\frac{V_4{}^2}{2g} = 10 + 0 + \frac{V_3{}^2}{2g}$$

Express all velocities in terms of V_3:

$$-\frac{5(0.25 V_3)^2}{2g} + 80 - 12\frac{(0.563 V_3)^2}{2g} = 10 + \frac{V_3{}^2}{2g}$$

$$V_3 = 29.7 \text{ fps}$$

$$Q = A_3 V_3 = \frac{\pi}{4}\left(\frac{3}{12}\right)^2 29.7 = 1.45 \text{ cfs}$$

Head loss in suction pipe:

$$h_L = 5\frac{V_6{}^2}{2g} = \frac{5(0.25 V_3)^2}{2g} = \frac{0.312 V_3{}^2}{2g}$$

$$= 4.2 \text{ ft}$$

Head loss in discharge pipe:

$$h_L = 12 \frac{V_4{}^2}{2g} = \frac{12(0.563 V_3)^2}{2g} = 52.1 \text{ ft}$$

$$\frac{V_3{}^2}{2g} = 13.7 \text{ ft} \qquad \frac{V_4{}^2}{2g} = 4.3 \text{ ft} \qquad \frac{V_6{}^2}{2g} = 0.86 \text{ ft}$$

The energy line and hydraulic grade line are drawn on the figure to scale. Inspection of the figure shows that the pressure head on the suction side of the pump is $p_B/\gamma = 14.94$ ft. Likewise, the pressure head at any point in the pipe may be found if the figure is to scale.

Illustrative example 4.6: Given the two-dimensional flow as shown in the accompanying figure. Determine the flow rate. Assume no head loss. The hydraulic grade line is represented by the water surface in the region where the

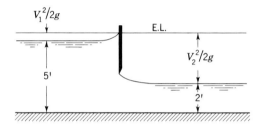

Illustrative Example 4.6

streamlines are parallel. The energy line is a distance $V^2/2g$ above the water surface, assuming $\alpha \doteq 1.0$. If there is no head loss, the energy line is horizontal. Writing the energy equation from section (1) to (2), we have

$$5 + \frac{V_1{}^2}{2g} = 2 + \frac{V_2{}^2}{2g} \tag{a}$$

But from continuity,

$$(5 \times 1)V_1 = (2 \times 1)V_2 \tag{b}$$

Substituting Eq. (b) into Eq. (a), we get

$$V_1 = 6.05 \text{ fps} \qquad V_2 = 15.1 \text{ fps}$$

$$Q = (5 \times 1)6.05 = 30.25 \text{ cfs (for 1 ft of width perpendicular to figure)}$$

$$\frac{V_1{}^2}{2g} = 0.56 \text{ ft} \qquad \frac{V_2{}^2}{2g} = 3.56 \text{ ft}$$

4.14. PRESSURE IN FLUID FLOW

Strictly speaking, the equations that have been derived apply to flow along a single streamline. They may, however, be used for stream tubes

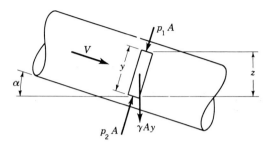

Fig. 4.10

of large cross-sectional area by taking average values. The case of pressure over a section will now be considered.

Figure 4.10 shows a small prism of a flowing fluid. The forces acting on the faces of the prism at right angles to the direction of flow and in the plane of the sketch are p_1A and p_2A as shown. Forces in the direction of motion balance out if the flow is steady and uniform. Summing forces in the direction at right angles to the flow, we get

$$p_1A + \gamma Ay \cos \alpha - p_2A = 0$$

where y is the dimension of the prism as shown, and A is its cross-sectional area. From this we get $p_2 - p_1 = \gamma y \cos \alpha = \gamma z$, which is similar to Eq. (2.2). That is, in any plane normal to the direction of flow, the pressure varies according to the hydrostatic law if the flow is uniform and steady. The average pressure is then the pressure at the center of gravity of such an area. The pressure is lowest near the top of the pipe, and cavitation, if it were to occur, would appear there first. On a horizontal diameter through the pipe the pressure is everywhere the same. Since the velocity is higher near the center than near the walls, it follows that the local energy head is also higher near the center. This emphasizes the fact that a flow equation applies along the same streamline, but not between two streamlines, any more than between two streams in two separate channels.

Static pressure. In a flowing fluid the pressure measured at right angles to the flow is called the *static pressure*. This is the value given by piezometer tubes and other devices explained in Sec. 11.2.

Stagnation pressure. The center streamline in Fig. 3.11 shows that the velocity becomes zero at the stagnation point. If p_0/γ denotes the static-pressure head at some distance away where the velocity is V_0, while p_s/γ denotes the pressure head at the stagnation point, then, applying Eq. (4.8) to these two points, $p_0/\gamma + 0 + V_0^2/2g = p_s/\gamma + 0 + 0$, or the stagnation pressure is

$$p_s = p_0 + \gamma \frac{V_0{}^2}{2g} = p_0 + \rho \frac{V_0{}^2}{2} \tag{4.33}$$

The quantity $\gamma V_0{}^2/2g$, or $\rho V_0{}^2/2$, is called the *dynamic* pressure.

Equation (4.33) applies to a fluid where compressibility may be disregarded. In Sec. 9.8 it is shown that for a compressible fluid

$$p_s = p_0 + \gamma_0 \frac{V_0{}^2}{2g} \left(1 + \frac{V_0{}^2}{4c^2} + \cdots \right) \tag{4.34}$$

where c is the acoustic velocity (Appendix 2). For air at 70°F, $c = 1{,}130$ fps. If $V_0 = 226$ fps, the error in neglecting the compressibility factor, which is the value in the parentheses, is only 1 per cent. But for higher values of V_0, the effect becomes much more important. Equation (4.34) is, however, restricted to values of V_0/c less than 1.

4.15. JET TRAJECTORY

A free liquid jet in air will describe a *trajectory*, or path under the action of gravity, with a vertical velocity component which is continually changing. The trajectory is a streamline, and consequently, if air friction is neglected, Bernoulli's theorem may be applied to it, with all the pressure terms zero. Thus the sum of the elevation and velocity head must be the same for all points of the curve. The energy grade line is a horizontal line at distance $V^2/2g$ above the nozzle, where V is the velocity leaving the nozzle (Fig. 4.11).

The equation for the trajectory may be obtained by applying Newton's equations of uniformly accelerated motion to a particle of the liquid passing from the nozzle to point P, whose coordinates are x, z, in time t. Then $x = V_x t$ and $z = V_z t - \frac{1}{2}gt^2$. Evaluating t from the first equation and substituting it in the second gives

$$z = \frac{V_z}{V_x} x - \frac{g}{2V_x{}^2} x^2 \tag{4.35}$$

This is seen to be the equation of an inverted parabola having its vertex at $x_0 = V_x V_z/g$ and $z_0 = V_z{}^2/2g$. Since the velocity at the top of the trajectory is horizontal and equal to V_x, the distance from this point to the energy gradient is evidently $V_x{}^2/2g$. This may be obtained in another way by considering that $V^2 = V_x{}^2 + V_z{}^2$. Dividing each term by $2g$ gives the relations shown in Fig. 4.11.

If the jet is initially horizontal, as in the flow from a vertical orifice, $V_x = V$ and $V_z = 0$. Equation (4.35) is then readily reduced to an

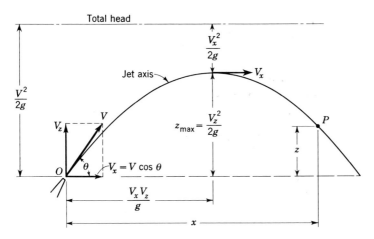

Fig. 4.11. Jet trajectory.

expression for the jet velocity in terms of the coordinates from the vena contracta to any point of the trajectory, z now being positive downward:

$$V = x \sqrt{\frac{g}{2z}} \qquad (4.36)$$

Illustrative example 4.7: If a jet is inclined upward 30° from the horizontal, what must be its velocity to reach over a 10-ft wall at a horizontal distance of 60 ft, neglecting friction?

$$V_x = V \cos 30° = 0.866V$$
$$V_z = V \sin 30° = 0.5V$$

From Newton's laws,

$$x = 0.866Vt = 60$$
$$z = 0.5Vt - 16.1t^2 = 10$$

From the first equation, $t = 69.3/V$. Substituting this in the second equation,

$$0.5V \frac{69.3}{V} - \frac{1}{2} \times 32.2 \left(\frac{69.3}{V}\right)^2 = 10$$

from which $V^2 = 3,140$, or $V = 56$ fps.

4.16. FLOW IN A CURVED PATH

The energy equations previously developed applied fundamentally to flow along a streamline or along a stream of large cross section if certain average values were used. Now conditions will be investigated in a direction normal to a streamline. In Fig. 4.12 is shown an element of

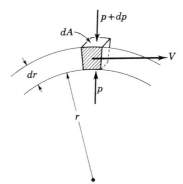

Fig. 4.12

fluid moving in a horizontal plane[1] with a velocity V along a curved path of radius r. The element has a linear dimension dr in the plane of the paper and an area dA normal to the plane of the paper. The mass of this fluid element is $\rho\, dA\, dr$, and the normal component of acceleration is V^2/r. Thus the centripetal force acting upon it is $\rho\, dA\, dr\, V^2/r$. As the radius increases from r to $r + dr$, the pressure will change from p to $p + dp$. Thus the resultant force in the direction of the center of curvature is $dp\, dA$. Equating these two forces,

$$dp = \rho\, \frac{V^2}{r}\, dr \qquad (4.37)$$

When the flow is in a straight line for which r is infinity, the value of dp is zero. That is, no difference in pressure can exist in the horizontal direction transverse to flow in a straight line.

As dp is positive if dr is positive, the equation shows that pressure increases from the concave to the convex side of the stream, but the exact way in which it increases depends upon the way in which V varies with the radius. In the next two sections two important practical cases will be presented in which V varies in two different ways.

4.17. FORCED VORTEX

A fluid may be made to rotate as a solid body without relative motion theoretically between particles, either by the rotation of a containing vessel or by stirring the contained fluid, so as to force it to rotate. Thus an *external torque* is applied. A common example is the rotation of liquid within a centrifugal pump or of gas in a centrifugal compressor.

---

[1] A more generalized analysis of flow along a curved path in a vertical or inclined plane leads to a result that includes z terms.

Cylindrical vortex. If the entire body of fluid rotates as a solid, then in Eq. (4.37) V varies directly with r; that is, $V = r\omega$, where ω is the imposed angular velocity. Inserting this value in Eq. (4.37), we have

$$dp = \rho\omega^2 r \, dr = \frac{\gamma}{g} \omega^2 r \, dr$$

Between any two radii r_1 and r_2, this integrates as

$$\frac{p_2}{\gamma} - \frac{p_1}{\gamma} = \frac{\omega^2}{2g} (r_2^2 - r_1^2) \tag{4.38}$$

If p_0 is the value of the pressure when $r_1 = 0$, this becomes

$$\frac{p}{\gamma} = \frac{\omega^2}{2g} r^2 + \frac{p_0}{\gamma} \tag{4.39}$$

which is seen to be the equation of a parabola. In Fig. 4.13 it is seen that, if the fluid is a liquid, the pressure head p/γ at any point is equal to z, the depth of the point below the free surface. Hence the preceding equations may also be written as

$$z_2 - z_1 = \frac{\omega^2}{2g} (r_2^2 - r_1^2) \tag{4.40}$$

and
$$z = \frac{\omega^2}{2g} r^2 + z_0 \tag{4.41}$$

where z_0 is the elevation when $r_1 = 0$. Equations (4.40) and (4.41) are the equations of the free surface, if one exists, or in any case are the equations for any surface of equal pressure; these are a series of paraboloids as shown by the dotted lines in Fig. 4.13a.

For the open vessel shown in Fig. 4.13a, the pressure head at any point is equal to its depth below the free surface. If the liquid is confined within a vessel, as shown in Fig. 4.13b, the pressure along any radius will vary in just the same way as if there were a free surface. Hence the two are equivalent.

The axis of the open vessel was assumed to be vertical. The axis of the closed vessel may be in any direction. However, pressure varies with elevation as well as with the radius, and a more general equation, considering both these factors at the same time, is

$$\frac{p_2}{\gamma} - \frac{p_1}{\gamma} + z_2 - z_1 = \frac{\omega^2}{2g} (r_2^2 - r_1^2) \tag{4.42}$$

Equation (4.38) is the special case where $z_1 = z_2$, and Eq. (4.40) is the special case where $p_1 = p_2$. If the axis of rotation of the closed vessel were horizontal, the paraboloid that represents the pressure would be somewhat

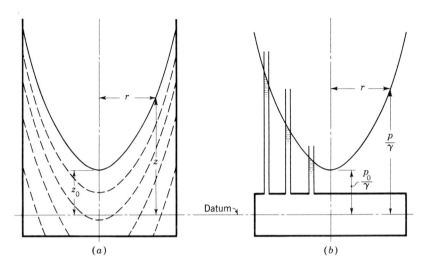

Fig. 4.13.   Forced vortex.   (*a*) Open vessel.   (*b*) Closed vessel.

distorted, since, at a given radius, the pressure at the top would be less than that at the bottom by the amount $z_2 - z_1$.

Inserting the value of p/γ from Eq. (4.39), but letting $p_0/\gamma = 0$, in the expression for total head, which is the constant in the Bernoulli equation (4.9), we have $H = p/\gamma + V^2/2g = (r\omega)^2/2g + V^2/2g$.   As p and V both increase or decrease together, which is just the opposite of the situation in linear flow, it is seen that H cannot be the same for different circular streamlines.   In fact, as in this special case $V = r\omega$, it follows that $H = 2(r\omega)^2/2g$.   That is, H increases as the square of r.

Spiral vortex.   So far the discussion has been confined to the rotation of all particles in concentric circles.   Suppose that there is now superimposed a flow with a velocity having radial components, either outward or inward.   If the height of the walls of the open vessel in Fig. 4.13*a* were less than that of the liquid surface as shown, and if liquid were supplied to the center at the proper rate by some means, then it is obvious that liquid would flow outward.   If, on the other hand, liquid flowed into the tank over the rim from some source at a higher elevation and were drawn out at the center, the flow would be inward.   The combination of this approximately radial flow with the circular flow would result in path lines that were some form of spirals.

If the closed vessel in Fig. 4.13*b* is arranged with suitable openings near the center and also around the periphery, and if it is provided with vanes, as shown in Fig. 4.14, it becomes either a centrifugal pump impeller or a turbine runner, as the case may be.   These vanes constrain the flow

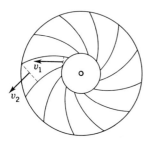

Fig. 4.14. Flow through rotor.

of the liquid and determine both its relative magnitude and its direction. If the area of the passages normal to the direction of flow is a, the equation of continuity fixes the relative velocities, since

$$Q = a_1 v_1 = a_2 v_2 = \text{constant}$$

This relative flow is the flow as it would appear to an observer or a camera, revolving with the vessel. The pressure difference due to this superimposed flow alone is found by the energy equation, neglecting friction losses, to be $p_2/\gamma - p_1/\gamma = (v_1{}^2 - v_2{}^2)/2g$.

Hence, for the case of rotation with flow, the total pressure difference between two points is found by adding together the pressure differences due to the two flows considered separately. That is,

$$\frac{p_2}{\gamma} - \frac{p_1}{\gamma} = \frac{\omega^2}{2g}(r_2{}^2 - r_1{}^2) + \frac{v_1{}^2 - v_2{}^2}{2g} \tag{4.43}$$

Of course, friction losses will modify this result to some extent. It is seen that Eq. (4.38) is a special case of Eq. (4.43) when $v_1 = v_2$ either when both are finite or when $v_1 = v_2 = 0$.

For a forced vortex with spiral flow, energy is put into the fluid in the case of a pump and extracted from it in the case of a turbine. In the limiting case of zero flow, when all path lines become concentric circles, energy input from some external source is still necessary for any real fluid in order to maintain the rotation. Thus a forced vortex is characterized by a transfer of mechanical energy from an external source and a consequent variation of H as a function of the radius from the axis of rotation.

4.18. FREE OR IRROTATIONAL VORTEX

In the free vortex there is no expenditure of energy whatever from an outside source, and the fluid rotates by virtue of some rotation previously imparted to it or because of some internal action. Some examples are a whirlpool in a river, the rotary flow that often arises in a shallow vessel when liquid flows out through a hole in the bottom (as is often seen when water empties from a bathtub), and the flow in a centrifugal-pump case just outside the impeller or that in a turbine case as the water approaches the guide vanes.

As no energy is imparted to the fluid, it follows that, neglecting friction, H is constant throughout; that is, $p/\gamma + z + V^2/2g = $ constant.

Cylindrical vortex. In mechanics, force equals mass times acceleration, or force equals time rate of change of momentum. If force is multiplied by a distance, the result is torque, and if time rate of change of momentum is multiplied by a distance, the product is called the time rate of change of *angular* momentum. The angular momentum of a particle of mass m rotating in a circular path of radius r with a velocity V is mVr.

As there is no torque applied in the case of a free vortex, it follows that the angular momentum is constant, and thus $rV = C = $ constant, where the value of C is determined by knowing the value of V at some radius r. Inserting $V = C/r$ in Eq. (4.37), we obtain

$$dp = \rho \frac{C^2}{r^2} \frac{dr}{r} = \frac{\gamma}{g} \frac{C^2}{r^3} dr$$

Between any two radii r_1 and r_2 this integrates as

$$\frac{p_2}{\gamma} - \frac{p_1}{\gamma} = \frac{C^2}{2g}\left(\frac{1}{r_1{}^2} - \frac{1}{r_2{}^2}\right) = \frac{V_1{}^2}{2g}\left[1 - \left(\frac{r_1}{r_2}\right)^2\right] \qquad (4.44)$$

If there is a free surface, the pressure head p/γ at any point is equal to the depth below the surface. Also, at any radius the pressure varies in a vertical direction according to the hydrostatic law. Hence this equation is merely a special case where $z_1 = z_2$.

As $H = p/\gamma + z + V^2/2g = $ constant, it follows that at any radius r

$$\frac{p}{\gamma} + z = H - \frac{V^2}{2g} = H - \frac{C^2}{2gr^2} = H - \frac{V_1{}^2}{2g}\left(\frac{r_1}{r}\right)^2 \qquad (4.45)$$

Assuming the axis to be vertical, the pressure along the radius can be found from this equation by taking z constant; and for any constant pressure p, values of z, determining a surface of equal pressure, can be found. If p is zero, the values of z determine the free surface, if one exists.

Equation (4.45) shows that H is the asymptote approached by $p/\gamma + z$ as r approaches infinity and V approaches zero. On the other hand, as r approaches zero, V approaches infinity, and $p/\gamma + z$ approaches minus infinity. Since this is physically impossible, the free vortex cannot

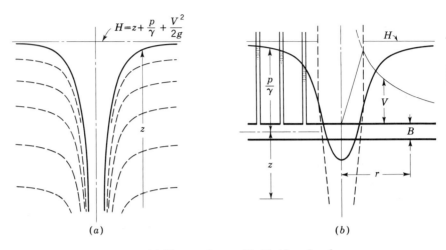

Fig. 4.15. Free vortex. (*a*) Free surface. (*b*) Fluid enclosed.

extend to the axis of rotation. In reality, since high velocities are attained as the axis is approached, the friction losses, which vary as the square of the velocity, become of increasing importance and are no longer negligible. Hence the assumption that H is constant no longer holds. The core of the vortex tends to rotate as a solid body as in the central part of Fig. 4.15*b*.

Spiral vortex. If a radial flow is superimposed upon the concentric flow previously described, the path lines will then be spirals. If the flow is out through a circular hole in the bottom of a shallow vessel, the surface of a liquid takes the form shown in Fig. 4.15*a*, with an air *core* sucked down the hole. If an outlet symmetrical with the axis is provided in the arrangement shown in Fig. 4.15*b*, we might have a flow either radially inward or radially outward. If the two plates shown are a constant distance B apart, the radial flow with a velocity V_r is then across a series of concentric cylindrical surfaces whose area is $2\pi r B$. Thus

$$Q = 2\pi r B V_r = \text{constant}$$

from which it is seen that $rV_r = \text{constant}$. Thus the radial velocity varies in the same way with r that the circumferential velocity did in the preceding discussion of the free cylindrical vortex. Hence the pressure variation with the radial velocity is the same, and thus the pressure distribution shown in Fig. 4.15*b* applies exactly to the case of spiral flow, as well as to pure rotation in a free vortex.

Illustrative example 4.8: An air duct of 2- by 2-ft-square cross section turns a bend of radius 4 ft as measured to the center line of the duct. If the measured pressure difference between the inside and outside walls of the bend is 1 in. of water, estimate the rate of air flow in the duct. Assume standard sea-level conditions in the duct, and *assume ideal flow* around the bend.

This is an application of the free vortex of Sec. 4.18. From Appendix 3, Table A.3, ρ (air) $= 0.002377$ slug/ft³. Thus

$$\frac{p_2}{\gamma} - \frac{p_1}{\gamma} = \frac{1}{12}\left(\frac{1.938}{0.002377}\right) = 68 \text{ ft of air}$$

From Eq. (4.44),
$$\frac{p_2}{\gamma} - \frac{p_1}{\gamma} = \frac{C^2}{2g}\left(\frac{1}{r_1{}^2} - \frac{1}{r_2{}^2}\right)$$

Thus, with $\qquad r_1 = 3$ ft $\qquad r_2 = 5$ ft $\qquad 68 = \dfrac{C^2}{64.4}\left(\dfrac{1}{3^2} - \dfrac{1}{5^2}\right)$

$$C = 248 \text{ ft}^2/\text{sec}$$

Thus, with $Q = \int V\, dA$ and $V = C/r$, while $dA = B\, dr$, where B is the width of the duct,

$$Q = BC\int_{r_1}^{r_2}\frac{dr}{r} = BC \ln\frac{r_2}{r_1} = 2 \times 248 \ln\frac{3}{5}$$
$$= 2 \times 248 \times 0.511 = 254 \text{ cfs} = 15,240 \text{ cfm}$$

PROBLEMS

4.1. In laminar flow through a circular pipe the velocity profile is a parabola, the equation of which is $u = u_m[1 - (r/r_0)^2]$, where u is the velocity at any radius r, u_m is the maximum velocity in the center of the pipe where $r = 0$, and r_0 is the radius to the wall of the pipe. From Prob. 3.3, $V = 0.5u_m$. Prove that $\alpha = 2$. (*Note:* Let $dA = 2\pi r\, dr$.)

4.2. Assume the velocity profile for turbulent flow in a circular pipe to be approximated by a parabola from the axis to a point very close to the wall where the local velocity is $u = 0.7u_m$, where u_m is the maximum velocity at the axis. The equation for this parabola is $u = u_m[1 - 0.3(r/r_0)^2]$. Prove that $\alpha = 1.031$.

4.3. Assume an open rectangular channel with the velocity at the surface twice that at the bottom and with the velocity varying as a straight line from top to bottom. Prove that $\alpha = 1\tfrac{1}{9}$.

4.4. Find α for the case of a two-dimensional laminar flow.

4.5. Assume frictionless flow in a long, horizontal, conical pipe, the diameter of which is 2 ft at one end and 4 ft at the other. The pressure head at the smaller end is 16 ft of water. If water flows through this cone at the rate of 125.6 cfs, find the velocities at the two ends and the pressure head at the larger end.

4.6. A vertical pipe 3 ft in diameter and 60 ft long has a pressure head at the upper end of 18 ft of water. When the flow of water through it is such that the mean velocity is 15 fps, the friction loss is $h_L = 4$ ft. Find the pressure head at the lower end of the pipe when the flow is (a) downward; (b) upward.

4.7. A conical pipe has diameters at the two ends of 1.5 and 4.5 ft and is 50 ft long. It is vertical, and the friction loss is $h_L = 8$ ft for flow of water in either direction when the velocity at the smaller section is 30 fps. If the smaller section is at the top and the pressure head there is 6.5 ft of water, find the pressure head at the lower end when the flow is (*a*) downward; (*b*) upward.

4.8. A pipeline supplies water to a hydroelectric power plant, the elevation of which is 2,000 ft below the level of the water at intake to the pipe. If 10 per cent of this total, or 200 ft, is lost in friction in the pipe, what will be the value of ΔI, and if the specific heat of water is 1 Btu/(lb)(°F), what will be the rise in temperature if there is no heat transfer?

4.9. A pipeline supplies water to a hydroelectric plant from a reservoir in which the water temperature is 60°F. (*a*) Suppose that in the length of the pipe there is a total loss of heat to the surrounding air of 0.30 Btu/lb of water and the temperature of the water at the power house is 59.9°F. What is the friction loss per pound of water? (*b*) Suppose that there is in the length an absorption of heat from hot sunshine of 3.0 Btu/lb of water and the temperature of the water at the power house is 63.2°F. What is the friction loss per pound of water? [Specific heat of water may be taken as 1 Btu/(lb)(°F).]

4.10. In the figure, the pipe AB is of uniform diameter. The pressure at A is 20 psi and at B is 30 psi. In which direction is the flow, and what is the friction loss in feet of the fluid if the liquid has a specific weight of (*a*) 30 pcf; (*b*) 100 pcf?

Fig. Prob. 4.10

4.11. A pipeline conducts water from a reservoir to a powerhouse, the elevation of which is 800 ft lower than that of the surface of the reservoir. The water is discharged through a nozzle with a jet velocity of 220 fps, and the diameter of the jet is 8 in. Find the horsepower of the jet and the horsepower lost in friction between reservoir and jet.

4.12. A pump lifts water at the rate of 200 cfs to a height of 400 ft, and the friction loss in the pipe is 30 ft. What is the horsepower required if the pump efficiency is 90 per cent?

4.13. A turbine is located at an elevation 600 ft below that of the surface of the water at intake. The friction in the pipeline leading to it is 25 ft, and the turbine efficiency is 90 per cent. What will be the horsepower delivered by it if the flow is 100 cfs?

4.14. A pump circulates water at the rate of 2,000 gpm in a closed circuit holding 10,000 gal. The net head developed by the pump is 300 ft, and the pump efficiency is 90 per cent. Assuming the bearing friction to be negligible and that there is no loss of heat from the system, find the temperature rise in the water in 1 hr.

4.15. The diameters of the suction and discharge pipes of a pump are 6 and 4 in., respectively. The discharge pressure is read by a gage at a point 5 ft above the center line of the pump, and the suction pressure is read by a gage 2 ft below the center line.   If the pressure gage reads 20 psi and the suction gage reads a vacuum of 10 in. Hg when gasoline ($s = 0.75$) is pumped at the rate of 1.2 cfs, find the power delivered to the fluid.

4.16. An air compressor takes 60°F air at 0.076 pcf and discharges it at 0.12 pcf at 80°F in a 10- by 14-in. duct.   If the rate of flow is 4 lb/sec, find the horsepower put into the fluid by the compressor.

4.17. Water enters a pump through a 10-in.-diameter pipe at 5 psi.   It leaves the pump at 20 psi through a 6-in.-diameter pipe.   If the flow rate is 5 cfs, find the horsepower delivered to the water by the pump.

4.18. In Fig. 4.9, neglect head loss and assume water is flowing.   If $h = 16$ ft and the lower reservoir is 15 ft higher than the constriction, find the highest permissible temperature of the water in order that there be no cavitation. The diameter of the constriction is three-fourths the diameter of the pipe where it joins the downstream tank.   Atmospheric pressure is 14.2 psia.

4.19. Repeat Prob. 4.18, but in this case let the water temperature be 60°F. Find the minimum permissible diameter of the constriction in order that there be no cavitation.

4.20. Air flows isothermally through a long, horizontal pipe of uniform diameter. At a section where the pressure is 150 psia the velocity is 80 fps.   Because of fluid friction, the pressure at a distant section is 30 psia.   (*a*) What is the increase in kinetic energy per pound of air?   (*b*) What is the amount of thermal energy in Btu per pound of air that must be transferred in order to maintain the temperature constant?

4.21. If the temperature of the air in Prob. 4.20 is 70°F and the diameter of the pipe is 3 in., find the total heat transferred in Btu per hour.

4.22. Dry saturated steam at a pressure of 100 psia and a temperature of 327.8°F expands through a suitable nozzle to a pressure of 15 psia.   For frictionless adiabatic flow, steam tables give $E_1 = 1186.6$ and $E_2 = 1048.1$ Btu/lb. If the initial velocity is negligible, find the final jet velocity.

4.23. For Prob. 4.22 assume that the friction is such that the actual jet velocity is 2,400 fps.   What must then be the value of E_2'?   If Eq. (4.21) were used, what would be the value of the coefficient by which the ideal jet velocity must be multiplied to give the actual jet velocity?

4.24. Air ($\gamma = 0.075$ pcf) is flowing.   If $u = 13.0$ fps, determine the readings on manometers a and b in the figure.

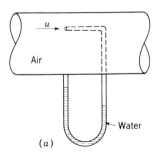

(*a*)

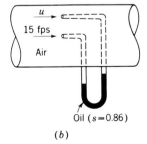

(*b*)

Fig. Prob. 4.24

4.25. Assume ideal fluid.   The pressure at section (1) in the figure is 10 psi. (*a*) Determine the reading on the manometer.   (*b*) If the downstream piezometer were replaced with a pitot tube, what would be the manometer reading?

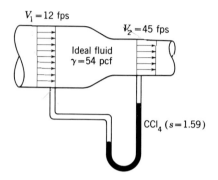

$V_1 = 12$ fps

$V_2 = 45$ fps

Ideal fluid
$\gamma = 54$ pcf

CCl_4 ($s = 1.59$)

Fig. Prob. 4.25

4.26. Take the situation depicted in Illustrative Example 4.5.   Suppose all data are the same except for the pump, which, instead of developing 80 ft of head, delivers 100 hp to the water.   Determine the flow rate.   Plot the energy line and hydraulic grade line, and determine the pressure on the suction side of the pump.

4.27. Referring to the figure, assume the flow to be frictionless in the siphon. Find the rate of discharge in cubic feet per second and the pressure head at *B* if the pipe has a uniform diameter of 6 in.

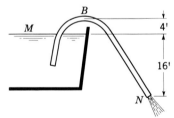

B

M

4'

16'

N   **Fig. Prob. 4.27**

4.28. In Prob. 4.27 assume that the friction loss between intake and *B* is 2 ft and between *B* and *N* is 3 ft.   What is the pressure head at *B*?

4.29. Neglect friction and assume that the minimum pressure allowable in the siphon of Prob. 4.27 is a vacuum of -32 ft of water.   What would then be the maximum difference in elevation between *M* and *N*, instead of the 16 ft shown in the sketch?

4.30. Referring to the figure, assume that liquid flows from A to C at the rate of 6 cfs and that the friction loss between A and B is negligible but that between B and C it is $0.1V_B^2/2g$. Find the pressure heads at A and C.

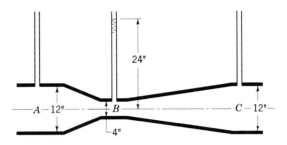

Fig. Prob. 4.30

4.31. In the figure, the diameter of the vertical pipe is 4 in., and that of the stream discharging into the air at E is 3 in. Neglecting all losses of energy, what are the pressure heads at B, C, and D?

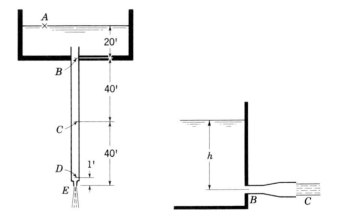

Fig. Prob. 4.31   **Fig. Prob. 4.32**

4.32. Referring to the figure, at B the diameter of the tube is 1 in., and the diameter of the jet discharging into the air at C is 1.5 in. If $h = 6$ ft and all friction losses are neglected, what are the values of the velocity and the pressure head at B?

4.33. What is the rate of discharge in cubic feet per second in Prob. 4.32? What would it be if the tube were cut off at B?

4.34. Pump P in the figure draws up liquid in a suction pipe at a velocity of 10 fps. Assume that the friction losses in the pipe are $2V^2/2g$ and that the barometer pressure is 14.500 psia. What would be the maximum allowable value of z if the liquid were (*a*) water at a temperature of 60°F; (*b*) gasoline with a vapor pressure of 8 psia and a specific weight of 45 pcf?

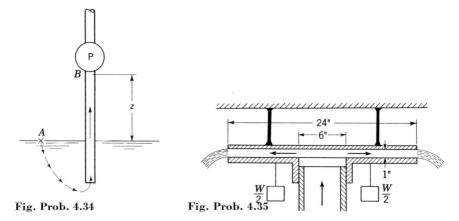

Fig. Prob. 4.34   **Fig. Prob. 4.35**

4.35. The upper circular plate in the figure is horizontal and is fixed in position, while the lower annular plate is free to move vertically and is not supported by the pipe in the center. Water is admitted at the center at the rate of 2 cfs and discharges into the air around the periphery. The annular plate weighs 5 lb, and the weight of water on it should be considered. If the distance between the two plates is maintained at 1 in., what total weight W can be supported?

4.36. In Prob. 4.35 what is the pressure head where the radius is 3 in., and what is it at a radius of 6 in.?

4.37. If in Fig. 3.11 the velocity of the undisturbed field is 20 fps, the velocities near the surface at radii from the "source" making angles with the axis of 0, 60, 120, 150° are 0, 18.6, 25.2, 23.3 fps, respectively. What will be the elevation of the surface of a liquid relative to that of the free surface of the undisturbed field? (This problem illustrates the way in which the water surface drops alongside a bridge pier or past the side of a moving ship.)

4.38. If the body shown in Fig. 3.11 is not two-dimensional but is a solid of revolution about a horizontal axis, the flow will be three-dimensional and the streamlines will be differently spaced. Also, the distance between the stagnation point and the "source" will be $d/4$, where d is the diameter at a great distance from the stagnation point. At points near the surface at radii from the source making angles with the axis of 0, 60, 120, and 150°, the velocities are 0, 15.0, 22.8, and 21.2 fps, respectively, when the velocity of the undisturbed field is 20 fps. If the body is an airship and the atmospheric pressure in the undisturbed field is 12 psia, what will be the pressures at these points, for air temperature of 39.3°F?

4.39. In Prob. 4.38 assume the body is a submarine with diameters at the four points of 0, 8.0, 13.86, and 15.44 ft, respectively. If the submarine is submerged in the ocean with its axis 50 ft below the surface, find the pressures in pounds per square inch at these points along the top and along the bottom.

4.40. Find the stagnation pressure on the nose of a submarine moving at 15 knots in sea water ($\gamma = 64$ pcf) when it is 80 ft below the surface.

4.41. Plot the stagnation pressure on an object as it passes through air at sea level as a function of velocity. Repeat for movement through air at 5,000-ft elevation. Let V vary from zero to c.

4.42. By manipulation of Eq. (4.35), demonstrate that it represents a standard parabola of the form $z - z_0 = a(x - x_0)^2$, where a is a constant and x_0 and z_0 are the coordinates of the vertex.

4.43. Find the maximum ideal horizontal range of a jet having an initial velocity of 100 fps. At what angle of inclination is this obtained?

4.44. It is required to throw a fire stream so as to reach the window in the wall shown in the figure. Assuming a jet velocity of 80 fps and neglecting air friction, find the angle (or angles) of inclination which will achieve this result.

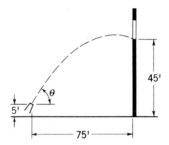

Fig. Prob. 4.44

4.45. Freshwater sewage effluent is discharged from a horizontal outfall pipe on the floor of the ocean at a point where the depth is 100 ft. The jet is observed to rise to the surface at a point 85 ft horizontally from the end of the pipe. Assuming the ocean water to have a specific gravity of 1.03 and neglecting fluid friction and mixing of the jet with the ocean water, find the velocity at the end of the outfall. [*Note:* In this case the jet is submerged, and it is no longer possible to neglect the density of the surrounding medium; hence the value of g in Eqs. (4.35) and (4.36) must be adjusted accordingly.]

4.46. A closed vessel 18 in. in diameter completely filled with fluid is rotated at 1,700 rpm. What will be the pressure difference between the circumference and the axis of rotation in feet of the fluid and in pounds per square inch if the fluid is (*a*) air with a specific weight of 0.075 pcf; (*b*) water at 68°F; (*c*) oil with a specific weight of 50 pcf?

4.47. An open cylindrical vessel partially filled with water is 3 ft in diameter and rotates about its axis, which is vertical. How many revolutions per minute would cause the water surface at the periphery to be 4 ft higher than the water surface at the axis? What would be the necessary speed for the same conditions if the fluid were mercury?

4.48. In Fig. 4.14 suppose that the vanes are all straight and radial, that $r_1 = 0.25$ ft, $r_2 = 0.75$ ft, and that the height perpendicular to the plane of the figure is constant at $b = 0.2$ ft. Then $a = 2\pi rb$. If the speed is 1,200 rpm and the flow of liquid is 7.54 cfs, find the difference in the pressure head between the outer and the inner circumferences, neglecting friction losses. Does it make any difference whether the flow is outward or inward?

4.49. In the figure, a centrifugal pump with an impeller 12 in. in diameter is surrounded by a casing which has a constant height of 1.5 in. between sections a and b and then enlarges into the *volute* at c. Water leaves the impeller at a with a velocity of 60 fps at an angle with the tangent of $\alpha = 15°$. (*a*) What will be the magnitude and direction of the velocity at b? (*b*) Neglecting friction, what will be the gain in pressure head from a to b?

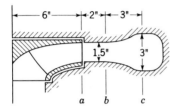

Fig. Prob. 4.49

4.50. For the case given in Prob. 4.49, find the magnitude and direction of the velocity at c. What is the gain in pressure head between b and c?

4.51. In the figure is shown a spiral case for a large vertical-shaft turbine. To assist in supporting the weight of a generator on the floor above the turbine, columns are inserted in the casing in the form of stay vanes in a casting known as a speed ring. These vanes should conform to natural stream-lines. (Guide vanes, which do direct the course of the water, are inside the speed ring, and the runner is in the very center. These details are not shown.) In the figure let $r_1 = 18$ ft, $r_2 = 8$ ft, $r_3 = 6$ ft, $A_1 = 200$ ft^2, $B_2 = 3$ ft, $B_3 = 2.5$ ft, $\alpha_1 = 40°$. If the water enters the turbine case at (1) with a velocity of 8 fps, find the tangential and radial components of velocity at entrance to and exit from the speed ring. What should be the directions of the stay vanes at entrance and at exit?

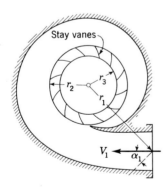

Fig. Prob. 4.51

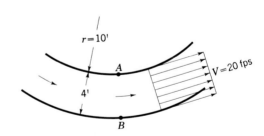

Fig. Prob. 4.52

4.52. In the figure is shown a two-dimensional ideal flow in a vertical plane. If the pressure at A is 5 psi, find the pressure at B.

4.53. Repeat Prob. 4.52; let $V = 20$ fps, but assume the velocity profile is parabolic.

FIVE

BASIC HYDRODYNAMICS

In this chapter we discuss various mathematical methods of describing the flow of ideal fluids. The presentation here provides only an introduction to the vast subject of hydrodynamics, but gives some notion of the possibilities of a rigorous mathematical approach to ideal-flow problems.

5.1. DIFFERENTIAL EQUATION OF CONTINUITY

In Chap. 3 a very practical, but special, form of the equation of continuity was presented. For some purposes a more general three-dimensional form is desired. Also, in that chapter the concept of the flow net was explained largely on an intuitive basis. To reach a more fundamental understanding of the mechanics of the flow net, it is necessary to consider the differential equations of continuity and irrotationality (Sec. 5.2) which give rise to the orthogonal network of streamlines and equipotential lines.

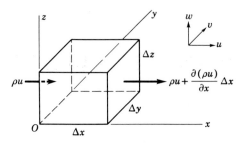

Fig. 5.1

Aside from application to the flow net, the differential form of the continuity equation has an important advantage over the one-dimensional form which was derived in Sec. 3.4 in that it is perfectly general for two- or three-dimensional fluid space and for either steady or unsteady flow.

Figure 5.1 shows three coordinate axes x, y, z mutually perpendicular and fixed in space. Let the velocity components in these three directions be u, v, w, respectively. Consider now a small parallelepiped, having sides Δx, Δy, Δz. In the x direction the rate of mass flow into this box through the left-hand face is approximately $\rho u \, \Delta y \, \Delta z$, this expression becoming exact in the limit as the box is shrunk to a point. The corresponding rate of mass flow out of the box through the right-hand face is $\left[\rho u + \dfrac{\partial(\rho u)}{\partial x} \, \Delta x \right] \Delta y \, \Delta z$. Thus the net rate of mass flow into the box in the x direction is $-[\partial(\rho u)/\partial x] \, \Delta x \, \Delta y \, \Delta z$. Similar expressions may be obtained for the y and z directions. The sum of the rates of mass inflow in the three directions must equal the time rate of change of the mass in the box, or $(\partial \rho / \partial t) \, \Delta x \, \Delta y \, \Delta z$. Summing up, applying the limiting process, and dividing both sides of the equation by the volume of the parallelepiped, which is common to all terms, we get

$$-\frac{\partial(\rho u)}{\partial x} - \frac{\partial(\rho v)}{\partial y} - \frac{\partial(\rho w)}{\partial z} = \frac{\partial \rho}{\partial t} \tag{5.1}$$

which is the equation of continuity in its most general form. If the flow is steady, ρ does not vary with time, but it may vary in space. Since $\partial(\rho u)/\partial x = \rho(\partial u/\partial x) + u(\partial \rho/\partial x)$, it follows that for steady flow the equation may be written

$$u \frac{\partial \rho}{\partial x} + v \frac{\partial \rho}{\partial y} + w \frac{\partial \rho}{\partial z} + \rho \left(\frac{\partial u}{\partial x} + \frac{\partial v}{\partial y} + \frac{\partial w}{\partial z} \right) = 0 \tag{5.2}$$

In the case of an incompressible fluid, whether the flow is steady or not, the equation of continuity becomes

$$\frac{\partial u}{\partial x} + \frac{\partial v}{\partial y} + \frac{\partial w}{\partial z} = 0 \tag{5.3}$$

For two-dimensional flow, application of the same procedure to an elemental volume in polar coordinates yields for steady flow the following equations:

For compressible fluid:

$$\frac{1}{r}(\rho v_r) + \frac{\partial}{\partial r}(\rho v_r) + \frac{\partial}{r\,\partial\theta}(\rho v_t) = 0 \tag{5.4}$$

For incompressible fluid:

$$\frac{v_r}{r} + \frac{\partial v_r}{\partial r} + \frac{\partial v_t}{r\,\partial\theta} = 0 \tag{5.5}$$

where v_r and v_t represent the velocities in the radial and tangential directions, respectively.

Illustrative example 5.1:   Check these flows for continuity:

(a) $u = -2y$, $v = 3x$; (b) $u = 0$, $v = 3xy$; (c) $u = 2x$, $v = -2y$.   Continuity for incompressible fluid is satisfied if $\partial u/\partial x + \partial v/\partial y = 0$.

(a) $\dfrac{\partial(-2y)}{\partial x} + \dfrac{\partial(3x)}{\partial y} = 0 + 0 = 0$ (continuity is satisfied)

(b) $\dfrac{\partial(0)}{\partial x} + \dfrac{\partial(3xy)}{\partial y} = 0 + 3x \neq 0$ (continuity is not satisfied)

(c) $\dfrac{\partial(2x)}{\partial x} + \dfrac{\partial(-2y)}{\partial y} = 2 - 2 = 0$ (continuity is satisfied)

5.2. ROTATIONAL AND IRROTATIONAL FLOW

Irrotational flow may be briefly described as flow in which each element of the moving fluid suffers no *net* rotation from one instant to the next, with respect to a given frame of reference.   The classic example of irrotational motion (although not of a fluid) is that of the carriages on a Ferris wheel.   Each carriage describes a circular path as the wheel revolves, but does not rotate with respect to the earth.   In irrotational flow, however, a fluid element may deform as shown in Fig. 5.2a, where the axes

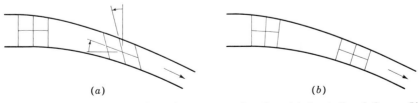

(a)   (b)

Fig. 5.2.   Two-dimensional flow along a curved path.   (a) Irrotational flow.   (b) Rotational flow.

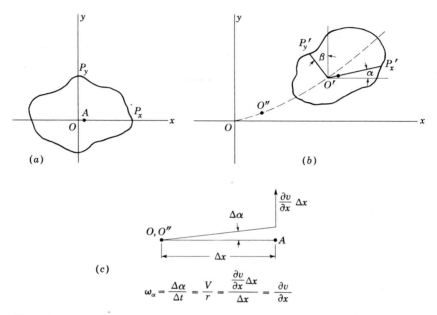

Fig. 5.3

of the element rotate equally toward or away from each other.   As long as the algebraic average rotation is zero, the motion is irrotational.

In Fig. 5.2*b* is depicted an example of rotational flow.   In this case there is a net rotation of the fluid element.   Actually, the deformation of the element in Fig. 5.2*b* is less than that of Fig. 5.2*a*.

Let us now express the condition of irrotationality in mathematical terms.   It will help to restrict the discussion at first to two-dimensional motion in the *xy* plane.   Consider the fluid moving about to be composed of hypothetical discrete elements having no particular shape.   At any instant we may find such an element at the origin of our frame, and we may locate in the element two mutually perpendicular axes, such as OP_x and OP_y (Fig. 5.3*a*).   An instant later this element may have moved to a new location, O' (Fig. 5.3*b*), with the axes rotated to the new positions OP_x' and OP_y' (generally no longer perpendicular to each other).   The rate of rotation (or angular deformation) of OP_x is, from $\omega = V/r$, as shown in Fig. 5.3*c*,

$$\omega_\alpha = \frac{\partial v}{\partial x}$$

while for OP_y it is

$$\omega_\beta = -\frac{\partial u}{\partial y}$$

with the negative sign because $+u$ is directed to the right. The rate of rotation of the element about the z axis is now defined to be ω_z, the average of ω_α and ω_β, thus:

$$\omega_z = \frac{1}{2}\left(\frac{\partial v}{\partial x} - \frac{\partial u}{\partial y}\right) \tag{5.6}$$

But the criterion we originally stipulated for irrotational flow was that the rate of rotation be zero. Therefore the flow is irrotational in the xy plane if $\partial v/\partial x - \partial u/\partial y = 0$. In three-dimensional flow there are corresponding expressions for the components of angular-deformation rates about the x and y axes. Finally, for the general case, *irrotational flow* is defined to be that for which

$$\omega_x = \omega_y = \omega_z = 0 \tag{5.7}$$

Illustrative example 5.2 Determine whether these flows are rotational or irrotational. (a) $u = -2y$, $v = 3x$; (b) $u = 0$, $v = 3xy$; (c) $u = 2x$, $v = -2y$. If

$$\frac{\partial v}{\partial x} - \frac{\partial u}{\partial y} = 0 \qquad \text{(flow is irrotational)}$$

(a) $\dfrac{\partial(3x)}{\partial x} - \dfrac{\partial(-2y)}{\partial y} = 3 + 2 \neq 0$ (flow is rotational)

(b) $\dfrac{\partial(3xy)}{\partial x} - \dfrac{\partial(0)}{\partial y} = 3y - 0 \neq 0$ (flow is rotational)

(c) $\dfrac{\partial(-2y)}{\partial x} - \dfrac{\partial(2x)}{\partial y} = 0 - 0 = 0$ (flow is irrotational)

5.3. CIRCULATION AND VORTICITY

To get a better understanding of the character of a flow field, we should acquaint ourselves with the concept of *circulation*. Let the streamlines of Fig. 5.4 represent a two-dimensional *flow field*, while L represents any closed path in this field. The circulation Γ is defined mathematically as a *line integral* of the velocity about a closed path. Thus

$$\Gamma = \oint_L \mathbf{V} \cdot d\mathbf{L} = \oint_L V \cos \beta \, dL \tag{5.8}$$

where $\mathbf{V}$ is the velocity at the element $d\mathbf{L}$ of the path, and β is the angle between it and the tangent to the path (in the positive direction) at that point. Equation (5.8) is analogous to the common equation in mechanics for work done as a body moves along a curved path while the force makes some angle with the path. The only difference here is the substitution of a velocity for a force.

Evaluation of Eq. (5.8) about any closed curve generally involves a tedious step-by-step integration. Some valuable information is acquired, however, by evaluating the circulation of the two-dimensional flow field of Fig. 5.5 by taking the line integral around the boundary of the indicated element. Since the element is of differential size, the resulting circulation is also differential. Thus, starting at A and proceeding counterclockwise,

$$d\Gamma = \frac{u_A + u_B}{2} dx + \frac{v_B + v_C}{2} dy - \frac{u_C + u_D}{2} dx - \frac{v_D + v_A}{2} dy \quad (5.9)$$

where the values of u_A, u_B, u_C, u_D and v_A, v_B, v_C, v_D are as indicated in Fig. 5.5. Substituting these values into Eq. (5.9), expanding, combining terms, and disregarding those of higher order yield

$$d\Gamma = \left(\frac{\partial v}{\partial x} - \frac{\partial u}{\partial y}\right) dx \, dy \quad (5.10)$$

The *vorticity* $\xi(xi)$ is defined as the circulation per unit of enclosed area. Thus

$$\xi = \frac{d\Gamma}{dx \, dy} = \frac{\partial v}{\partial x} - \frac{\partial u}{\partial y} \quad (5.11)$$

Comparing Eq. (5.11) with Eq. (5.7), we see that an irrotational flow is one for which the vorticity $\xi = 0$. Similarly, if the flow is rotational, $\xi \neq 0$.

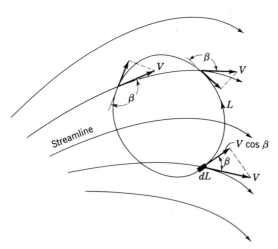

Fig. 5.4. Circulation around a closed path in a two-dimensional velocity field.

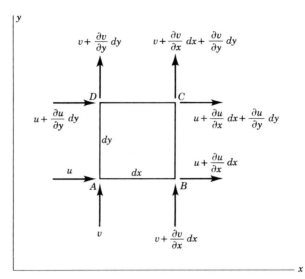

Fig. 5.5

Using a similar procedure for polar coordinates, we find

$$\xi = \frac{\partial v_t}{\partial r} + \frac{v_t}{r} - \frac{\partial v_r}{r \, \partial \theta} \tag{5.12}$$

Illustrative example 5.3:   Check these flows for continuity and determine the vorticity of each: (a) $v_t = 6r$, $v_r = 0$; (b) $v_t = 0$, $v_r = -5/r$.
Applying Eqs. (5.5) and (5.12),

(a) $\dfrac{0}{r} + \dfrac{\partial(0)}{\partial r} + \dfrac{\partial(6r)}{r \, \partial \theta} = 0$ (continuity is satisfied)

$\xi = \dfrac{\partial(\partial r)}{\partial r} + \dfrac{6r}{r} - \dfrac{\partial(0)}{r \, \partial \theta} = 6 + 6 - 0 = 12$ (flow is rotational)

(b) $-\dfrac{5/r}{r} + \dfrac{\partial(-5r^{-1})}{\partial r} + \dfrac{\partial(0)}{r \, \partial \theta} = -\dfrac{5}{r^2} + \dfrac{5}{r^2} + 0 = 0$ (continuity is satisfied)

$\xi = \dfrac{\partial(0)}{\partial r} + \dfrac{0}{r} - \dfrac{\partial(-5/r)}{r \, \partial \theta} = 0$ (flow is irrotational)

5.4. THE STREAMFUNCTION

The streamfunction ψ, based on the continuity principle, is a mathematical expression that describes a flow field.   In Fig. 5.6 are shown two adjacent streamlines of a two-dimensional flow field.   Let $\psi(x,y)$ represent the streamline nearest the origin.   Then $\psi + d\psi$ is representative of the second streamline.   Since there is no flow across a streamline, we can let ψ

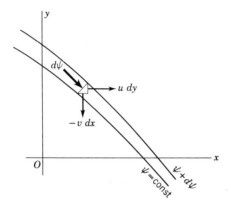

Fig. 5.6.   Streamfunction.

be indicative of the flow carried through the area from the origin O to the first streamline.   And thus $d\psi$ represents the flow carried between the two streamlines of Fig. 5.6.   From continuity referring to the triangular fluid element of Fig. 5.6, we see that for an incompressible fluid

$$d\psi = -v\,dx + u\,dy \tag{5.13}$$

The total derivative $d\psi$ may also be expressed as

$$d\psi = \frac{\partial\psi}{\partial x}\,dx + \frac{\partial\psi}{\partial y}\,dy \tag{5.14}$$

Comparing these last two equations, we note that

$$u = \frac{\partial\psi}{\partial y} \quad\text{and}\quad v = -\frac{\partial\psi}{\partial x} \tag{5.15}$$

Thus, if ψ can be expressed as a function of x and y, we can find the velocity components (u and v) at any point of a two-dimensional flow field by application of Eq. (5.15).   Conversely, if u and v are expressed as functions of x and y, we can find ψ by integrating Eq. (5.13).   However, it should be noted that since the derivation of ψ is based on the principle of continuity, the streamfunction exists only if continuity is satisfied.

5.5. BASIC FLOW FIELDS

In this section several basic flow fields that are commonly encountered will be discussed.   The simplest of all flows is that where the streamlines are straight, parallel, and evenly spaced as indicated in Fig. 5.7.   In this case $v = 0$ and $u = $ constant.   Thus, from Eq. (5.13), $d\psi = u\,dy$, and hence $\psi = Uy$, where U is the velocity of flow.   If the distance between streamlines is a, the values of ψ for the streamlines are as indicated in Fig. 5.7.

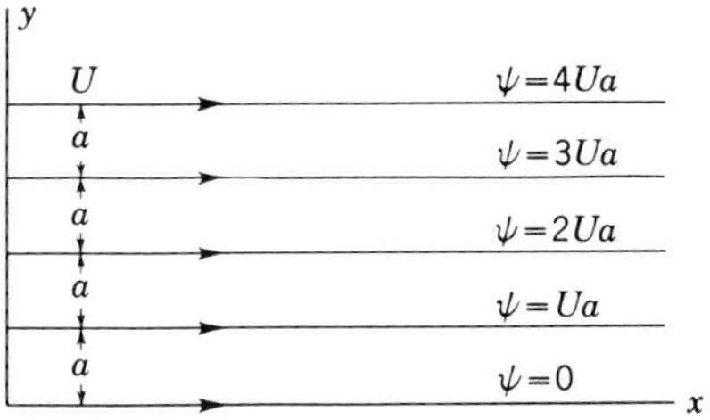

y

U

a

$\psi = 4Ua$

a

$\psi = 3Ua$

a

$\psi = 2Ua$

a

$\psi = Ua$

a

$\psi = 0$

x

Fig. 5.7. Rectilinear flow field.

Another flow field of general interest is that of a *source* or a *sink*. In the case of a source, the flow field consists of radial streamlines symmetrically spaced as shown in Fig. 5.8. If q is the *source strength*, or rate of flow from the source, it is at once apparent that $\psi = q\theta/2\pi$. Customarily, for this case, the $\psi = 0$ streamline is defined as that coincident with the direction of the x axis. From inspection of the flow field it is obvious that $v_t = 0$ and $v_r = q/2\pi r$. Thus $v_r \rightarrow 0$ as $r \rightarrow \infty$. For a sink (inward flow), the streamfunction is expressible as $\psi = -q\theta/2\pi$.

Flow fields may be combined to give other fields of importance. For example, let us combine a source and sink of equal strength with a rectilinear flow. Let $2a$ be the distance between the source and sink. Referring to Fig. 5.9 and defining θ_1 and θ_2 as shown, we can write for the combined field

$$\psi = Uy + \frac{q\theta_1}{2\pi} - \frac{q\theta_2}{2\pi} \tag{5.16}$$

Transforming the last two terms of this equation to cartesian coordinates by replacing the θ's with appropriate trigonometric functions, we get

$$\psi = Uy + \frac{q}{2\pi} \left(\arctan \frac{y}{x+a} - \arctan \frac{y}{x-a} \right) \tag{5.17}$$

This equation will permit one to plot streamlines by determining values of ψ at various points in the flow field having coordinates (x,y). Lines of

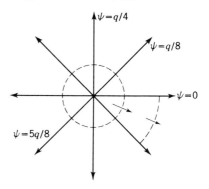

Fig. 5.8. Source flow field.

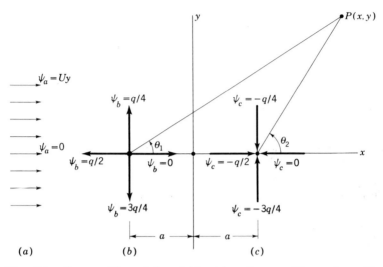

Fig. 5.9. Superposition of flow fields: (*a*) uniform rectilinear flow; (*b*) source; (*c*) sink. Source and sink are of equal strength and a distance 2*a* apart along the *x* axis.

constant ψ are streamlines. The resulting flow field for this case is shown in Fig. 5.10. The $\psi = 0$ line produces a closed curve (oval), and thus the flow field represents ideal flow past a body of that shape. By using different values of a and different relationships between U and q, it is possible to describe a whole array of two-dimensional flow fields about ovals of various shapes. The location of stagnation points S may be found by solving for x after substituting $\psi = 0$ and $y = 0$ into Eq. (5.17).

The flow field of Fig. 5.10 is for an ideal fluid and of course does not represent the flow picture for a real fluid, where there will be separation with the formation of a wake on the downstream side of the body (Fig. 13.10). However, on the upstream side of the body where the boundary layer is thin, the flow of a real fluid is well represented by Fig. 5.10.

In the example (page 131), if $a \rightarrow 0$, the oval approaches a circle. However, the flow field will reduce mathematically to uniform rectilinear flow since the source and sink will cancel each other out. Suppose we define a *doublet* as a source-sink combination for which $2qa = m$, a constant. Permitting a to approach zero, the streamfunction of the doublet imposed on the uniform flow field is then

$$\psi = Uy - \frac{m \sin \theta}{2\pi r} \qquad (5.18)$$

Taking $\psi = 0$ to determine the form of the closed-body contour and noting

$$\psi = Uy + \frac{q}{2\pi}\left(\tan^{-1}\frac{y}{x+a} - \tan^{-1}\frac{y}{x-a}\right)$$

As an example let $U = 0.80$, $q = 2\pi$, $a = 2$. Thus,

$$\psi = 0.80y + \tan^{-1}\frac{y}{x+2} - \tan^{-1}\frac{y}{x-2}$$

Let

$$A = \frac{y}{x+2} \quad \text{and} \quad B = \frac{y}{x-2}$$

x	y	$\dfrac{y}{x+2}$	$\dfrac{y}{x-2}$	Degrees			Radians		
				$\tan^{-1}A$	$\tan^{-1}B$	$0.8y$	$\tan^{-1}A$	$\tan^{-1}B$	ψ
0	2	$\frac{2}{2}$	$-\frac{2}{2}$	45°00′	135°00′	1.60	0.78	2.36	0.02
0	3	$\frac{3}{2}$	$-\frac{3}{2}$	56°19′	123°41′	2.40	0.98	2.16	1.22
0	4	$\frac{4}{2}$	$-\frac{4}{2}$	63°26′	116°34′	3.20	1.11	2.04	2.27
2	2	$\frac{2}{4}$	∞	26°34′	90°00′	1.60	0.46	1.57	0.49
2	3	$\frac{3}{4}$	∞	36°54′	90°00′	2.40	0.64	1.57	1.47
5	1	$\frac{1}{7}$	$\frac{1}{3}$	8°08′	18°26′	0.80	0.14	0.32	0.62
5	2	$\frac{2}{7}$	$\frac{2}{3}$	15°55′	33°42′	1.60	0.28	0.59	1.29
8	1	$\frac{1}{10}$	$\frac{1}{6}$	5°43′	9°28′	0.80	0.10	0.17	0.73
8	2	$\frac{2}{10}$	$\frac{2}{6}$	11°19′	18°26′	1.60	0.19	0.32	1.47

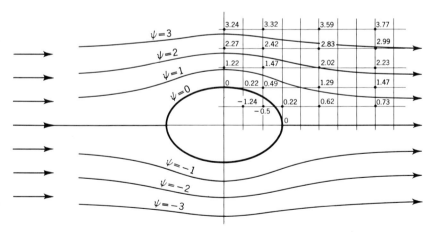

Fig. 5.10.   Flowfield for source and sink of equal strength in uniform rectilinear flowfield.

that $y = r \sin \theta$, we get

$$0 = Ur \sin \theta - \frac{m \sin \theta}{2\pi r}$$

or

$$r = \sqrt{\frac{m}{U2\pi}} = \text{constant}$$

Therefore the closed-body contour for this case is a circle and Eq. (5.18) is the streamfunction for two-dimensional flow about a circular cylinder. Further mention of this flow is made in Sec. 13.11, where lift and circulation are discussed.

5.6. VELOCITY POTENTIAL

For two-dimensional flow the velocity potential $\varphi(x,y)$ is defined in cartesian coordinates as

$$u = \frac{\partial \varphi}{\partial x} \qquad \text{and} \qquad v = \frac{\partial \varphi}{\partial y} \tag{5.19}$$

The corresponding expressions in polar coordinates are

$$v_r = \frac{\partial \varphi}{\partial r} \qquad \text{and} \qquad v_t = \frac{\partial \varphi}{r\,\partial \theta} \tag{5.20}$$

If we substitute the expressions of Eq. (5.19) into the continuity equation [Eq. (5.3)], we get

$$\frac{\partial^2 \varphi}{\partial x^2} + \frac{\partial^2 \varphi}{\partial y^2} = 0 \tag{5.21}$$

This is known as the Laplace equation; it is of importance in both solid mechanics and fluid mechanics.

If the expressions of Eq. (5.19) are substituted into the equation for vorticity [Eq. (5.11)], we get

$$\xi = \frac{\partial v}{\partial x} - \frac{\partial u}{\partial y} = \frac{\partial}{\partial x}\left(+\frac{\partial \varphi}{\partial y}\right) - \frac{\partial}{\partial y}\left(+\frac{\partial \varphi}{\partial x}\right) = +\frac{\partial^2 \varphi}{\partial x\,\partial y} - \frac{\partial^2 \varphi}{\partial y\,\partial x} = 0$$

Since $\xi = 0$, the flow is irrotational, and thus, if a velocity potential exists, the flow must be irrotational.   Conversely, if the flow is rotational, the velocity potential φ does not exist.

The rotation of fluid particles requires the application of torque, which in turn depends on shearing forces.   Such forces are possible only in a viscous fluid.   In inviscid (or ideal) fluids there can be no shears and hence no torques.   An irrotational flow that also satisfies the two-dimensional form of the continuity equation will satisfy the Laplace equation (Eq. 5.21).   Such a flow may be represented by a *flow net* (Sec. 3.7) and is usually referred to as *potential flow*.

5.7. ORTHOGONALITY OF STREAMLINES AND EQUIPOTENTIAL LINES

It was noted in Eq. (5.14) that

$$d\psi = \frac{\partial \psi}{\partial x}\, dx + \frac{\partial \psi}{\partial y}\, dy$$

Similarly,
$$d\varphi = \frac{\partial \varphi}{\partial x}\, dx + \frac{\partial \varphi}{dy}\, \partial y$$

From Eqs. (5.15) and (5.19) we can express these two equations as

$$d\psi = -v\, dx + u\, dy$$

and
$$d\varphi = u\, dx\; v\, dy$$

Along a streamline, $\psi =$ constant, so $d\psi = 0$, and from the first equation we get $dy/dx = v/u$. Along an equipotential line, $\varphi =$ constant, so $d\varphi = 0$, and from the second equation we get $dy/dx = -u/v$. Geometrically, this tells us that the streamlines and equipotential lines are *orthogonal*, or everywhere perpendicular to each other.

The equipotential lines $\varphi = C_i$ and the streamlines $\psi = K_i$, where the C_i and the K_i have equal increments between adjacent lines, form a network of intersecting perpendicular lines which is called the flow net (Fig. 5.11). The small quadrilaterals must evidently be squares as their size approaches zero, for $\partial \varphi/\partial x = \partial \psi/\partial y$, or for finite increments, $\Delta \varphi/\Delta x = \Delta \psi/\Delta y$. The difference in value of the streamfunction between adjacent streamlines is called the *strength* of the stream tube bounded by

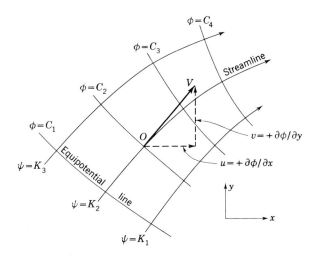

Fig. 5.11

the two streamlines, and it represents the two-dimensional flow through the tube.[1]

Referring to Fig. 5.11, the maximum velocity at any point O is seen to be tangential to the streamline. This velocity is given by $V = -\partial\varphi/\partial s$, where s is measured along the streamline. The expression $\partial\varphi/\partial s$ is also known as the *gradient* of the velocity potential. Thus the velocity is often written in convenient vector notation as $\mathbf{V} = -\text{grad } \varphi$, which holds for either two- or three-dimensional flow. The absolute velocity may always be written as the vector sum of its components; thus, in three dimensions,

$$V = |\mathbf{V}| = \sqrt{u^2 + v^2 + w^2} \tag{5.22}$$

It should be emphasized once again that the velocity potential exists only if the flow is irrotational. Thus, in order for a flow net to exist, a basic requirement is that the flow be irrotational.

An interesting application of the flow net to real flow is the case of laminar flow through porous media. In such a case the velocity head is negligible and the energy equation may be written as

$$\left(\frac{p_1}{\gamma} + z_1\right) - \left(\frac{p_2}{\gamma} + z_2\right) = h_L$$

where the head loss h_L is directly proportional to velocity for laminar flow.

Taking the differential, we get

$$-d\left(\frac{p}{\gamma} + z\right) = dh_L = \frac{V}{K}\,ds$$

where ds is the distance along the streamline, and K is constant of proportionality.

Hence

$$V = -K\frac{d(p/\gamma + z)}{ds} = \frac{\partial\varphi}{\partial s} \tag{5.23}$$

Thus we see that $\varphi = K(p/\gamma + z)$. The constant K is commonly referred to as the coefficient of permeability. Excellent discussions of the application of flow nets to flow through porous media are available in the literature.[2]

---

[1] Consider flow in the direction of the x axis in a stream tube bounded by $\psi = K_1$ and $\psi = K_2$. Let y_1 and y_2 represent the graphical locations of the two streamlines. The flow through the tube is then given by

$$Q = \int_{y_1}^{y_2} u\,dy = -\int_{y_1}^{y_2}\frac{\partial\psi}{\partial y}\,dy = -\int_{K_1}^{K_2} d\psi = K_1 - K_2$$

[2] H. R. Vallentine, "Applied Hydrodynamics," chap. 3, Butterworth & Co. (Publishers), Ltd., London, 1959. A. Casagrande, "Seepage through Dams," *J. New Engl. Water Works Assoc.*, vol. 51, pp. 131–172, 1937.

5.8. EULER'S EQUATION FOR UNSTEADY FLOW IN THREE DIMENSIONS

The energy equations developed in Chap. 4 are for steady flow only. They are also directly applicable to flow in channels with solid boundaries, but it is not obvious that they are applicable to flow in space, such as that of flow around a submerged object. In space flow it is desirable to consider not only the conditions along a streamline, but also the relations between different streamlines. In this situation we are greatly aided by the fact that for fluids of low viscosity, such as water and air, the flow is practically frictionless, except for a thin layer in the immediate vicinity of the surface of the solid and for the turbulent wake in the rear of an object.

Consider the small volume of fluid in Fig. 5.12, which is similar to Fig. 5.1, the mass of which is $\rho \, \Delta x \, \Delta y \, \Delta z$. The forces acting upon this mass are the normal pressure forces on the faces, the body force, which is here restricted to gravity, and the friction forces due to viscosity. The latter are tangential to the faces. The expressions for the friction forces are complicated, and the equations involving them cannot be integrated except in very special cases. Hence viscous forces will be neglected, and the following equations are for a frictionless fluid only.

In the direction of the z axis the net pressure force is

$$- \left(\frac{\partial p}{\partial z} \Delta z \right) (\Delta x \, \Delta y)$$

assuming the opposite faces to be parallel and equal in area. There are similar pressure forces in the x and y directions. If z is taken as vertical, as shown in Fig. 5.12, there is, in this one direction only, the body force of gravity, which is $-g\rho \, \Delta x \, \Delta y \, \Delta z$. The minus signs in both expressions are because the forces act downward, while z is considered as positive upward. If Newton's equation, force equals mass times acceleration, is

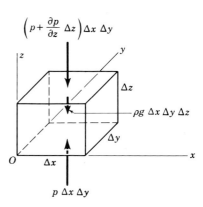

Fig. 5.12

written for the components in the z direction,

$$-\frac{\partial p}{\partial z}(\Delta x\,\Delta y\,\Delta z) - g\rho(\Delta x\,\Delta y\,\Delta z) = \rho(\Delta x\,\Delta y\,\Delta z)a_z$$

where a_z is the component of acceleration. If the finite dimensions in Fig. 5.12 are shrunk to infinitesimal values and the mass is factored out, the equation for unit mass is

$$-\frac{1}{\rho}\frac{\partial p}{\partial z} - g = a_z \tag{5.24}$$

and similar expressions apply in the x and y directions, except for the omission of $-g$. As a_z may vary both with space and time,

$$a_z = u\frac{\partial w}{\partial x} + v\frac{\partial w}{\partial y} + w\frac{\partial w}{\partial z} + \frac{\partial w}{\partial t} \tag{5.25}$$

and there are similar expressions for a_x and a_y.

Inserting the value of a_z from Eq. (5.25) into Eq. (5.24), we have Euler's equation for motion in one direction, but in general the flow equations are written for three directions, and components of the body force appear in all three. In order to simplify the equation still further, we shall consider a one-dimensional flow along a streamline in the s direction at an angle θ with the z axis. This is essentially rotating the coordinate system through the angle θ, and thus the u and v terms in Eq. (5.25) become zero, giving

$$-\frac{1}{\rho}\frac{\partial p}{\partial s} - g\cos\theta = V\frac{\partial V}{\partial s} + \frac{\partial V}{\partial t}$$

where V is now the velocity along the streamline s. (In general,

$$V = \sqrt{u^2 + v^2 + w^2}$$

but by rotating the axes so that the streamline lies along the z axis, u and v are zero.) We observe that $\cos\theta = dz/ds$ and $V\,\partial V/\partial s = \partial/\partial s(V^2/2)$. Substituting these expressions in the preceding equation and multiplying through by ds gives

$$\frac{1}{\rho}\frac{\partial p}{\partial s}ds + g\frac{dz}{ds}ds + \frac{\partial}{\partial s}\frac{V^2}{2}ds = -\frac{\partial V}{\partial t}ds \tag{5.26}$$

We now integrate each term where possible along the streamline s for one particular instant of time. Thus the partials with respect to s become total derivatives, so that the first term becomes dp/ρ and the third term becomes $d(V^2/2)$. As ρ is a variable, the first term may be integrated by parts by the form $\int u\,dv = uv - \int v\,du$. Transferring the second part of this first term to the right-hand side produces the equation

$$\left[\frac{p}{\rho} + gz + \frac{V^2}{2}\right]_1^2 = -\int_1^2 \frac{p}{\rho^2}\,\partial\rho - \int_1^2 \frac{\partial V}{\partial t}\,ds \qquad (5.27)$$

Equation (5.27) is entirely general for the motion of a *compressible* fluid in *unsteady* flow. If the flow is steady, the last term is zero. If p can then be expressed as a function of ρ, it may be possible to integrate the first term on the right-hand side of Eq. (5.27), and we then would have the flow equation for a *compressible* fluid in frictionless *steady* flow.

If the fluid is incompressible, the first term on the right side of Eq. (5.27) is zero. Dividing the remaining terms by g and also changing signs,

$$\left[\frac{p}{\gamma} + z + \frac{V^2}{2g}\right]_2^1 = \frac{1}{g}\int_1^2 \frac{\partial V}{\partial t}\,ds \qquad (5.28)$$

which is the flow equation for an *incompressible* fluid in frictionless *unsteady* flow.

If the flow is steady, the last term is again zero, and we have

$$\left(\frac{p_1}{\gamma} + z_1 + \frac{V_1^2}{2g}\right) - \left(\frac{p_2}{\gamma} + z_2 + \frac{V_2^2}{2g}\right) = 0$$

which is Bernoulli's theorem [Eq. (4.8)] for the frictionless steady flow of an incompressible fluid.

A value of deriving Eq. (5.28) from Euler's general equation of motion is that it gives us the nature of the term to use for unsteady flow, which was not obtained in Sec. 4.4. Reference to Eq. (5.28) will be made in Chap. 12, where unsteady-flow problems are discussed.

PROBLEMS

5.1. Given the streamfunction $\psi = 8xy$. Check for continuity and determine the vorticity.

5.2. Does a streamfunction exist for a flow defined by $u = 2$, $v = 8x$? Does a potential function exist?

5.3. Given the streamfunction $\psi = 3x - 2y$. Is this a potential flow? Does it satisfy the Laplace equation?

5.4. Plot a flow net for the flow defined by $\psi = 5x - y$.

5.5. A source of strength 8π is located at $(2,0)$. Another source of strength 16π is located at $(-3,0)$. For the combined flow field produced by these two sources: (*a*) find the location of the stagnation point; (*b*) plot the $\psi = 0$, $\psi = 4\pi$, $\psi = 8\pi$ lines; (*c*) find the values of ψ at $(0,2)$ and at $(3,-1)$; (*d*) find the velocity at $(-2,5)$.

5.6. For the two-dimensional flow of a frictionless incompressible fluid against a flat plate normal to the initial velocity, the streamfunction is given by $\psi = -2axy$, while its *conjugate function*, the velocity potential, is

$$\phi = -a(x^2 - y^2)$$

where a is a constant and the flow is symmetrical about the yz plane (Fig. 5.1). By direct differentiation demonstrate that these functions satisfy Eq. (5.21). Using a scale of 1 in. = 1 unit of distance, plot in the first quadrant the streamlines given by $\psi = -2a, -4a, -6a, -8a$, and the equipotential lines given by $\phi = 0, \pm 2a, \pm 4a, \pm 6a, \pm 8a$. Observe that this flow net also gives the ideal flow around an inside square corner.

5.7. In Prob. 5.6 determine the velocity components u and v, and demonstrate that they satisfy the differential equations for continuity and irrotational flow. In which direction is the flow? Prove that the absolute velocity is given by $V = 2ar$, where r is the radius to the point from the origin. Now assume that the linear scale is 1 in. = 1 ft. Determine the constant a such that the flow net of Prob. 5.6 will represent a flow of 3 ft²/sec between any two adjacent streamlines. What are the dimensions of a? Draw curves of equal velocity for values of 3, 6, 9, 12 fps. How does the velocity vary along the surface of the plate?

5.8. The three-dimensional counterpart of the flow in Probs. 5.6 and 5.7 is that of flow along the y axis approaching the plate in the xz plane. As the flow must be symmetrical about the y axis, the traces of stream and equipotential surfaces in the xy plane will be representative of those in all planes containing the y axis. The velocity potential is now given by $\phi = -a(x^2/2 - y^2)$, and the streamfunction by $\psi = ax^2y$. Notice that these functions no longer satisfy Eq. (5.21). Why not? Again plot in the first-quadrant streamlines and equipotential lines for the values given in Prob. 5.6. The velocities u and v may still be determined by Eq. (5.19). Prove that the absolute velocity for this case is given by $V = a\sqrt{x^2 + 4y^2}$. With the value of $a = \frac{3}{2}$ found in Prob. 5.7, draw curves of equal velocity for values of 3, 6, 9, 12 fps. How does the velocity vary along the surface? What is the total flow between any two adjacent stream surfaces?

5.9. For the two-dimensional flow around any angle α, the velocity potential and streamfunction are given in polar coordinates as $\phi = -ar^{\pi/\alpha} \cos (\pi/\alpha)\theta$ and $\psi = -ar^{\pi/\alpha} \sin (\pi/\alpha)\theta$, respectively. Prove that the functions given in Prob. 5.6 are a specialization of these expressions for $\alpha = \pi/2$. Take the case of $\alpha = 3\pi/2$, and plot streamlines and equipotential lines for the values given in Prob. 5.6. Compare the velocity at the corner with that at the corner in Prob. 5.6.

5.10. The flow around the body of Fig. 3.11 may be considered as that due to the sum of two velocity potentials, $\phi_1 = -Ux$, representing an undisturbed flow of velocity U in the x direction, and $\phi_2 = -S \ln r$, representing the radial flow from a source located inside the body behind the stagnation point. To relate U and S, it is observed that the total flow $2\pi S$ from the source (which is hydrodynamically equivalent to the body itself) must be equal to the flow of the main stream which is not passing through the body of width b, or $2\pi S = Ub$. This gives

$$\phi_2 = -\frac{Ub}{2\pi} \ln r$$

The distance from the stagnation point to the source is determined by setting the radial velocity from the source, $v_r = -\partial\phi/\partial r$, equal and opposite to the undisturbed velocity U. Prove that this establishes the source at a distance $b/2\pi$ behind the stagnation point. The absolute velocity

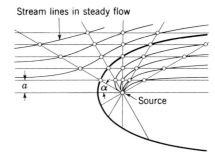

Stream lines in steady flow

Source

Fig. Prob. 5.10

at any point of the field may be determined by the vector sum of the two components U and v_r.

There follows an ingenious method of plotting the boundary of such a streamlined body, as shown in the figure. Suppose that the streamlines in the undisturbed flow are spaced a distance a apart, where $b/2a = n$, an integer. Next divide the upper half of the source into n radial sectors, each of angle α, that is, $n\alpha = \pi$. Then the undisturbed flow between the x axis and the first streamline is associated with the source flow in the first sector from the stagnation point. Thus the intersection of the first streamline with the first radial line must be a point on the boundary of the body, through which there can be no flow. Similarly, the intersection of the horizontal line at $2a$ with the radial line at 2α forms another point, and so on. Further streamlines can be plotted by connecting successive intersections of the original horizontal lines with the radial lines, recognizing that the same flow must exist between any adjacent pair of streamlines. Thus the intersection of a horizontal line ea above the axis with a radial line at $f\alpha$ from the stagnation point must lie on a streamline which is $(e - f)a$ distant from the axis in the undisturbed region.

Assume a value of $U = 20$ fps and a two-dimensional flow past a streamlined body for which $b = 36$ ft. Compute the distances from the source to the stagnation point and to the surface of the body at a radius $90°$ to the axis. What is the value of the source velocity at the latter point?

5.11. What is the magnitude of the velocity of the fluid along the surface at the $90°$ point in the preceding problem? (Compare with the results of Prob. 3.12.) What is its direction relative to the axis?

5.12. Find the distance and the two velocities called for in the preceding two problems for an angle of $30°$. (Compare with Prob. 3.12.)

5.13. Using the method described in Prob. 5.10, plot the boundary of the body and a set of streamlines for a steady two-dimensional flow past a body such as that of Fig. 3.11, for $b = 36$ ft, using a scale of 1 in. = 6 ft.

5.14. An ideal fluid flows in a two-dimensional $90°$ bend. The inner and outer radii of the bend are 0.4 and 1.4 ft. Sketch the flow net and estimate the velocity at the inner and outer walls of the bend if the velocity in the 1.0-ft-wide straight section is 10 fps. Develop an analytic expression for the streamfunction, in this case noting that $v_t = -\partial\psi/\partial r$ and $v_r = \partial\psi/r\,\partial\theta$.

5.15. Combine the uniform flow defined by $u = 16$ fps with the doublet $2qa = m$, where $q = 10$ cfs/ft and $a = 2$ in. Sketch the streamlines for $\psi = -3$, -2, -1, $-\frac{1}{2}$, 0, $\frac{1}{2}$, 1, 2, and 3 cfs/ft. Use a scale of 1 in. = 1 in.

5.16. A flow field is defined by the streamfunction $\psi = 15r \sin \theta - 30 \ln r - (20/r) \sin \theta$. Sketch this flow field. Calculate the velocities at $r = 3$ for $\theta = 0, 45, 90, 150, 210,$ and $315°$.

5.17. The components of the velocities of a certain flow system are

$$u = -\frac{Q}{2\pi} \frac{x}{x^2 + y^2} + By + C$$

$$v = -A \frac{y}{x^2 + y^2} + Dx + E$$

(*a*) Calculate a value of A consistent with continuous flow. (*b*) Sketch the streamlines for this flow system, assuming $B = C = D = E = 0$.

5.18. A cylindrical drum with a 2-ft radius is securely held in position in an open channel of rectangular section. The channel is 10 ft wide, and the flow rate is 240 cfs. Water flows beneath the drum as shown in the figure. Sketch the flow net, and determine as accurately as you can the pressure at several points along the surface AB. Neglect fluid friction. Sketch the pressure distribution, and by numerical integration determine the horizontal thrust on the cylinder.

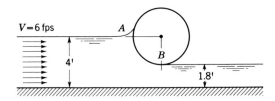

Fig. Prob. 5.18

SIX

MOMENTUM AND DYNAMIC FORCES IN FLUID FLOW

6.1. DYNAMIC FORCE

Whenever the velocity of a stream of fluid is changed either in direction or in magnitude, a force is required. By the law of action and reaction, an equal and opposite force is exerted by the fluid upon the body producing the change. This is called a *dynamic* force, to distinguish it from the forces due to hydrostatic pressure.

Previously, two important fundamental propositions were presented: the continuity equation and the energy equation. A third basic concept, the *impulse-momentum principle*, will now be developed. It is of particular importance in flow problems where the determination of forces is involved.

6.2. DEVELOPMENT OF THE IMPULSE - MOMENTUM PRINCIPLE

Newton's law $\mathbf{F} = m\mathbf{a} = m\,d\mathbf{V}/dt$ may also be written as $\mathbf{F}\,dt = m\,d\mathbf{V}$, where the left-hand term is impulse and the right-hand term is the resulting change in momentum. In the case of a steady stream impinging on a slightly curved vane as in Fig. 6.1, the resulting force $\mathbf{F}$ of the vane against the fluid is the summation of all the elementary forces acting along the entire surface of the vane; their summation could be found if piezometers were connected at various points along the vane.

Let us now turn our attention to Fig. 6.2, which sketches a control volume of fluid composed of the section of fluid in contact with the vane (i.e., the fluid between sections 1 and 2 of Fig. 6.1). In time dt let us suppose that a filament of fluid moves from position MN to $M'N'$. Let the distance moved by the particles at M during the time dt be ds_1, while the particles at N will have moved ds_2.

In steady flow there is no change in either mass or velocity of the body of fluid between sections 1 and 2, and thus its momentum is constant. Hence the change in momentum of the fluid particles within the control volume is the difference between that of the fluid entering and that of the fluid leaving the control volume. The momentum of the fluid entering the control volume can be expressed as $(\rho_1 A_1\,ds_1)\,V_1$, while that leaving the control volume is $(\rho_2 A_2\,ds_2)\,V_2$. In steady flow the mass entering at section 1 must equal that leaving at section 2; hence $\rho_1 A_1\,ds_1 = \rho_2 A_2\,ds_2$. Dividing both sides of this expression by dt gives the continuity condition: $\rho_1 A_1 V_1 = \rho_2 A_2 V_2 = \rho Q$. Hence, in time dt the momentum entering the control volume is $\rho Q V_1\,dt$, while that leaving is $\rho Q V_2\,dt$.

As $\mathbf{V}$, $\Delta\mathbf{V}$, and $\mathbf{F}$ are vector quantities, it is convenient to take

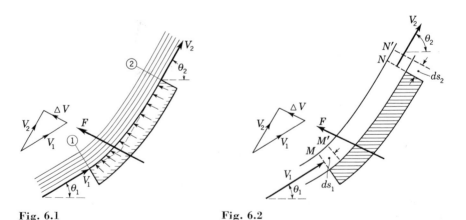

Fig. 6.1   Fig. 6.2

components, the x component of the change of momentum being $\rho Q\,dt\,(V_2\cos\theta_2 - V_1\cos\theta_1)$. Equating this to the x component of the impulse, $F_x\,dt$,

$$F_x = \rho Q(V_2\cos\theta_2 - V_1\cos\theta_1) = \rho Q\,\Delta V_x \tag{6.1}$$

In similar manner the y component is

$$F_y = \rho Q(V_2\sin\theta_2 - V_1\sin\theta_1) = \rho Q\,\Delta V_y \tag{6.2}$$

As $|\mathbf{F}| = \sqrt{F_x{}^2 + F_y{}^2}$ and $|\Delta\mathbf{V}| = \sqrt{\Delta V_x{}^2 + \Delta V_y{}^2}$, the value of the resultant dynamic force exerted by the body *on* the fluid is

$$\mathbf{F} = \rho Q\,\Delta\mathbf{V} \tag{6.3}$$

The direction of $\mathbf{F}$ will be the same as that of $\Delta\mathbf{V}$, as in Figs. 6.1 and 6.2. The direction of the force exerted by the fluid *on the body* will be opposite to this and might be represented as $\mathbf{F} = \rho Q(-\Delta\mathbf{V})$. As previously stated, the resultant force, as shown in Fig. 6.1, is the summation of all the infinitesimal forces along the surface, but the impulse-momentum principle shows that the resultant force is a function of only the conditions at entrance and at exit. Thus we avoid the complications of the internal details. However, internal factors along the path, such as friction, will affect the numerical value of quantities at exit. In the case of multiple inlets and outlets, the respective $(\rho Q\,\Delta\mathbf{V})$'s may be added vectorially.

In the mechanics of solids we are usually concerned only with a tangible definite body of mass m. In fluid mechanics we are usually unable to consider a specific mass, but must deal with a succession of particles flowing past a given section. It is seen that the momentum law enables this to be done.

6.3. MOMENTUM CORRECTION FACTOR

If the velocity is not uniform over a section, the momentum transferred across that section is greater than that computed by using the mean velocity. Thus the momentum transferred across an elementary area dA, where the local velocity is u, is $(\rho u\,dA)u = \rho u^2\,dA$, and the momentum transfer across the entire section is $\rho\int_A u^2\,dA$, while that computed by using the mean velocity is $\rho QV = \rho AV^2$. Hence the correction factor by which the latter should be multiplied is

$$\beta = \frac{1}{AV^2}\int_A u^2\,dA \tag{6.4}$$

For laminar flow in a circular pipe, $\beta = \tfrac{4}{3}$, but for turbulent flow in circular pipes, it usually ranges from 1.005 to 1.05, as shown by Eq. (8.32b). For open-channel flow it may be greater. Unless otherwise specified, the value of β in the ensuing discussion will be taken as 1.0.

6.4. DYNAMIC FORCES ON A STATIONARY BODY

To find the force exerted by a jet upon a stationary object, it is necessary to find the value of $\Delta \mathbf{V}$ in Eq. (6.3). The direction of the force on the object will be opposite to that of $\Delta \mathbf{V}$. The following example illustrates these points.

Illustrative example 6.1: In Fig. 6.3 it may be assumed that $\theta = 30°$, $V_1 = 100$ fps, and the stream is a jet of water with an initial diameter of 2 in. Assume friction losses such that $V_2 = 80$ fps. Find the dynamic force of the water on the vane.

This problem is best solved by taking a free-body diagram of the element of fluid in contact with the blade. The forces acting on this element, disregarding gravity and friction, are as shown in the sketch. The forces $(F_{B/W})_x$ and $(F_{B/W})_y$ represent the components of force of blade on water in the x and y directions.

Applying Eq. (6.3) along the x axis,

$$-(F_{B/W})_x = \rho Q(V_{2_x} - V_{1_x}) = 1.94(0.0218 \times 100)(0.866 \times 80 - 100)$$
$$= 4.22(-30.7) = -129.5 \text{ lb}$$

Hence $(F_{B/W})_x = +129.5$ lb

The plus sign indicates that the assumed direction of $(F_{B/W})_x$ was correct.

Applying Eq. (6.3) along the y axis,

$$+(F_{B/W})_y = \rho Q(V_{2_y} - V_{1_y}) = 4.22(0.50 \times 80 - 0) = 168.5 \text{ lb}$$

Thus the dynamic force of the blade on the fluid is the resultant of a 129.5-lb component to the left and a 168.5-lb component upward in the y direction. Equal and opposite to this is the force of the fluid on the blade (downward and to the right). The resultant force is 213 lb at an angle of 48.8° below the horizontal.

It should be noted that this is the dynamic force. To get the total force of fluid on the vane, an estimate of the weight of liquid on the vane should be added to the 168.5 lb to get the total force downward on the vane.

It will be seen that, if θ is less than 90°, friction increases the value of F_x over its value if there were no friction. If θ is greater than 90°, friction decreases

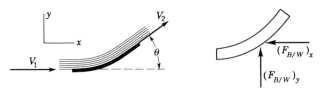

Fig. 6.3

the value of F_x.   On the other hand, friction decreases the value of F_y for any value of the angle θ.   It is assumed in this discussion that θ is the angle of deflection from the initial direction of the jet.

6.5. DYNAMIC FORCE ON FLAT PLATE

As a special case of the preceding example, consider Fig. 6.4, which shows a circular jet of area A and velocity V striking a flat plate normally.   In accordance with Eq. (6.3), the total dynamic force exerted is

$$F = \rho Q \,\Delta V = \frac{\gamma A V}{g}\, V = \gamma A \,\frac{V^2}{g} = \rho A V^2 \qquad (6.5)$$

where V is assumed to be uniform over the section of the jet.   This is practically true for a jet from a nozzle, and thus the value of β will be very close to unity.

In Fig. 6.4 streamlines and pressure variation on the plate are shown plotted to scale from actual measurements.   It is assumed in Eq. (6.5) that all the fluid has been turned through an angle of 90°, and thus $\Delta V_x = V$, but this may not be strictly true.   As the fluid flows radially outward in all directions, the depth must continually decrease if the cross-sectional area is to be constant, as it must be unless the velocity is diminished by friction.   Hence the total force measured on such a plate may be slightly less than the value given by Eq. (6.5).   However, for all practical purposes, the streamlines become nearly parallel to the plate, at a radius about four times that of the jet, and the dynamic intensity of pressure approaches zero.

If the plate is much smaller than this, Eq. (6.5) does not apply and a purely empirical coefficient must be used.

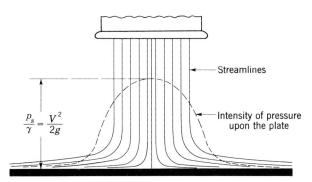

Streamlines

Intensity of pressure upon the plate

$$\frac{p_s}{\gamma} = \frac{V^2}{2g}$$

Fig. 6.4.   A free jet impinging upon a large flat plate perpendicular to the jet.   (Plotted to scale from actual measurements.)

The intensity of pressure at the center of the plate, due to dynamic action, is the stagnation pressure; that is, $p_s = \rho V^2/2 = \gamma V^2/2g$. The dynamic pressure then decreases to very nearly zero as the radius increases, as shown in Fig. 6.4. If p' denotes the dynamic pressure on the plate at any radius r,

$$F_R = 2\pi \int_0^R p'r\,dr$$

where F_R represents the dynamic force on that portion of the plate having a radius R with center coincident with the center of the jet. If R is sufficiently large, so that the velocity of practically all the fluid is turned through 90°, the value of this integral should be the same as that given by Eq. (6.5). Once again it should be noted that to get the total force of the fluid on the plate one must add the weight of water on the plate to the dynamic force. The weight of water that should be added includes all that below the section of jet where the streamlines are no longer parallel.

6.6. REACTION OF A JET

In Fig. 6.5 consider a jet issuing steadily from a tank which is large enough so that the velocity within it may be neglected. Let the area of the jet be A_2 and its velocity V_2, and assuming an ideal fluid, $V_2 = \sqrt{2gh}$. Applying the impulse-momentum principle, the force exerted upon the fluid to change its velocity from 0 to V_2 is

$$F_2 = \rho Q(V_2 - 0) = \rho A_2 V_2{}^2 = 2\gamma h A_2 \qquad (6.6)$$

As this is the value of the force upon the fluid, there must be an equal force exerted upon the tank in a direction opposite to V_2. A physical

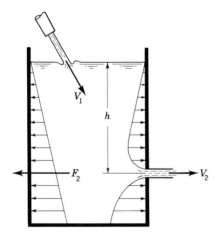

Fig. 6.5

explanation for this is that the pressure over the central portion of the orifice is reduced to zero gage pressure and that there is also a lowered pressure on the tank walls immediately adjacent to the orifice, while at the same depth and on the opposite side of the tank the pressure over a corresponding area is γh. It is seen that in the ideal case the reaction of the jet is twice the force exerted upon an area the same size as the jet and at the same depth below the surface.

Also suppose that in Fig. 6.5 a jet of fluid from a nozzle is discharged into the tank at the same rate ρQ and with a velocity V_1. As this jet velocity is reduced to zero within the tank, the value of ΔV_1 is V_1. Hence the force exerted *upon* the tank by the jet is

$$F_1 = \rho Q V_1$$

Therefore the total dynamic force exerted upon the tank is the vector sum of these two separate forces, F_1 and F_2.

From Eqs. (6.1) and (6.2) it may be seen that the resultant dynamic force exerted upon a body having fluid influx and efflux may be considered as being made up of two concentrated forces, $F_1 = \rho Q V_1$ at entrance and $F_2 = \rho Q V_2$ at exit, the former being in the same direction as V_1 and the latter in the opposite direction to V_2. This is true whether the velocity between (1) and (2) is 0, as in Fig. 6.5, or whether it is not zero, as indicated in Figs. 6.1 and 6.2.

6.7. DYNAMIC FORCE EXERTED ON PRESSURE CONDUITS

When a flowing stream is confined, as in a pipe under pressure, there will be forces due to static pressure as well as the dynamic force due to change in velocity. Consider the fluid as flowing horizontally to the right in Fig. 6.6. The dynamic force exerted upon the fluid is to the right and is $F = \rho Q(V_2 - V_1)$. This is the resultant of all the forces acting upon the fluid. These forces are the static forces on the two end sections and the summation of the forces from the pipe wall. The intensity of pressure at the wall will decrease as the diameter decreases, because of the increase in velocity head. If gravity is disregarded as unimportant, the summation of all components normal to the pipe axis must be zero because of symmetry, and the resultant force exerted by the pipe walls is N_x and is in an axial direction. Because of fluid friction, N_x will be increased over the value indicated in Fig. 6.6 if the flow is to the right. If the flow is to the left, friction will decrease the value of N_x and may even cause it to be directed to the right.

However, assuming an ideal fluid and assuming N_x to be directed as

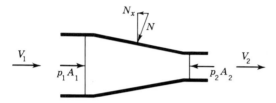

Fig. 6.6

shown, equating the sum of all forces to the time rate of change of momentum gives

$$p_1A_1 - p_2A_2 - N_x = \rho Q(V_2 - V_1) \tag{6.7}$$

In Eq. (6.7) each term can be evaluated independently, except N_x, which is the quantity we wish to find. Rewriting Eq. (6.7), the result is

$$N_x = p_1A_1 - p_2A_2 - \rho Q(V_2 - V_1) \tag{6.8}$$

This is the value of the total dynamic force exerted by the reducer on the fluid. The force of the fluid on the reducer is of course equal and opposite to that of the reducer on the fluid.

If the flow were to the left in Fig. 6.6, a similar analysis would apply, but it is necessary to be consistent in regard to plus and minus signs.

Consideration of the weight of fluid between sections 1 and 2 in Fig. 6.6 results in the conclusion that pressures are larger on the bottom half of the pipe than on the upper half. Also, once again it is the conditions at the end sections of the control volume that govern the analysis. What occurs within the flow between sections 1 and 2 is unimportant so far as the determination of dynamic forces is concerned. In Fig. 6.7 is shown a schematic representation of the pressure distribution within the reducer. The integrated effect of all these pressures is equivalent in the x direction to N_x and in the y direction to the weight of fluid between sections 1 and 2.

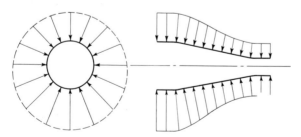

Fig. 6.7.   Pressure distribution in a reducer.

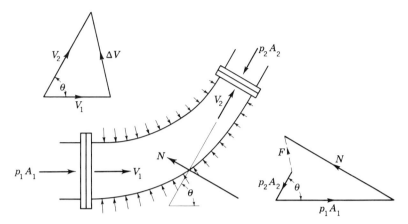

Fig. 6.8.   Forces on a reducing bend.

If the fluid undergoes a change in both direction and velocity, as in the reducing pipe bend in Fig. 6.8, the procedure will be similar to that in the preceding case, except that it is convenient to deal with components. Neglecting the weight of the fluid between sections 1 and 2, applying Eq. (6.3) by summing up forces acting on the fluid in the x direction, and equating them to the change in fluid momentum in the x direction give

$$N_x = p_1 A_1 - p_2 A_2 \cos \theta - \rho Q(V_2 \cos \theta - V_1) \tag{6.9}$$

Similarly, in the y direction,

$$N_y = p_2 A_2 \sin \theta + \rho Q V_2 \sin \theta \tag{6.10}$$

In a specific case, if the numerical values determined by these equations are positive, then the assumed directions are correct. A negative value for either one merely indicates that that component is in the direction opposite from that assumed.

Note that $\mathbf{F} = \rho Q \, \Delta \mathbf{V}$ is the resultant of all the forces acting on the fluid, which includes the pressure forces on the two ends, while $\mathbf{N}$ is the force exerted by the bend. The value of N is $\sqrt{N_x^2 + N_y^2}$, and it is represented by the closing line in the force diagram shown in Fig. 6.8. The total force exerted by the fluid on the bend is equal to N, but it is opposite to the direction shown in the figure.

It may be seen that such a force tends to move the portion of the pipe considered. Hence, where such changes in velocity or alignment occur, a large pipe will usually be "anchored" by attaching it to a concrete block of sufficient weight to provide the necessary resistance.

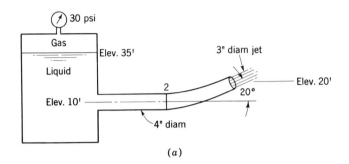

(a)

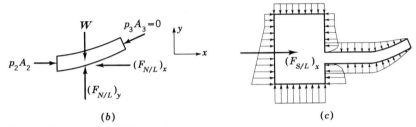

(b)   (c)

Illustrative Example 6.2

Illustrative example 6.2: In the accompanying figure (a) is shown a curved pipe section that is attached to the straight pipe section as shown. Determine the dynamic force of the liquid ($\gamma = 55$ pcf) on the curved pipe, and find the horizontal component of the jet reaction. All significant data are given in the figure. Assume an ideal liquid. The energy equation between sections 1 and 3 gives

$$\frac{30 \times 144}{55} + 35 = 20 + \frac{V_3^2}{2g}$$

and $V_3 = 77.6$ fps   (jet velocity)

$$Q = A_3 V_3 = 3.81 \text{ cfs}$$

$$V_2 = \frac{Q}{A_2} = 43.5 \text{ fps}$$

Energy equation between section 2 and 3 gives

$$10 + \frac{p_2(144)}{55} + \frac{(43.5)^2}{64.4} = 20 + \frac{(77.6)^2}{2g}$$

and $p_2 = 28.3$ psi

The free-body diagram of the forces acting on the liquid contained in the curved pipe is shown in (b) of the figure. Applying Eq. (6.3),

$$p_2 A_2 - p_3 A_3 \cos 20° - (F_{N/L})_x = \rho Q(V_3 \cos 20° - V_2)$$

where $(F_{N/L})_x$ represents the force of the curved pipe on the liquid in the x direction.

Since section 3 is a jet in contact with the atmosphere, $p_3 = 0$. Thus

$$28.3 \left(\frac{\pi}{4} \times 4^2 \right) - (F_{N/L})_x = \left(1.94 \times \frac{55}{62.4} \right) (3.81)(77.6 \times 0.94 - 43.5)$$

$$356 - (F_{N/L})_x = 192$$
$$(F_{N/L})_x = +164 \text{ lb}$$

where the plus sign indicates that the assumed direction is correct. In the y direction the $p_2 A_2$ force has no component. Estimating the weight of liquid W as 100 lb,

$$(F_{N/L})_y = \rho Q(77.6 \times 0.342 - 0) + 100 = +273 \text{ lb}$$

The resultant force of liquid on the curved pipe is equal and opposite to that of nozzle on liquid. The resultant force of liquid on the curved pipe is $[(164)^2 + (273)^2]^{1/2} = 318$ lb downward and to the right at an angle of $59°00'$ with the horizontal. The horizontal jet reaction is best found by taking a free-body diagram of the liquid in the system as shown in (c) of the figure:

$$(F_{S/L})_x = \rho Q(V_3 \cos 20° - 0) = 475 \text{ lb}$$

where $(F_{S/L})_x$ represents the force of the system on the liquid in the x direction. $(F_{S/L})_x$ is equivalent to the integrated effect of the x components of the pressure vectors shown in (c). Equal and opposite to $(F_{S/L})_x$ is the force of the liquid on the system, i.e., the jet reaction. Hence the horizontal jet reaction is a 475-lb force to the left. Thus there is a 164-lb force tending to push the nozzle off the pipe to the right, while at the same time there is a 475-lb force tending to move the entire system to the left.

6.8. RELATION BETWEEN ABSOLUTE AND RELATIVE VELOCITIES

In much of the work that follows it will be necessary to deal with both absolute and relative velocities of the fluid. The absolute velocity $\mathbf{V}$ of a body (Fig. 6.9) is its velocity relative to the earth. The relative velocity $\mathbf{v}$ of a body is its velocity relative to a second body, which may in turn be in motion relative to the earth. The absolute velocity $\mathbf{V}$ of the first body is the vector sum of its velocity $\mathbf{v}$ relative to the second body and the absolute velocity $\mathbf{u}$ of the latter. The relation of the three is thus

$$\mathbf{V} = \mathbf{u} + \mathbf{v} \tag{6.11}$$

Let us define α and β as the angles made by the absolute and relative

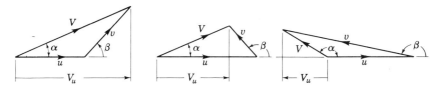

Fig. 6.9. Relative and absolute velocity relations.

velocities of a fluid, respectively, with the linear velocity u of some solid body. It is seen from Fig. 6.9 that, whatever the shape of the velocity vector triangle,

$$V \sin \alpha = v \sin \beta$$

$$V \cos \alpha = u + v \cos \beta$$

6.9. DYNAMIC FORCE UPON BODY IN TRANSLATION

The dynamic force exerted by a stream upon a single moving object can be determined by Eq. (6.3) provided the flow is steady and the body has a motion of translation along the line of action of the stream initially. If the latter condition is not fulfilled, the case becomes the complex one of unsteady flow.

There are two principal differences between the action upon a stationary and a moving object. One is that it is necessary to consider both absolute and relative velocities, which may make the determination of $\Delta \mathbf{V}$ more difficult. The other is in regard to the amount of fluid that strikes the single moving object in any time interval. If the cross-sectional area of a stream is A_1 and its velocity is V_1, then the rate at which fluid is emitted from the nozzle is $G = \gamma Q = \gamma A_1 V_1$. But the amount of fluid which strikes the body per unit time will be less than this if the body is moving away from the nozzle. As an extreme case, suppose the object to be moving in the same direction as the jet and with the same or a higher velocity. It is clear that none of the fluid will act upon it. If it is moving with a velocity less than that of the jet, the amount of fluid that strikes it per unit time will be proportional to the difference between the two velocities, i.e., to $v_1 = V_1 - u$. If G' denotes the weight of fluid per second striking an object moving with a velocity u which is in the same direction as V_1, then

$$G' = \gamma Q' = \gamma A_1 (V_1 - u) = \gamma A_1 v_1 \tag{6.12}$$

An explanation for the difference between G and G' may also be seen by considering Fig. 6.10, where the fluid issues from a nozzle at the rate of $G = \gamma A_1 V_1$ per unit time. But in the same interval of time the object will have moved away from the nozzle the distance u, and the volume of fluid between the two will have been increased by the amount $A_1 u$.

Thus, for this special case of a single object in translation in the same direction as the stream initially, the component of the force exerted upon it in the direction of motion is

$$F_u = \frac{G'}{g} \Delta V_u = \frac{\gamma A_1 v_1}{g} \Delta V_u \tag{6.13}$$

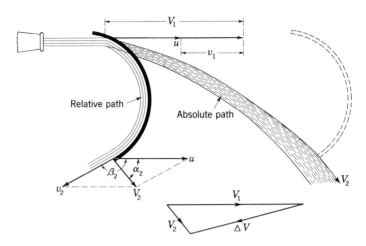

Fig. 6.10. Jet acting on a vane in translation.

where the subscript u denotes the component in the same direction as u. (It will be seen later that this same subscript is used to represent the tangential direction for a point on a rotating body.)

It can be proved that $\Delta V_u = \Delta v_u$. Referring to Fig. 6.10, it is seen that $V_{2_u} = V_2 \cos \alpha_2$ and $V_{1_u} = V_1 \cos \alpha_1 = V_1$. Therefore

$$\Delta V_u = V_{2_u} - V_{1_u} = V_2 \cos \alpha_2 - V_1$$

But $V_1 = u + v_1$, so $\Delta V_u = V_2 \cos \alpha_2 - v_1 - u$. Now, $v_{2_u} = v_2 \cos \beta_2$ and $v_{1_u} = v_1 \cos \beta_1 = v_1$. Therefore $\Delta v_u = v_{2_u} - v_{1_u} = v_2 \cos \beta_2 - v_1$. But $v_2 \cos \beta_2 = V_2 \cos \alpha_2 - u$. So

$$\Delta v_u = V_2 \cos \alpha_2 - u - v_1$$

Hence $\Delta V_u = \Delta v_u$. Thus Eq. (6.13) for the force on a single body may also be written as

$$F_u = \frac{G'}{g} \Delta v_u = \frac{\gamma A v_1}{g} \Delta v_u \tag{6.14}$$

In Fig. 6.10, by the time a particle of fluid which strikes the moving vane at the instant it is in the position shown by the solid line has reached the point of outflow from the vane, the latter will have reached the position shown by the dotted line. Thus two paths may be traced for the fluid, one relative to the moving vane, which is as it would appear to an observer (or a camera) moving with the vane, and the other relative to the earth, termed the *absolute path*, as it would appear to an observer (or a camera) stationary with respect to the earth.

A study of Fig. 6.10 shows that the direction of the relative velocity at outflow from the vane is determined by the shape of the latter, but the relative velocity at entrance, just *before* the fluid strikes the vane, is determined solely by the relation between V_1 and u. Just *after* the fluid strikes the vane, its relative velocity must be tangent to the vane surface. To avoid excess energy loss, these two directions should agree; otherwise there will be an abrupt change in velocity and direction of flow at this point.

There are few instances where a stream of fluid impinges on a single body or vane. More commonly, the jet is directed on a series of vanes as with a Pelton wheel (Fig. 15.1). In such a case the effective flow impinging on each of the series of closely spaced buckets is $Q = A_1V_1$, since whatever flow does not impinge on the first bucket will impinge on the second one, and so on around the circle. Thus the component of force exerted on a series of vanes is expressible as

$$F_u = \frac{G}{g} \Delta V_u = \frac{\gamma A_1 V_1}{g} \Delta V_u = \frac{\gamma A_1 V_1}{g} \Delta v_u \qquad (6.15)$$

Illustrative example 6.3: A 2-in.-diameter water jet with a velocity of 100 fps impinges on a single vane moving in the same direction at a velocity of 60 fps. If $\beta_2 = 150°$ and friction losses over the vane are such that $v_2 = 0.9v_1$, compute the force exerted by the water on the vane.

The velocity vector diagrams at entrance and exit to the vane are shown in the accompanying figure. Since $v_2 = 0.9 \times 40 = 36$ fps,

$$V_2 \sin \alpha_2 = v_2 \sin \beta_2 = 36 \times 0.5 = 18 \text{ fps} \qquad (a)$$

$$V_2 \cos \alpha_2 = u + v_2 \cos \beta_2 = 60 + 36(-0.866) = 28.8 \text{ fps} \qquad (b)$$

Solving (a) and (b) simultaneously yields $V_2 = 34$ fps, $\alpha_2 = 32°$. Hence

$$-F_u = \rho Q'(V_2 \cos \alpha_2 - V_1) = 1.94(0.0218)(100 - 60)(28.8 - 100) = -120.3 \text{ lb}$$

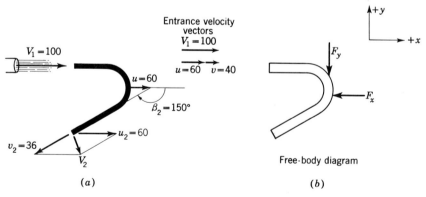

(a)   (b)

Illustrative Example 6.3. (a) Exit velocity vectors. (b) Free-body diagram.

So $F_u = 120.3$ lb.   The force of vane on water is to the left as assumed; hence force of water on vane is 120.3 lb to the right.

$$-F_y = \rho Q'(V_2 \sin \alpha_2 - 0) = 1.94(0.0218)(40)(-18) = -30.3 \text{ lb}$$

Thus $F_y = 30.3$ lb in the direction shown.   The force of water on the vane is equal and opposite and thus 30.3 lb upward.   If the blade were one of a series of blades,

$$-F_u = \rho Q(V_2 \cos \alpha_2 - V_1) = 1.94(0.0218)(100)(28.8 - 100) = -301 \text{ lb}$$

For the case of a series of blades, energy considerations could have been used for the solution.   The horsepower of the original jet is

$$\text{HP}_{\text{in}} = \frac{\gamma Q(V_1{}^2/2g)}{550} = \frac{62.4(0.0218 \times 100)[(100)^2/64.4]}{550} = 38.4$$

The horsepower of the water as it leaves the system is

$$\text{HP}_{\text{out}} = \frac{\gamma Q(V_2{}^2/2g)}{550} = 4.44$$

The horsepower transferred to the blades (i.e., out of the fluid) is

$$\text{HP}_{\text{transfer}} = \frac{Fu}{550} = \frac{(301)(60)}{550} = 32.8$$

An equation for conservation of energy expressed in terms of power is

$$\text{HP}_{\text{in}} - \text{HP}_{\text{out}} - \text{HP}_{\text{transfer}} - \text{HP}_{\text{friction loss}} = 0$$

Thus $$38.4 - 4.4 - 32.8 = \text{HP}_{\text{friction loss}}$$

Therefore $$\text{HP}_{\text{friction loss}} = 1.2$$

That this is so may be verified by computing

$$\frac{\gamma Q(v_1{}^2/2g) - \gamma Q(v_2{}^2/2g)}{550} = \frac{62.4(0.0218 \times 100)[(40)^2 - (36)^2]}{550(64.4)} = 1.2$$

It should be noticed that the horsepower loss due to friction is small.   Commonly, in problems of this type, an assumption that $v_1 = v_2$ will give good results.

6.10. JET PROPULSION

In Sec. 6.6 an expression was derived for the reaction of a jet from a stationary tank.   Assume now that the tank in Fig. 6.5 moves to the left with a velocity u.   If the orifice is small compared with the size of the tank, the relative velocity within the latter may be disregarded, as may also any change in h for a short interval of time.   Thus the absolute velocity of the fluid within the tank is $V_1 = u$ to the left.   If the jet issues from the orifice with a relative velocity v_2, taking velocities to the right as positive, its absolute velocity will be $V_2 = v_2 - u$.   Hence

$$\Delta V = V_2 - V_1 = (v_2 - u) - (-u) = v_2$$

The same result is obtained directly by noting that for translation

$\Delta V = \Delta v = v_2$. Thus the force of reaction for this case is independent of the velocity of the tank, and Eq. (6.6) applies for either rest or motion.

Rocket. Both the fuel and the oxygen for combustion are contained within a rocket which is analogous to the tank of Fig. 6.5 if the entering stream at (1) is omitted. The only difference is that the exit pressure p_0 of the gases leaving the orifice or nozzle at (2) may exceed the atmospheric pressure p_a. If A_2 equals the area of the jet, the rocket thrust is

$$F = \rho A_2 v_2{}^2 + (p_0 - p_a)A_2 \qquad (6.16)$$

and this is independent of the speed of the rocket.

Jet engine. By *jet engine* is meant a device which carries its fuel only and takes in the air for combustion from the atmosphere. It is analogous to the tank of Fig. 6.5, including the intake of fluid at (1), except that the velocity of the air received is usually in the same straight line as the velocity of the exit jet at (2). There are three forms of jet engines, but the dynamic equation is the same for all three. The *ram jet* must be brought up to a high speed by rockets or some other means, and then it scoops in the air from in front and compresses it by virtue of the stagnation pressure due to its speed. The *turbojet* can take off from the ground, for in it the air is compressed by a compressor driven by a gas turbine, the exhaust from which supplies the jet propulsion. Then there is a *pulsating* machine, which scoops in air in cycles. The inlet is then closed, the fuel-air mixture is exploded; a jet then gives the device a spurt; and the process is repeated.

The thrust is

$$F = \frac{(G_a + G_f)v_2 - G_a u}{g} \qquad (6.17)$$

where u = velocity of flight

G_a = weight of air taken in per second

G_f = weight of fuel consumed per second

The thrust will vary with the speed of flight. Usually $p_0 = p_a$, and so the second term of Eq. (6.16) is not included in Eq. (6.17).

6.11. TORQUE IN ROTATING MACHINES

When a fluid flows through a rotor, its radius usually varies along its path. Hence it is desirable to compute torque rather than a force. The resultant torque is the summation of the torques produced by all the elementary forces, but it has been shown that the latter may be considered as equivalent to two single forces, one concentrated at entrance to and the other at exit from any device. For steady flow these equivalent forces have been shown to be $\rho Q V_1$ and $\rho Q V_2$. Referring to Figs. 6.11 and 6.12 and taking moments, the torque produced is

$$T = \rho Q (r_1 V_1 \cos \alpha_1 - r_2 V_2 \cos \alpha_2) \qquad (6.18)$$

If T as given by this equation is positive, it is the value of the torque exerted by the fluid on the runner and shaft of a turbine. The torque delivered by the turbine is less than this by virtue of the mechanical friction. If the value of T is negative, it represents the torque exerted on the fluid by the impeller of a pump or compressor or fan. The torque input to the shaft of such a machine is greater than this because of mechanical friction.

Equation (6.18) and subsequent equations that may be derived from it are correct, but it is difficult to determine the numerical values to be used in them. Thus fluid particles in different streamlines may flow with different velocities, and it is necessary to estimate what the average velocity may be. Also, it is known that the average direction of a stream is often different from that of the vane which it is supposed to follow, but as yet there is no exact knowledge as to the amount of deviation in every case. Thus even the average velocity is not given precisely by dividing the flow by the cross-sectional area of a rotor passage. Furthermore, the entrance or exit edges of vanes are not always parallel to the axis of rotation, and thus the radii will be different for different streamlines.

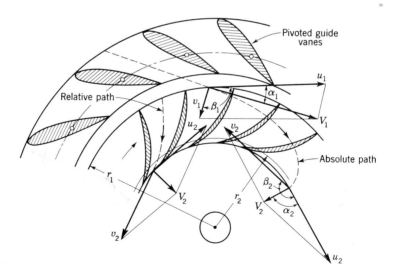

Fig. 6.11. Radial-flow hydraulic turbine.

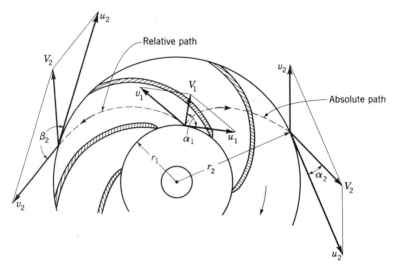

Fig. 6.12.   Centrifugal-pump impeller with radial flow.

Fig. 6.13.   Radial-flow-pump impeller rotating at 200 rpm.   (*a*) Instantaneous photo showing relative flow.   (*b*) Time exposure showing absolute flow.   (*Photographs from California Institute of Technology Hydrodynamics Laboratory.*)

Despite these defects, the theory is useful. It shows the shape or nature of the performance curves of a given machine; it shows the influence of each separate factor; and it shows the direction in which changes in design should be made in order to alter the characteristics which have been found by test of an existing machine.

It is immaterial in the use of Eq. (6.18) and subsequent equations whether the fluid flows radially inward, as in Fig. 6.11, or radially outward, as in Fig. 6.13 or remains at a constant distance from the axis, as in Figs. 6.14 and 6.15. In any case, r_1 is the radius at entrance and r_2 is that at exit. In Figs. 6.11 to 6.13 may be seen the absolute and the relative paths of flow.

Figures 6.11 to 6.13 show two-dimensional flow in planes normal to the axis of rotation. This is known as *radial* flow. The streamlines and velocity triangles lie in the plane of the paper and are readily represented. In *axial* flow, as in Figs. 6.14 and 6.15, a particle of fluid remains at a constant distance from the axis, and the streamlines are helices on coaxial cylinders. A streamline and its velocity triangles are shown on a developed cylinder for the corresponding radius.

Mixed flow is intermediate between these two extremes, and velocities have radial, axial, and tangential components. A streamline is a conical helix with a varying radius from the axis of rotation. Needless to say, this is a complicated three-dimensional-flow situation.

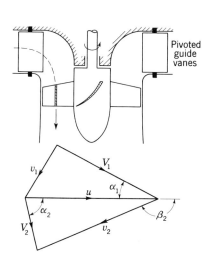

Fig. 6.14. Axial-flow hydraulic turbine.

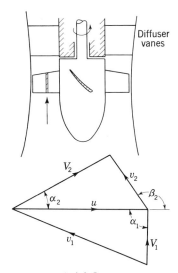

Fig. 6.15. Axial-flow pump.

6.12. HEAD EQUIVALENT OF MECHANICAL WORK

If Eq. (6.18) is multiplied by angular velocity ω, the product represents the rate at which mechanical energy is delivered *by* the fluid to a turbine or at which mechanical energy is delivered *to* the fluid by a pump. From Eqs. (4.14) and (4.15) $\gamma QH = T\omega$. Replacing H by a specific value h'' and noting that, when Eq. (6.18) is multiplied by ω, $r_1\omega = u_1$ and $r_2\omega = u_2$, we have $\gamma Qh'' = T\omega = \rho Q(u_1 V_1 \cos \alpha_1 - u_2 V_2 \cos \alpha_2)$, or

$$h'' = \frac{u_1 V_1 \cos \alpha_1 - u_2 V_2 \cos \alpha_2}{g} \qquad (6.19)$$

which is the *head utilized* by a turbine or the *head imparted* to the fluid by the impeller of a pump.

If the value of h'', as determined by Eq. (6.19), is positive, it is the mechanical work done by the fluid on the vanes of a turbine runner per unit weight of fluid. If the value is negative, it is the mechanical work done on the fluid by the impeller of a pump or similar device per unit weight of fluid. Obviously, the work done by or on the fluid is equal to the loss or gain of energy, respectively, of the fluid.

6.13. FLOW THROUGH ROTATING CHANNEL

The equation to be derived is sometimes called the equation of *relative velocities*, because the absolute velocities of the energy equation are replaced by relative velocities. The usual energy equation may be written between entrance to and exit from a passage which is itself rotating about some axis, but in addition to the friction loss h_L there is an additional loss h'', due to the fact that the fluid is delivering mechanical work and losing energy thereby. (If the passage is that of a pump, the numerical value of h'' will be negative.) Thus

$$\left(\frac{p_1}{\gamma} + z_1 + \frac{V_1{}^2}{2g}\right) - \left(\frac{p_2}{\gamma} + z_2 + \frac{V_2{}^2}{2g}\right) = h_L + \frac{u_1 V_1 \cos \alpha_1 - u_2 V_2 \cos \alpha_2}{g}$$

By trigonometry, $V^2 = v^2 + u^2 + 2vu \cos \beta$, and

$$uV \cos \alpha = u(u + v \cos \beta)$$

Inserting these values, the equation is reduced to

$$\left(\frac{p_1}{\gamma} + z_1 + \frac{v_1{}^2 - u_1{}^2}{2g}\right) - \left(\frac{p_2}{\gamma} + z_2 + \frac{v_2{}^2 - u_2{}^2}{2g}\right) = h_L \qquad (6.20)$$

If there is no flow, both v_1 and v_2 become zero and the equation reduces to that of a forced vortex [Eq. (4.42)]. If there is no rotation, both u_1 and u_2 become zero, the relative velocities become absolute velocities, and the equation becomes the usual energy equation. The frame of reference having been changed, the mechanical work done does not appear as a separate term in Eq. (6.20).

In the usual type of flow encountered in hydraulic machinery the head lost in fluid friction is proportional to the square of the velocity and arbitrarily may be expressed as

$$h_L = k \frac{v_2^2}{2g} \tag{6.21}$$

It may be seen that Eq. (6.20) is broader than Bernoulli's theorem, since the latter is only a special case. It serves to relate conditions at different points in a rotating passage, just as the normal energy equation does for stationary channels. Thus, if there is no change in pressure in flow over a rotating vane, so that $p_1 = p_2$, then

$$v_1^2 - u_1^2 = v_2^2 - u_2^2 + kv_2^2 \tag{6.22}$$

where the z terms are omitted because the difference between z_1 and z_2 is either zero or relatively negligible in most cases when this equation would be applied. The equation is ordinarily used to find v_2 when v_1 is known.

If the fluid completely fills the passage, then $Q = a_1v_1 = a_2v_2$, which determines v_2. The equation may then be used to find the value of $p_1 - p_2$.

6.14. REACTION WITH ROTATION

The force of reaction of a jet from a stationary body is given in Sec. 6.6 and from a body in translation in Sec. 6.10. Since Sec. 6.13 develops the equation for the flow through a channel in rotation, we are now ready to consider the force of reaction of a fluid discharged from a rotating body.

A familiar object to illustrate this subject is the rotating lawn sprinkler. In Fig. 6.16 assume that the cross-sectional area of the arms is so large relative to the area of the jets that fluid-friction loss in the arms may be neglected. Water enters at the center, where $r_1 = 0$, so that in Eq. (6.20), $u_1 = 0$. With the sprinkler arms lying in a horizontal plane, $z_1 - z_2 = 0$, and for the jets discharging into the air, p_2 is atmospheric pressure and will be regarded as zero. Since friction is neglected, $h_L = 0$, and if we let $h = p_1/\gamma + v_1^2/2g$, Eq. (6.20) applied to Fig. 6.16 becomes

$$v_2 = \sqrt{2gh + u_2^2} \tag{6.23}$$

If a_2 denotes the sum of the areas of all the jets (two in the figure shown), then $Q = a_2v_2$. This shows that the discharge is a function of

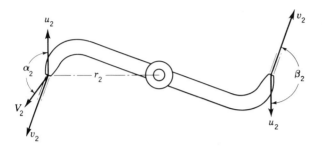

Fig. 6.16

the rotative speed, since $u_2 = r_2\omega$. The tangential component of the absolute velocity of discharge is $V_\mu = u_2 + v_2 \cos \beta_2$, and hence the tangential component of the force of reaction is

$$F_u = \frac{\gamma Q}{g} \Delta V_u = \frac{\gamma a_2 v_2}{g} (0 - V_u) = - \frac{\gamma a_2 v_2}{g} (u_2 + v_2 \cos \beta_2)$$

As the radius is a factor in any rotating body, it is usually better to compute torque rather than a force. In this case the torque is

$$T = F_u r_2 = - \frac{\gamma a_2 r_2}{g} v_2 (u_2 + v_2 \cos \beta_2) \qquad (6.24)$$

The ideal maximum, or runaway, speed is when $T = 0$, and this will be the case when $u_2 = -v_2 \cos \beta_2$ and when $V_2 \cos \alpha_2 = 0$ or $\alpha_2 = 90°$. Because of mechanical friction this condition will never be realized. Of the total power supplied to the sprinkler, the greater part is lost in the kinetic energy of the jets. The total power *developed* by the sprinkler is used in overcoming its own friction. If there were more arms, with larger orifices, so as to discharge more water, there could be a surplus of power which would be useful power delivered. A primitive turbine constructed in this manner was known as Barker's mill.

6.15. MOMENTUM PRINCIPLE APPLIED TO PROPELLERS

In the case of a fan in a duct or pump in a pipeline, the cross section of the fluid affected by the fan is the same upstream as it is downstream, and the principal effect of the fan is to increase the pressure in the duct. In the case of a propeller revolving in free air, however, this is not so. The pressure must necessarily be the same at a distance either upstream or downstream from the propeller. How, then, may the revolving blades be considered to do work on the air? This situation may be analyzed by consideration of the *slipstream*, or *propeller race*, which is nothing more than the body of air affected by the propeller (Fig. 6.17). It is customary to replace the propeller in simple slipstream theory with a stationary *actuating disk* across which the pressure is made to rise, as shown in the pressure profile below the slipstream. We thereby neglect the rotational effect of the propeller, together with the helical path of vortices shed from the blade tips (Sec. 13.8). The thrust force will be given by the pressure change at the disk times the area of the disk,

$$F_T = \frac{\pi D^2}{4} \Delta p \qquad (6.25)$$

By Newton's second law, this force must equal the rate of change of momentum of the fluid upon which it acts. If we let Q be the rate of flow through the slipstream,

$$F_T = Q\rho\Delta V \qquad (6.26)$$

where ΔV is the change in the slipstream velocity before and after the

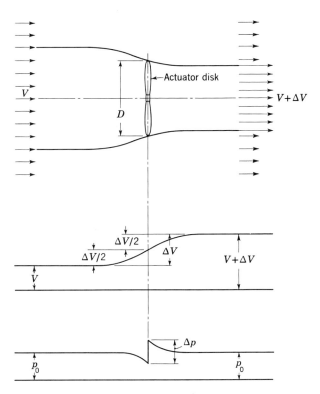

Fig. 6.17. Slipstream of propeller in free air.

propeller (in the case of a propeller moving forward through still fluid ΔV represents the backward velocity of the slipstream). If we now write the Bernoulli equation from a point upstream where the velocity is V to a point downstream where it is $V + \Delta V$, recognizing that the pressure terms at these points cancel and that the disk adds $\Delta p/\gamma$ ft-lb of energy per pound of fluid to the flow,

$$\frac{V^2}{2g} + \frac{\Delta p}{\gamma} = \frac{(V + \Delta V)^2}{2g} \tag{6.27}$$

Solving Eqs. (6.25) and (6.26) for Q in terms of Δp and substituting in Eq. (6.27) results in

$$Q = \frac{\pi D^2}{4}\left(V + \frac{\Delta V}{2}\right) \tag{6.28}$$

This shows that the velocity at the disk is the average of the upstream and downstream velocities. Equation (6.27) may now be solved for the velocity change ΔV (or velocity of the slipstream), yielding

$$\Delta V = -V + \sqrt{V^2 + \frac{8F_T}{\pi D^2 \rho}} \tag{6.29}$$

We may utilize the slipstream analysis to determine the maximum efficiency possible by a propulsive device of any kind. The power output is given by

$$P_{\text{out}} = F_T V = (\rho Q\, \Delta V)V$$

The power lost in kinetic energy of the slipstream is

$$P_{\text{lost}} = Q\rho \frac{(\Delta V)^2}{2}$$

The total power input is the output plus the loss (and this neglects the eddy losses from a rotating propeller), and the maximum possible efficiency is given by the ratio of power output to power input:

$$e_{\text{max}} = \frac{Q\rho V\, \Delta V}{Q\rho V\, \Delta V + Q\rho[(\Delta V)^2/2]}$$

$$= \frac{1}{1 + \Delta V/2V} \tag{6.30}$$

The efficiency is seen to be a function of the ratio $\Delta V/V$. The efficiency approaches 100 per cent as ΔV approaches zero, but if $\Delta V = 0$, the propeller produces no force. The actual maximum efficiency of an aircraft propeller may be in the neighborhood of 85 per cent.

A windmill is essentially the opposite of a propeller in that the function of the windmill is to extract energy from the wind. The slipstream for a windmill expands as it passes the *actuated disk*, and the pressure drops, as does the velocity.

Illustrative example 6.4:   Find the thrust and efficiency of two 6.5-ft-diameter propellers through which flows a total of 20,000 cfs of air (0.072 pcf).   The propellers are attached to an airplane moving at 175 mph through still air.   Neglect eddy losses. Velocity of air relative to airplane is

$$V = \frac{175 \times 44}{30} = 257 \text{ fps}$$

Velocity of air through the actuating disk is

$$V + \frac{\Delta V}{2} = \frac{1}{2} \times \frac{20,000}{(\pi/4)(6.5)^2} = 301 \text{ fps}$$

Thus
$$\Delta V = 2(301 - 257) - 88 \text{ fps}$$

$$F_T = \rho Q \, \Delta V = \frac{0.072}{32.2} (20,000)(88) = 3,940 \text{ lb}$$

$$e = \frac{1}{1 + \Delta V/2V} = \frac{1}{1 + 88/514} = 0.855 = 85.5 \%$$

6.16. OTHER APPLICATIONS OF THE MOMENTUM PRINCIPLE

In addition to the cases that have already been discussed, there are numerous other fluid-flow situations where the momentum principle is useful.   It is used to develop the concept of the shock wave (Sec. 9.12) and to develop the equations of the hydraulic jump (Sec. 10.18).   Another application is that of finding the forces exerted on open-flow structures. The magnitudes of such forces may generally be found by application of the momentum principle.   The application to this type of problem can best be discussed with an illustrative example

Illustrative example 6.5:   This water passage is 10 ft wide normal to the accompanying figure.   Determine the horizontal force acting on the crosshatched structure.   Assume ideal flow.

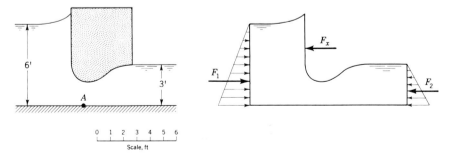

Illustrative Example 6.5

In free-surface flow such as this where the streamlines are parallel, the water surface is coincident with the hydraulic grade line. Writing an energy equation from the upstream section to the downstream section,

$$6 + \frac{V_1{}^2}{2g} = 3 + \frac{V_2{}^2}{2g} \qquad (a)$$

From continuity,
$$6(10)V_1 = 3(10)V_2 \qquad (b)$$

Substituting Eq. (b) into Eq. (a) yields

$$V_1 = 8.05 \text{ fps} \qquad V_2 = 16.1 \text{ fps}$$
$$Q = A_1 V_1 = A_2 V_2 = 483 \text{ cfs}$$

Next take a free-body diagram of the element of water shown in the figure and apply Eq. (6.3).

$$F_1 - F_2 - F_x = \rho Q(V_2 - V_1)$$

where F_x represents the force of the structure on the water in the horizontal direction.

$$62.4(3)(10 \times 6) - 62.4(1.5)(10 \times 3) - F_x = 1.94(483)(16.1 - 8.05)$$

and
$$F_x = 890 \text{ lb}$$

The positive sign means that the assumed direction is correct. Hence the force of the water on the structure is equal and opposite, namely, 890 lb to the right.

The momentum principle will not permit one to obtain the vertical component of the force of the water on the structure. If the pressure distribution at the boundary of the structure were known or could be estimated, one could approximate the vertical component of the force by computing the integrated effect of the pressure-distribution diagram.

PROBLEMS

6.1. For laminar flow as in Prob. 4.1, prove that $\beta = \frac{4}{3}$.

6.2. For the turbulent-flow case as approximated in Prob. 4.2, prove that $\beta = 1.014$.

6.3. For laminar flow between two stationary parallel plates such as to give two-dimensional flow, find (a) the ratio of mean velocity to maximum velocity; (b) α; (c) β. Once again, for this case the velocity profile is parabolic as in Prob. 6.1.

6.4. If a jet of any fluid of an area A and with a velocity V is deflected through an angle θ without any change in the magnitude of the velocity, prove that $F = (2\gamma A/g)V^2 \sin(\theta/2)$.

6.5. If a jet of any fluid is deflected through an angle θ and fluid friction reduces V_2 to $0.8V_1$, derive an equation for the dynamic force exerted.

6.6. In Fig. 6.3 assume that $\theta = 120°$, that the jet is water with a velocity of 100 fps, and that the jet diameter is 2 in. If friction loss is neglected, find (a) the component of dynamic force in the same direction as the jet; (b) the component of the dynamic force normal to the jet; (c) the magnitude and direction of the resultant dynamic force exerted on the body.

6.7. Solve Prob. 6.6 assuming that friction is such as to reduce V_2 to 80 fps.

6.8. Suppose the jet in Prob. 6.6 were to strike a large flat plate normally. What would be the dynamic force on the plate?

6.9. In Prob. 6.8 what would be the stagnation pressure, and what would be the average dynamic pressure on a circular plate if the area of the plate were 20 times the area of the jet? Assume that the center of the jet is coincident with the center of the plate.

6.10. Using Fig. 6.4 as a guide, estimate the significant weight of water on the plate of Prob. 6.9 and add it to the dynamic force to obtain the total force of liquid on the plate.

6.11. A 2-in.-diameter water jet with a velocity of 100 fps impinges vertically downward on a 4-in.-diameter circular plate. The center of the jet is coincident with the center of the plate. Assuming that Fig. 6.4 gives an accurate picture of the flow pattern, determine as accurately as you can the dynamic force of the water on the plate.

6.12. A horizontal jet of water issues from an orifice in the side of a tank under a head h_1 and strikes a large plate a short distance away which covers the end of a horizontal tube in the side of a second tank. The second tank contains oil ($\gamma = 52$ pcf) at rest. The height of the oil above the tube is h_2. The jet diameter is three-fourths of the inside diameter of the tube. The jet and tube are at the same elevation. If the impact of the water is just sufficient to hold the plate in place, find the relation between h_1 and h_2. Neglect the weight of the plate and assume ideal flow.

6.13. In Prob. 6.12 consider the effect of the weight of the plate. Find h_2 if $h_1 = 10$ ft, weight of plate = 50 lb, jet diameter = 1.5 in., and coefficient of friction between plate and tube = 0.6.

6.14. Find the magnitude and direction of the resultant force of the fluid on the compressor shown in the figure. Air ($\gamma = 0.075$ pcf) enters at A through a 3-ft² area at a velocity of 10 fps. Air is discharged at B through a 2-ft² area at a velocity of 12 fps.

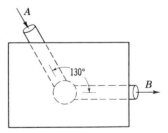

Fig. Prob. 6.14

6.15. On the end of a 6-in.-diameter pipe is a nozzle which discharges a 2-in.-diameter jet. The pressure in the pipe is 55 psi, and the pipe velocity is 10 fps. The jet discharges into the air. If the fluid is water, what is the axial force exerted upon the nozzle? Neglect fluid friction.

6.16. Water under a pressure of 50 psi flows with a velocity of 10 fps through a right-angle bend having a uniform diameter of 12 in. Assuming no drop in pressure, what is the resultant force acting upon the bend? What is its direction?

6.17. Water enters a reducing right-angle bend with a velocity of 8 fps and a pressure of 5.0 psi. The diameter of the bend at entrance is 24 in., and at exit it is 18 in. Neglecting any friction loss, find the magnitude and the direction of the resultant force on the bend.

6.18. In Fig. 6.6 the diameters are 36 and 24 in. At the larger end the pressure is 100 psi and the velocity is 8 fps. Find the resultant force on the conical reducer, neglecting any friction, if the flow is (a) to the right; (b) to the left.

6.19. Determine the magnitude and direction of the force exerted by the liquid (γ = 62.4 pcf) on the double nozzle of the figure. Both nozzle jets have a velocity of 40 fps. The axes of the pipe and both nozzles all lie in a horizontal plane. Neglect friction.

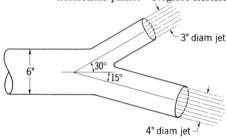

Fig. Prob. 6.19

6.20. In Prob. 6.19, what angle should the 4-in. jet make with the axis of the pipe so that the resultant force is along the pipe axis?

6.21. Find the pull on the bolts in the figure. Neglect the weight of the water and assume ideal flow.

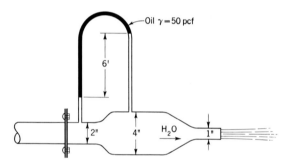

Fig. Prob. 6.21

6.22. A 6-in.-diameter water jet having a velocity of 30 fps at section A is directed vertically upward against the cone as shown in the figure. What must be the weight of the cone if it is held in the position shown? Neglect friction.

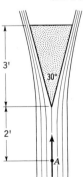

Fig. Prob. 6.22

6.23. Repeat Prob. 6.22 for the case where the jet velocity is 15 fps. Make appropriate assumptions.

6.24. A jet of water 3 in. in diameter has a velocity of 120 fps. It strikes a single vane, which has an angle $\beta_2 = 90°$ and which has a motion of translation in the same direction as the jet, with a velocity u. When u has values of 0, 40, 60, 80, 100, and 120 fps, find values of (a) G'; (b) $V_2 \cos \alpha_2$; (c) ΔV_u; (d) Δv_u; (e) F_u. Assume $v_2 = 0.9v_1$.

6.25. If the jet in Prob. 6.24 strikes a single vane for which $\beta_2 = 180°$, all other data remaining the same, find values of (a) G'; (b) v_2; (c) V_2; (d) ΔV; (e) Δv; (f) F_u. Assume $v_2 = 0.9v_1$.

6.26. In Prob. 6.25 assume all data the same except that friction loss in flow over the vane is such that $v_2 = 0.8v_1$. Find the results called for in Prob. 6.25.

6.27. Assume that all data are the same as in Prob. 6.26 except that $\beta_2 = 150°$. Find (a) $v_2 \cos \beta_2$; (b) $V_2 \cos \alpha_2$; (c) ΔV_u; (d) Δv_u; (e) F_u.

6.28. Suppose the single vane of Illustrative Example 6.3 is traveling to the left toward the nozzle at 20 fps. What then would be the force components exerted by the water on the vane?

6.29. A series of vanes is acted on by a 3-in. water jet having a velocity of 100 fps, $\alpha_1 = \beta_1 = 0°$. Find the required blade angle β_2 in order that the force acting on the vane in the direction of the jet is 200 lb. Neglect friction. Solve for vane velocities of 100, 80 and 50 fps.

6.30. A 2-in.-diameter air jet impinges on a series of blades. The absolute velocities are shown in the figure. Assume $\gamma = 0.076$ pcf and neglect friction. What horsepower is transmitted to the blades? Find also the velocity of the blades.

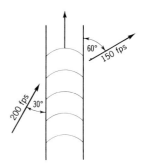

Fig. Prob. 6.30

6.31. In Prob. 6.30 determine the necessary blade angles at entrance and exit. Assume the air enters the blade smoothly.

6.32. The water jet in the figure, moving at 50 fps, is divided by the splitter so that one-third of the water is diverted toward A. Calculate the *magnitude* and *direction* of the force of the water on this single stationary blade. Assume ideal flow.

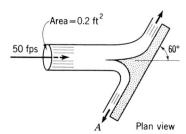

Fig. Prob. 6.32

6.33. For the conditions of Prob. 6.32 compute the magnitude and direction of the resultant force on the single blade if it is moving to the right at a velocity of 10 fps.

6.34. Suppose the blade of Prob. 6.32 is one of a series of blades which are moving to the right at 10 fps. Determine the horizontal force on the blade system, and compute the horsepower transferred to the blades. Compute the horsepower of the jet and of the water leaving the blade system to verify an energy balance (Illustrative Example 6.3).

6.35. Find the thrust developed when water is pumped in through a 10-in.-diameter pipe in the bow of a boat at $v = 5$ fps and emitted through a 6-in.-diameter pipe in the stern of the boat.

6.36. An ideal liquid ($\gamma = 62.4$ pcf) flows from a 2-ft-diameter tank as shown in the figure. The jet diameter is 3 in. If the static coefficient of friction between the tank and floor is 0.56, determine the minimum value of h at which the tank will commence to move to the left. The tank itself weighs 100 lb.

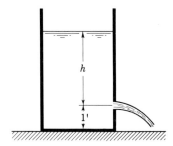

Fig. Prob. 6.36

6.37. A typical rocket has a propellant flow rate of 24.1 lb/sec through a nozzle with a throat area of 10.3 in.² The exit area of the nozzle is 51.5 in.², the exhaust velocity is 6,670 fps, and the specific weight of the exhaust gases is 0.0101 pcf. The nozzle is designed to expand the gases down to 14.7 psia at exit. Find the rocket thrust (*a*) at sea level and (*b*) at an elevation of 20,000 ft where the barometer pressure is 6.75 psia.

6.38. A turbojet at a speed of 600 fps takes in air at the rate of 40 lb/sec. The air/fuel ratio is 30:1, and the exhaust velocity is 2,000 fps. Find the thrust.

6.39. The absolute velocity of water entering a turbine runner is 60 fps, and that leaving is 15 fps. $\alpha_1 = 20°$, $\alpha_2 = 80°$, $r_1 = 1.6$ ft, $r_2 = 1.0$ ft, $n = 300$ rpm, and $Q = 170$ cfs. Find (a) torque exerted by water; (b) horsepower delivered to shaft; (c) head converted into mechanical work.

6.40. The absolute velocity of a jet of steam impinging upon the blades of a steam turbine is 4,000 fps, and that leaving is 2,800 fps. $\alpha_1 = 20°$, $\alpha_2 = 150°$, $u_1 = u_2 = 500$ fps, and $r_1 = r_2 = 0.5$ ft. Find the torque exerted on the rotor and the horsepower developed on it if $G = 0.4$ lb/sec.

6.41. Water enters a rotating wheel with a relative velocity of 200 fps. $r_1 = 4.0$ ft, and $n = 420$ rpm. There is no pressure drop in flow over the vanes. Assume $k = 0.2$. Find the relative velocity at discharge if (a) $r_2 = 3.0$ ft; (b) $r_2 = 5.0$ ft.

6.42. Water enters a rotating wheel which is so proportioned that the passages are completely filled. $Q = 400$ cfs, $a_1 = 10$ ft², $a_2 = 8$ ft², $r_1 = 1.5$ ft, $r_2 = 1.0$ ft, and $n = 540$ rpm. Assume $k = 0.2$. Find the drop in pressure head between entrance and exit.

6.43. If a jet of fluid strikes a single body moving in the same direction with a velocity u, flows over it without friction loss, and leaves with a relative velocity in the direction of β_2, prove that $F_u = (\gamma A_1/g)(1 - \cos \beta_2)$ $(V_1 - u)^2$.

6.44. A locomotive tender running at 20 mph scoops up water from a trough between the rails, as shown in the figure. The scoop delivers water at a point 8 ft above its original level and in the direction of motion. The area of the stream of water at entrance is 50 in.². The water is everywhere under atmospheric pressure. Neglecting all losses, what is the absolute velocity of the water as it leaves the scoop? What is the force acting on the tender caused by this? What is the minimum train speed at which water will be delivered to the tender?

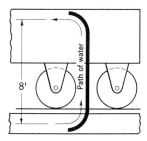

Fig. Prob. 6.44

6.45. A jet of steam is 1 in. in diameter and has a velocity of 4,000 fps. The specific volume is 20 ft³/lb. What is the horsepower in the jet? What is the force of reaction?

6.46. A jet of water with an area of 3 in.² and a velocity of 200 fps strikes a single vane which reverses it through 180° without friction loss. Find the force exerted if the vane moves (a) in the same direction as the jet with a velocity of 80 fps; (b) in a direction opposite to that of the jet with a velocity of 80 fps.

6.47. When a turbine runner is held so that it cannot rotate, the discharge under a head of 50 ft is found to be 29.5 cfs. $\alpha_1 = 35°$, $\beta_2 = 155°$, $r_1 = 0.70$ ft, $r_2 = 0.42$ ft, $A_1 = 0.837$ ft², $a_2 = 0.882$ ft². What is the value of the torque at zero speed? Neglect shock loss.

6.48. Develop Eq. (6.20) by making the substitutions indicated in the text.

6.49. A paddlewheel with vanes that are all straight and radial is to be used as a crude centrifugal pump. $r_1 = 3$ in., $r_2 = 9$ in., and the height perpendicular to the plane of the figure is 0.2 ft. If the speed is 1,200 rpm and the flow is 3,380 gpm, find the difference in pressure between the inner and outer circumference, neglecting friction losses. Express the answer in pounds per square inch. Which point is at the higher pressure? Compute the torque required to drive the pump. What is the horsepower requirement? Verify that the horsepower requirement is equal to the difference between the horsepower of the outflow minus the horsepower of the inflow.

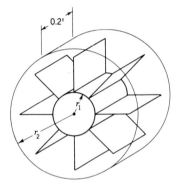

Fig. Prob. 6.49

6.50. Given a lawn sprinkler such as that in Fig. 6.16 with $\beta_2 = 160°$, and the total area of the jets at a radius of 15 in. is 0.0008 ft². When $h = 144$ ft, compute the rate of discharge, the torque exerted by the water, and the horsepower developed if the rotative speed of the sprinkler is 400 rpm. Neglect fluid friction, but note that the calculated torque is that required to overcome mechanical friction and air resistance.

6.51. Repeat Prob. 6.50 for the case where some external object prevents the sprinkler from rotating.

6.52. How fast would the sprinkler of Prob. 6.50 rotate if there were no mechanical friction or air resistance (i.e., consider the case where $T = 0$)? This is known as runaway speed.

6.53. At what speed will the sprinkler of Prob. 6.50 develop maximum horsepower?

6.54. The flow from a lawn sprinkler such as Fig. 6.16 is 30 gpm, $\beta_2 = 180°$, and the total area of the jets is 0.0012 ft². The jets are located 10 in. from the center of rotation. Determine the speed of rotation if there is no friction.

6.55. For the case depicted in Illustrative Example 6.4, determine the pressure rise across the propellers and the required horsepower input to each propeller.

6.56. Consider the case of a windmill (essentially the opposite of a propeller), apply the momentum and energy principles, and determine the maximum theoretical efficiency based on an input energy available from the wind velocity in a stream tube having a cross section equivalent to that of the windmill blade circle.

6.57. A 20-in.-diameter household fan drives air ($\gamma = 0.076$ pcf) at a rate of

1.60 lb/sec. Find the thrust exerted by the fan. What is the pressure difference on the two sides of the fan? Find the efficiency and the required horsepower to drive the fan. Neglect losses.

6.58. A 14-in. electric fan is placed on a frictionless mount and is observed to exert a thrust of 0.5 lb. Find the approximate velocity of the slipstream of standard air (sea level) which it produces. If 45 per cent of the power supplied to the blades is lost in eddies and friction and if the driving motor has an efficiency of 60 per cent, find the required electrical input in watts.

6.59. A fan sucks air from outside to inside a building through an 18-in.-diameter duct. The density of the air is 0.0022 slug/ft³. If there is a vacuum just upstream of the fan equivalent to 1.8 in. of water, determine the flow rate of the air in cubic feet per second. What thrust must the fan support be designed to withstand?

6.60. In Illustrative Example 6.5 suppose the passage narrowed down to a width of 8 ft at the second section. With the same depths find the flow rate and the horizontal force of the water on the structure.

6.61. Flow occurs over a spillway as shown in the figure. Determine the horizontal force of water on the spillway per foot of spillway length. Assume ideal flow.

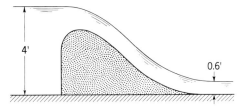

Fig. Prob. 6.61

6.62. A hydraulic jump (Sec. 10.18) occurs in a "diamond-shaped" transparent closed conduit as shown in the figure. The conduit is horizontal, and the water depth just upstream of the jump is 2.0 ft. The conduit is completely full of water downstream of the jump. Pressure-gage readings are as shown in the figure. Compute the flow rate. Note that, because of turbulence in the jump, there is a substantial energy loss. Hence ideal flow cannot be assumed.

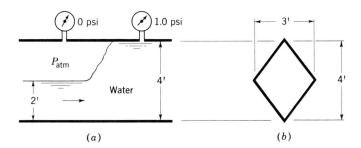

Fig. Prob. 6.62.   (a) Profile along channel.   (b) Cross section.

SEVEN

SIMILITUDE AND
DIMENSIONAL ANALYSIS

7.1. DEFINITION AND USES

It is usually impossible to determine all the essential facts for a
given fluid flow by pure theory, and hence dependence must often
be placed upon experimental investigations. The number of
tests to be made can be greatly reduced by a systematic program
based on dimensional analysis and specifically on the laws of
similitude or similarity, which permit the application of certain
relations by which test data can be applied to other cases.

Thus the similarity laws enable us to make experiments with
a convenient fluid such as water or air, for example, and then
apply the results to a fluid which is less convenient to work with,
such as gas, steam, or oil. Also, in both hydraulics and aeronautics, valuable results can be obtained at a minimum cost by
tests made with small-scale models of the full-size apparatus.
The laws of similitude make it possible to determine the perform-

ance of the *prototype*, which means the full-size device, from tests made with the model. It is not necessary that the same fluid be used for the model and its prototype. Neither is the model necessarily smaller than its prototype. Thus the flow in a carburetor might be studied in a very large model. And the flow of water at the entrance to a small centrifugal-pump runner might be investigated by the flow of air at the entrance to a large model of the runner.

A few other examples where models may be used are ships in towing tanks, airplanes in wind tunnels, hydraulic turbines, centrifugal pumps, spillways of dams, river channels, and the study of such phenomena as the action of waves and tides on beaches, soil erosion, and the transportation of sediment.

It should be emphasized that the model need not necessarily be different in size from its prototype. In fact, it may be the same device, the variables in the case being the velocity and the physical properties of the fluid.

7.2. GEOMETRIC SIMILARITY

One of the desirable features in model studies is that there be geometric similarity, which means that the model and its prototype be identical in shape but differ only in size. The important consideration is that the flow patterns be geometrically similar. If the scale ratio[1] is denoted by L_r, which means the ratio of the linear dimensions of the prototype to corresponding dimensions in the model, it follows that areas vary as L_r^2 and volumes as L_r^3. Complete geometric similarity is not always easy to attain. Thus the surface roughness of a small model may not be reduced in proportion unless it is possible to make its surface very much smoother than that of the prototype. In the study of sediment transportation, it may not be possible to scale down the bed materials without having material so fine as to be impractical. Thus fine powder does not simulate the behavior of sand. Again in the case of a river, the horizontal scale is usually limited by the available floor space, and this same scale used for the vertical dimensions may produce a stream so shallow that capillarity has an appreciable effect and also the slope may be such that the flow is laminar. In such cases it is necessary to use a distorted model, which means that the vertical scale is larger than the horizontal scale. If the horizontal scale is denoted by L_r and the vertical scale by $L_{r'}$, the cross section area ratio is $L_r L_{r'}$.

---

[1] In this text we shall define $L_r = L_p/L_m$ as the *scale ratio*. The reciprocal of this, $\lambda = L_m/L_p$, will be referred to as the *model ratio*, or model scale. Thus a model ratio of $1:20$ corresponds to a scale ratio of $20:1$.

7.3. KINEMATIC SIMILARITY

This implies geometric similarity and in addition that the ratio of the velocities at all corresponding points is the same.   If subscripts p and m denote prototype and model, respectively, the velocity ratio V_r is

$$V_r = \frac{V_p}{V_m} \tag{7.1}$$

and its value in terms of L_r will be determined by dynamic considerations, as explained in the following section.

As time T is dimensionally L/V, the time scale is

$$T_r = \frac{L_r}{V_r} \tag{7.2}$$

and in a similar manner the acceleration scale is

$$a_r = \frac{L_r}{T_r^2} \tag{7.3}$$

7.4. DYNAMIC SIMILARITY

If two systems are dynamically similar, corresponding forces must be in the same ratio in the two.   Forces that may act on a fluid element include those due to gravity F_G, pressure F_P, viscosity F_V, and elasticity F_E. Also, if the element of fluid is at a liquid-gas interface, there are forces due to surface tension F_T.   If the summation of forces on a fluid element does not add up to zero, the element will accelerate in accordance with Newton's law.   Such an unbalanced force system can be transformed into a balanced system by adding an inertia force F_I that is equal and opposite to the resultant R of the acting forces.   Thus, generally,

$$\Sigma \mathbf{F} = \mathbf{F}_G + \mathbf{F}_P + \mathbf{F}_V + \mathbf{F}_E + \mathbf{F}_T = \mathbf{R}$$

and
$$\mathbf{F}_I = -\mathbf{R}$$

Thus
$$\mathbf{F}_G + \mathbf{F}_P + \mathbf{F}_V + \mathbf{F}_E + \mathbf{F}_T + \mathbf{F}_I = 0$$

These forces may be expressed in simplest terms as follows:

Gravity: $\quad F_G = Mg = \rho L^3 g$

Pressure: $\quad F_P = (\Delta p)A = (\Delta p)L^2$

Viscosity: $\quad F_V = \mu \left(\dfrac{du}{dy}\right) A = \mu \left(\dfrac{V}{L}\right) L^2 = \mu V L$

Elasticity: $\quad F_E = EA = EL^2$

Surface tension: $\quad F_T = \sigma L$

Inertia: $\quad F_I = Ma = \rho L^3 \dfrac{L}{T^2} = \rho L^4 T^{-2} = \rho V^2 L^2$

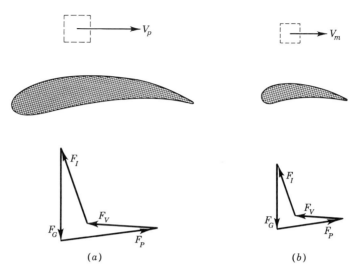

Fig. 7.1. (a) Prototype. (b) Model. $L_r = L_p/L_m$; $V_r = V_p/V_m$.

In many flow problems some of these forces are either not present or insignificant. In Fig. 7.1 are depicted two geometrically similar flow systems. Let it be assumed that they also possess kinematic similarity and that the forces acting are F_G, F_P, F_V, and F_I. Then dynamic similarity will be achieved if

$$\frac{F_{G_p}}{F_{G_m}} = \frac{F_{P_p}}{F_{P_m}} = \frac{F_{V_p}}{F_{V_m}} = \frac{F_{I_p}}{F_{I_m}}$$

where subscripts p and m refer to prototype and model as before. These relations can be expressed as

$$\left(\frac{F_I}{F_G}\right)_p = \left(\frac{F_I}{F_G}\right)_m \qquad \left(\frac{F_I}{F_P}\right)_p = \left(\frac{F_I}{F_P}\right)_m \qquad \left(\frac{F_I}{F_V}\right)_p = \left(\frac{F_I}{F_V}\right)_m$$

Each of the quantities is dimensionless. With four forces acting, there are three independent expressions that must be satisfied; for three forces there are two independent expressions; and so on. The significance of the dimensionless ratios is discussed in the following paragraphs.

Reynolds number. In the flow of a fluid through a completely filled conduit, gravity does not affect the flow pattern. It is also obvious that capillarity is of no practical importance, and hence the significant forces are inertia and fluid friction due to viscosity. The same is true of an airplane at speeds below that at which compressibility of the air is appreciable. Also, for a submarine submerged far enough so as not to produce waves on the surface, the only forces involved are those of friction and inertia.

Considering the ratio of inertia forces to friction forces, the parameter obtained is called the *Reynolds number*, or N_R, in honor of Osborne Reynolds, who presented this in a publication of his experimental work in 1882, but it was Lord Rayleigh ten years later who developed the theory of dynamic similarity. The ratio of these two forces is

$$N_R = \frac{F_I}{F_V} = \frac{L^2 V^2 \rho}{L V \mu} = \frac{L V \rho}{\mu} = \frac{L V}{\nu} \qquad (7.4)$$

For any consistent system of units, N_R is a dimensionless number. The linear dimension L may be any length that is significant in the flow pattern. Thus, for a pipe completely filled, it might be either the diameter or the radius, and the numerical value of N_R will vary accordingly. General usage in this country prescribes L as the pipe diameter.

If two systems, such as a model and its prototype, or two pipelines with different fluids, are to be dynamically equivalent so far as inertia and viscous friction are concerned, they must both have the same value of N_R. For the same fluid in both cases, the equation shows that a high velocity must be used with a model of small linear dimensions. It is also possible to compare the action of fluids of very different viscosities provided only that L and V are so chosen as to give the same value of N_R.

It is seen that for the velocity ratio of Eq. (7.1), $V_r = (\nu/L)_r$, and from Eq. (7.2), $T_r = (L^2/\nu)_r$ for the same value of N_R.

Froude number. Considering inertia and gravity forces alone, a ratio is obtained called a *Froude number*, or N_F, in honor of William Froude, who experimented with flat plates towed lengthwise through water in order to estimate the resistance of ships due to wave action. The ratio of inertia forces to gravity forces is

$$\frac{\rho L^2 V^2}{\rho g L^3} = \frac{V^2}{gL}$$

Although this is sometimes defined as a Froude number, it is more common to use the square root so as to have V in the first power, as in the Reynolds number. Thus a Froude number is

$$N_F = \frac{V}{\sqrt{gL}} \qquad (7.5)$$

Systems involving gravity and inertia forces are the wave action set up by a ship, the flow of water in open channels, the forces of a stream on a bridge pier, the flow over a spillway, the flow of a stream from an orifice, and other cases where gravity is a dominant factor.

A comparison of Eqs. (7.4) and (7.5) shows that the two cannot be satisfied at the same time with a fluid of the same viscosity, since one requires that the velocity vary inversely as L, while the other requires it to vary directly as $\sqrt{L}$. If both friction and gravity are involved, it is necessary to decide which of the two factors is more important or more useful. In the case of a ship, the towing of a model will give the total resistance, from which must be subtracted the empirically computed skin friction to determine the wave-making resistance, and the latter may be even smaller than the former. But for the same Froude number, the wave-making resistance of the full-size ship may be determined from this result. A computed skin friction for the ship is then to be added to this value to give the total ship resistance. The details of such calculations are deferred to Chap. 13.

In the flow of water in open channels fluid friction is a factor, as well as gravity and inertia, and apparently we face the same difficulty here. However, for flow in an open channel there is usually fully developed turbulence, so that the hydraulic friction loss is exactly proportional to V^2, as will be shown later, and thus fluid friction is independent of the Reynolds number with rare exceptions, and so is a function of the Froude number alone.

The only way to satisfy Eqs. (7.4) and (7.5) for both a model and its prototype is to use fluids of very different viscosities in the two cases. Sometimes this can be done, but often it is either impractical or impossible.

For the computation of N_F, the length L must be some linear dimension that is significant in the flow pattern. For a ship it is commonly taken as the length at the waterline. For an open channel it is taken as the depth of flow.

From Eq. (7.5), V varies as $\sqrt{gL}$, and if g is considered a constant, as is usually the case, then from Eq. (7.1),

$$V_r = \frac{V_p}{V_m} = \sqrt{\frac{L_r}{1}} \qquad \text{(for same } N_F\text{)}$$

and from Eq. (7.2) the ratio of time for prototype to model is

$$T_r = \frac{T_p}{T_m} = \sqrt{\frac{L_r}{1}} \qquad \text{(for same } N_F\text{)}$$

while $a_r = 1$.

A knowledge of the time scale is useful in the study of cyclic phenomena such as waves and tides.

Since the velocity varies as $\sqrt{L_r}$ and the cross section area as L_r^2, it follows that

$$\frac{Q_p}{Q_m} = \frac{L_r^{5/2}}{1} \qquad \text{(for same } N_F\text{)}$$

As previously stated, it is usually necessary to use a river model with an enlarged vertical scale. In this case the velocity varies as $\sqrt{L_{r'}}$, and hence

$$\frac{Q_p}{Q_m} = \frac{L_r L_{r'}^{3/2}}{1}$$

Mach number. Where compressibility is important, it is necessary to consider the ratio of the fluid velocity (or the velocity of a solid through a stationary fluid) to that of a sound wave in the same medium. This ratio, called the *Mach number* in honor of the Austrian scientist Mach, is

$$N_M = \frac{V}{c} \tag{7.6}$$

where c is the acoustic velocity (or celerity) in the medium in question.[1] If N_M is less than 1, the flow is called *subsonic;* if it is equal to 1, the flow is *sonic;* if it is greater than 1, the flow is called *supersonic;* and for extremely high values of N_M the flow is called *hypersonic.*

Weber number. In a few cases of flow, surface tension may be important, but normally this is negligible. The ratio of inertia forces to surface tension is $\rho V^2 L^2/\sigma L$, the square root of which is known as the *Weber number:*

$$N_W = \frac{V}{\sqrt{\sigma/\rho L}} \tag{7.7}$$

An illustration of its application is at the leading edge of a very thin sheet of liquid flowing over a surface.

Euler number. The ratio of the inertia forces to the pressure forces is known as the *Euler number.* It is expressed in a variety of ways, one form being

$$N_E = \frac{V}{\sqrt{2(\Delta p/\rho)}} = \frac{V}{\sqrt{2g(\Delta p/\gamma)}} \tag{7.8}$$

If only pressure and inertia influence the flow, the Euler number for any boundary form will remain constant. If other parameters (viscosity, gravity, etc.) cause the flow pattern to change, however, N_E will also change. The expression for N_E [(Eq. 7.8)] may be recognized as being equivalent to the coefficient of velocity, discussed in Chap. 11.

Illustrative example 7.1: A certain submerged body is to move horizontally through oil (γ = 52 pcf, μ = 0.0006 lb-sec/ft²) at a velocity of 45 fps. To study the

---

[1] The ratio of inertia forces to elastic forces $\rho V^2 L^2/E L^2 = \rho V^2/E$ is called the *Cauchy number.* Appendix 2 shows that the celerity c of an acoustic wave is given by $\sqrt{E/\rho}$. Hence the Cauchy number is the square of the Mach number.

characteristics of this motion, an enlarged model of the body is tested in 60°F water. The model ratio is 8:1. Determine the velocity at which this enlarged model should be pulled through the water to achieve dynamic similarity. If the drag force on the model is 0.80 lb, predict the drag force on the prototype. Since the body is submerged, there is no wave action, and thus viscosity and inertia are the predominant forces. This requires that the Reynolds criterion be satisfied.

$$\left(\frac{DV}{\nu}\right)_p = \left(\frac{DV}{\nu}\right)_m \qquad \text{where } \frac{D_m}{D_p} = \frac{8}{1}$$

$$\nu_m = 1.22 \times 10^{-5} \text{ lb-sec/ft}^2 \qquad \text{(Appendix 3, Table A.1)}$$

$$\nu_p = \frac{\mu}{\rho} = \frac{0.0006}{52/32.2} = 0.000322 \text{ lb-sec/ft}^2$$

$$\frac{D_p(45)}{0.000322} = \frac{(8D_p)V_m}{1.22 \times 10^{-5}}$$

$$V_m = 0.213 \text{ fps}$$

$$F \propto \rho V^2 L^2 \qquad \text{hence} \qquad \frac{F_p}{F_m} = \frac{\rho_p V_p{}^2 L_p{}^2}{\rho_m V_m{}^2 L_m{}^2}$$

$$\frac{F_p}{F_m} = \frac{(52/32.2)(45)^2 1}{1.94(0.213)^2(8)^2} = 580$$

$$F_p = 580 F_m \qquad F_p = 580(0.8) = 465 \text{ lb}$$

7.5. COMMENTS ON MODELS

In the use of models it is essential that the fluid velocity should not be so low that laminar flow exists when the flow in the prototype is turbulent. Also, conditions in the model should not be such that surface tension is important if such conditions do not exist in the prototype. For example, the depth of water flowing over the crest of a model spillway should not be too low.

While model studies are very important and valuable, it is necessary to exercise some judgment in transferring results to other cases, and often a scale effect must be allowed for.

Neither is it always necessary or desirable that these various ratios be adhered to in every case. Thus, in tests of model centrifugal pumps, geometric similarity is essential, but it is desirable to operate at such a rotative speed that the peripheral velocity and all fluid velocities are the same as in the prototype, since only in this way may cavitation be detected.

The roughness of a model should be scaled down in the same ratio as the other linear dimensions, which means that a small model should have surfaces that are much smoother than those in its prototype. But this requirement imposes a limit on the scale that can be used if true geometric similarity is to be had. However, in the case of a river model with a vertical scale larger than the horizontal scale, it may be necessary to make the model surface rough in order to simulate the flow conditions in the actual stream.   As any distorted model lacks the proper similitude, no simple rule can be given for this; the roughness should be determined by trial until the flow conditions are judged to be typical of those in the prototype.

7.6. VACUUM AND BAROMETRIC PRESSURE

In the case of a siphon, such as that shown in Fig. 7.2, there is a vacuum at its summit, and if the siphon is to operate, the absolute pressure at the summit should equal or exceed the vapor pressure.   An exact solution should consider the friction losses in the lengths of conduit involved, but we shall here confine ourselves to the ideal case of frictionless flow with all loss occurring after exit from the siphon.   Thus the absolute pressure at the summit is ideally

$$p_2 = p_a - \gamma \left(z + \frac{V^2}{2g} \right) = p_a - \gamma(z + h) \tag{7.9}$$

where p_a is the atmospheric or barometer pressure and where it is assumed that $V^2/2g = h$.

If the model siphon were enclosed in a chamber (Fig. 7.2b) having an absolute pressure $(p_a)_m$, the absolute pressure at point 2 of the model would be

$$(p_2)_m = (p_a)_m - \lambda\gamma(z + h) \tag{7.10}$$

where the model ratio $\lambda = L_m/L_p = 1/L_r$.

If $(p_a)_m$ were made equal to p_a, that is, if the model were tested at atmospheric conditions,

$$p_2 = (p_2)_m - (1 - \lambda)\gamma(z + h) \tag{7.11}$$

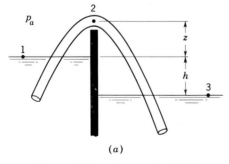

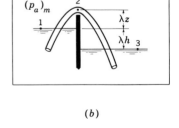

(a)   (b)

Fig. 7.2.   (a) Prototype.   (b) Model.

Thus the minimum pressure in the prototype would be less than that in the smaller model. Hence the model might operate, but the full-size siphon would not. In order that they be comparable, the same minimum pressure should exist in each, and equating p_2 and $(p_2)_m$ of Eqs. (7.9) and (7.10), we obtain

$$(p_a)_m = p_a - (1 - \lambda)\gamma(z + h) \tag{7.12}$$

which shows that the entire model siphon should be enclosed in a tank in which there is a partial vacuum to produce an absolute pressure $(p_a)_m$ much less than the normal atmospheric pressure. It is apparent that there is also a limit beyond which it is impossible to go. Combining Eqs. (7.9) and (7.12), we obtain

$$(p_a)_m = \lambda p_a + (1 - \lambda)p_2 \tag{7.13}$$

and by substituting the minimum allowable pressure p_2 for the prototype, this determines the maximum absolute pressure under which the model siphon should operate assuming no head loss.[1]

Illustrative example 7.2: A 1:50 model of a boat has a wave resistance of 0.06 lb when operating at 3 fps. Find the corresponding prototype wave resistance. Find also the corresponding horsepower requirements for model and prototype. Gravity and inertia forces predominate in this case; hence Froude's criterion should be used:

$$(N_F)_p = (N_F)_m = \left(\frac{V}{\sqrt{gL}}\right)_p = \left(\frac{V}{\sqrt{gL}}\right)_m$$

Since both the model and prototype are acted upon by the earth's gravitational field, the g's can be canceled out. Thus

$$\frac{V_p{}^2}{L_p} = \frac{V_m{}^2}{L_m}$$

and

$$\frac{V_p{}^2}{V_m{}^2} = \frac{L_p}{L_m} = L_r = 50$$

Since

$$F \propto \rho V^2 L^2$$

Therefore

$$\frac{F_p}{F_m} = \frac{\rho L_p{}^2 V_p{}^2}{\rho L_m{}^2 V_m{}^2} = L_r{}^2 L_r = L_r{}^3$$

$$F_p = L_r{}^3 F_m = (50)^3 0.06 = 7,500 \text{ lb}$$

$$\text{HP}_m = \frac{F_m V_m}{550} = \frac{0.06(3)}{550} = 0.000328$$

$$\text{HP}_p = \frac{F_p V_p}{550} = \frac{7,500(\sqrt{50} \times 3)}{550} = 290$$

[1] K. C. Reynolds, Notes on the Laws of Similitude as Applied to Experiments with Models, p. 762, and A. C. Chick, Dimensional Analysis and the Principles of Similitude as Applied to Hydraulic Experiments with Models, p. 800, in John R. Freeman (ed.), "Hydraulic Laboratory Practice," American Society of Mechanical Engineers, New York, 1929. Hydraulic Models, *ASCE Manuals Eng. Practice* 25, 1942.

Also it may be noted that

$$HP_r = F_r V_r = L_r{}^3 L_r{}^{\frac{1}{2}} = L_r{}^{\frac{7}{2}}$$

Thus $\qquad\qquad HP_p = L_r{}^{\frac{7}{2}} HP_m = 290$

7.7. DIMENSIONAL ANALYSIS

Fluid-mechanics problems may be approached by *dimensional analysis*, a mathematical technique making use of the study of dimensions. Dimensional analysis is related to similitude; however, the approach is different. In dimensional analysis, from a general understanding of fluid phenomena, one first predicts the physical parameters that will influence the flow, and then, by grouping these parameters in dimensionless combinations, a better understanding of the flow phenomena is made possible. Dimensional analysis is particularly helpful in experimental work because it provides a guide to those things that significantly influence the phenomena; thus it indicates the direction in which experimental work should go.

Physical quantities may be expressed in either the force-length-time (FLT) system or in the mass-length-time (MLT) system. These two systems are interrelated through Newton's law which states that force equals mass times acceleration, $F = ma$, or

$$F = M \frac{L}{T^2}$$

Through this relation, conversion can be made from one system to the other. The dimensions used in either system may be in English units or in metric units. Details on the English and metric systems of units and conversion factors are presented in Appendix 1.

To illustrate the steps in a dimensional-analysis problem, let us consider the drag force F_D exerted on a sphere as it moves through a viscous liquid. We must visualize the physical problem to consider what physical factors influence the drag force. Certainly, the size of the sphere must enter the problem; also, the velocity of the sphere must be important. The fluid properties involved are the density ρ and the viscosity μ. Thus we can write

$$F_D = f(D, V, \rho, \mu)$$

Here D, the sphere diameter, is used to represent sphere size.

We want to determine how these variables are interrelated. Our approach is to satisfy dimensional homogeneity. That is, we want the dimensions on one side of the equation to correspond to those on the other. The preceding expression may be written as a power equation

$$F_D = C D^a V^b \rho^c \mu^d$$

where C is a dimensionless constant.   Using the MLT system and substituting the proper dimensions,

$$\frac{ML}{T^2} = L^a \left(\frac{L}{T}\right)^b \left(\frac{M}{L^3}\right)^c \left(\frac{M}{LT}\right)^d$$

To satisfy dimensional homogeneity the exponents of each dimension must be identical on both sides of the equation.   Thus

$$\text{For } M: \qquad 1 = c + d$$
$$\text{For } L: \qquad 1 = a + b - 3c - d$$
$$\text{For } T: \qquad -2 = -b - d$$

Since we have three equations with four unknowns, we must express three of the unknowns in terms of the fourth.   Solving for a, b, and c in terms of d, we get

$$a = 2 - b \qquad b = 2 - d \qquad c = 1 - d$$

Thus
$$F_D = CD^{2-d}V^{2-d}\rho^{1-d}\mu^d$$

and grouping variables according to their exponents,

$$F_D = C(\rho)(D^2V^2)\left(\frac{VD\rho}{\mu}\right)^{-d}$$

It may be noted that the quantity $VD\rho/\mu$ is a Reynolds number.   Thus the original power equation can be expressed as

$$F_D = f'(N_R)\rho D^2 V^2$$

or
$$\frac{F_D}{\rho D^2 V^2} = f'(N_R)$$

The result indicates that the drag on a sphere is equal to some coefficient times $\rho D^2 V^2$, where the coefficient is a function of the Reynolds number. This is indeed true, as indicated by the discussion of drag on a sphere in Sec. 13.7.

The foregoing approach to dimensional analysis is commonly referred to as the *Rayleigh method*, after Lord Rayleigh, who originally proposed it. Another more generalized approach is through use of the *Buckingham* II *theorem*.   This theorem states that if there are n dimensional variables in a dimensionally homogeneous equation, described by m fundamental dimensions, they may be grouped in $n - m$ dimensionless groups.   Thus, in the preceding example, $n = 5$ and $m = 3$ (M, L, and T) and $n - m = 2$; these dimensionless groups were N_R and $F_D/\rho D^2 V^2$.   Buckingham referred to these dimensionless groups as II terms.   The advantage of the II theorem is that it tells one ahead of time how many dimensionless groups are to be expected.

Applying the Π theorem to the preceding example, one would proceed as follows:

$$f'(F_D,D,V,\rho,\mu) = 0$$

where $n = 5$, $m = 3$, so $n - m = 2$. Thus we can write

$$\phi(\Pi_1,\Pi_2) = 0$$

The problem now is to find the Π's by arranging the five parameters into two dimensionless groups. Taking ρ, D, and V as the primary variables, the Π terms are:

$$\Pi_1 = \rho^{a_1}D^{b_1}V^{c_1}\mu^{d_1}$$

$$\Pi_2 = \rho^{a_2}D^{b_2}V^{c_2}F_D{}^{d_2}$$

The values of the exponents are determined as before, noting that since the Π's are dimensionless, they can be replaced with $M^0L^0T^0$. Experience in fluid mechanics has shown that these dimensionless groups commonly take the form of a Reynolds number, Froude number, or Mach number. Hence one should always be on the lookout for them when using dimensional analysis. Working with Π_1,

$$M^0L^0T^0 = \left(\frac{M}{L^3}\right)^{a_1} L^{b_1} \left(\frac{L}{T}\right)^{c_1} \left(\frac{M}{LT}\right)^{d_1}$$

$$M: \quad 0 = a_1 + d_1$$

$$L: \quad 0 = -3a_1 + b_1 + c_1 - d_1$$

$$T: \quad 0 = -c_1 - d_1$$

Solving for a_1, b_1, and c_1 in terms of d_1,

$$a_1 = -d_1 \qquad b_1 = -d_1 \qquad c_1 = -d_1$$

Thus

$$\Pi_1 = \rho^{-d_1}D^{-d_1}V^{-d_1}\mu^{d_1} = \left(\frac{\mu}{\rho D V}\right)^{d_1} = \left(\frac{\rho D V}{\mu}\right)^{-d_1} = N_R$$

Working in a similar fashion with Π_2, one gets

$$\Pi_2 = \frac{F_D}{\rho D^2 V^2}$$

Finally, $\phi(\Pi_1,\Pi_2) = 0$ may be expressed as

$$\Pi_1 = \phi'(\Pi_2) \qquad \text{or} \qquad \Pi_2 = \phi''(\Pi_1)$$

So

$$\frac{F_D}{\rho D^2 V^2} = \phi''(N_R)$$

nd

$$F_D = \phi''(N_R)\rho D^2 V^2$$

It should be emphasized that dimensional analysis does not provide a complete solution to fluid problems. It provides a partial solution only. The success of dimensional analysis depends entirely on the ability of the individual using it to define the parameters that are applicable. If one omits an important variable, the results are incomplete and this may lead to incorrect conclusions. If one includes a variable that is totally unrelated to the problem, an additional insignificant dimensionless group will result. Thus, to use dimensional analysis successfully, one must be familiar with the fluid phenomena involved.

Illustrative example 7.3: Derive an expression for the flow rate q over the spillway shown in the accompanying figure per foot of spillway perpendicular to the sketch. Assume that the sheet of water is relatively thick so that surface-tension effects may be neglected. Assume also that gravity effects predominate so strongly over viscosity that viscosity may be neglected.

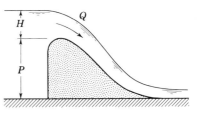

Illustrative Example 7.3

Under the assumed conditions the variables that effect q would be the head H, the acceleration of gravity g, and possibly the spillway height P. Thus

$$q = f(H,g,P)$$

or
$$f'(q,H,g,P) = 0$$

In this case $n = 4$, and $m = 2$, since only kinematic properties are involved. Hence, according to the Π theorem, there are $n - m = 2$ dimensionless groups, and

$$\phi(\Pi_1,\Pi_2) = 0$$

Using q and H as the basic variables,

$$\Pi_1 = q^{a_1}H^{b_1}g^{c_1}$$
$$\Pi_2 = q^{a_2}H^{b_2}P^{c_2}$$

Working with Π_1,

$$L^0 T^0 = \left(\frac{L^3}{TL}\right)^{a_1} L^{b_1} \left(\frac{L}{T^2}\right)^{c_1}$$

$$L: \quad 0 = 2a_1 + b_1 + c_1$$
$$T: \quad 0 = -a_1 - 2c_1$$

Hence
$$c_1 = -\tfrac{1}{2}a_1 \qquad b_1 = -\tfrac{3}{2}a_1$$

$$\Pi_1 = q^{a_1}H^{-\frac{3}{2}a_1}g^{-\frac{1}{2}a_1} = \left(\frac{q}{g^{\frac{1}{2}}H^{\frac{3}{2}}}\right)^{a_1}$$

Working with Π_2,

$$L^0 T^0 = \left(\frac{L^3}{TL}\right)^{a_2} L^{b_2} L^{c_2}$$

$$L: \quad 0 = 2a_2 + b_2 + c_2$$
$$T: \quad 0 = -a_2$$

Hence

$$a_2 = 0 \qquad c_2 = -b_2$$

$$\Pi_2 = q^0 H^{b_2} P^{-b_2} = \left(\frac{H}{P}\right)^{b_2}$$

Finally, $\phi(\Pi_1, \Pi_2) = 0$ can be written as

$$\Pi_1 = \phi'(\Pi_2)$$

$$\frac{q}{\sqrt{g}\, H^{3\!/_2}} = \phi'\left(\frac{H}{P}\right)$$

or

$$q = \phi'\left(\frac{H}{P}\right)\sqrt{g}\, H^{3\!/_2}$$

Thus dimensional analysis indicates that the flow rate per unit length of spillway is proportional to $\sqrt{g}$ and to $H^{3\!/_2}$. The flow rate also is affected by the H/P ratio. This relationship is discussed in Sec. 11.20.

If viscosity were included as one of the variables, another dimensionless group would have resulted. This dimensionless group would have had the form of a Reynolds number. With surface tension included as a variable, the resulting dimensionless group would have been a Weber number.

PROBLEMS

7.1. What is the value of Reynolds number for water at 68°F flowing with a velocity of 5 fps in a pipe 6 in. in diameter? Note that $L = D$.

7.2. What is the value of Reynolds number for air at a pressure of 100 psia and a temperature of 150°F flowing at a velocity of 80 fps in a pipe 6 in. in diameter?

7.3. A model airplane has linear dimensions that are one-twentieth those of its prototype. If the plane is to fly at 400 mph, what must be the air velocity in the wind tunnel for the same Reynolds number if the air temperature and pressure are the same?

7.4. A model airplane has dimensions that are one-twentieth those of its prototype. It is desired to test it in a pressure wind tunnel at a speed the same as that of the prototype. If the air temperature is the same and the Reynolds number is the same, what must be the pressure in the wind tunnel relative to the atmospheric pressure?

7.5. What flow rate of 70°F air at 50 psia in a 1-in.-diameter pipe will give dynamic similarity to a 250-gpm flow of 60°F water in a 4-in.-diameter pipe?

7.6. A 1:30 scale model of a submarine is tested in a wind tunnel. It is desired to know the drag on the submarine when it is operating at 10 knots in 40°F ocean water. At what velocity should the object be tested in a wind tunnel containing 70°F air at atmospheric pressure? If the drag on the model is 80 lb, what would be the drag on the prototype? At what velocity should the test be conducted when testing in a water tunnel if the water temperature is 65°F? What would be the drag on this model?

7.7. For a prototype and model having the same Reynolds numbers, express Q_r, F_r, and HP_r in terms of L_r.

7.8. A flowmeter for gas measurement registers a pressure drop of 1.0 psi when the flow through it is 0.16 lb/sec. The gas ($\gamma = 0.35$ pcf, $\mu = 2.4 \times 10^{-6}$ lb-sec/ft²) is flowing in a ¾-in.-diameter pipe. An enlarged model that is geometrically similar is to be tested in a 6-in.-diameter pipe. What flow rate of 80°F water will achieve dynamic similarity? What would be the pressure drop across the water meter?

7.9. A ship 600 ft long is to operate at a speed of 25 mph. If a model is 10 ft long, what should be its speed in feet per second to give the same Froude number? What is the value of the Froude number?

7.10. The flow over a spillway is 5,000 cfs. For dynamic similarity, what should be the model scale if the model flow rate is to be 45 cfs? The force on a certain area of the model is measured to be 1.0 lb. What would be the force on the corresponding area of the prototype?

7.11. A ship 600 ft long is to operate at a speed of 25 mph in ocean water whose viscosity is 1.2 centipoises and specific weight is 64 pcf. What should be the kinematic viscosity of a fluid used with the model so that both the Reynolds number and the Froude number would be the same? Does such a liquid exist? Assume the model is 10 ft long.

7.12. A 1:500 model is constructed to study tides. What length of time in the model corresponds to a day in the prototype? Suppose this model could be transported to the moon and tested there. What then would be the time relationship between the model and prototype?

7.13. On the earth a vertical water jet issuing upward from a nozzle at a velocity of 80 fps will rise to a height of approximately 100 ft. To get a water jet to rise to a height of 100 ft on the moon, what must be its velocity? Neglect atmospheric resistance. Gravity of moon equals ⅙ × gravity of earth.

7.14. A sectional model of a spillway 3 ft high is placed in a laboratory flume of 10-in. width. Under a head of 0.375 ft the flow is 0.70 cfs. What flow does this represent in the prototype if the model scale is 1:25 and the spillway is 650 ft long?

7.15. One wishes to model the flow about a missile when traveling at 1,000 mph through the atmosphere at elevation 10,000 ft. The model is to be tested in a wind tunnel at standard atmospheric conditions with 70°F air. What air speed in the wind tunnel is required for dynamic similarity?

7.16. A model of a supersonic aircraft is tested in a variable-density wind tunnel at 1,200 fps. The air is at 100°F with a pressure of 18 psia. At what velocity should this model be tested to maintain dynamic similarity if the air were at 120°F with pressure of 24 psia?

7.17. Verify that Eq. (7.13) results from Eqs. (7.9) and (7.12).

7.18. A model siphon is built to a model scale of 1:20. The prototype (Fig. 7.2a) having dimensions $z = 8$ ft and $h = 12$ ft will be installed in the mountains at a 7,000-ft elevation. Engineers wish to investigate the possibility of cavitation at the crown of the siphon when the absolute pressure in the prototype at section 2 is 3.0 psia. Specify the required pressure within the chamber that encloses the model. Assume the temperatures of the prototype water and model water are identical.

7.19. Refer to Prob. 7.18 and specify the required pressure in the chamber if the prototype water has a temperature of 50°F while the model water is at 70°F.

7.20. For the pipe bend shown in the figure, a model study of possible cavitation when the velocity is 8 fps is desired.   The bend is to be installed at sea level.   What model scale should one use if the model is to be placed in a chamber having a vacuum of 10 in. Hg?   Assume that the drop in energy head between the reservoir and the bend is negligible and that the water temperatures in prototype and model are identical.   Note that Eq. (7.13) cannot be used here.

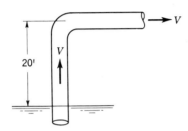

Fig. Prob. 7.20

7.21. Consider the pipe bend of Prob. 7.20.   What chamber pressure should be used with a 1:5 model if the prototype velocity is to be 16 fps?

7.22. Arrange the following groups into dimensionless parameters: (a) τ, V, ρ; (b) Δp, V, γ, g; (c) F, ρ, L, V; (d) V, L, ρ, σ.

7.23. Find the dimensions of torque, energy, power, force, and momentum in the FLT system.   Repeat for the MLT system.

7.24. By dimensional analysis derive an expression for the power developed by an engine in terms of the torque and rotative speed.

7.25. Derive an expression for the velocity of rise of an air bubble in a stationary liquid.   Consider the effect of surface tension as well as other variables.

7.26. Derive an expression for the drag on a submerged torpedo.   The parameters involved are the size of the torpedo L, the velocity of the torpedo V, the viscosity of the water μ, and the density of the water ρ.

7.27. Derive an expression for the drag on a surface vessel.   Use the same parameters as in Prob. 7.26, and add the acceleration due to gravity g, to account for the effect of wave action.

7.28. Derive an expression for the drag on an aircraft flying at supersonic speed.

7.29. Using dimensional analysis, derive an expression for small flow rates over a spillway.   The parameters involved are height of spillway P, head on the spillway H, acceleration due to gravity g, viscosity of liquid μ, density of liquid ρ, and surface tension σ.

7.30. Use dimensional analysis to derive an expression for the height of capillary rise in a glass tube.

EIGHT

STEADY FLOW
OF INCOMPRESSIBLE FLUIDS
IN PIPES

In this chapter some of the aspects of steady flow in pipes are discussed. The discussion is limited to *incompressible fluids*, that is, to those for which $\gamma \approx$ constant. This includes all liquids. In this chapter isothermal conditions are assumed so as to eliminate thermodynamic effects, some of which are discussed in Chap. 9. Gases flowing with very small pressure drops may be considered *incompressible*, for then $\gamma \approx$ constant.

8.1. LAMINAR AND TURBULENT FLOW

If the head loss in a given length of uniform pipe is measured at different values of the velocity, it will be found that, as long as the velocity is low enough to secure laminar flow, the head loss, due to friction, will be directly proportional to the velocity, as shown in Fig. 8.1. But with increasing velocity, at some point B, where visual observation in a transparent tube would show that the flow

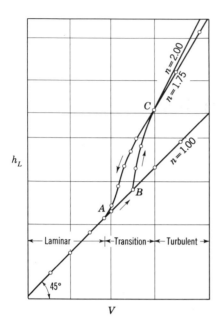

h_L

Laminar — | — Transition — | — Turbulent —

45°

V

Fig. 8.1. Log-log plot for flow in a uniform pipe.

changes from laminar to turbulent, there will be an abrupt increase in the rate at which the head loss varies. If the logarithms of these two variables are plotted on linear scales or if the values are plotted directly on logarithmic cross-sectional paper, it will be found that, after a certain transition region has been passed, lines will be obtained with slopes ranging from about 1.75 to 2.00.

It is thus seen that for laminar flow the drop in energy due to friction varies as V, while for turbulent flow the friction varies as V^n, where n ranges from about 1.75 to 2. The lower value of 1.75 for turbulent flow is found for pipes with very smooth walls; as the wall roughness increases, the value of n increases up to its maximum value of 2.

The points in Fig. 8.1 were plotted directly from Osborne Reynolds' measurements and show decided curves in the transition zone where values of n are even greater than 2. If the velocity is gradually reduced from a high value, the line BC will not be retraced. Instead, the points lie along curve CA. Point B is known as the *higher critical* point, and A as the *lower critical* point.

However, velocity is not the only factor that determines whether the flow is laminar or turbulent. The criterion is Reynolds number, which has been discussed in Sec. 7.4. For a circular pipe the significant linear dimension L may be taken as the diameter D, and thus

$$N_R = \frac{DV\rho}{\mu} = \frac{DV}{\nu} \tag{8.1}$$

where any consistent system of units may be used, since N_R is a dimensionless number.[1]

8.2. CRITICAL REYNOLDS NUMBER

The upper critical Reynolds number, corresponding to point B of Fig. 8.1, is really indeterminate and depends upon the care taken to prevent any initial disturbance from affecting the flow. Its value is normally about 4,000, but laminar flow in circular pipes has been maintained up to values of N_R as high as 50,000. However, in such cases this type of flow is inherently unstable, and the least disturbance will transform it instantly into turbulent flow. On the other hand, it is practically impossible for turbulent flow in a straight pipe to persist at values of N_R much below 2,000, because any turbulence that is set up will be damped out by viscous friction. This lower value is thus much more definite than the higher one and is really the dividing point between the two types of flow. Hence this lower value will be defined as the *true critical* Reynolds number. However, this lower critical value is subject to slight variations. Its value will be higher in a converging pipe and lower in a diverging pipe than in a straight pipe. Also, its value will be less for flow in a curved pipe than in a straight one, and even for a straight uniform pipe its value may be as low as 1,000, where there is an excessive degree of roughness. However, for normal cases of flow in straight pipes of uniform diameter and usual roughness, the critical value may be taken as $N_R = 2,000$.

For water at 75°F the kinematic viscosity is 1.00×10^{-5} ft²/sec, and for this case the critical Reynolds number is obtained when

$$DV = N_R \nu = 2{,}000 \times 10^{-5}$$

Thus, for a pipe 1 in. in diameter,

$$V_{\text{crit}} = 12 \times 2{,}000 \times 10^{-5} = 0.24 \text{ fps}$$

Or if the velocity were 2.4 fps, the diameter would be only 0.1 in. Velocities or pipe diameters as small as these values are not often encountered in practical engineering, though they may be found in certain laboratory instruments. Hence, for such fluids as water and air, practically all cases

---

[1] It is sometimes convenient to use a "hybrid" set of units and compensate by a correction factor. Thus $N_R = 15.28Q/d\nu = 22{,}740G/(d \times \text{centipoises})$, where d is the diameter in inches, ν is kinematic viscosity in square feet per second, and Q and G are as defined in the Notation, in the front of the book. The last form is especially convenient in the case of gases; and it also shows that in a pipe of uniform diameter the Reynolds number is constant along the pipe even for a compressible fluid where the density and velocity vary, if there is no appreciable variation in temperature to alter the absolute viscosity of the gas.

of engineering importance are in the turbulent-flow region. But if the fluid is a viscous oil, laminar flow is often encountered.

8.3. HYDRAULIC RADIUS

For conduits having noncircular cross sections, some value other than the diameter must be used for the linear dimension in the Reynolds number. Such a quality is the *hydraulic radius*, defined as

$$R = \frac{A}{P} \tag{8.2}$$

where A is the cross-sectional area of the flowing fluid, and P is the *wetted perimeter*, that portion of the perimeter of the cross section where there is contact between fluid and solid boundary. For a circular pipe flowing full, $R = \pi r^2 / 2\pi r = r/2$, or $D/4$. Thus R is not the radius of the pipe, and hence the term "radius" is misleading. If a circular pipe is exactly half full, both the area and the wetted perimeter are half the preceding values; so R is $r/2$, the same as if it were full. But if the depth of flow in a circular pipe is 0.8 times the diameter, for example, $A = 0.6736D^2$ and $P = 2.214D$, then $R = 0.304D$, or $0.608r$.

The hydraulic radius is a convenient means for expressing the shape as well as the size of a conduit, since for the same cross-sectional area the value of R will vary with the shape.

In evaluating Reynolds number for a noncircular conduit it is customary to substitute $4R$ for D in Eq. (8.1).

8.4. GENERAL EQUATION FOR FRICTION

The following discussion applies to either laminar or turbulent flow and to any shape of cross section.

Consider steady flow in a conduit of uniform cross section A (Fig. 8.2). The pressures at sections 1 and 2 are p_1 and p_2, respectively. The distance between sections is L. For equilibrium in steady flow, the summation of forces acting on any fluid element must be equal to zero. Thus, in the direction of flow,

$$p_1 A - p_2 A - \gamma L A \sin \alpha - \tau_0 (PL) = 0 \tag{8.3}$$

where τ_0 is the shear force per unit area at the pipe wall. Noting that $\sin \alpha = (z_2 - z_1)/L$ and dividing each term by γA,

$$\frac{p_1}{\gamma} - \frac{p_2}{\gamma} - z_2 + z_1 = \tau_0 \frac{PL}{\gamma A} \tag{8.4}$$

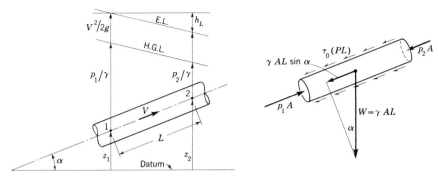

Fig. 8.2

Noting from the left-hand sketch of Fig. 8.2 that

$$h_L = (z_1 + p_1/\gamma) - (z_2 + p_2/\gamma)$$

and substituting R for A/P,

$$h_L = \tau_0 \frac{L}{R\gamma} \tag{8.5}$$

For a smooth conduit, where wall roughness may be neglected for the present, it may be assumed that the fluid shear at the wall is some function of ρ, μ, V and some characteristic linear dimension, which will here be taken as the hydraulic radius R. Thus

$$\tau_0 = K R^a \rho^b \mu^c V^d \tag{8.6}$$

where K is a dimensionless number but is not necessarily a constant. Substituting in Eq. (8.6) dimensional values of F, L, and T for force, length, and time, we get[1]

$$FL^{-2} = K L^a (FL^{-4}T^2)^b (FL^{-2}T)^c (LT^{-1})^d$$

As the dimensions on the two sides of the equation must be alike,

$$\begin{aligned}
&\text{For } F: & 1 &= b + c \\
&\text{For } L: & -2 &= a - 4b - 2c + d \\
&\text{For } T: & 0 &= 2b + c - d
\end{aligned}$$

The solution of these three simultaneous expressions in terms of n is $a = n - 2$, $b = n - 1$, $c = 2 - n$.

---

[1] Here we are using the FLT system, while in Chap. 7 the MLT system was used. It makes no difference which system is used since the results are the same.

Inserting these values of the exponents in Eq. (8.6), the result is

$$\tau_0 = K R^{n-2} \rho^{n-1} \mu^{2-n} V^n \tag{8.7}$$

This may be rearranged as

$$\tau_0 = K \left(\frac{RV\rho}{\mu}\right)^{n-2} \rho V^2 = 2K N_R^{n-2} \rho \frac{V^2}{2} \tag{8.8}$$

for it is seen that $RV\rho/\mu$ is a Reynolds number, with R as the characteristic length.

Grouping the dimensionless terms on the right side of Eq. (8.8) into a single term C_f, we get

$$C_f = 2K N_R^{n-2} \tag{8.9}$$

Hence
$$\tau_0 = C_f \rho \frac{V^2}{2} \tag{8.10}$$

Inserting this value of τ_0 in Eq. (8.5) and noting that $\gamma = \rho g$,

$$h_L = C_f \frac{L}{R} \frac{V^2}{2g} \tag{8.11}$$

which may be applied to any shape of cross section.

8.5. PIPES OF CIRCULAR CROSS SECTION

In Sec. 8.3 it is shown that for a circular pipe flowing full $R = D/4$. Substituting this value in Eq. (8.11), the result is

$$h_L = f \frac{L}{D} \frac{V^2}{2g} \tag{8.12}$$

where
$$f = 4C_f = 8K N_R^{n-2} \tag{8.13}$$

Equation (8.12) is known as the *pipe-friction equation*, and the names of Darcy, Fanning, and Weisbach have been associated with it. Like the coefficient C_f, the friction factor f is dimensionless and is also some function of Reynolds number. Modern research has been directed toward determining the way in which f varies with N_R and also with pipe roughness. As L/D is the ratio of two linear dimensions, it is also an abstract number. The pipe-friction equation expresses the fact that the head lost in friction in a given pipe can be expressed in terms of the velocity head. The equation is dimensionally homogeneous and may be used with any consistent system of units.

Applying Eq. (8.5) to a circular pipe, $h_L = \tau_0 2L/r_0 \gamma$, where r_0 is the radius to the pipe wall. Likewise, for any concentric cylindrical body of fluid of smaller diameter than the pipe, $h_L = \tau 2L/r\gamma$, where r is the radius to *any* point. From this it follows that the unit shear in a circular pipe at any radius r is

$$\tau = \frac{\tau_0}{r_0} r \tag{8.14}$$

or the unit shear is zero at the center of the pipe and increases linearly with the radius to a maximum value τ_0 at the wall as in Fig. 8.3.

From Eqs. (8.10) and (8.13) we obtain

$$\tau_0 = \frac{f}{4} \rho \frac{V^2}{2} = \frac{f}{4} \gamma \frac{V^2}{2g} \tag{8.15}$$

By the aid of this equation, τ_0 may be computed for any experimentally determined value of f.

Dimensional analysis gives us the proper form for an equation but does not yield a numerical result since it is not concerned with abstract numerical factors. Hence it shows in Eq. (8.7) that whatever the value of the exponent of V, the exponents of all the other quantities involved are then determined. It also shows that Eq. (8.12) is a rational expression for pipe friction. But the numerical values of such quantities as K, n, and f must be determined by other means.

8.6. LAMINAR FLOW IN CIRCULAR PIPES

In Sec. 1.10 it was noted that for laminar flow $\tau = \mu \, du/dy$, where u is the value of the velocity at a distance y from the wall. As $y = r_0 - r$, it is also seen that $\tau = -\mu \, du/dr$; in other words, the minus sign indicates that u decreases as r increases. The coefficient of viscosity μ is a constant for any particular fluid at a constant temperature, and therefore if the shear varies from zero at the center of the pipe to a maximum at the wall, it follows that the velocity profile must have a zero slope at the center and have a continuously steeper velocity gradient as the wall is approached.

In order to determine the velocity profile for laminar flow in a circular pipe the expression for τ in laminar flow will be inserted in the general relation

$$h_L = \frac{\tau 2L}{r\gamma}$$

so that we have

$$h_L = -\mu \frac{du}{dr} 2 \frac{L}{r\gamma}$$

From this

$$du = -\frac{h_L \gamma}{2\mu L} r \, dr$$

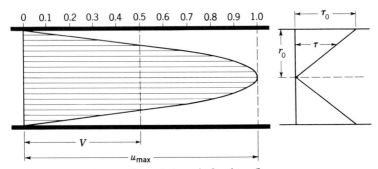

Fig. 8.3. Velocity profile and shear in laminar flow.

Integrating and determining the constant of integration from the fact that $u = u_{max}$ when $r = 0$, we obtain

$$u = u_{max} - \frac{h_L\gamma}{4\mu L}\, r^2 \qquad (8.16)$$

From this equation it is seen that the velocity profile is a parabola, as shown in Fig. 8.3.

From the fact that the velocity at the wall is zero, that is, $u = 0$ when $r = r_0$, the value of the velocity at the center is

$$u_{max} = \frac{h_L\gamma}{4\mu L}\, r_0{}^2 = \frac{h_L\gamma}{16\mu L}\, D^2 \qquad (8.17)$$

Equation (8.16) may be multiplied by a differential area $dA \doteq 2\pi r\, dr$ and the product integrated from $r = 0$ to $r = r_0$ to find the rate of discharge. As in previous cases, the rate of discharge is proportional to the volume of a solid bounded by the velocity profile. In this case the solid is a paraboloid with a maximum height proportional to u_{max}. The mean height of a paraboloid is one-half the maximum height, and hence the mean velocity V is $0.5u_{max}$. Thus

$$V = \frac{h_L\gamma}{32\mu L}\, D^2 \qquad (8.18)$$

From this last equation, noting that $\gamma = g\rho$ and $\mu/\rho = \nu$, the loss of head in friction is given by

$$h_L = 32\, \frac{\mu}{\gamma}\, \frac{L}{D^2}\, V = 32\nu\, \frac{L}{gD^2}\, V \qquad (8.19)$$

which is the Hagen-Poiseuille law for laminar flow in tubes. Hagen, a German engineer, experimented with water flowing through small brass tubes and published his results in 1839. Poiseuille, a French scientist, experimented with water flowing through capillary tubes in order to determine the laws of flow of blood through the veins of the body and published his studies in 1840.

From Eq. (8.19) it is seen that in laminar flow the loss of head is proportional to the first power of the velocity, or $n = 1$. This is verified by experiment, as shown in Fig. 8.1. The striking feature of this equation is that it involves no empirical coefficients or experimental factors of any kind, except for the physical properties of the fluid such as viscosity and density (or specific weight). From this it would appear that in laminar flow the friction is independent of the roughness of the pipe wall. That this is true is also borne out by experiment.

Dimensional analysis shows that the friction loss may also be expressed by Eq. (8.12). Equating (8.12) and (8.19) and solving for the friction factor f, we obtain $f = 64\nu/DV$, or

$$f = \frac{64}{N_R} \tag{8.20}$$

Hence, if N_R is less than 2,000, we may use Eq. (8.19) to find pipe friction head loss or we may use Eq. (8.12) with the value of f as given by Eq. (8.20).

8.7. ENTRANCE CONDITIONS IN LAMINAR FLOW

In the case of a pipe leading from a reservoir, if the entrance is rounded so as to avoid any initial disturbance of the entering stream, all particles will start to flow with the same velocity, except for a very thin film in contact with the wall. Particles next to the wall have a zero velocity, but the velocity gradient is here extremely steep, and with this slight exception, the velocity is uniform across the diameter, as shown in Fig. 8.4. As the fluid progresses, the streamlines in the vicinity of the wall

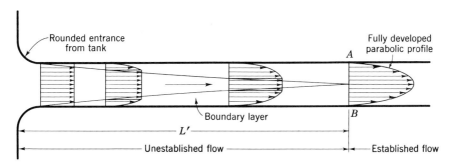

Fig. 8.4. Velocity profiles along a pipe in laminar flow.

are slowed down by friction emanating from the wall, but as Q is constant for successive sections, the velocity in the center must be accelerated, until the final velocity profile is a parabola, as shown in Fig. 8.3. Theoretically, an infinite distance is required for this, but it has been established both by theory and by observation that the maximum velocity in the center of the pipe will reach 99 per cent of its ultimate value in the distance $L' = 0.058 N_R D$. Thus, for the critical value $N_R = 2,000$, the distance L' of Fig. 8.4 equals 116 pipe diameters. In other cases of laminar flow below this critical point, the distance L' will be correspondingly less.[1]

In the entry region of length L' the flow is *unestablished;* that is, the velocity profile is changing. In this region the flow can be visualized as consisting of a central core in which there are no frictional effects and an annular zone extending from the core outward to the pipe wall. This outer zone increases in thickness as it moves along the wall and is known as the *boundary layer.* Viscosity in the boundary layer acts to transmit the effect of boundary shear inwardly into the flow. At section AB the boundary layer has grown until it occupies the entire section of the pipe. At this point, for laminar flow, the velocity profile is a perfect parabola. Beyond section AB the velocity profile does not change, and the flow is known as *established flow.*

As shown in Prob. 4.1 for a circular pipe, the kinetic energy of a stream with a parabolic velocity profile is $2V^2/2g$, where V is the mean velocity. At the entrance of the pipe the velocity is uniformly V across the diameter, except for an extremely thin layer next to the wall. Thus, at the entrance to the pipe, the kinetic energy per unit weight is practically $V^2/2g$. Hence, in the distance L', there is a continuous increase in kinetic energy accompanied by a corresponding decrease in pressure head. Therefore, at a distance L' from the entrance, the pressure head is less than the static value by $2V^2/2g$ plus the friction loss in this distance.

Laminar flow has been dealt with rather fully, not merely because it is of importance in problems involving fluids of very high viscosity, but especially because it permits a simple and accurate rational analysis. The general approach used here is of some assistance in the study of turbulent flow, where conditions are so complex that rigid mathematical treatment is impossible.

8.8. TURBULENT FLOW IN CIRCULAR PIPES

Viscosity in laminar flow may be explained, especially in the case of gases, by the aid of the kinetic theory. This is that gases are composed of

---

[1] H. L. Langhaar, Steady Flow in the Transition Length of a Straight Tube, *J. Appl. Mech.*, vol. 10, p. 55, 1942.

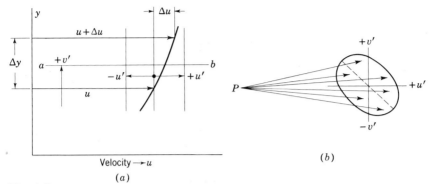

Fig. 8.5

molecules which continually move at random in all directions at high velocities, a continuous interchange of momentum being the result of their collisions with each other. The average distance traveled between collisions is called the *mean free path.*

Consider a body of fluid moving to the right in Fig. 8.5a, with a velocity u which increases with y. Because of molecular motion, molecules will cross the line ab, even in laminar flow, and will thereby transport momentum. On the average, the velocities of the molecules in the slower-moving fluid below the line will be less than those of the faster-moving fluid above; the result is that the molecules which cross from below tend to slow down the faster-moving fluid. Likewise, the molecules which cross the line ab from above tend to speed up the slower-moving fluid below. The result is the production of a shear stress along the surface whose trace is ab, the value of which is given in Sec. 1.10 as $\tau = \mu\, du/dy$. The viscosity coefficient is a property of the fluid and depends upon the weight and number of molecules that cross over through a unit area in unit time. It is a constant in a given flow, but the shear stress varies as the velocity gradient du/dy.

First expression. In the modern conception of turbulent flow, a similar mechanism is assumed. In turbulent flow a multitude of small eddies are created by the viscous shear between adjacent particles. These eddies grow in size and then completely disappear as their particles merge into adjacent eddies. There is thus a continuous mixing of particles, with a consequent transfer of momentum. Thus molecules are considered to be replaced by minute but finite masses; molecular velocity is replaced by turbulent fluctuations of velocity; and the mean free path is replaced by a *mixing length*, which is the average distance perpendicular to the mean axial velocity in which a small mass changes its initial velocity and accommodates itself to its new surroundings. Hence, by analogy, the shear stress along the plane through ab in Fig. 8.5 may be defined in the case of turbulent flow as

$$\text{Turbulent shear} = \eta \frac{du}{dy} \tag{8.21}$$

But unlike μ, the *eddy-viscosity coefficient* η is not a constant for a given fluid, but depends upon the turbulence of the stream, and it also varies according to its position in the stream. Its magnitude may range from zero to many thousand times the value of μ. However, its numerical value is of less interest than its physical concept. In general, the total shear stress is the sum of the laminar shear plus the turbulent shear; i.e.,

$$\tau = \mu \frac{du}{dy} + \eta \frac{du}{dy} \tag{8.22}$$

In turbulent flow the local axial velocity has been shown, in Sec. 3.3, to have fluctuations of plus and minus u', and there are also fluctuations of plus and minus v' normal to u. As it is obvious that there can be no values of v' next to a smooth wall and perpendicular to it, there can be no turbulent shear there. Hence, near a smooth wall, the shear is due to viscosity alone.

At a distance from the wall the value of du/dy becomes very small in turbulent flow, and hence the viscous shear becomes negligible in comparison with the turbulent shear. The latter can be large, even though du/dy is small, because of the possibility of η being very large. This is due to the great turbulence that may exist at an appreciable distance from the wall. But in the central portion of the pipe, where du/dy is zero, there can be no shear at all. Hence, in turbulent flow as well as in laminar flow, the shear stress is a maximum at the wall and decreases linearly to zero at the axis, as shown in Fig. 8.3.

Second expression. Another expression for turbulent shear stress may be obtained which is different from that in Eq. (8.21). Thus in Fig. 8.5a, if a mass m of fluid below ab, where the temporal mean axial velocity is u, moves upward into a zone where the temporal mean axial velocity is $u + \Delta u$, its initial momentum in the axial direction must be increased by $m \Delta u$. Conversely, a mass m which moves from the upper zone to the lower will have its axial momentum decreased by $m \Delta u$. Hence this transfer of momentum back and forth across ab will produce a shear in the plane through ab proportional to Δu. This shear is possible only because of the velocity profile shown. If the latter were vertical, Δu would be zero and there could be no shear.

In detail consider that at every point in turbulent flow there are also velocity fluctuations of $+u'$ and $-u'$ in an axial direction and $+v'$ and

$-v'$ normal to the axis.   Consider an area dA in the plane ab and normal to v'.   Because of turbulent fluctuations, small masses of fluid will be carried across this area at a rate $\rho v' \, dA$ and will undergo a change in velocity and hence in momentum in the axial direction.

Consider first a mass moving upward with a velocity $+v'$: it will transport into the upper zone a momentum $\rho \, dA \, v'(u \pm u')$.   It is apparent in Fig. 8.5a that while the velocity fluctuations were equally plus and minus in the lower zone, *in the new environment* the values of $-u'$ predominate over the values of $+u'$ and hence as before there will be on the average a retardation of the fluid in the upper zone.

If the distance Δy in Fig. 8.5a is so chosen that the average value of u' in the *new zone* is equal to Δu, the two streams will be separated by the mixing length.   Thus, over a period of time, the turbulent shear force on the area dA will be $\tau \, dA = \rho \, dA \, v' \, \Delta u = -\rho \, dA \, \overline{u'v'}$, where $\overline{u'v'}$ is the temporal average of the product.   Thus, along ab per unit area,

$$\text{Turbulent shear} = -\rho \overline{u'v'} \tag{8.23}$$

which is an alternative form for Eq. (8.21).

The minus sign appears in Eq. (8.23) because the product $\overline{u'v'}$ on the average is negative.   As an aid in this problem, consider two lines of automobiles moving in the same direction in adjacent lanes.   Assume that in lane A the average speed is 30 mph and in lane B it is 29 mph, which makes Δu correspond to 1 mph.   If there are spaces between the cars so that drivers can shift lanes, it is obvious that there is a tendency for cars in lane A to be slowed down and those in lane B to be speeded up as a result of such shifting back and forth.   Most analogies have limitations, and here we shall impose the limitation that the velocity fluctuations in each lane are the same as Δu.   Thus in lane A the speeds will continually fluctuate between 29 and 31 mph, while in lane B they will range between 28 and 30 mph.   Now if at a certain instant when cars in lane A are moving at 31 mph and those in B are traveling at 28 mph a car from lane B shifts over into lane A, it will be 3 mph *slower* than the rest.   But if the shift takes place when cars in lane A are going 29 mph and those in lane B are at 30 mph, the B car will be traveling 1 mph *faster* than those in lane A.   The shift might also be made at the instant when cars in both lanes are traveling at the same speed of 30 mph, but on the *average* cars from lane B will contribute a negative velocity to lane A, and on the average this will be the same as Δu.   Corresponding conclusions could be drawn if we considered cars from lane A shifting over to lane B.

The minus sign is present in Eq. (8.23) because on a time average $+v'$ is associated with $-u'$ values more than it is with $+u'$ values, and hence the value of the shear is really positive.   Similarly, when the elementary mass moves downward across ab with a velocity $-v'$, the $+u'$ values will then predominate over the $-u'$ values.   This is so because of the correlation between u' and v' due to the velocity gradient.   If the latter were zero, there would be no correlation and no shear.

This is shown in another way in Fig. 8.5b, where the velocity vectors at fixed point P in the stream fluctuate in both magnitude and direction in turbulent flow.   If a hot-wire anemometer were used with an oscilloscope, on a screen would be seen an oval-shaped cloud, denser in the center because more velocity vectors would terminate in that region, fading away on the outer edges.   There is no sharp boundary, but most of the vectors would terminate within the oval shown.   If there were no correlation and no shear, this oval would be replaced by a circle.   If there were perfect correlation so that $+v' = -u'$ and the two were always numerically equal at the same times, the oval would reduce to the 45° dotted line shown.   But with the actual correlation, Fig. 8.5b shows more combinations of $+v'$ and $-u'$ than of $+v'$ and $+u'$.   Similarly, for a movement of the minute mass downward, the temporal mean value of $\overline{u'v'}$ is also negative because on the average $-v'$ is associated with $+u'$ more often than the reverse.

Therefore, while the temporal mean values of u' and v' are individually equal to zero, the temporal mean value of their product is not zero because of the correlation.

Prandtl reasoned that in any turbulent flow u' and v' must be proportional to each other and of the same order of magnitude.   He also introduced the concept of the mixing length l, which has been defined previously.   This concept assumes that a small mass of fluid moves this distance and then suddenly acquires a new velocity.   Actually, there is a gradual change all the way.   Despite this, the theory does provide a framework for the following reasoning.   As $\Delta u = l\, du/dy$, Prandtl assumed $u' = l\, du/dy$, and if u' varies with v', it follows that $\overline{u'v'}$ varies as $l^2(du/dy)^2$.   As the numerical value of l is not known, it is arbitrarily assumed of such a value as to absorb the constant of proportionality, and thus the total shear stress is

$$\tau = \mu \frac{du}{dy} + \rho l^2 \left(\frac{du}{dy}\right)^2 \tag{8.24}$$

This equation expresses terms that can be measured.   Thus in any experiment where the pipe friction is determined, τ_0 can be computed by Eq. (8.15), and τ at any radius is then found by Eq. (8.14).   A traverse of the velocity across a pipe diameter will give u at any radius, and the velocity profile will give du/dy at any radius.   Thus Eq. (8.24) enables the Prandtl mixing length l to be found as a function of the pipe radius. The purpose of all of this is to enable us to develop theoretical equations for the velocity profile in turbulent flow, and from this in turn to develop theoretical equations for f, the friction coefficient.[1]

8.9. LAMINAR SUBLAYER IN TURBULENT FLOW

In Fig. 8.4 it is shown that, for laminar flow, if the fluid enters with no initial disturbance, the velocity is uniform across the diameter except for an exceedingly thin film at the wall, inasmuch as the velocity next to any wall is zero. But as flow proceeds down the pipe, the velocity profile changes because of the growth of a laminar boundary layer which continues until the boundary layers from opposite sides meet at the pipe axis and then there is fully developed laminar flow.

If the Reynolds number is above the critical value, so that the flow is turbulent, the initial condition is much like that in Fig. 8.4. But as the laminar boundary layer increases in thickness, a point is soon reached where a transition occurs and the boundary layer becomes turbulent. This turbulent boundary layer generally increases in thickness much more rapidly, and soon the two from opposite sides meet at the pipe axis, and there is then fully developed turbulent flow.

This initial laminar boundary layer may be given a Reynolds number such as $N_{Rx} = Ux/\nu$, where U is the uniform velocity and x is the distance measured from the initial point. When x has such a value that this N_{Rx} is about 300,000, the transition occurs to the turbulent boundary layer. Fully developed turbulent flow will be found at about 50 pipe diameters from the pipe entrance for a smooth pipe with no special disturbance at entrance; otherwise the turbulent boundary layers from the two sides will meet within a shorter distance. It is this fully developed turbulent flow that we shall consider in all that follows.

There can be no turbulence next to a smooth wall since it is impossible for v' to have any value at a solid boundary. Therefore immediately adjacent to a smooth wall there will be a laminar sublayer, as shown in Fig. 8.6, within which the shear is due to viscosity alone. This laminar sublayer is extremely thin, usually only a few thousandths of an inch, but

---

[1] T. von Kármán has developed an equation from which l may be determined from the velocity profile alone, but the value will not be identical with that determined by Eq. (8.24). His expression is $l = K(du/dy)/(d^2u/dy^2)$, where K is a universal constant the value of which has been determined by many experiments to be 0.40. See T. von Kármán, Turbulence and Skin Friction, *J. Aeronaut. Sci.*, vol. 1, no. 1, January, 1934, and Some Aspects of the Turbulence Problem, *Mech. Eng.*, July, 1935, p. 407.

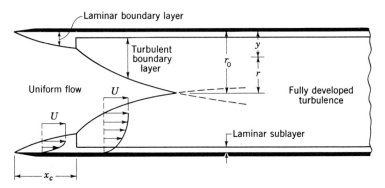

Fig. 8.6. Development of boundary layer in a pipe (scales much distorted).

its effect is great because of the very steep velocity gradient within it and as $\tau = \mu \, du/dy$. At a distance from the wall the viscous effect becomes negligible, but the turbulent shear is then large. Between the two there must be a transition zone where both types of shear are significant. It is evident that there can be no sharp lines of demarcation separating these three zones, inasmuch as one must merge gradually into the other.

By plotting a velocity profile from the wall on the assumption that the flow is entirely laminar and plotting another velocity profile on the assumption that the flow is entirely turbulent (Sec. 8.10), the two will intersect, as shown in Fig. 8.7. It is obvious that there can be no abrupt change in profile at this point of intersection, but that one curve must merge gradually into the other, as shown by the experimental points.

Any value taken for the thickness of this laminar sublayer must be purely arbitrary. The simultaneous solution of the equations for the two curves, together with some experimental factors, will give the value of y for point b as

$$\delta = 11.6 \frac{\nu}{\sqrt{\tau_0/\rho}} \tag{8.25}$$

where δ is referred to as the nominal thickness of the laminar sublayer. The transition curve ac determined by measurements indicates that a is a better limit of the laminar-sublayer thickness. Present information is that the thickness of the laminar sublayer out to point a is approximately

$$\delta' = 5 \frac{\nu}{\sqrt{\tau_0/\rho}} \tag{8.26}$$

In a circular pipe the laminar velocity profile has been shown to be a parabola, but in this extremely thin region near the wall it can scarcely be distinguished from a straight line.

The transition zone may be said to extend from a to c in Fig. 8.7. For the latter point the value of y has been estimated to be about $30\nu/\sqrt{\tau_0/\rho}$. Beyond this the flow is so turbulent that viscous shear is negligible.

From Eq. (8.15)

$$\sqrt{\frac{\tau_0}{\rho}} = \sqrt{\frac{fV^2}{8}}$$

and making this substitution in Eq. (8.26), we obtain

$$\delta' = \frac{14.12\nu}{V\sqrt{f}} \tag{8.27}$$

from which it is seen that the higher the velocity or the lower the kinematic viscosity, the thinner the laminar sublayer. Thus, for a given constant pipe diameter, the thickness of the laminar sublayer decreases as the Reynolds number increases.

It is now in order to discuss what is meant by a smooth wall. There is no such thing in reality as a mathematically smooth surface. But if the irregularities on any actual surface are such that the projections do not pierce through the laminar sublayer, the surface is smooth from the fluid-mechanics viewpoint. But if the projections do extend beyond the sub-

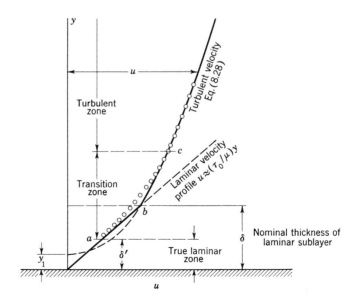

Fig. 8.7. Velocity profile near a solid wall (vertical scale greatly exaggerated).

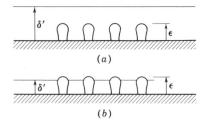

(a)

(b)

Fig. 8.8. Turbulent flow near boundary. (a) Relatively low N_R, $\delta' > \epsilon$. (b) Relatively high N_R, $\delta' < \epsilon$.

layer, this laminar layer is broken up and the surface is then hydraulically rough.

Inasmuch as the thickness of the laminar sublayer in a given pipe will decrease with an increase in Reynolds number, it is seen that the same pipe may be hydraulically smooth at low Reynolds numbers and rough at high Reynolds numbers. Thus, even the smoothest of pipes may behave as a rough pipe if the Reynolds number is high enough. It is also apparent that, with increasing Reynolds number, there is a gradual transition from smooth to rough pipe flow. These concepts are depicted schematically in Fig. 8.8, where ϵ is the height of the roughness projection.

8.10. VELOCITY PROFILE IN TURBULENT FLOW

If the viscous shear is considered as negligible outside of the laminar sublayer, an equation for the velocity profile in the turbulent zone may be developed by considering the last term in Eq. (8.24). Prandtl reasoned that near the wall, but outside the laminar sublayer, l would be proportional to y, where y is the distance from the wall; that is, $y = r_0 - r$. He also assumed that, in this small distance, $\tau = \tau_0$, since the velocity profile is practically a straight line in this narrow zone. Therefore, from Eq. (8.24), these assumptions give $\tau_0 = K^2 \rho y^2 (du/dy)^2$, where K is a constant the value of which has been determined by many experiments to be about 0.40. Therefore

$$du = \frac{1}{K}\sqrt{\frac{\tau_0}{\rho}}\frac{dy}{y}$$

from which

$$u = 2.5\sqrt{\frac{\tau_0}{\rho}}\ln y + C$$

The constant may be evaluated by noting that $u = u_{\max}$ when $y = r_0$. With this value of C and replacing y by $r_0 - r$, the equation becomes

$$u = u_{\max} - 5.75\sqrt{\frac{\tau_0}{\rho}}\log_{10}\frac{r_0}{r_0 - r} \qquad (8.28)$$

Although this equation is derived by assuming certain relations very near to the wall, it has been found to hold practically to the axis of the pipe.

Starting with the derivation of Eq. (8.24), this entire development is open to argument at nearly every step. But the fact remains that Eq. (8.28) agrees very closely with actual measurements of velocity profiles for both smooth and rough pipes. However, there are two zones in which it is defective. At the axis of the pipe du/dy must be zero. But Eq. (8.28) is logarithmic and does not have a zero slope at $r = 0$, and hence the velocity profile has a sharp point at the axis, as shown in Fig. 8.9, whereas it must in reality be rounded at the axis. But this discrepancy affects only a very small area and involves very slight error in computing the rate of discharge.

Equation (8.28) is also not applicable very close to the wall. In fact it indicates that when $r = r_0$, the value of u is minus infinity. Also the equation indicates that $u = 0$, not at the wall, but at a small distance from it, shown as y_1 in Fig. 8.7. However, this discrepancy is well within the confines of the laminar sublayer, where the equation is not supposed to apply. As the laminar sublayer is very thin, the flow within it has very little effect upon the total rate of discharge.

Hence, although Eq. (8.28) is not perfect, it is reliable except for these two small areas, and thus the rate of discharge may be determined with a high degree of accuracy by using the value of u given by it and integrating over the area of the pipe. Thus $Q = \int u \, dA = 2\pi \int_0^{r_0} ur \, dr$, and dividing by the pipe area πr_0^2 and integrating, the mean velocity is

$$V = u_{\max} - 2.5 \sqrt{\frac{\tau_0}{\rho}} \left[\ln r_0 - \frac{2}{r_0^2} \int_0^{r_0} r \ln (r_0 - r) \, dr \right]^*$$

This equation reduces to

$$V = u_{\max} - \tfrac{3}{2} \times 2.5 \sqrt{\frac{\tau_0}{\rho}} = u_{\max} - 1.326 V \sqrt{f} \qquad (8.29)$$

From this last equation the *pipe factor*, which is the ratio of the mean to the maximum velocity, may be obtained. It is

$$\frac{V}{u_{\max}} = \frac{1}{1 + 1.326 \sqrt{f}} \qquad (8.30)$$

---

* The integration of this term results in indeterminate values at $r = r_0$, as we should expect, inasmuch as the equation for u does not really apply close to the wall. However, these have been shown to reduce to negligible quantities. See B. A. Bakhmeteff, "The Mechanics of Turbulent Flow," p. 70, Princeton University Press, Princeton, N.J., 1941.

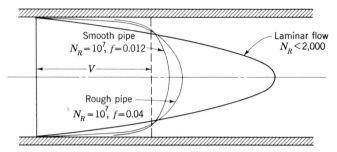

Fig. 8.9. Velocity profiles.

Using the relation of Eq. (8.30) in Eq. (8.28) and replacing $\sqrt{\tau_0/\rho}$ by $\sqrt{fV^2/8}$, the result is

$$u = (1 + 1.326\sqrt{f})\,V - 2.04\sqrt{f}\,V\,\log_{10}\frac{r_0}{r_0 - r} \qquad (8.31)$$

which enables a velocity profile to be plotted for any mean velocity and any value of f in turbulent flow. In Fig. 8.9 may be seen profiles for both a smooth and a rough pipe plotted from this equation. The only noticeable difference between these and measured profiles is that the latter are more rounded at the axis of the pipe.[1]

Comparing Fig. 8.9 with Fig. 8.3, it may be seen that the velocity profiles for turbulent flow are very much flatter in the central portion and much steeper near the wall. It is also seen that the profile is flatter in the central portion for a very smooth pipe than it is for a very rough one.

As a theoretical equation has now been derived for the velocity profile for turbulent flow, in circular pipes, it is also possible to derive equations for the kinetic-energy and momentum-correction factors when mean velocities are used. These values are[2]

$$\alpha = 1 + 2.7f \qquad (8.32a)$$

$$\beta = 1 + 0.977f \qquad (8.32b)$$

Illustrative example 8.1: The head loss in 200 ft of 6-in.-diameter pipe is known to be 25 ft-lb/lb when oil ($s = 0.90$) of viscosity 0.0008 lb-sec/ft² flows at

---

[1] Although the preceding theory agrees very well with experimental data, it is not absolutely correct throughout the entire range from the axis to the pipe wall, and present indications are that some slight shift in the numerical constants will agree somewhat more closely with test data. Thus, in Eqs. (8.30) and (8.31) the 1.326 may be replaced by 1.435, and in Eq. (8.31), although many writers use 2 instead of 2.04, a better practical value seems to be 2.15.

[2] L. F. Moody, Some Pipe Characteristics of Engineering Interest, *Houille Blanche*, May–June, 1950.

20 cfs. Determine the centerline velocity, the shear stress at the wall of the pipe, and the velocity at 2 in. from center line.

The first step is to determine whether the flow is laminar or turbulent.

$$V = \frac{Q}{A} = \frac{2}{0.196} = 10.2 \text{ fps}$$

$$N_R = \frac{DV\rho}{\mu} = \frac{0.5(10.2)(0.9 \times 1.94)}{0.0008} = 11,100$$

Since $N_R > 2,000$, the flow is turbulent. Using Eq. (8.12), the friction factor can be found:

$$f = \frac{h_L D(2g)}{lV^2} = \frac{25(0.5)64.4}{200(10.2)^2} = 0.039$$

From Eq. (8.30),

$$u_{max} = V(1 + 1.326 \sqrt{f}) = 12.9 \text{ fps}$$

Equation (8.15) yields

$$\tau_0 = \frac{f\rho V^2}{8} = \frac{0.039(0.9 \times 1.94)(10.2)^2}{8} = 0.89 \text{ psf}$$

Finally,

$$u_{2 \text{ in.}} = 12.9 - 5.75 \sqrt{\frac{\tau_0}{\rho}} \log_{10} {}^3\!/_1$$

$$u_{2 \text{ in.}} = 12.9 - 1.96 = 10.94 \text{ fps}$$

Note that if the flow had been laminar, the velocity profile would have been parabolic and the centerline velocity would have been twice the average velocity.

8.11. PIPE ROUGHNESS

Unfortunately, there is as yet no scientific way of measuring or specifying the roughness of commercial pipes. Several experimenters have worked with pipes with artificial roughness produced by various means so that the roughness could be measured and described by geometrical factors, and it has been proved that the friction is dependent not only upon the size and shape of the projections, but also upon their distribution or spacing. Much remains to be done before this problem is completely solved.

The most noteworthy efforts in this direction have been made by a German engineer Nikuradse, a student of Prandtl's. He coated several different sizes of pipe with sand grains which had been segregated by sieving so as to obtain different sizes of grain of reasonably uniform diameters. The diameters of the sand grains may be represented by ϵ, which is known as the *absolute* roughness. In Sec. 8.4 dimensional analysis of pipe flow showed that for a smooth-walled pipe the friction factor f is a function of Reynolds number. A general approach, including ϵ as a parameter, reveals that $f = \phi(N_R, \epsilon/D)$. The term ϵ/D is known as the *relative* roughness. In his experimental work Nikuradse had values of ϵ/D ranging from 0.000985 to 0.0333.

In the case of artificial roughness such as this, the roughness is uniform, whereas in commercial pipes it is irregular both in size and in distribution. However, the roughness of commercial pipe may be described by ϵ, which means that the pipe has the same value of f at a high Reynolds number that would be obtained if the pipe were coated with sand grains of a uniform size ϵ.

For pipes it has been found that if $\delta' > 1.7\epsilon$, the laminar sublayer completely submerges the effect of ϵ. Von Kármán, using information from Eq. (8.28) and data from Nikuradse's experiments, developed an equation for friction factor for such a case:

$$\frac{1}{\sqrt{f}} = 2 \log_{10} N_R \sqrt{f} - 0.8 \qquad (8.33)$$

This equation applies to any pipe as long as $\delta' > 1.7\epsilon$; when this condition prevails, the flow is known as *smooth flow*. The equation has been found to be reliable for smooth pipes for all values of N_R over 4,000. For such pipes, i.e., drawn tubing, brass, glass, etc., it can be extrapolated with confidence for values of N_R far beyond any present experimental values because it is functionally correct, assuming wall surface so smooth that projections do not pierce the laminar sublayer, which becomes increasingly thinner with increasing N_R. That this is so is evident from the fact that the formula yields a value of $f = 0$ for $N_R = \infty$. This is in accord with the facts because N_R is infinite for a fluid of zero viscosity, and for such a case f must be zero.

Blasius[1] has shown that for Reynolds numbers between 3,000 and 100,000 the friction factor for a very smooth pipe may be expressed approximately as

$$f = \frac{0.316}{N_R^{0.25}} \qquad (8.34)$$

He also found that over this range of Reynolds numbers the velocity profile in a smooth pipe is closely approximated by the expression

$$\frac{u}{u_{\max}} = \left(\frac{y}{r_0}\right)^{1/7} \qquad (8.35)$$

where $y = r_0 - r$, the distance from the pipe wall. This equation is commonly referred to as the *seventh-root law* for turbulent-velocity distribu-

---

[1] H. Blasius, Das Ähnlichkeitsgesetz bei Reibungsvorgängen in Flüssigkeiten, *Forsch. Gebiete Ingenieurw.*, vol. 131, 1913.

tion.   Though it is not absolutely accurate, it is useful because it is easy to work with mathematically.

At high Reynolds numbers δ' becomes smaller.   If $\delta' < 0.08\epsilon$, it has been found that the pipe behaves as a *wholly* rough pipe; i.e., its friction factor is independent of the Reynolds number.   For such a case von Kármán found that the friction factor could be expressed as

$$\frac{1}{\sqrt{f}} = 2 \log_{10} \frac{D}{\epsilon} + 1.14 \tag{8.36}$$

The values of f from this equation correspond to the values from the chart (Fig. 8.10), where the lines become horizontal.

In the gap where $1.7\epsilon > \delta' > 0.08\epsilon$ neither smooth flow [Eq. (8.33)] nor wholly rough flow [Eq. (8.36)] applies.   Colebrook[1] found that in this intermediate range an approximate relationship was

$$\frac{1}{\sqrt{f}} = -2 \log_{10} \left(\frac{\epsilon/D}{3.7} + \frac{2.51}{N_R \sqrt{f}} \right) \tag{8.37}$$

8.12. CHART FOR FRICTION FACTOR

As the preceding equations for f are very inconvenient for use, it is preferable to obtain numerical values from a chart, such as Fig. 8.10, prepared by Moody.   This chart is based on the best information available and has been plotted with the aid of the dimensionally correct equations of the preceding section.

As a matter of convenience, values for air and water at 60°F have been placed at the top of the chart to save the necessity of computing Reynolds number for those two typical cases.   For water at 60°F, $N_R = 6,839 \times$ diameter in inches $\times$ velocity in feet per second.   For air at 60°F and atmospheric pressure, $N_R = 527.4 \times$ diameter in inches $\times$ velocity in feet per second.

The chart shows that there are four zones: laminar flow; a critical range where values are uncertain because the flow might be either laminar or turbulent; a transition zone, where f is a function of both Reynolds number and relative pipe roughness; and a zone of complete turbulence where the value of f is independent of Reynolds number and depends solely upon the relative roughness.

There is no sharp line of demarcation between the transition zone and the zone of complete turbulence.   Moody has divided them by a dashed

---

[1] C. F. Colebrook, Turbulent Flow in Pipes, with Particular Reference to the Transition Region between the Smooth and Rough Pipe Laws, *J. Inst. Civil Engrs. (London)*, February, 1939.

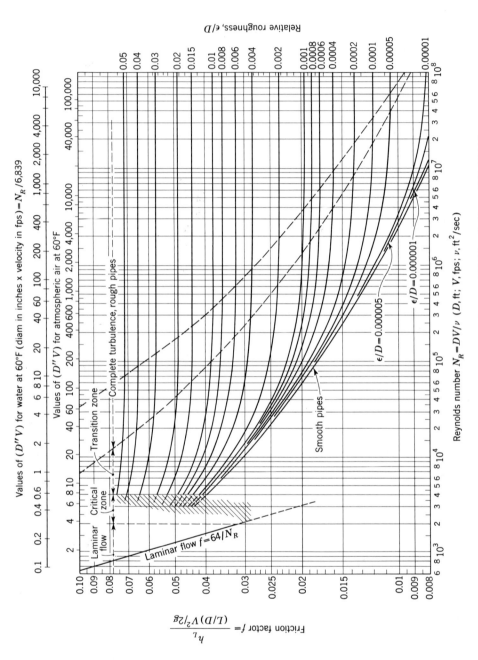

Fig. 8.10. Friction factor for pipes. (*From Lewis F. Moody, Trans. ASME, vol. 66, p. 672, 1944.*)

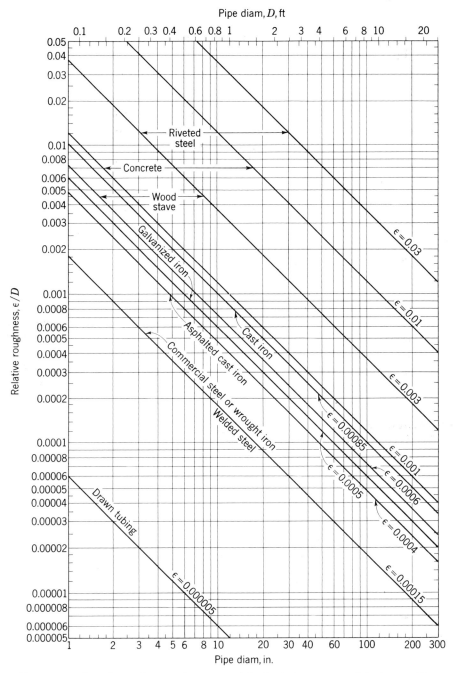

Fig. 8.11. Roughness factors (ϵ expressed in feet) for commercial pipes. (*From Lewis F. Moody, Trans. ASME, vol. 66, p. 673, 1944.*)

line, but the one to its right has been suggested by R. J. S. Pigott, for which he has given the very simple relation that

$$N_R = \frac{3,500}{\epsilon/D}$$

For use with this chart, values of ϵ may be obtained from Table 8.1. As the ratio ϵ/D is dimensionless, any units may be used provided they are the same for both. Values of ϵ/D for commercial pipe may conveniently be found from Fig. 8.11, which has also been prepared by Moody. In the use of these charts, as well as in Eq. (8.12), the exact value of the internal diameter of the pipe should be used. Except in large sizes, these values differ somewhat from the nominal sizes, and especially so in the case of very small pipes.

With reference to the values of ϵ, it must be observed that these are given here for new, clean pipes, and even in such cases there may be considerable variation in the values. Consequently, in practical cases, the value of f may be in error by ± 5 per cent for smooth pipes and by ± 10 per cent for rough ones. For old pipes values of ϵ may be much higher, but there is much variation in the degree with which pipe roughness increases with age, since so much depends upon the nature of the fluid being transported. In small pipes there is the added factor that deposits materially reduce the internal diameter. Hence much judgment must be used in estimating a value of ϵ, and consequently of f.

For complete turbulence, where the friction is directly proportional to V^2 and independent of Reynolds number, values of f may be determined

Table 8.1   Values of absolute roughness ϵ for new pipes

	Feet	Inches
Drawn tubing, brass, lead, glass, centrifugally spun cement, bituminous lining, transite...	0.000005	0.00006
Commercial steel or wrought iron..........	0.00015	0.0018
Welded-steel pipe......................	0.00015	0.0018
Asphalt-dipped cast iron.................	0.0004	0.0048
Galvanized iron........................	0.0005	0.006
Cast iron, average.....................	0.00085	0.0102
Wood stave............................	0.0006 to 0.003	0.0072 to 0.036
Concrete..............................	0.001 to 0.01	0.012 to 0.12
Riveted steel.........................	0.003 to 0.03	0.036 to 0.36

Note: $\dfrac{\epsilon}{D} = \dfrac{\epsilon \text{ in feet}}{D \text{ in feet}} = \dfrac{\epsilon \text{ in inches}}{\text{diameter in inches}}.$

for any assumed relative roughness. Most practical problems come within the transition zone, and there it is necessary to have also a definite value of Reynolds number. Hence, if the problem is to determine the friction loss for a given size of pipe with a given velocity, the solution is a direct one. But if the unknown quantities are either the diameter or the velocity or both, the Reynolds number is unknown. However, the value of f changes very slowly with large changes in Reynolds number; so the problem may readily be solved by assuming either a Reynolds number or a value of f to start with and then obtaining the final solution by trial. Since f will generally have a value between 0.01 and 0.07, it is best to assume f initially and work from there (Illustrative Example 8.2). Only one or two trials will usually suffice. This procedure is practically the only one that can be employed where other losses in addition to pipe friction enter into the problem.[1]

Illustrative example 8.2: For the conditions of Illustrative Example 8.1, determine the absolute roughness ϵ for the pipe and compute the thickness δ' of the true laminar sublayer. Also determine the friction factor of this pipe at very high Reynolds numbers.

Referring to Fig. 8.10, the chart indicates an ϵ/D value of 0.007 for $N_R = 11,100$ and $f = 0.039$. Thus

$$\epsilon = 0.007D = 0.042 \text{ in.}$$

$$\delta' = \frac{14.12\nu}{V\sqrt{f}} = \frac{14.12(0.0008)}{10.2\sqrt{0.039}\,(0.9 \times 1.94)} = 0.0032 \text{ ft} = 0.038 \text{ in.}$$

At very high Reynolds numbers the chart indicates that $f = 0.034$. This value may be verified by application of Eq. (8.36).

8.13. PIPE FRICTION IN NONCIRCULAR CONDUITS

Most pipes used in engineering practice are of circular cross section; however, rectangular ducts and cross sections of other geometry are occasionally used. Some of the foregoing equations may be modified for application to noncircular sections by use of the hydraulic-radius concept.

The hydraulic radius was defined (Sec. 8.3) as $R = A/P$, where A is the cross-sectional area and P is the wetted perimeter. For a circular pipe flowing full,

$$R = \frac{A}{P} = \frac{\pi D^2/4}{\pi D} = \frac{D}{4} \tag{8.38}$$

or
$$D = 4R \tag{8.39}$$

---

[1] Charts involving these same functional relations may be plotted with different coordinates from those in Fig. 8.10 and may be more convenient for certain specific purposes, but it is believed that the form shown is best both for instruction purposes and for general use.

These values may be substituted into Eq. (8.12) and into the expression for Reynolds number.   Thus

$$h_L = \frac{f}{4} \frac{l}{R} \frac{V^2}{2g} \tag{8.40}$$

$$N_R = \frac{(4R)V\rho}{\mu} \tag{8.41}$$

From these two expressions the head loss in noncircular conduits can be calculated by use of Fig. 8.10, where ϵ/D is replaced by $\epsilon/4R$.   This approach gives good results for turbulent flow, but for laminar flow the results are poor, because in such flow frictional phenomena are caused by viscous action throughout the body of the fluid, while in turbulent flow the frictional effect is accounted for largely by the region close to the wall; i.e., it depends on the wetted perimeter.

8.14. EMPIRICAL EQUATIONS FOR PIPE FLOW

The presentation of friction loss in pipes given in Secs. 8.1 to 8.12 incorporates the best knowledge available on this subject, as far as the application to fluids in general is concerned.   Admittedly, however, the trial-and-error type of solution, especially when encumbered with computations for relative roughness and Reynolds number, becomes tedious when repeated often for similar conditions, as with a single fluid such as water. It is natural, therefore, that certain empirical design formulas have been developed, applicable only to specialized fluids and conditions but very convenient in the specified range.   Perhaps the best example of such a formula is that of Hazen and Williams, applicable only to the flow of water in pipes larger than 2 in. and at velocities less than 10 fps, but widely used in the waterworks industry.   This formula was designed for flow in both pipes and open channels and is given in the form

$$V = 1.318C_1R^{0.63}S^{0.54} \tag{8.42}$$

where R is the hydraulic radius (Sec. 8.3), and $S = h_L/L$, the slope of the hydraulic grade line.   The advantage of this formula over the standard pipe-friction formula is that the roughness coefficient C_1 is not a function of the Reynolds number and trial solutions are therefore eliminated. Values of C_1 range from 140 for very smooth, straight pipe down to 110 for new riveted-steel and vitrified pipe and to 90 or 80 for old and tuberculated pipe.

Another empirical formula, which will be discussed in detail in the next chapter, is the Manning formula,

$$V = \frac{1.486}{n} R^{2/3}S^{1/2} \tag{8.43}$$

where n is a roughness coefficient, varying from 0.009 for the smoothest brass or glass pipe, to 0.014 for average drainage tile or vitrified sewer pipe, to 0.021 for corrugated iron, and up to 0.035 for tuberculated cast-iron pipe. The Manning formula applies to about the same flow range as does the Hazen-Williams formula.

Nomographic charts and diagrams have been developed for the application of Eqs. (8.42) and (8.43). The attendant lack of high accuracy is not important in the design of water-distribution systems, since it is seldom possible to predict the capacity requirements with any significant accuracy.

8.15. MINOR LOSSES

Losses due to the *local* disturbances of the flow in conduits such as projecting gaskets, elbows, valves, and similar items are called *minor* losses. In the case of a very long pipe or channel, these other losses are usually insignificant in comparison with the friction in the length considered. But if the length of pipe or channel is very short, these so-called minor losses may actually be major losses. Thus, in the case of the suction pipe of a pump, the loss of head at entrance, especially if a strainer and a foot valve are installed, may be very much greater than the friction loss in the short inlet pipe.

Whenever the velocity of a flowing stream is altered either in direction or in magnitude, eddy currents are set up and create a loss of energy in excess of the pipe friction in that same length. The magnitude of this localized loss is proportional to the abruptness of the velocity change. Though the disturbing factor is usually confined to a very short length of path, the effects may not disappear for a considerable distance downstream. Thus an elbow in a pipe may occupy only a small length but the disturbance in the flow will extend for a long distance downstream.

The most common sources of minor loss are described in the remainder of this chapter. Such losses may be represented in one of two ways. They may be expressed as $kV^2/2g$, where k must be determined for each case, or they may be represented as being equivalent to a certain length of straight pipe, usually expressed in terms of the number of pipe diameters.

8.16. LOSS OF HEAD AT ENTRANCE

Referring to Fig. 8.12, it may be seen that, as fluid from the reservoir enters the pipe, the streamlines tend to converge, much as though this were a jet issuing from a sharp-edged orifice, so that at B a maximum velocity and a minimum pressure are found. At B the central stream is surrounded by fluid which is in a state of turbulence but has very little

forward motion.   Between B and C the fluid is in a very disturbed condition because the stream expands and the velocity decreases while the
pressure rises.   From C to D the flow is normal.

It is seen that the loss of energy at entrance is distributed along the
length AC, a distance of several diameters.   The increased turbulence
and vortex motion in this portion of the pipe cause the friction loss to be
much greater than in a corresponding length where the flow is normal, as
is shown by the drop of the total-energy line.   Of this total loss, a portion
h' would be due to the normal pipe friction.   Hence the difference between
this and the total, or h_e', is the true value of the extra loss caused at
entrance.

It is apparent that at section C the pressure head is less than the
static pressure head in the reservoir by an amount equal to the velocity
head acquired plus the total friction loss in AC.

The entrance loss is caused primarily by the turbulence created by
the enlargement of the stream after it passes section B, and this enlargement in turn depends upon how much the stream contracts as it enters
the pipe.   Thus it is very much affected by the conditions at the entrance
to the pipe.   Values of the entrance-loss coefficients have been determined experimentally.   If the entrance to the pipe is well rounded or
bell-mouthed (Fig. 8.13a), there is no contraction of the stream entering
and the coefficient of loss is correspondingly small.   In fact it is less than
0.1 and is often assumed to be about 0.04, or even neglected altogether.
A conical entrance with a total included angle of between 30 and 60°
gives an entrance loss of about $0.18V^2/2g$, where V is the mean velocity

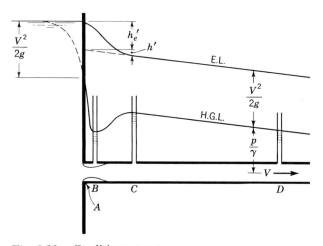

Fig. 8.12.   Conditions at entrance.

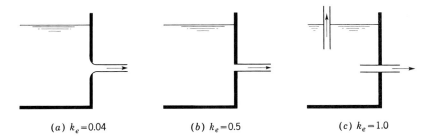

(a) $k_e = 0.04$ (b) $k_e = 0.5$ (c) $k_e = 1.0$

Fig. 8.13. Entrance losses.

in the pipe itself. For a flush entrance, such as shown in Fig. 8.13b, k_e has a value of about 0.5. A reentrant tube, such as shown in Fig. 8.13c, produces a maximum contraction of the entering stream because the streamlines come from around the outside wall of the pipe, as well as more directly from the fluid in front of the entrance. The degree of the contraction depends upon how far the pipe may project within the reservoir and also upon how thick the pipe walls are, compared with its diameter. With very thick walls, the conditions approach that of a flush entrance. For these reasons the loss coefficients for reentrant tubes vary, generally having a value of about 0.8.

Thus the loss of head at entrance may be expressed as

$$h_e' = k_e \frac{V^2}{2g} \tag{8.44}$$

where V is the mean velocity in the pipe, and k_e is the loss coefficient whose general values are shown in Fig. 8.13.

8.17. LOSS OF HEAD AT DISCHARGE

When a fluid with a velocity V is discharged from the end of a pipe into a reservoir which is so large that the velocity within it is negligible, the entire kinetic energy of the stream is dissipated. Hence the discharge loss is

$$h_d' = \frac{V^2}{2g} \tag{8.45}$$

That this is true may be shown by writing an energy equation between (a) and (c) in Fig. 8.14. Taking the datum plane through (a) and recognizing that the pressure head of the fluid at (a) is y, its depth below the surface, $H_a = y + 0 + V^2/2g$ and $H_c = 0 + y + 0$. Therefore

$$h_d' = H_a - H_c = \frac{V^2}{2g}$$

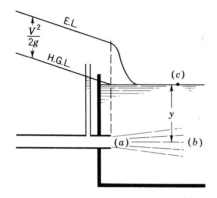

Fig. 8.14.   Discharge loss.

The discharge loss coefficient is 1.0 under all conditions; hence the only way to reduce the discharge loss is to reduce the value of V by means of a diverging tube.   This is the reason for a diverging draft tube from a reaction turbine (Sec. 16.6).

As contrasted with entrance loss, it must here be emphasized that discharge loss occurs *after* the fluid *leaves* the pipe,[1] while entrance loss occurs *after* the fluid *enters* the pipe.

8.18. LOSS DUE TO CONTRACTION

Sudden contraction.   The phenomena attending the sudden contraction of a flow are shown in Fig. 8.15.   There is a marked drop in pressure due both to the increase in velocity and to the loss of energy in turbulence.   It is noted that in the corner upstream at section C there is a rise in pressure because the streamlines here are curving, so that the centrifugal action causes the pressure at the pipe wall to be greater than in the center of the stream.   The dashed line indicates the pressure variation along the centerline streamline from sections B to C.

From C to E the conditions are similar to those described for entrance. The loss of head may be represented by

$$h_c' = k_c \frac{V_2^2}{2g} \tag{8.46}$$

where k_c has the values given in Table 8.2.

Table 8.2

D_2/D_1	0.0	0.1	0.2	0.3	0.4	0.5	0.6	0.7	0.8	0.9	1.0
k_c	0.50	0.45	0.42	0.39	0.36	0.33	0.28	0.22	0.15	0.06	0.00

[1] In a short pipe where the discharge loss may be a major factor, it might be well to use the correction factor α, as explained in Sec. 4.1 [see also Eq. (8.32)].

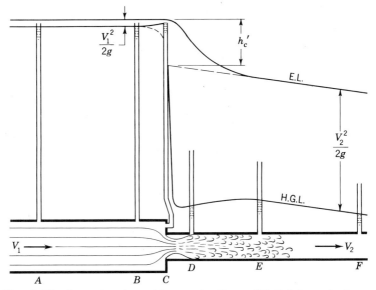

Fig. 8.15. Loss due to sudden contraction. (*Plotted to scale from observations made by Daugherty.*)

The entrance loss of Sec. 8.16 is a special case where $D_2/D_1 = 0$.

Gradual contraction. In order to reduce the foregoing losses, abrupt changes of cross section should be avoided. Inspection of Fig. 8.15 shows that the principal cause of loss is due to the contraction of the stream as it enters the smaller pipe. This may be prevented by changing from one diameter to the other by means of the smooth curve AC of Fig. 8.16. With this construction there will be no additional loss in the

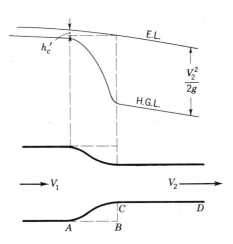

Fig. 8.16. Loss due to gradual contraction.

length CD. However, because of the higher average velocity in the portion AC, there will be a greater loss than in the same length of pipe of the original diameter. This loss is identical with that in a nozzle of the same form as the portion AC and is practically negligible. Ordinarily, it will be about $0.04V_2{}^2/2g$ or even less.

For ease in manufacture the curved portion AC of Fig. 8.16 may be replaced with a frustum of a cone. Such a geometry will result in a somewhat higher head loss. If the angle of the cone is too great, the conditions of sudden contraction will be approached, because of the tendency of the streamlines to converge downstream from C. On the other hand, if the angle of the cone is too small, the distance AB will be unduly large, and since the average velocity in this conical section will be higher than that in the larger straight pipe, the friction loss in the reducer will be somewhat greater than in the length of straight pipe which it replaces. A total angle of 20 to 40° is about the proper amount of taper for a converging conical section. The head loss for such a case is about $0.1V_2{}^2/2g$.

In converging flow, as in Fig. 8.16, the conversion of pressure into kinetic energy is a very efficient process.

8.19. LOSS DUE TO ENLARGEMENT

Sudden enlargement. The conditions at a section of sudden enlargement are shown in Fig. 8.17. There is a rise in pressure because

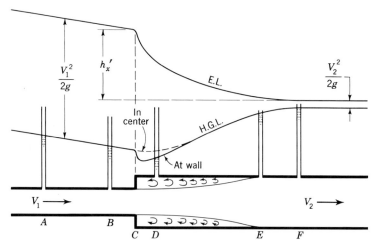

Fig. 8.17. Loss due to sudden enlargement. (*Plotted to scale from observations made by Daugherty. Velocity the same as in Fig. 8.15.*)

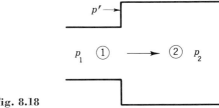

Fig. 8.18

of the decrease in velocity, but this rise is not so great as it would be if it were not for the loss in energy. There is a state of excessive turbulence from C to F beyond which the flow is normal. The drop in pressure just beyond section C, which was measured by a piezometer not shown in the illustration, is due to the fact that the pressures at the wall of the pipe are in this case less than those in the center of the pipe.

Figures 8.15 and 8.17 are both drawn to scale from test measurements for the same diameter ratios and the same velocities and show that the loss due to sudden expansion is greater than the loss due to a corresponding contraction.

An expression for the loss of head in a sudden enlargement can be derived as follows. In Fig. 8.18, section (2) corresponds to section F in Fig. 8.17, which is a section where the velocity profile has become normal again and marks the end of the region of excess energy loss due to the turbulence created by the sudden enlargement. In Fig. 8.18 assume that the pressure at (2) in the ideal case without friction is p_0. Then in this ideal case

$$\frac{p_0}{\gamma} = \frac{p_1}{\gamma} + \frac{V_1^2}{2g} - \frac{V_2^2}{2g}$$

If in the actual case the pressure at (2) is p_2 while the average pressure on the annular ring is p', then, equating the resultant force on the body of fluid between (1) and (2) to the time rate of change of momentum between (1) and (2), we obtain

$$p_1 A_1 + p'(A_2 - A_1) - p_2 A_2 = \frac{\gamma}{g}(A_2 V_2^2 - A_1 V_1^2)$$

From this $$\frac{p_2}{\gamma} = \frac{A_1}{A_2}\frac{p_1}{\gamma} + \frac{A_2 - A_1}{A_2}\frac{p'}{\gamma} + \frac{A_1}{A_2}\frac{V_1^2}{g} - \frac{V_2^2}{g}$$

The loss of head is $h_x' = (p_0 - p_2)/\gamma$, and noting that

$$A_1 V_1 = A_2 V_2$$

and that $A_1V_1{}^2 = A_1V_1V_1 = A_2V_2V_1$, we obtain

$$h_x' = \frac{(V_1 - V_2)^2}{2g} + \left(1 - \frac{A_1}{A_2}\right)\left(\frac{p_1}{\gamma} - \frac{p'}{\gamma}\right)$$

It is usually assumed that $p' = p_1$, in which case the loss of head due to sudden enlargement is

$$h_x' = \frac{(V_1 - V_2)^2}{2g} \tag{8.47}$$

Although it is possible that under some conditions p' will equal p_1, it is also possible for it to be either more or less than that value, in which case the loss of head will be either less or more than that given by Eq. (8.47). The exact value of p' will depend upon the manner in which the fluid eddies around in the corner adjacent to this annular ring. However, the present information is that the deviation from Eq. (8.47) is quite small and of negligible importance.

The discharge loss of Sec. 8.17 is seen to be a special case where A_2 is infinite compared with A_1 or $V_2 = 0$, so that Eq. (8.47) will reduce to Eq. (8.45).

Gradual enlargement. To minimize the loss accompanying a reduction in velocity, a diffuser such as shown in Fig. 8.19 may be used. The diffuser may be given a curved outline, or it may be a frustum of a cone. In Fig. 8.19 the loss of head will be some function of the angle of divergence and also of the ratio of the two areas, the length of the diffuser being determined by these two variables.

In flow through a diffuser the total loss may be considered as made up of two factors. One is the ordinary pipe friction loss, which may be represented by

$$h_L = \int \frac{f}{D} \frac{V^2}{2g} \, dL$$

In order to integrate the foregoing, it is necessary to express the variables f, D, and V as functions of L. For our present purpose it is sufficient,

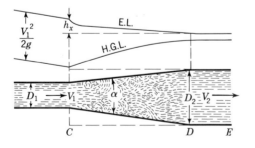

Fig. 8.19. Loss due to gradual enlargement.

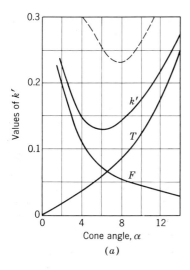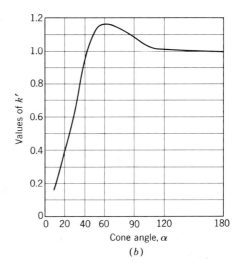

Fig. 8.20. Loss in conical diffuser.

however, merely to note that the friction loss increases with the length of the cone. Hence, for given values of D_1 and D_2, the larger the angle of the cone, the less its length and the less the pipe friction, which is indicated by the curve marked F in Fig. 8.20a. However, in flow through a diffuser, there is an additional turbulence loss set up by induced currents which produce a vortex motion over and above that which normally exists. This additional turbulence loss will naturally increase with the degree of divergence, as is indicated by the curve marked T in Fig. 8.20a, and if the rate of divergence is great enough, there may be a separation at the walls and eddies flowing backward along the walls. The total loss in the diverging cone is then represented by the sum of these two losses, marked k'. This is seen to have a minimum value at 6° for the particular case chosen, which is for a very smooth surface. If the surface were rougher, the value of the friction F would be increased. This increases the value of k', which is indicated by the dotted curve, and also shifts the angle for minimum loss to 8°. Thus the best angle of divergence increases with the roughness of the surface.

It has been found that the excess turbulence loss, produced by secondary or induced currents, is independent of the roughness of the surface of the cone. But it is a function of the viscosity of the fluid. The higher the viscosity, the less the amount of eddying in the fluid and the lower the value of T. But with a higher viscosity, the normal pipe friction F would be greater, and thus the best angle of divergence increases with an increase of viscosity.

It has been seen that the loss due to a sudden enlargement is very nearly represented by $(V_1 - V_2)^2/2g$. The loss due to a gradual enlargement is expressed as

$$h' = k' \frac{(V_1 - V_2)^2}{2g} \tag{8.48}$$

Values of k' as a function of the cone angle α are shown in Fig. 8.20b, for a wider range than appears in (a).[1] It is of interest to note that at an angle slightly above 40° the loss is the same as that for a sudden enlargement, which is 180°, and that between these two the loss is greater than for a sudden enlargement, being a maximum at about 60°. This is because the induced currents set up are worse within this range.

Converging flow where pressure is being converted into kinetic energy is stable, and the process is efficient. Diverging flow where kinetic energy is being transformed back into pressure is inherently unstable, subject to eddies and separation with much turbulence, and is inherently less efficient. Converging flow renders the velocity more uniform across a diameter; diverging flow increases the variation of velocity across a diameter.

8.20. LOSS IN PIPE FITTINGS

The loss of head in pipe fittings may be expressed as $kV^2/2g$, where V is the velocity in a pipe of the nominal size of the fitting. Typical values of k are given in Table 8.3. If preferred, the actual pipe length may be increased by values obtained from the L/D ratios given in the table. However, it must be recognized that these fittings create so much turbulence that the loss caused by them is proportional to V^2, and hence this latter method should be restricted to the case where the pipe friction itself is in the zone of complete turbulence. For very smooth pipes, it is better to use the k values when determining the loss through fittings.

8.21. LOSS IN BENDS AND ELBOWS

In flow around a bend or elbow there is an increase in pressure along the outer wall and a decrease in pressure along the inner wall. As the normal velocity and pressure distribution are approached downstream, the inner wall pressure must rise again. Since the velocity is zero, it cannot

[1] A. H. Gibson, *Engineering* (*London*), Feb. 16, 1912. These values were based on area ratios of 1:9, 1:4, 1:2.25 and gave one curve up to an angle of about 30°. Beyond that the three ratios gave three curves which differed as much as about 18 per cent at 60°, where the turbulence was a predominating factor, and then drew together again as 180° was approached. The curve here shown is a composite of these three.

*Table 8.3   Values of loss factors for pipe fittings**

Fitting	k	L/D
Globe valve, wide open............	10	350
Angle valve, wide open............	5	175
Close return bend................	2.2	75
T, through side outlet.............	1.8	67
Short-radius elbow...............	0.9	32
Medium-radius elbow.............	0.75	27
Long-radius elbow...............	0.60	20
45° elbow......................	0.42	15
Gate valve, wide open...........	0.19	7

* Flow of Fluids through Valves, Fittings, and Pipe, *Crane Co., Tech. Paper* 409, p. 20, May, 1942. Values based on tests by Crane Co. and at the University of Wisconsin, the University of Texas, and Texas College.

decrease to provide for a pressure increase, and hence there may be separation (Figs. 3.12 and 13.7) from the inner wall.

The result of the unbalanced condition is to produce a secondary flow, as shown in Fig. 8.21. This combines with the axial velocity to form a double spiral flow which persists for some distance. Thus not only is there some loss of energy within the bend itself, but this distorted flow condition persists for some distance downstream until dissipated by viscous friction. Thus the velocity in the pipe may not become normal again within as much as 100 pipe diameters downstream from the bend. In fact, more than half the friction loss produced by a bend or elbow takes place in the straight pipe following it.

Most of the loss of head in a sharp bend may be eliminated by the use of a vaned elbow, such as is shown in Fig. 8.22. The vanes prevent much

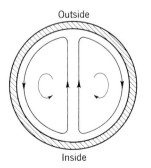

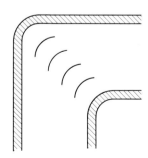

Fig. 8.21. Secondary flow in bend.

Fig. 8.22. Vaned elbow.

of the velocity-profile distortion and the secondary flow that would otherwise occur.

The loss produced by a bend is greatly dependent upon the ratio of the radius of curvature to the diameter of the pipe, and combinations of different pipe bends placed close together cannot be treated by adding up the losses of each one considered separately. The total loss depends not only upon the spacing between the bends, but also upon the relations of the directions of the bends and the planes in which they are located.

The problem of the friction loss produced by a bend is complicated, and much work has yet to be done before it is placed upon a certain and systematic basis. Pigott has proposed the following formula for k_b in the expression $k_b V^2/2g$ to express the head loss due to a 90° bend, to which must be added the friction in the length of pipe occupied by the bend.[1]

$$ k_b = 0.106 \left(\frac{R}{D}\right)^{-2.5} + 2,000f^{2.5} \tag{8.49} $$

where R is the radius of curvature of the bend and D is the diameter of the pipe, both in the same units. As f is a function of Reynolds number for the pipe, this makes the friction loss in the bend also a function of N_R.

For cast 90° elbows, $R/D = 0.58$ for short-radius elbows and 1.78 for long-radius elbows. The bend loss is nearly proportional to the angle of the bend for steel pipe and drawn tubing, but for cast-iron 45° elbows, it is 60 per cent of the value for a 90° elbow, and for a return bend, that is, 180°, it is 140 per cent of the value for a 90° elbow.

8.22. SOLUTION OF PIPE - FLOW PROBLEMS

We have examined the fundamental fluid mechanics associated with the frictional loss of energy in pipe flow. While the interest of the scientist extends very little beyond this, it is the task of the engineer to apply these fundamentals to various types of practical problem. Pipe-flow problems may be classified according to whether the solution may be obtained by direct computation or whether it requires a trial-and-error procedure. In the direct-solution problem the size, length, and roughness of the pipe are given, together with the rate of discharge. The head loss may be found by application of the pipe-friction equation, together with consideration of minor losses. This determines the slope of the energy grade line and such quantities as the water-surface elevation in one or more reservoirs.

The indirect-solution problems are of two principal types: (1) given pipe lengths, diameters, and head loss, find the flow; and (2) given the

---

[1] R. J. S. Pigott, Pressure Losses in Tubing, Pipe, and Fittings, *Trans. ASME*, vol. 72, p. 679, July, 1950.

flow and the hydraulic gradient, find the required diameter.   The feature of these problems which requires the trial-and-error solution, of course, is the variation of the friction factor f with Reynolds number, as shown in Fig. 8.10.   As the latter involves the velocity, which is an unknown quantity in this case, the problem must be commenced by assuming a reasonable value of f.   Figure 8.10 shows that the value of f is closely bracketed by the relative roughness if it is known that the flow is in or near the zone of complete turbulence.   If this is not known or suspected, it may be helpful to consider a reasonable velocity, perhaps in the neighborhood of 5 to 10 fps for ordinary pipe flow, in order to obtain a first value of f. This will then lead, through the pipe-friction and energy equations, to a *computed* velocity and Reynolds number.   This determines a more accurate value of f, and it will generally be necessary to repeat the solution for new values of V and Q.   As f varies but little within a small range of N_R, a third trial will rarely be necessary.

The following example illustrates the method of solution for flow through a pipeline of uniform diameter.

Illustrative example 8.3:   Referring to Fig. 8.23, find the flow rate though a new 10-in.-diameter cast-iron pipe of length 5,000 ft, with $z_1 = 260$ ft.   Consider the entrance to be sharp-cornered, nonprojecting.

With no further information, we make the first choice of f based on a velocity of 8 fps in a 10-in. pipe.   With ϵ/D of 0.001 (from Fig. 8.11), we find $f = 0.020$ in Fig. 8.10.   From Sec. 8.16 we choose a value of $k_e = 0.5$ for the loss at entrance. Then, writing the energy equation between the water surface and the free jet,

$$0 + 260 + 0 = 0 + 0 + \frac{V_2{}^2}{2g} + \left(0.5 + 0.02 \times \frac{5,000}{10/12}\right) \frac{V_2{}^2}{2g}$$

This gives $V_2{}^2/2g = 2.14$ and $V_2 = 11.75$ fps.   We may now confirm the trial value of f by returning to Fig. 8.10, with $D''V = 10 \times 11.75 = 117.5$ and $\epsilon/D = 0.001$. Again, the chart shows $f = 0.020$, so no repeat solution is required, even though the first assumption of velocity was little more than half the final value.   The flow is $Q = A_2 V_2 = 0.545 \times 11.75 = 6.40$ cfs.

In the foregoing example it may be seen that with this length of pipe it would have made very little difference if the entrance loss and also the velocity head at discharge had been neglected altogether.   It is generally conceded that, for pipes of length greater than 1,000 diameters, the error incurred by neglecting minor losses is less than that inherent in selecting a value of f.   In applying this rule one must of course use common sense and recall that a valve, for example, is a minor loss only when it is wide open.   Partially closed, it may be the most important loss in the system.

In case the pipe does not discharge into the air at (2) but the liquid there is under some pressure, the term for p_2/γ will not be zero as in the above example.   Thus the foregoing solution of a type 1 problem is perfectly general.

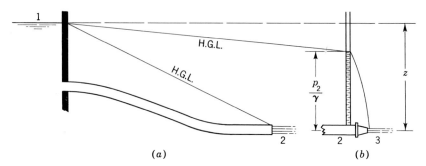

Fig. 8.23. Discharge from a reservoir. (*a*) Free discharge. (*b*) With nozzle.

Another example of flow from a reservoir is that of a penstock leading to an impulse turbine. In this case the pipe does not discharge freely but ends in a nozzle, which has a known or assumed loss coefficient. The head loss in the nozzle is associated with the high issuing velocity head and is therefore not a minor loss. The procedure is to employ the equation of continuity to place all losses in terms of the velocity head in the pipe. This is the logical choice for the "common unknown" because the trial-and-error solution will again be built around the pipe friction loss rather than the nozzle loss.

Illustrative example 8.4: In Fig. 8.23 suppose that the pipeline of the preceding example is now fitted with a nozzle at the end which discharges a jet 2.5 in. in diameter and which has a loss coefficient of 0.11. Find the flow rate. Let point (2) now refer to the pipe at the base of the nozzle and point (3) be in the jet. The head loss in the nozzle is $0.11 V_3{}^2/2g$. Writing the energy equation between (1) and (3), neglecting entrance loss,

$$0 + 260 + 0 = 0 + 0 + \frac{V_3{}^2}{2g} + 6{,}000f\,\frac{V_2{}^2}{2g} + 0.11\,\frac{V_3{}^2}{2g}$$

By the continuity equation, $V_3{}^2/2g = (10/2.5)^4 V_2{}^2/2g = 256 V_2{}^2/2g$. Thus

$$260 = (1.11 \times 256 + 6{,}000f)\,\frac{V_2{}^2}{2g}$$

A trial value of f is selected. Let $f = 0.02$ for the first assumption. Then $260 = (284 + 120)V_2{}^2/2g$, from which

$$\frac{V_2{}^2}{2g} = \frac{260}{404} = 0.644$$

and $V_2 = 8.02\,\sqrt{0.644} = 6.45$ fps. With $10 \times 6.45 = 64.5$ and $\epsilon/D \doteq 0.001$, Fig. 8.10 shows $f = 0.0203$. In this case the first solution may be considered sufficiently accurate, but in general the value of f determined from the chart may be materially different from that assumed, and a second trial may be necessary.

The rate of discharge is $Q = A_2 V_2 = 0.545 \times 6.45 = 3.52$ cfs, and

$$V_3 = 16 V_2 = 16 \times 6.45 = 103.2 \text{ fps}$$

As additional information, $H_2 = 260 - 0.02 \times 6{,}000 \times 0.644 = 182.72$ ft, and the pressure head $p_2/\gamma = 182.72 - 0.644 = 182.08$ ft.

This example shows that the addition of the nozzle has reduced the discharge but has given a much higher jet velocity.

We may change Illustrative Examples 8.3 and 8.4 into type 2 problems by specifying the rate of discharge and finding the required diameter. Although this type of problem can be attacked in exactly the same way as by the foregoing procedure, the solution is facilitated by a slightly different procedure if the length is so great that the minor losses are negligible. From the continuity equation, $V = Q/A = 4Q/\pi D^2$. Substituting this expression for V in the pipe-friction equation,

$$h_L = f \frac{L}{D} \frac{V^2}{2g}$$

and rearranging, we obtain

$$\frac{D^5}{f} = \frac{8LQ^2}{\pi^2 g h_L} = \text{constant} \tag{8.50}$$

A value of f may be assumed more or less arbitrarily and an approximate value of the pipe diameter computed by this equation. This determines the velocity, Reynolds number, and relative roughness. A new value of f is determined with the aid of Fig. 8.10, and the computation may be repeated if necessary. In general, the diameter so obtained will not be a standard pipe size, and the size selected will usually be the next largest commercially available size. In planning for the future capacities it must be recalled that scale deposits will increase the roughness and reduce the cross-sectional area. For pipes in water service, the absolute roughness ϵ of old pipes (twenty years and more) may increase over that of new pipes by threefold for concrete or cement-lined steel, up to twenty-fold for cast iron, and even to fortyfold for tuberculated wrought-iron and steel pipe.

If the minor losses and the velocity head in the pipe are not negligible in comparison with the pipe friction, the problem may be attacked by expressing such losses in equivalent lengths of pipe, if possible, and the solution reduces to the case just described. In considering problems of pipe size, it is important to realize that, for constant f, Q varies as $D^{5/2}$, or to achieve a 100 per cent increase in flow, the diameter need be increased only 32 per cent.

8.23. PIPELINE WITH PUMP OR TURBINE

If a pump lifts a fluid from one reservoir to another, as in Fig. 8.24, not only does it do work in lifting the fluid the height z, but also it has to

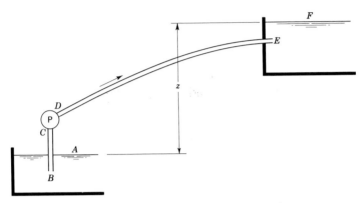

Fig. 8.24. Pipeline with pump between two reservoirs.

overcome the friction loss in the suction and discharge piping. This friction head is equivalent to some added lift, so that the effect is the same as if the pump lifted the fluid a height $z + \Sigma h_L$, without loss. Hence the power delivered to the liquid by the pump is $\gamma Q(z + \Sigma h_L)$. The power required to run the pump is greater than this, depending on the efficiency of the pump. The total pumping head h_p for this case is

$$h_p = z + \Sigma h_L \qquad (8.51)$$

If the pump discharges a stream through a nozzle, as shown in Fig. 8.25, not only has the liquid been lifted to a height z, but also it has received a kinetic energy head of $V_2^2/2g$, where V_2 is the velocity of the jet. Thus the total pumping head is now

$$h_p = z + \frac{V_2^2}{2g} + \Sigma h_L \qquad (8.52)$$

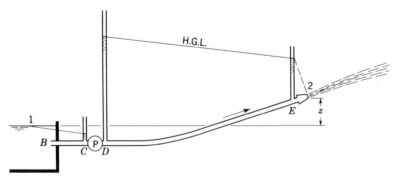

Fig. 8.25. Pipeline with pump and nozzle.

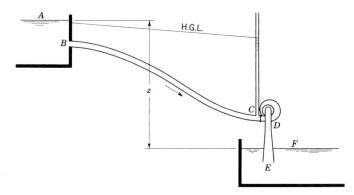

Fig. 8.26. Pipeline with turbine.

In any case the total pumping head may be determined by writing the energy equation between any point upstream from the pump and any other point downstream, as in Eq. (4.12). For example, if the upstream reservoir were at a higher elevation than the downstream one, then the z's in the two foregoing equations would have negative signs.

The machine that is employed for converting the energy of flow into mechanical work is called a *turbine*. In flowing from the upper tank in Fig. 8.26 to the lower, the fluid loses potential energy head equivalent to z. This energy is expended in two ways, part of it in hydraulic friction in the pipe and the remainder in the turbine. Of that which is delivered to the turbine, a portion is lost in hydraulic friction and the rest is converted into mechanical work.

The power delivered to the turbine is decreased by the friction loss in the pipeline, and its value is given by $\gamma Q(z - \Sigma h_L)$. The power delivered by the machine is less than this, depending upon both the hydraulic and mechanical losses of the turbine. The head under which the turbine operates is

$$h = z - \Sigma h_L \qquad (8.53)$$

where Σh_L is the loss of head in the supply pipe and does not include the head loss in the draft tube (DE in Fig. 8.26), since the draft tube is considered an integral part of the turbine. The draft tube has a gradually increasing cross-sectional area which results in a reduced velocity at discharge. This enhances the efficiency of the turbine because of the reduced head loss at discharge (Sec. 8.17). It should be noted that the h of Eq. (8.53) is equal and opposite to the h_t of Eq. (4.13). The h represents the energy head transferred to the turbine from the fluid, while h_t is the energy head removed from the fluid by the turbine.

Illustrative example 8.5: A pump is located 15 ft above the surface of a liquid ($\gamma = 52$ pcf) in a closed tank. The pressure in the space above the liquid surface is 5 psi. The suction line to the pump is 50 ft of 6-in.-diameter pipe ($f = 0.025$). The discharge from the pump is 200 ft of 8-in.-diameter pipe ($f = 0.030$). This pipe discharges in a submerged fashion to an open tank whose free liquid surface is 10-ft lower than the liquid surface in the pressure tank. If the pump puts 2.0 hp into the liquid, determine the flow rate and find the pressure in the pipe on the suction side of the pump.

From Eq. (4.14),

$$\text{HP} = \frac{\gamma Q h_p}{550} = 2 = \frac{52 Q h_p}{550}$$

Thus

$$h_p = \frac{21.2}{Q}$$

Writing the energy equation from one liquid surface to the other,

$$\frac{5(144)}{52} - 0.5 \frac{V_6{}^2}{2g} - 0.025 \left(\frac{50}{6/12}\right) \frac{V_6{}^2}{2g} + h_p - 0.030 \left(\frac{200}{8/12}\right) \frac{V_8{}^2}{2g} - \frac{V_8{}^2}{2g} = -10$$

This reduces to

$$23.9 + h_p - 2.48Q^2 = 0$$

or

$$23.9 + \frac{21.2}{Q} - 2.48Q^2 = 0$$

By trial,

$$Q = 3.48 \text{ cfs}$$

To obtain pressure at the suction side of the pump,

$$\frac{5(144)}{52} - 0.5 \frac{V_6{}^2}{2g} - 0.025 \left(\frac{50}{6/12}\right) \frac{V_6{}^2}{2g} = 15 + \frac{p}{\gamma} + \frac{V_6{}^2}{2g}$$

where

$$V_6 = \frac{3.48}{0.196} = 17.7 \text{ fps}$$

from which

$$\frac{p}{\gamma} = -20.5 \text{ ft}$$

In this type of problem one should check the absolute pressure against the vapor pressure of the liquid to see that vaporization does not occur.

8.24. BRANCHING PIPES

Suppose that three reservoirs A, B, and C of Fig. 8.27 are connected to a common junction J by pipes 1, 2, and 3, in which the friction losses are h_1, h_2, and h_3, respectively. It is supposed that all pipes are sufficiently long, so that minor losses and velocity heads may be neglected. Actually, any one of the pipes may be considered leading to or from some destination other than the reservoir shown by simply replacing the reservoir with a piezometer tube in which the water level is the same as that of the reservoir surface. The continuity and energy equations require that the flow entering the junction equal the flow leaving it and that the pressure head at J (which may be represented schematically by

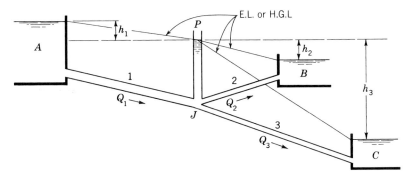

Fig. 8.27. Branching pipes.

the open piezometer shown, with water at elevation P) be common to all pipes. That is, for the condition shown:

1. $Q_1 = Q_2 + Q_3$.
2. Elevation P is common to all.

If P is below the surface of B, then the flow will be out of B and $Q_1 + Q_2 = Q_3$. The diagram suggests several problems, three of which will be discussed below:

1. Given all pipe lengths and diameters, the surface elevations of two reservoirs, and the flow from one, find the surface elevation of the third reservoir. This is a direct-solution problem. Suppose that Q_1 and the elevations of A and B are given. The head loss h_1 is determined directly by the pipe-friction equation, using Fig. 8.10 to determine the proper value of f. This fixes P and h_2. The flow in pipe 2 may then be determined, assuming a reasonable value of f and adjusting it if necessary. Condition 1 then determines Q_3, which in turn determines h_3 and the surface elevation of C.

2. Given all pipe lengths and diameters, the elevations of water surfaces of two reservoirs, and the flow to the third, find the elevation of the surface in the third reservoir. Suppose Q_2 and the surface elevations of A and C are given. Then the quantities $Q_1 - Q_3$ and $h_1 + h_3$ are known. These relations are solved simultaneously for their component parts in one of two ways: (a) by assuming successive distributions of the flows Q_1 and Q_2 satisfying the first relation, until a distribution is found which also satisfies the head-loss relation; (b) by assuming successive elevations of the piezometer level P, which is to say, distributions of h_1 and h_3 satisfying the second relation above, until a level is found which also satisfies the

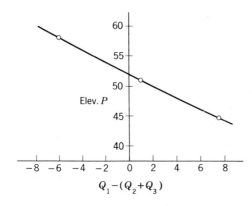

$$Q_1 - (Q_2 + Q_3)$$

Fig. 8.28

discharge relation. With P known and h_2 determined by the given discharge Q_2, the elevation of B is easily obtained.

3. Given all pipe lengths and diameters and the elevations of all three reservoirs, find the flow in each pipe. This is the classic *three-reservoir problem*, and it differs from the foregoing cases in that it is not immediately evident whether the flow is *into* or *out of* reservoir B. This direction is readily determined by first assuming no flow in pipe 2; that is, the piezometer level P is assumed at the elevation of the surface of B. The head losses h_1 and h_3 then determine the flows Q_1 and Q_3, and depending on whether $Q_1 > Q_3$ or $Q_1 < Q_3$, the condition of continuity is determined as $Q_1 = Q_2 + Q_3$ or $Q_1 + Q_2 = Q_3$, respectively. From this point the solution proceeds as in (*b*) of case 2 above. The piezometer level is moved up or down by trial until the resulting flow distribution satisfies the continuity relation. In reaching the final adjusted level it is helpful to make a small plot such as is shown in Fig. 8.28 for the case where $Q_1 = Q_2 + Q_3$. Two or three points, with one fairly close to the axis, determine a curve which intersects the vertical axis at the equilibrium level of P, that is, for the condition $Q_1 - (Q_2 + Q_3) = 0$.

8.25. PIPES IN SERIES

The discussion in Sec. 8.22 was restricted to the case of a single pipe. If the pipe is made up of sections of different diameters, as shown in Fig. 8.29, the continuity and energy equations establish the following two simple relations which must be satisfied:

$$Q = Q_1 = Q_2 = Q_3 \tag{8.54}$$

$$h_L = h_{L1} + h_{L2} + h_{L3} + \cdots \tag{8.55}$$

If the rate of discharge is given, the head loss may be found directly by adding the contributions from the various sections, as in Eq. (8.55). If the total head loss is given and the flow is required, the procedure is to write Eq. (8.55) for the head loss in each length in terms of the dimensions applying to it; i.e.,

$$h_L = f_1 \frac{L_1}{D_1} \frac{V_1^2}{2g} + f_2 \frac{L_2}{D_2} \frac{V_2^2}{2g} + \cdots$$

where the values of the friction factor f are chosen from Fig. 8.10 to be in the range of reasonable values for the given pipes. By the equation of continuity, the individual section losses may be expressed in terms of one of the velocity heads. When minor losses are to be included, these may also be placed as additive terms in Eq. (8.55) and expressed in terms of the same velocity head. Thus, for any pipeline, no matter how complex, the total loss of head may be written as

$$h_L = y \frac{V^2}{2g} \qquad (8.56)$$

This equation may now be solved for V, and then Q can be computed. For better accuracy the assumed values of f may be adjusted and a second solution obtained.

Another method of solving this problem is to place all pipes in terms of equivalent lengths of one given pipe size, usually the one which figures most prominently in the system. By equivalent length is meant a length L_e of pipe of a certain diameter D_e which for the same flow will give the same head loss as the pipe of length L and diameter D under consideration. Thus, from the pipe-friction and continuity equations,

$$L_e = L \frac{f}{f_e} \frac{D_e}{D} \frac{V^2/2g}{V_e^2/2g} = L \frac{f}{f_e} \left(\frac{D_e}{D} \right)^5 \qquad (8.57)$$

In case empirical formulas or pipe diagrams are being used, the equivalent

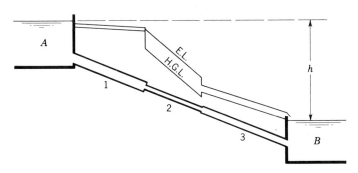

Fig. 8.29.   Compound pipes in series.

length is established by the relation $S = h_L/L$, or $L_e = L(S/S_e)$, where the values of the hydraulic slope are obtained for any assumed rate of discharge.

The equivalent-length method is especially useful where there are minor losses, such as bends, which are already expressed in terms of equivalent lengths of pipe. The compound-pipe problem is then reduced to that of a single pipe of a certain total length, and it may be solved by the methods previously outlined.

Illustrative example 8.6: Suppose that, in Fig. 8.29, pipes 1, 2, and 3 are 1,000 ft of 12 in., 500 ft of 8 in., and 800 ft of 10 in., respectively, of new cast iron. If $h = 30$ ft, find the rate of flow Q from A to B.

(a) *By the equivalent-velocity-head method.* From Fig. 8.11, $\epsilon/D = 0.00085$, 0.0013, and 0.001 for pipes 1, 2, and 3, and from Fig. 8.10 we may assume $f_1 = 0.019$, $f_2 = 0.021$, and $f_3 = 0.020$. Then

$$30 = 0.019 \left(\frac{1{,}000}{1}\right)\frac{V_1{}^2}{2g} + 0.021 \left(\frac{500 \times 12}{8}\right)\frac{V_2{}^2}{2g} + 0.020 \left(\frac{800 \times 12}{10}\right)\frac{V_3{}^2}{2g}$$

From continuity, $\dfrac{V_2{}^2}{2g} = \dfrac{V_1{}^2}{2g}\left(\dfrac{D_1}{D_2}\right)^4 = \dfrac{V_1{}^2}{2g}\left(\dfrac{12}{8}\right)^4 = 5.06\,\dfrac{V_1{}^2}{2g}$

Similarly, $V_3{}^2/2g = 2.07 V_1{}^2/2g$, and thus

$$30 = \frac{V_1{}^2}{2g}\left[0.019\left(\frac{1{,}000}{1}\right) + 0.021\left(\frac{500 \times 12}{8}\right)5.06 + 0.020\left(\frac{800 \times 12}{10}\right)2.07\right]$$

rom which $V_1 = 3.74$ fps.

Computing the values of $D''V$ and applying them to Fig. 8.10, adjusted values of the friction factor will be found to be $f_1 = 0.020$, $f_2 = 0.0215$, $f_3 = 0.0205$, giving an adjusted flow of 2.90 cfs, in this case little different from the first trial. As two of the pipes are shorter than 1,000 diameters, minor losses should be included for good accuracy.

(b) *By the equivalent-length method.* Choose the 12-in. pipe as the standard. Using the above adjusted values of f in Eq. (8.57),

Pipe 2: $L_e = 500 \left(\dfrac{0.0215}{0.020}\right)\left(\dfrac{12}{8}\right)^5 = 4{,}080$ ft of 12-in. pipe

Pipe 3: $L_e = 800 \left(\dfrac{0.0205}{0.020}\right)\left(\dfrac{12}{10}\right)^5 = 2{,}040$ ft of 12-in. pipe

Add pipe 1 = 1,000 ft of 12-in. pipe
Total $L_e = \overline{7{,}120}$ ft of 12-in. pipe

Then $30 = 0.020 \times 7{,}120(V_1{}^2/2g)$, or $V_1 = 3.68$ fps, and $Q = 2.90$ cfs, as above.

8.26. PIPES IN PARALLEL

In the case of flow through two or more parallel pipes, as in Fig. 8.30, the continuity and energy equations establish the following relations which must be satisfied:

$$Q = Q_1 + Q_2 + Q_3 \qquad (8.58)$$

since $h_L = h_{L1} = h_{L2} = h_{L3} \qquad (8.59)$

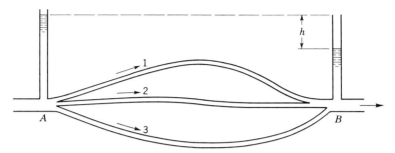

Fig. 8.30.   Compound pipes in parallel.

as the pressures at A and B are common to all pipes.   If the head loss is
given, the total discharge may be computed directly by adding the contributions from the various circuits, as in Eq. (8.58).   If the total flow is
given and the head loss and distribution of the flow among the circuits are
required, the procedure is to write Eq. (8.59) for the flow in each circuit in
terms of the dimensions applying to it.   This may be accomplished by
observing that the loss of head in any circuit is

$$h_L = \left(f\frac{L}{D} + \sum k \right) \frac{V^2}{2g}$$

where Σk is the sum of the minor-loss coefficients, which may usually be
neglected if the pipe is longer than 1,000 diameters.   Solving for V and
then Q, the following is obtained for pipe 1:

$$Q_1 = A_1 V_1 = A_1 \sqrt{\frac{2gh_L}{f_1(L_1/D_1) + \Sigma k}} = C_1 \sqrt{h_L} \qquad (8.60)$$

where C_1 is constant for the given pipe, except for the change in f with
Reynolds number.   The flows in the other pipes may be similarly
expressed, using reasonable values of f from Fig. 8.10.   Finally, Eq.
(8.58) becomes

$$Q = C_1 \sqrt{h_L} + C_2 \sqrt{h_L} + C_3 \sqrt{h_L} = \sqrt{h_L} (C_1 + C_2 + C_3)$$

This enables a first determination of h_L and the distribution of flows and
velocities in the pipes.   Adjustments in the values of f may be made
next, if indicated, and finally a corrected determination of h_L and the distribution of flows.

As a variation of the foregoing method, an approximate solution of
parallel pipes may be obtained by assuming a reasonable value of h_L and
computing the resulting individual flows and the *percentage* distribution
of flow.   This percentage distribution will not change greatly with the
magnitude of the flow and may then be applied to find the actual dis-

tribution of the total discharge. The accuracy of the solution may be checked by comparing the computed head losses in the separate circuits. They should be the same.

It is instructive to compare the solution methods for pipes in parallel with those for pipes in series. The role of the head loss in one case becomes that of the discharge rate in the other, and vice versa. The student is already familiar with this situation from the elementary theory of d-c circuits. The flow corresponds to the electrical current, the head loss to the voltage drop, and the frictional resistance to the ohmic resistance. The outstanding deficiency in this analogy occurs in the variation of potential drop with flow, which is with the first power in the electrical case ($E = IR$) and with the second power in the hydraulic case ($h_L \sim V^2 \sim Q^2$) for common turbulent flow.

8.27. PIPE NETWORKS

An extension of compound pipes in parallel is a case frequently encountered in municipal distribution systems, in which the pipes are interconnected so that the flow to a given outlet may come by several different paths, as shown in Fig. 8.31. Indeed, it is frequently impossible to tell by inspection which way the flow travels, as in pipe BE. Nevertheless, the flow in any network, however complicated, must satisfy the basic relations of continuity and energy as follows:

1. The flow into any junction must equal the flow out of it.
2. The flow in each pipe must satisfy the pipe-friction laws for flow in a single pipe.
3. The algebraic sum of the head losses around any closed circuit must be zero.

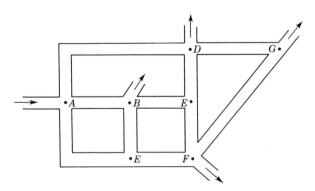

Fig. 8.31. Pipe network.

Pipe networks are generally too complicated to solve analytically, as was possible in the simpler cases of parallel pipes (Sec. 8.26). A practical procedure is the method of successive approximations, introduced by Cross.[1] It consists of the following elements, in order:

1. By careful inspection assume the most reasonable distribution of flows that satisfies condition 1.

2. Write condition 2 for each pipe in the form

$$h_L = KQ^n \qquad (8.61)$$

where K is a constant for each pipe. For example, the standard pipe-friction equation in the form of Eq. (8.60) would yield $K = 1/C^2$ and $n = 2$ for constant f. The empirical formulas (8.42) and (8.43) are seen to be readily reducible to the desired form. Minor losses within any circuit may be included, but minor losses at the junction points are neglected.

3. To investigate condition 3, compute the algebraic sum of the head losses around each elementary circuit, $\Sigma h_L = \Sigma KQ^n$. Consider losses from clockwise flows as positive, counterclockwise negative. Only by good luck will these add to zero on the first trial.

4. Adjust the flow in each circuit by a correction, ΔQ, to balance the head in that circuit and give $\Sigma KQ^n = 0$. The heart of this method lies in the determination of ΔQ. For any pipe we may write

$$Q = Q_0 + \Delta Q$$

where Q is the correct discharge and Q_0 is the assumed discharge. Then, for each pipe,

$$h_L = KQ^n = K(Q_0 + \Delta Q)^n = K(Q_0{}^n + nQ_0{}^{n-1} \Delta Q + \cdots)$$

If ΔQ is small compared with Q_0, the terms of the series after the second one may be neglected. Now, for a circuit, with ΔQ the same for all pipes,

$$\Sigma h_L = \Sigma KQ^n = \Sigma KQ_0{}^n + \Delta Q \Sigma KnQ_0{}^{n-1} = 0$$

As the corrections of head loss in all pipes must be summed *arithmetically*, we may solve this equation for ΔQ,

$$\Delta Q = \frac{-\Sigma KQ_0{}^n}{\Sigma |KnQ_0{}^{n-1}|} = \frac{-\Sigma h_L}{n\Sigma |h_L/Q_0|} \qquad (8.62)$$

as, by Eq. (8.61), $h_L/Q = KQ^{n-1}$. It must be emphasized again that the numerator of Eq. (8.62) is to be summed algebraically, with due

[1] Hardy Cross, Analysis of Flow in Networks of Conduits or Conductors, *Univ. Ill. Eng. Expt. Sta. Bull.* 286, 1936.

account of sign, while the denominator is summed arithmetically. The negative sign in Eq. 8.62 indicates that when there is an excess of head loss around a loop in the clockwise direction, the ΔQ must be subtracted from clockwise Q_0's and added to counterclockwise ones. The reverse is true if there is a deficiency of head loss around a loop in the clockwise direction.

5. After each circuit is given a first correction, the losses will still not balance because of the interaction of one circuit upon another (pipes which are common to two circuits receive two independent corrections, one for each circuit). The procedure is repeated, arriving at a second correction, and so on, until the corrections become negligible.

Either form of Eq. (8.62) may be used to find ΔQ. As values of K appear in both numerator and denominator of the first form, values proportional to the actual K may be used to find the distribution. The second form will be found most convenient for use with pipe-friction diagrams for water pipes.

Illustrative example 8.7: In Fig. 8.32 the method of successive approximations is applied to a simple pipe network of two loops. For simplicity, n is taken equal to 2 and the value of K for each pipe is made a simple integer.

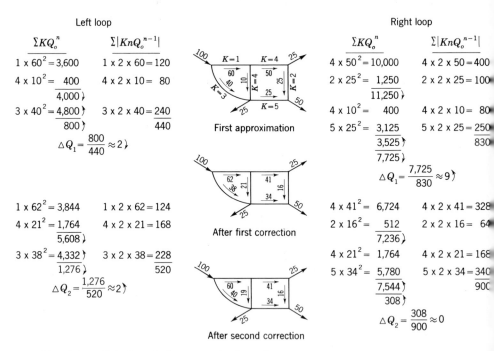

Left loop

ΣKQ_o^n	$\Sigma \lvert KnQ_o^{n-1} \rvert$
$1 \times 60^2 = 3{,}600$	$1 \times 2 \times 60 = 120$
$4 \times 10^2 = 400$	$4 \times 2 \times 10 = 80$
$\overline{4{,}000\,\rangle}$	
$3 \times 40^2 = 4{,}800\,\rangle$	$3 \times 2 \times 40 = 240$
$\overline{800\,\rangle}$	$\overline{440}$
$\Delta Q_1 = \dfrac{800}{440} \approx 2\,\rangle$	

First approximation

After first correction

$1 \times 62^2 = 3{,}844$	$1 \times 2 \times 62 = 124$
$4 \times 21^2 = 1{,}764$	$4 \times 2 \times 21 = 168$
$\overline{5{,}608\,\rangle}$	
$3 \times 38^2 = 4{,}332\,\rangle$	$3 \times 2 \times 38 = 228$
$\overline{1{,}276\,\rangle}$	$\overline{520}$
$\Delta Q_2 = -\dfrac{1{,}276}{520} \approx 2\,\rangle$	

After second correction

Right loop

ΣKQ_o^n	$\Sigma \lvert KnQ_o^{n-1} \rvert$
$4 \times 50^2 = 10{,}000$	$4 \times 2 \times 50 = 400$
$2 \times 25^2 = 1{,}250$	$2 \times 2 \times 25 = 100$
$\overline{11{,}250\,\rangle}$	
$4 \times 10^2 = 400$	$4 \times 2 \times 10 = 80$
$5 \times 25^2 = 3{,}125$	$5 \times 2 \times 25 = 250$
$\overline{3{,}525\,\rangle}$	$\overline{830}$
$\overline{7{,}725\,\rangle}$	
$\Delta Q_1 = \dfrac{7{,}725}{830} \approx 9\,\rangle$	

$4 \times 41^2 = 6{,}724$	$4 \times 2 \times 41 = 328$
$2 \times 16^2 = 512$	$2 \times 2 \times 16 = 64$
$\overline{7{,}236\,\rangle}$	
$4 \times 21^2 = 1{,}764$	$4 \times 2 \times 21 = 168$
$5 \times 34^2 = 5{,}780$	$5 \times 2 \times 34 = 340$
$\overline{7{,}544\,\rangle}$	$\overline{900}$
$\overline{308\,\rangle}$	
$\Delta Q_2 = \dfrac{308}{900} \approx 0$	

Fig. 8.32. Solution of pipe network of two loops.

An attractive feature of the approximation method is that errors in computation have the same effect as errors in judgment and will eventually be corrected by the process.

The pipe-network problem lends itself well to solution by use of a digital computer.[1] Programming takes time and care, but once set up, there is great flexibility and many man-hours of labor can be saved.

PROBLEMS

8.1. An oil with a kinematic viscosity of 0.00015 ft²/sec flows through a pipe of diameter 6 in. Below what velocity will the flow be laminar?

8.2. An oil with a kinematic viscosity of 0.005 ft²/sec flows through a 3-in.-diameter pipe with a velocity of 10 fps. Is the flow laminar or turbulent?

8.3. Hydrogen at atmospheric pressure and a temperature of 50°F has a kinematic viscosity of 0.0011 ft²/sec. Determine the maximum laminar flow rate in pounds per second in a 2-in.-diameter pipe. At this flow rate what is the average velocity?

8.4. What is the hydraulic radius of a rectangular air duct 6 by 14 in.?

8.5. Steam with a specific weight of 0.25 pcf flows with a velocity of 100 fps through a circular pipe. The friction factor f was found to have a value of 0.016. What is the shearing stress at the wall?

8.6. If the oil of Prob. 8.2 weighs 58 pcf, what will be the flow rate and head loss in a 3,000-ft length of 4-in.-diameter pipe when the Reynolds number is 800?

8.7. In Prob. 8.2 what will be the approximate distance from the pipe entrance to the first point at which the flow is established?

8.8. With laminar flow in a circular pipe, at what distance from the center line does the average velocity occur?

8.9. Find the head loss when oil ($s = 0.9$) of viscosity 0.007 ft²/sec flows in a 3-in.-diameter pipe at a rate of 5 gpm.

8.10. With laminar flow in a circular pipe, find the velocities at $0.1r$, $0.3r$, $0.5r$, $0.7r$, and $0.9r$. Plot the velocity profile.

8.11. Prove that the centerline velocity is twice the average velocity when laminar flow occurs in a circular pipe.

8.12. When laminar flow occurs in a two-dimensional passage, find the relation between the average and maximum velocities.

8.13. Tests made on a certain 12-in.-diameter pipe showed that, when $V = 10$ fps, $f = 0.015$. The fluid used was water at 60°F, at which temperature its specific weight is 62.37 pcf. Find the unit shear at the wall and at radii of 0, 0.2, 0.3, 0.5, 0.75 times the pipe radius.

8.14. The absolute viscosity of water at 60°F is 0.0113 poise, or 0.0000236 lb-sec/ft². If at a distance of 3 in. from the center of the pipe of Prob. 8.13 the velocity profile gives a value for du/dy of 4.34 per second, find the viscous shear and the turbulent shear at that radius.

8.15. What is the value of the mixing length l in Prob. 8.14, and what is the value of the ratio l/r_0?

---

[1] Lyle N. Hoag and Gerald Weinberg, Pipeline Network Analysis by Electronic Digital Computer, *J. Am. Water Works Assoc.*, vol. 49, pp. 517–529, 1957.

8.16. If water at 60°F enters a pipe with a uniform velocity of 10 fps, what is the distance at which the transition occurs from a laminar to a turbulent boundary layer?

8.17. If the thickness of this initial laminar boundary layer is given by $4.91 \sqrt{vx/U}$, what is the thickness reached by it at the point of transition in Prob. 8.16?

8.18. If water in a pipe is at a temperature of 60°F, the mean velocity is 12 fps, and the value of f is 0.015, what is the thickness of the laminar sublayer?

8.19. What will be the thickness of the laminar sublayer for the preceding problem if the velocity is increased to 20 fps?

8.20. For the data in Prob. 8.18, what is the distance from the wall to the assumed limit of the transition region where true turbulent flow begins?

8.21. Express Eq. (8.26) in terms of pipe diameter, friction factor, and Reynolds number.

8.22. Find the head loss in a 6-in.-diameter pipe having $\epsilon = 0.042$ in. when oil ($s = 0.90$) having a viscosity of 0.0008 lb-sec/ft² flows at a rate of 15 cfs. Determine the shear stress at the wall of the pipe and the velocity at 2.0 in. from center line.

8.23. When water at 150°F flows in a 0.75-in.-diameter copper tube at 1.0 gpm, find the head loss per 100 ft. What is the centerline velocity, and what is the value of δ'?

8.24. Repeat Prob. 8.23 for flow rates of 0.05 and 20 gpm.

8.25. The velocities in a 36-in.-diameter pipe are measured as 15.0 fps at $r = 0$ in. and 14.1 fps at $r = 4$ in. Approximately what is the flow rate?

8.26. When water at 50°F flows at 3.0 cfs in a 24-in. pipeline, the head loss is 0.0003 ft/ft. What will be the head loss when glycerin flows through this same pipe at the same rate?

8.27. With turbulent flow in a circular pipe prove that the mean velocity occurs at a distance of approximately $0.78r_0$ from the center line of the pipe.

8.28. Repeat Prob. 8.27 for the case of laminar flow.

8.29. Kerosene ($s = 0.81$) flows at a temperature of 80°F in a 2-in.-diameter brass pipeline at a rate of 10 gpm. (*a*) Find the head loss. (*b*) For the same head loss what would be the rate of flow if the temperature of the kerosene were raised to 120°F?

8.30. Air flows at 50 lb/min in a 4-in.-diameter welded-steel pipe at 100 psia and 60°F. Determine the head loss in 150 ft of this pipe. Assume the air to be of constant density.

8.31. Make a plot of the values of α and β versus N_R for brass pipes. Take an N_R range from 10^2 to 10^6. On the same plot show values of u_{max}/V.

8.32. The flow rate in a 12-in.-diameter pipe is 8 cfs. The flow is known to be turbulent, and the centerline velocity is 12.0 fps. Plot the velocity profile, and determine the head loss per foot of pipe.

8.33. What is the head loss per foot of pipe when oil ($s = 0.90$), having a viscosity of 2×10^{-4} lb-sec/ft², flows in a 2-in.-diameter welded-steel pipe at 0.15 cfs?

8.34. Air at 60°F and atmospheric pressure flows with a velocity of 20 fps through a 2-in.-diameter pipe. Find the head loss in 50 ft of pipe. ($\epsilon = 0.0001$ in.)

8.35. Consider water at 50°F flowing in a 36-in.-diameter concrete pipe ($e = 0.02$ in.). Determine N_R, u_{max}/V, τ_0, and δ' for flow rates of 20, 2, 0.2, and 0.02 cfs.

8.36. Find the flow rate when 60°F water causes a head loss of 0.25 ft in 100 ft of average cast-iron pipe. Diameter of pipe is 6 inches.

8.37. Gasoline with a kinematic viscosity of 0.000006 ft²/sec flows in a 12-in.-diameter smooth pipe. Find the flow rate when the head loss is 0.4 ft per 100 ft.

8.38. What size pipe is required to carry oil having a kinematic viscosity of 0.0002 ft²/sec at a rate of 8.0 cfs if the head loss is to be 0.4 ft-lb/lb per 100 ft of pipe length? Assume $\epsilon = 0.00015$ ft.

8.39. Air at 50 psia and temperature of 150°F flows in a 12- by 18-in. rectangular air duct at the rate of 1 lb/min. Find the head loss per 100 ft of duct. Express answer in feet of air flowing and in pounds per square inch. Assume $\epsilon = 0.0005$ in.

8.40. Find the approximate rate at which 60°F water will flow in a conduit shaped in the form of an equilateral triangle if the head loss is 2 ft per 100 ft. The cross-sectional area of the duct is 120 in.², and $\epsilon = 0.0018$ in.

8.41. Find the value of the Hazen-Williams coefficient C_1 for the water flow in Prob. 8.26.

8.42. A 12-in.-diameter pipe with a friction factor $f = 0.02$ conducts fluid between two tanks at 10 fps. The entrance and exit conditions to and from the pipe are flush with the wall of the tank. Find the ratio of the minor losses to the pipe friction loss if the length of the pipe is (a) 5 ft; (b) 100 ft; (c) 2,000 ft.

8.43. For a diameter ratio of 1:2 and a velocity of 20 fps in the smaller pipe, find the loss of head due to (a) sudden contraction; (b) sudden enlargement; (c) expansion in a conical diffuser with a total angle of 20 and 6°.

8.44. Prove that for a constant rate of discharge and a constant value of f the friction loss in a pipe varies inversely as the fifth power of the diameter.

8.45. A smooth pipe 12 in. in diameter and 300 ft long has a flush entrance and a submerged discharge. The velocity is 10 fps. If the fluid is water at 60°F, what is the total loss of head?

8.46. Suppose that the fluid in Prob. 8.45 were oil with a kinematic viscosity of 0.001 ft²/sec and a specific gravity of 0.925. What would be the head loss in feet of oil and in pounds per square inch?

8.47. Suppose that the fluid in Prob. 8.45 were dry saturated steam at a pressure of 29.82 psia, at which pressure its temperature is 250°F and its specific volume is 13.824 ft³/lb. If the velocity were also 10 fps, what would be the energy loss in head in feet of steam and in pounds per square inch?

8.48. Suppose that the velocity in Prob. 8.47 were 130 fps. What would be the head loss in pounds per square inch?

8.49. A smooth pipe consists of 50 ft of 8-in. pipe followed by 300 ft of 24-in. pipe with an abrupt change of cross section at the junction. It has a flush entrance and a submerged discharge. If it carries water at 60°F in the smaller pipe, with a velocity of 18 fps, what is the total frictional resistance?

8.50. In a 100-ft length of 4-in.-diameter wrought-iron pipe there are one open globe valve, one medium-radius elbow, and one pipe bend with a radius of curvature of 40 in. The bend is 90°, and its length is not included in the 100 ft. No entrance or discharge losses are involved. If the fluid is water at 72°F and the velocity is 6 fps, what is the total frictional resistance?

8.51. It has been found that with great care laminar flow can be maintained up to $N_R = 50,000$. Compute the friction head per 100 ft of pipe for a Reynolds number of 50,000 if (a) the flow is laminar; (b) the flow is turbulent in a smooth pipe; (c) the flow is turbulent in a rough pipe with $\epsilon/D = 0.05$. Consider two situations, one where the fluid is 60°F water, the other where the fluid is SAE 10 oil at 150°F. Pipe diameter is 2.0 inches.

8.52. Water at 60°F flows through 10,000 ft of 12-in.-diameter pipe between two reservoirs whose water-surface elevation difference is 200 ft. (a) Find the flow rate if $\epsilon = 0.0018$ in. (b) Find the flow rate if ϵ were twenty times larger.

8.53. How large a wrought-iron pipe is required to convey oil ($s = 0.9$, $\mu = 0.0008$ lb-sec/ft²) from one tank to another at a rate of 1.0 cfs if the pipe is 3,000 ft long and the difference in elevation of the free liquid surfaces is 40 ft?

8.54. If the diameter of a pipe is doubled, what effect does this have on the flow rate for a given head loss? Consider (a) laminar flow; (b) turbulent flow.

8.55. A 6-in.-diameter pipeline 400 ft long discharges a 2-in.-diameter jet into the atmosphere at a point which is 200 ft below the liquid surface at intake. The entrance to the pipe is a projecting one, with $k_e = 0.9$, and the nozzle loss coefficient is 0.05. Find the flow rate and the pressure head at the base of the nozzle, assuming $f = 0.03$.

8.56. A riveted steel pipe for which $\epsilon = 0.01$ ft. has an 8.5-ft diameter and is 1,900 ft long. It carries 60°F water at the rate of 300 cfs. What must be the difference in level at the two ends?

8.57. A pipe with an average diameter of 62 in. is 6,272 ft long and delivers water to a powerhouse at a point 1,375 ft lower in elevation than the water surface at intake. Assume $f = 0.025$. When the pipe delivers 300 cfs, what is its efficiency? What is the horsepower delivered to the plant?

8.58. An oil with a kinematic viscosity of 0.005 ft²/sec and a specific weight of 55 pcf flows through a 3-in. pipe ($\epsilon = 0.02$ in.). Find the drop in pressure in pounds per square inch per 100 ft of pipe. Horizontal pipe, $V = 10$ ft per sec.

8.59. California crude oil at 100°F, at which temperature its kinematic viscosity is 0.0004 ft²/sec, is pumped through a 2-in. pipe ($\epsilon = 0.001$ in.). Its specific weight is 59.8 pcf. (a) At what maximum velocity would the flow still be laminar? (b) What would then be the loss in energy head in pounds per square inch per 1,000 ft of pipe? (c) What would be the loss in energy head per 1,000 ft if the velocity were three times the value in (a)?

8.60. Water flows in a 6-in. vertical pipe with a velocity of 10 fps. The end of the pipe is 3 ft below the surface. Considering all losses and with $f = 0.025$, find the pressure at a point 10 ft above the surface of the water when the flow is (a) upward; (b) downward.

8.61. A horizontal pipe 6 in. in diameter and for which $f = 0.025$ projects into a body of water 3 ft below the surface. Considering all losses, find the pressure at a point 13 ft from the end of the pipe if the velocity is 10 fps and the flow is (a) from the pipe into the body of water; (b) from the body of water into the pipe.

8.62. A pipe runs from one reservoir to another, both ends of the pipe being under water. The intake is nonprojecting. The length of pipe is 500 ft, its diameter is 10.25 in., and the difference in water levels in the two reservoirs is 110 ft. If $f = 0.02$, what will be the pressure at a point 300 ft from the intake, the elevation of which is 120 ft lower than the surface of the water in the upper reservoir?

8.63. A pipe 850 ft long discharges freely into the air under a fall of 40 ft. Assume projecting pipe at entrance, $f = 0.0233$, and a diameter of 6.065 in.

What will be the rate of discharge? Assuming the diameter is 12.250 in. and $f = 0.0216$, what will be the rate of discharge? What is the ratio of the pipe areas, and what is the ratio of the discharges?

8.64. A pipeline runs from one reservoir to another, both ends being under water, and the intake end is nonprojecting. The difference in water levels in the two reservoirs is 110 ft, and the length of pipe is 500 ft. (*a*) What is the discharge if the pipe is 10.25 in. in diameter and $f = 0.022$? (*b*) When this same pipe is old, assume that the growth of tubercles has reduced the diameter to 9.5 in. and that $f = 0.06$. What will then be the rate of discharge?

8.65. A pump delivers water through 300 ft of 4-in. fire hose to a nozzle which throws a 1-in.-diameter jet. The loss coefficient of the nozzle is 0.04, and the value of f is 0.025. The nozzle is 20 ft higher than the pump, and it is required that the jet velocity be 70 fps. What must be the pressure in the hose at the pump?

8.66. A jet of water is discharged through a nozzle at a point 200 ft below the water level at intake. The jet is 4 in. in diameter, and the loss coefficient of the nozzle is 0.15. If the pipeline is 12 in. in diameter, 500 ft long, with a nonprojecting entrance, what is the pressure at the base of the nozzle? Assume $f = 0.015$.

8.67. It is desired to deliver 3 cfs of water at a point 10,000 ft distant with a loss of head of no more than 150 ft. What size of cast-iron pipe will be required?

8.68. Find an expression showing the relation between the discharge and the pipe diameter for a project where the available head loss is 50 ft and the length of the pipeline is 2 miles. The pipe is to be of the same size throughout its entire length. Take f for the pipe equal to 0.02. Plot a curve showing this relation, using diameters from 12 to 36 in. What is the ratio of the discharges for the 36- and 12-in. pipes in this problem? What are the ratios of the areas? Of their velocities?

8.69. A riveted-steel pipeline 2,000 ft long is 5 ft in diameter. The lower end is 140 ft below the level of the surface at intake and is joined to a turbine at this lower end. If the efficiency of the pipeline is 95 per cent, find the power delivered to the turbine.

8.70. Water at 140°F flows in 0.824-in.-diameter iron pipe ($\epsilon = 0.00015$ ft) of length 400 ft between points A and B. At point A the elevation of the pipe is 104.0 ft and the pressure 8.20 psi. At point B the elevation of the pipe is 99.5 ft and the pressure is 9.05 psi. Compute the flow rate as accurately as you can.

8.71. A 10-in. pipeline is 3 miles long. Let $f = 0.022$. If 4 cfs of water is to be pumped through it, the total actual lift being 20 ft, what will be the horsepower required if the pump efficiency is 70 per cent?

8.72. In Fig. 8.24 assume pipe diameter $= 10$ in., $BC = 20$ ft, $DE = 3,000$ ft, and $z = 135$ ft. Assume $f = 0.022$. If $Q = 7$ cfs of water and the pump efficiency is 80 per cent, what is the power required?

8.73. In Prob. 8.72, if the elevation of C above the water surface is 13 ft, that of D is 15 ft, and that of E is 110 ft, compute the pressures at C, D, and E.

8.74. Refer to Fig. 8.25. Suppose that water-surface elevation, elevation of pump, and elevation of nozzle tip are 100, 90, and 120 ft, respectively. Pipe BC is 40 ft long, 8 in. in diameter, $f = 0.025$; pipe DE is 200 ft long,

10 in. in diameter, $f = 0.030$; jet diameter is 6 in., and nozzle loss coefficient is 0.04. Assume the pump is 80 per cent efficient under all conditions of operation. Make a plot of flow rate and p_C/γ versus pump horsepower input. At what flow rate will cavitation occur in the pipe at C if the water is at 50°F and atmospheric pressure is 13.9 psia?

8.75. A 12-in. pipe 10,000 ft long for which $f = 0.02$ discharges freely into the air at an elevation 15 ft lower than the surface of the water at intake. It is necessary that the flow be doubled by inserting a pump. If the efficiency of the latter is 70 per cent, what will be the power required?

8.76. In Fig. 8.24 assume that the actual pipe diameter is 3 in., $BC = 20$ ft, $DE = 200$ ft, and $z = 70$ ft. The elevation of C above the water surface is 15 ft. Assume $f = 0.04$. (a) If the pressure head at C is to be -25 ft, what is the rate at which water is pumped? (b) If the efficiency of the pump is 60 per cent, what is the power required?

8.77. In Prob. 8.76 what is the pressure head at D if it is 2 ft higher in elevation than C? Compute $h_p = H_D - H_C$.

8.78. When a certain pump is delivering 1.2 cfs of water, a pressure gage at D (Fig. 8.25) reads 25 psi, while a vacuum gage at C reads 10 in. Hg. The pressure gage at D is 2 ft higher than the vacuum gage at C. The pipe diameters are 4 in. for the suction pipe and 3 in. for the discharge pipe. Find the power delivered to the water.

8.79. A certain turbine in a testing laboratory has been found to discharge 12 cfs under a head of 64 ft. It is to be installed at the end of a 12-in. pipe 500 ft long with a flush entrance. The total fall from the surface of the water at intake to the surface of the tailwater is 48 ft. Assume $f = 0.02$ for the pipe. What will be the net head on the turbine, the rate of discharge, and the power delivered to it?

8.80. If in Illustrative Example 8.5 the vapor pressure of the liquid is 2.0 psia and the atmospheric pressure is 14.4 psi, what is the maximum theoretical flow rate?

8.81. In Fig. 8.26 assume pipe diameter = 12 in., $BC = 200$ ft; $z = 120$ ft, and $f = 0.0217$. The entrance to the pipe at the intake is flush with the wall. (a) If $Q = 8$ cfs of water, what is the head supplied to the turbine? (b) What is the power delivered by the turbine if its efficiency is 75 per cent?

8.82. A turbine operating under a total fall of 120 ft ($z = 120$ ft) is supplied with water through 300 ft of 8-in. pipe. Let $f = 0.0225$. If the rate of discharge is such that 30 ft of head is lost in friction of the pipe, what will be the power delivered to the turbine?

8.83. Assume the total fall from one body of water to another is 120 ft. The water is conducted through 200 ft of 12-in. pipe with the entrance flush with the wall. Let $f = 0.0217$. At the end of the pipe is a turbine and draft tube which discharged 5 cfs of water when tested under a head of 43.8 ft in another location. What would be the rate of discharge through the turbine and the net head on it under the present conditions?

8.84. Refer to Fig. 8.23b. Suppose $z = 50$ ft and the pipe is 600 ft of 8-in.-diameter pipe ($f = 0.025$). Find the jet diameter that will result in the greatest jet horsepower. Assume the nozzle loss coefficient is 0.05.

8.85. A 6-in.-diameter pipe ($f = 0.032$) of length 100 ft connects two reservoirs whose water-surface elevations differ by 10 ft. The pipe entrance is flush, and the discharge is submerged. (a) Compute the flow rate. (b) If the last 10 ft of pipe were replaced with a conical diffuser with a cone angle of 10°, compute the flow rate.

8.86. Suppose that, in Fig. 8.27, pipe 1 is 36-in. smooth concrete, 5,000 ft long; pipe 2 is 24-in. new cast iron, 1,500 ft long; and pipe 3 is 18-in. new cast iron, 4,000 ft long. The elevations of water surfaces in reservoirs A and B are 200 and 150 ft, respectively, and the discharge Q_1 is 50 cfs. Find the elevation of the surface of reservoir C.

8.87. With the sizes and lengths of pipes given in Prob. 8.86, suppose that the surface elevations of reservoirs A and C are 200 and 125 ft, respectively, and the discharge Q_2 is 20 cfs into reservoir B. Find the surface elevation of reservoir B.

8.88. Suppose, in Prob. 8.87, that the discharge Q_2 is known to be 20 cfs from reservoir B. Find the elevation of the surface of reservoir B.

8.89. Suppose, in Fig. 8.27, that pipes 1, 2, and 3 are 3,000 ft of 24 in., 1,000 ft of 18 in., and 4,000 ft of 16 in., respectively, of new riveted-steel pipe. The surface elevations of reservoirs A, B, and C are 100, 60, and 0 ft, respectively. Find the flow in all pipes.

8.90. Suppose that, in Fig. 8.27, pipe 1 is 1,500 ft of 12-in. new cast-iron pipe, pipe 2 is 800 ft of 6-in. wrought-iron pipe, and pipe 3 is 1,200 ft of 8-in. wrought-iron pipe. The water surface of reservoir B is 20 ft below that of A, while the junction J is 35 ft below the surface of A. In place of reservoir C, pipe 3 leads away to some other destination but its elevation at C is 60 ft below A. When the pressure head at J is 25 ft, find the flow in each pipe and the pressure head at C.

8.91. Suppose that in Fig. 8.29 pipes 1, 2, and 3 are 500 ft of 3.068-in., 200 ft of 2.067-in., and 400 ft of 2.469-in. wrought-iron pipe. With a total head loss of 20 ft from A to B, find the flow of 60°F water by the equivalent-velocity-head method.

8.92. Repeat Prob. 8.89 for the case where the fluid is an oil ($s = 0.9$, $\mu = 0.0008$ lb-sec/ft^2).

8.93. Suppose that in Fig. 8.30 pipes 1, 2, and 3 are 500 ft of 2-in., 300 ft of 3-in., and 700 ft of 4-in., respectively. The pipes are all smooth brass. When the total flow of 80°F crude oil ($s = 0.855$) is 0.6 cfs, find the head loss from A to B and the flow in each pipe.

8.94. Repeat Prob. 8.93 for the case where the flow rate is 0.06 cfs.

8.95. A pipeline 800 ft long discharges freely at a point 150 ft below the water level at intake. The pipe projects into the reservoir. The first 500 ft is 12 in. in diameter, and the remaining 300 ft is 8 in. in diameter. Find the rate of discharge, assuming $f = 0.04$.

8.96. The junction of the two sizes of pipe in Prob. 8.95 is 120 ft below the surface of the water level. Find the pressure just above C and just below C, where C denotes the point of junction. Assume a sudden contraction at this point.

8.97. Three new cast-iron pipes, having diameters of 30, 24, and 18 in., respectively, each 500 ft long, are connected in series. The 30-in. pipe leads from a reservoir, and the 18-in. pipe discharges into the air at a point 12 ft below the water surface in the reservoir. Assuming all changes in section to be abrupt, find the rate of discharge of water at 60°F.

8.98. Suppose that, in Prob. 8.97, a 6-in. nozzle is placed at the outlet of the 18-in. pipe, preceded by an angle valve wide open. Find the new rate of discharge. Compare in Prob. 8.97 and 8.98 the percentage decrease in discharge caused by a 5 per cent increase in the pipe-friction factor (e.g., from 0.020 to 0.021).

8.99. In Fig. 8.30 suppose that the water enters at A from a large standpipe and that B is located 50 ft above a given datum plane. The three pipes are of the following dimensions: 1,200 ft of 6-in. pipe, 1,000 ft of 8-in. pipe, and 1,200 ft of 10-in. pipe, while the diameter at B is 16 in. All pipes are galvanized iron. Assume the velocity is negligible at A but is to be considered at B. If 14 cfs of water at 60°F is delivered at B under a pressure head of 100 ft, what must be the elevation of the water surface in the standpipe above the datum plane?

8.100. The pipes in the system shown in the figure are all new cast iron. With a flow of 20 cfs, find the head loss from A to D.

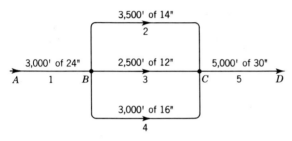

Fig. Prob. 8.100

8.101. With the same head loss as found in Prob. 8.100, find the percentage increase in the capacity of the system to be gained by adding another 12-in. pipe 2,500 ft long between B and C.

8.102. What should be the diameter of a single pipe from B to C of Prob. 8.100 such that it replaces pipes 2, 3, and 4 without altering the capacity for the same head loss from A to D?

8.103. Compute the flow in each pipe of the system shown in the figure, and determine the pressures at B and C. Pipe AB is 1,000 ft long, 6 in. in diameter, and $f = 0.03$; pipe BC (upper) is 600 ft long, 4 in. in diameter, and $f = 0.02$; pipe BC (lower) is 800 ft long, 2 in. in diameter, and $f = 0.04$; pipe CD is 400 ft long, 4 in. in diameter, and $f = 0.02$. The elevations are reservoir water surface, 100 ft; A, 80 ft; B, 50 ft; C, 40 ft; and D, 25 ft.

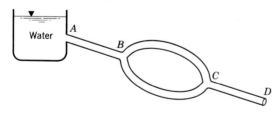

Fig. Prob. 8.103

8.104. A pump is installed to deliver water from a reservoir of surface elevation zero to another of elevation 200 ft. The 12-in.-diameter suction pipe ($f = 0.020$) is 40 ft long, and the 10-in.-diameter discharge pipe

($f = 0.032$) is 4,500 ft long. The pump head may be defined as $h_p = 300 - 20Q^2$, where h_p, the pump head, is in feet and Q in cubic feet per second. Compute the rate at which this pump will deliver the water. Also, what is the horsepower input to the water?

8.105. When fluid of specific weight 50 pcf flows in a 6-in.-diameter pipe, the frictional stress between the fluid and the pipe wall is 0.5 lb/ft². Calculate the head loss per foot of pipe. If the flow rate is 2.0 cfs, how much power is lost per foot of pipe?

8.106. Referring to the figure, when the pump develops 25 ft of head, the velocity of flow in pipe C is 4 fps. Neglecting minor losses, find (a) the flow rates in cubic feet per second in pipes A and B under these conditions and (b) the elevation of pipe B at discharge. The pipe characteristics are as follows: pipe A, 4,000 ft long, 2 ft in diameter, and $f = 0.03$; pipe B, 4,000 ft long, 1 ft in diameter, and $f = 0.03$; pipe C, 4,000 ft long, 2 ft in diameter, and $f = 0.02$.

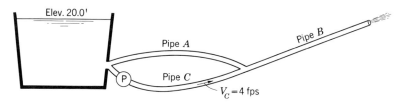

Fig. Prob. 8.106

8.107. An 8-in. new cast-iron pipe 1,000 ft long forms one link of a pipe network. If the velocities to be encountered are assumed to fall within the range of 2 to 8 fps, derive an equation for the flow of water at 60°F in this pipe in the form $h_L = KQ^n$. (*Hint:* Using the information in Figs. 8.10 and 8.11, set up two simultaneous equations corresponding to the ends of the desired velocity range, then solve for the unknowns K and n.)

8.108. Solve the pipe network shown in the figure, to find the flow in each pipe. For simplicity, take $n = 2.0$ and use the value of f for complete turbu-

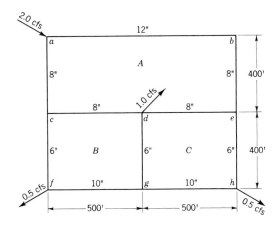

Fig. Prob. 8.108

lence, as given in Fig. 8.10.   All pipe is new cast iron.   If the pressure head at *a* is 100 ft, find the pressure head at *d* (which might represent a fire demand, for example).

8.109. Solve the pipe network shown in the figure.   The 12- and 16-in. pipes are of new cast iron, while the 18- and 24-in. sizes are of average concrete. Again, assume $n = 2.0$ and use the values of f from Fig. 8.10 for complete turbulence.   If the pressure at *h* is 80 psi, find the pressure at *f*.

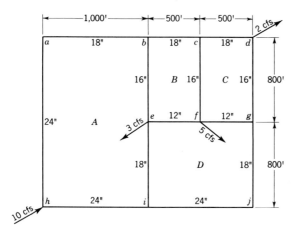

Fig. Prob. 8.109

NINE

STEADY FLOW
OF COMPRESSIBLE FLUIDS

The concepts of Chap. 8 are applicable to compressible fluids if the pressure variation in the flow system is very small. When the absolute pressure within the flow changes by not more than 5 per cent, for example, for the isothermal case, the change in density of a compressible fluid will be less than 5 per cent and for all practical purposes may be considered constant. Such an assumption, where $\Delta\rho/\rho < 0.05$, will lead to relatively good results in the isothermal case when the concepts of Chap. 8 are applied. If $\Delta\rho/\rho > 0.05$, however, the effects of compressibility must be considered. The purpose of this chapter is to investigate compressible-fluid problems that require such considerations. It will be seen that such problems are much more difficult than incompressible-fluid problems because of thermodynamic considerations. Moreover, the equations that are developed are considerably more complex than those for incompressible fluids.

9.1. FLOW OF COMPRESSIBLE FLUIDS IN PIPES

There is a distinct difference between the flow of compressible and incompressible fluids in pipes. When an incompressible fluid flows in a pipe of uniform diameter, the energy drops uniformly along the pipe, but with a compressible fluid this is not the case, as illustrated in Fig. 9.1. There is this difference because, with a compressible fluid, the drop in pressure along the pipe causes a decrease in density which, in order to satisfy continuity, results in an increased velocity. The increased velocity increases the rate at which energy is lost along the pipe.

The case of isothermal flow of a compressible fluid in a horizontal pipe will now be considered.

9.2. ISOTHERMAL FLOW IN HORIZONTAL PIPE

The flow of gas through a long uninsulated pipe in an isothermal environment may be assumed to approximate isothermal flow. For the sake of simplicity, the treatment here will be restricted to a horizontal pipe of uniform diameter. In this case the drop in pressure along the pipe is due both to the friction and to the increase in kinetic energy resulting from the expansion. As $d(V^2/2g) = V\,dV/g$, the energy equation [(Eq. 4.29)] for a differential length of pipe is

$$-\frac{dp}{\gamma} = f\frac{dx}{D}\frac{V^2}{2g} + \frac{V\,dV}{g} \tag{9.1}$$

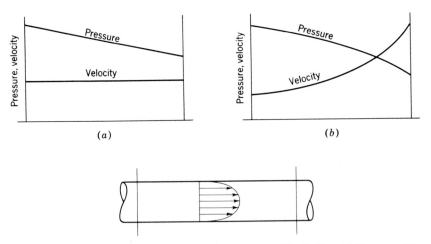

Fig. 9.1. Flow in a horizontal pipe. (a) Incompressible fluid. (b) Compressible fluid.

For a gas at usual pressure ranges the absolute viscosity is constant at any given temperature, and for isothermal expansion V varies inversely as γ, and so ρV is constant (Sec. 1.7). Therefore the Reynolds number is constant along the entire length of pipe, and consequently f is constant along the pipe for any given flow. From the perfect-gas law and the equation of continuity, $\gamma = p/RT$ and $V = G/\gamma A = GRT/pA$. Substituting these values in Eq. (9.1) and rearranging, we obtain

$$-\left(\frac{2gA^2}{G^2RT}\right) p \, dp = \frac{f}{D} \, dx + \frac{2 \, dV}{V}$$

For isothermal flow in a pipe of uniform diameter this equation is readily integrated for a length $L = x_2 - x_1$ to give

$$p_1{}^2 - p_2{}^2 = \frac{G^2RT}{gA^2}\left(f\frac{L}{D} + 2 \ln \frac{p_1}{p_2}\right) \tag{9.2}$$

where p_1/p_2 has replaced V_2/V_1, since for isothermal flow $p_1/p_2 = v_2/v_1$ and for constant diameter $V_2/V_1 = v_2/v_1$. This equation may be used to find G if all other values are given, but if G and other values at (1) are given, p_2 may be found by successive approximation. In most cases the last term is small compared with fL/D and may be neglected as a first approximation. If it proves to be significant, a second solution, using an approximate value of p_1/p_2, may be made if greater accuracy is desired. It may be noted that p and A involve the *same area units*, and so, for numerical work, it is usually more convenient to use p in pounds per square inch and A in square inches. There is a restriction to Eq. (9.2) that will be discussed in Sec. 9.9.

Illustrative example 9.1: Air flows isothermally at 65°F through a horizontal 10- by 14-in. rectangular duct at 100 lb/sec. If the pressure at a section is 80 psia, find the pressure at a second section 500 ft downstream from the first. Assume the duct surface is very smooth; hence the lowest curve of Fig. 8.10 may be used to determine f.

$$\gamma_1 = \frac{p}{RT} = \frac{80 \times 144}{53.3 \times (460 + 65)} = 0.41 \text{ pcf}$$

$$V_1 = \frac{G}{\gamma_1 A} = \frac{100}{0.41(140/144)} = 250 \text{ fps}$$

$$R = \frac{A}{P} = \frac{140}{48} = 2.92 \text{ in.} = 0.243 \text{ ft}$$

$$N_{R_1} = \frac{DV\rho}{\mu} = \frac{4RV_1\rho_1}{\mu_1} = \frac{4(0.243)(250)(0.41/32.2)}{3.78 \times 10^{-7}} = 8.2 \times 10^6$$

$$= N_{R_2} \quad \text{since } \rho_1 V_1 = \rho_2 V_2 \text{ and } \mu_1 = \mu_2$$

From Fig. 8.10, $f = 0.0085$. Substituting into Eq. (9.2) and neglecting the logarithm term,

$$(80 \times 144)^2 - p_2{}^2 = \frac{(100)^2 53.3(525)}{32.2(140/144)^2}\left[0.0085 \times \frac{500}{4(0.243)}\right]$$

from which $p_2 = 66.7$ psia. Substituting this value of p_2 into Eq. (9.2) and considering the logarithmic term yields $p_2 = 66.0$ psia.

9.3. THERMODYNAMIC CONSIDERATIONS

The material of the preceding section was presented to point out the physical difference between the flow of incompressible and compressible fluids in pipes. To further our understanding of the flow of compressible fluids, it will be advantageous in our discussion to review briefly some thermodynamic principles. First there is the perfect-gas law $pv = RT$, which was discussed in Sec. 1.7. Then we have the *equation of state* of the gas, which is

For isothermal conditions: $pv = $ constant

For adiabatic conditions: $pv^k = $ constant

where $k = c_p/c_v$, the ratio of the specific heats. The terms c_p and c_v are the specific heats at constant pressure and constant volume, respectively. If both c_p and c_v are expressed in Btu/(lb)(°R), the gas constant is expressible as

$$R = J(c_p - c_v) \tag{9.3}$$

where $J = 778$ ft-lb/Btu. Substituting $k = c_p/c_v$ into this equation, we get

$$c_p = \frac{k}{k-1}\frac{R}{J} \tag{9.4}$$

and

$$c_v = \frac{1}{k-1}\frac{R}{J} \tag{9.5}$$

Note that Eq. (9.4) was previously introduced, in Sec. 4.9.

An *isothermal* process is one in which there is no change in temperature, while an *adiabatic* process is one in which no heat is added to or taken away from the flow system. An *isentropic* process is a frictionless adiabatic process. The solution of a compressible-flow problem is similar to that of an incompressible one except that the equation of state of the compressible fluid must be introduced into the problem.

9.4. FUNDAMENTAL EQUATIONS APPLICABLE TO THE FLOW OF COMPRESSIBLE FLUIDS

The fundamental equations for the flow of compressible fluids have already been stated in Chaps. 3, 4, and 6. For convenience we restate them here.

Continuity. The expression for continuity for one-dimensional flow of a compressible fluid is

$$G = \gamma A V = \text{constant} \tag{9.6}$$

Energy equation. For one-dimensional flow of a compressible fluid the energy equation[1] is expressible as:

$$JE_1 + \frac{V_1^2}{2g} + Jq = JE_2 + \frac{V_2^2}{2g} \tag{9.7}$$

where the *enthalpy* $E = I + pv/J$.

Impulse-momentum equation. The impulse-momentum equation for one-dimensional flow of a compressible fluid is:

$$\mathbf{F} = \rho_2 Q_2 \mathbf{V}_2 - \rho_1 Q_1 \mathbf{V}_1 \tag{9.8}$$

Euler equation. For one-dimensional compressible flow in a circular pipe the Euler equation (Sec. 4.11) may be expressed as

$$\frac{dp}{\rho} + V \, dV = -\frac{2\tau \, ds}{\rho r} \tag{9.9}$$

In this equation and in Eq. (9.7) the z terms were dropped, for in the flow of compressible fluids they are almost always negligible compared with the other terms in the energy equation.

Acoustic velocity. In Appendix 2 it is shown that the acoustic velocity $c = \sqrt{E_v/\rho} = \sqrt{kgRT}$. This represents the celerity at which a pressure wave will travel through a compressible fluid. In Chap. 7 an important dimensionless parameter, the Mach number N_M, was mentioned. $N_M = V/c$, where V is the velocity of flow. If $N_M < 1$, the flow is subsonic; if $N_M = 1$, the flow is sonic; if $N_M > 1$, the flow is supersonic.

9.5. ISOTHERMAL FLOW

In isothermal flow $pv = \text{constant}$ and $I_1 = I_2$ so that Eq. (9.7) reduces to

$$\frac{V_1^2}{2g} + Jq = \frac{V_2^2}{2g} \tag{9.10}$$

This equation is applicable to both real and ideal fluids. It shows that if $A_1 = A_2$, heat energy must·be added to the fluid in the isothermal case if there is to be an increase in kinetic energy.

[1] The reader should review Sec. 4.9 for a discussion of the energy equation.

9.6. FRICTION HEAD LOSS IN ISOTHERMAL FLOW

The energy equations for compressible fluids contain no specific term for friction head loss. This is so because fluid friction transforms the kinetic energy of eddies into thermal energy and is therefore represented by changes in the numerical values of the other terms of the energy equation. We shall now derive an expression for friction head loss in *isothermal* flow of a compressible fluid. The Euler equation (9.9) may be expressed as

$$v \, dp + \frac{V \, dV}{g} = -dh_L \tag{9.11}$$

Integrating and noting that for isothermal flow $p_1 v_1 = p_2 v_2 = pv$, we get

$$h_L = p_1 v_1 \ln \frac{p_1}{p_2} + \frac{V_1^2 - V_2^2}{2g} \tag{9.12}$$

Relating this expression to Eq. (9.10), we can also write

$$h_L = p_1 v_1 \ln \frac{p_1}{p_2} - Jq \tag{9.13}$$

The following example shows some interesting relations between the head loss due to friction and the heat energy added to or taken away from the fluid.

Illustrative example 9.2: Air flows isothermally in a long pipe. At one section the pressure is 90 psia, the temperature is 80°F, and the velocity is 100 fps. At a second section some distance from the first the pressure is 15 psia. Find the energy head loss due to friction, and determine the thermal energy that must have been added to or taken from the fluid between the two sections. Since the flow is isothermal, $p_1 v_1 = p_2 v_2$, so $v_2/v_1 = p_1/p_2 = 6$. Thus $\rho_1/\rho_2 = 6$, and from continuity, $V_2 = 6V_1 = 600$ fps.

Applying Eq. (9.10), we get

$$\frac{(100)^2}{2g} + Jq = \frac{(600)^2}{2g}$$

$$Jq = \frac{(600)^2 - (100)^2}{2g} = 5,436 \text{ ft-lb/lb of air}$$

$$q = 5,436/778 = 7.0 \text{ Btu/lb of air}$$

Since q is positive, heat energy must be added to the fluid. The energy loss due to fluid friction may be found by application of Eq. (9.13).

$$h_L = RT \ln {}^{90}\!/_{15} - 5,436 = 53.3(540) \ln 6 - 5,436 = 46,334 \text{ ft-lb/lb}$$

An interesting observation is that, because the fluid receives heat in its flow, the total energy at (2) is greater than at (1). Thus friction merely means a degradation of mechanical energy but not a loss of energy.

9.7. IDEAL ADIABATIC (ISENTROPIC) FLOW

In an adiabatic flow $q = 0$, and hence Eq. (9.7) may be written as

$$JE_1 + \frac{V_1^2}{2g} = JE_2 + \frac{V_2^2}{2g} \tag{9.14}$$

From thermodynamics, $\Delta E = c_p \, \Delta T$; hence

$$c_p T_1 + \frac{V_1^2}{2g} = c_p T_2 + \frac{V_2^2}{2g} = c_p T_s \tag{9.15}$$

where T_s is the stagnation temperature (where V is zero). Thus, in adiabatic flow, the stagnation temperature is constant along a streamline regardless of whether or not the flow is frictionless.

From Eq. (9.4),

$$c_p T = \frac{kRT}{(k-1)J} = \frac{kp}{\gamma(k-1)J}$$

and for isentropic (frictionless) conditions, $(p_2/p_1)^{1/k} = \gamma_2/\gamma_1$. Making these substitutions in Eq. (9.15), we get

$$\frac{V_2^2 - V_1^2}{2g} = \frac{p_1}{\gamma_1} \frac{k}{k-1} \left[1 - \left(\frac{p_2}{p_1} \right)^{(k-1)/k} \right] = \frac{p_2}{\gamma_2} \frac{k}{k-1} \left[\left(\frac{p_1}{p_2} \right)^{(k-1)/k} - 1 \right] \tag{9.16}$$

This equation may also be derived by integrating the Euler equation $dp/\gamma + V \, dV/g = 0$ along a stream tube, while noting that $pv^k =$ constant.

The preceding equation may be transformed into other equivalent expressions by means of the perfect-gas law. One other form is

$$\frac{V_2^2 - V_1^2}{2g} = \frac{k}{k-1} RT_1 \left(1 - \frac{T_2}{T_1} \right) \tag{9.17}$$

9.8. STAGNATION PRESSURE

From Appendix 2, the acoustic velocity $c = \sqrt{kgRT}$. Substituting this relation in Eq. (9.17), noting that $V_1 = cN_M$, where N_M is the Mach number (Sec. 7.4), and applying Eq. (1.7) under adiabatic conditions, we get

$$\frac{V_2^2}{c_1^2} = N_{M_1}^2 + \frac{2}{k-1} \left[1 - \left(\frac{p_2}{p_1} \right)^{(k-1)/k} \right] \tag{9.18}$$

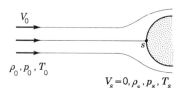

$V_s = 0, \rho_s, p_s, T_s$ **Fig. 9.2.**   Stagnation point.

Refer now to Fig. 9.2, which shows a stagnation point in compressible flow. At the stagnation point S the increased pressure causes a rise in density and temperature. At this point, $V_2 = 0$. Hence, for the situation depicted in Fig. 9.2, Eq. (9.18) may be expressed as

$$0 = \left(\frac{V_0}{c}\right)^2 + \frac{2}{k-1}\left[1 - \left(\frac{p_s}{p_0}\right)^{(k-1)/k}\right]$$

where c = acoustic velocity
   V_0 = velocity
   p_0 = pressure in undisturbed flow
Rearranging this equation, we get

$$\frac{p_s}{p_0} = \left[1 + \left(\frac{V_0}{c}\right)^2 (k-1)/2\right]^{k/(k-1)} \tag{9.19}$$

Substituting $k = \rho_0 c_0^2/p_0$ and expanding by the binomial theorem,

$$p_s = p_0 + \tfrac{1}{2}\rho_0 V_0^2 \left(1 + \frac{V_0^2}{4c^2} + \cdots\right)$$
$$= p_0 + \gamma_0 \frac{V_0^2}{2g}(1 + \tfrac{1}{4}N_{M_0}^2 + \cdots) \tag{9.20}$$

This equation is identical with Eq. (4.34), mentioned earlier. It is applicable only if $N_M < 1$. In determining stagnation pressure, the error from neglecting compressibility depends on the Mach number of the flow. At low Mach numbers the error is insignificant, but as N_M approaches unity, the error is sizable.

Illustrative example 9.3:   Find the stagnation pressure and temperature in nitrogen flowing at 600 fps if the pressure and temperature in the undisturbed flow field are 100 psia and 200°F, respectively. (See Appendix 3, Table A.4, for properties of gases.)

$$c = \sqrt{kgRT} = \sqrt{(1.4)(32.2)(55.1)(660)} = 1,282 \text{ fps}$$
$$N_M = 600/1,282 = 0.468$$
$$\rho_0 = \frac{kp_0}{c_0^2} = \frac{1.4(100 \times 144)}{(1,282)^2} = 0.0123 \text{ slug/ft}^3$$
$$p_s = 100(144) + \tfrac{1}{2}(0.0123)(600)^2[1 + \tfrac{1}{4}(0.468)^2]$$
$$= 14,400 + 2,200(1 + 0.055) = 16,720 \text{ psf} = 116 \text{ psi}$$

Applying Eq. (9.15),

$$c_p T_1 + \frac{V_1{}^2}{2g} = c_p T_s$$

$$(193)(660) + \frac{(600)^2}{64.4} = 193 T_s$$

$$T_s = 695°R = 235°F$$

9.9. EFFECT OF AREA VARIATION ON ONE - DIMENSIONAL COMPRESSIBLE FLOW

In steady flow the velocity of an *incompressible* fluid varies inversely with the area. This is not the case with a compressible fluid because variations in density will also influence the velocity. Moreover, the behavior of a compressible fluid, when there is a change in cross-sectional area, depends on whether the flow is *subsonic* ($N_M < 1$) or *supersonic* ($N_M > 1$). We shall now examine this phenomenon. In this discussion we shall confine our remarks to ideal flow.

The continuity equation (9.6) may be written in differential form as

$$\frac{dA}{A} + \frac{d\rho}{\rho} + \frac{dV}{V} = 0 \tag{9.21}$$

The Euler equation (9.9) for an *ideal* fluid may be expressed as

$$\frac{d\rho}{\rho} \frac{dp}{d\rho} + V\,dV = c^2 \frac{d\rho}{\rho} + V\,dV = 0 \tag{9.22}$$

Combining the two preceding equations, replacing V/c with N_M, and rearranging, we get

$$\frac{dA}{A} = (N_M{}^2 - 1) \frac{dV}{V} \tag{9.23}$$

From this equation we can arrive at some significant conclusions as follows:

1. For subsonic flow ($N_M < 1$):

If $\frac{dV}{V} > 0$, $\frac{dA}{A} < 0$ (area must decrease for increase in velocity).

If $\frac{dV}{V} < 0$, $\frac{dA}{A} > 0$ (area must increase for a decrease in velocity).

2. For supersonic flow ($N_M > 1$):

If $\frac{dV}{V} > 0$, $\frac{dA}{A} > 0$ (area must increase if velocity is to increase).

If $\frac{dV}{V} < 0$, $\frac{dA}{A} < 0$ (area must decrease if velocity is to decrease).

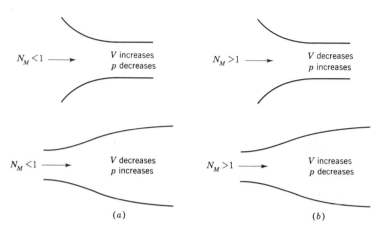

Fig. 9.3. Effect of area variation on compressible flow. (*a*) Subsonic flow. (*b*) Supersonic flow.

3. For sonic flow ($N_M = 1$):

$$\frac{dA}{A} = 0$$

Thus it is seen that subsonic and supersonic flows behave *oppositely* if there is an area variation. To accelerate a flow at subsonic velocity, a converging passage is required just as in the case of an incompressible flow. To accelerate a flow at supersonic velocity, however, a diverging passage is required. This is so because the decrease in fluid density exceeds the increase in flow velocity; hence, to satisfy continuity, the passage must diverge.

For sonic velocity it is noted that $dA/A = 0$. This condition occurs at the throat of a converging passage. The occurrence of sonic velocity in the throat of the passage requires a high-pressure differential to accelerate the flow the necessary amount to reach sonic velocity. The velocity at the throat will be a maximum, but will not necessarily be as great as sonic velocity. If sonic velocity is attained in the throat, the flow will become supersonic if the converging passage is followed by a diverging one. On the other hand, if the flow in the throat were not sonic, there would be a decrease in velocity in the following diverging passage. In Fig. 9.3 is shown the behavior of subsonic and supersonic flow through converging and diverging passages.

In Sec. 9.2 it was mentioned that there is a restriction to Eq. (9.2). From the preceding discussion we see that if the flow in the pipe of Sec. 9.2 is subsonic, then the maximum possible value of V_2 is the isothermal acoustic velocity.   Hence there is a maximum value of G for any length of pipe, since $G = \gamma_2 A_2 V_2$.   Another way of expressing the restriction is that there is a maximum length of pipe for any given flow.

9.10. COMPRESSIBLE FLOW THROUGH CONVERGING NOZZLE

Let us now consider one-dimensional flow of a compressible fluid through the converging nozzle of Fig. 9.4.   We shall assume isentropic conditions. If the velocity of approach is negligible, Eq. (9.16) can be expressed as

$$\frac{V_2{}^2}{2g} = \frac{p_2}{\gamma_2} \frac{k}{k-1} \left[\left(\frac{p_1}{p_2}\right)^{(k-1)/k} - 1 \right] \tag{9.24}$$

Noting that $c_2 = \sqrt{kgp_2/\gamma_2}$, the above equation can be rearranged to give

$$\left(\frac{V_2}{c_2}\right)^2 = N_{M_2}{}^2 = \frac{2}{k-1} \left[\left(\frac{p_1}{p_2}\right)^{(k-1)/k} - 1 \right] \tag{9.25}$$

Thus it is seen that the velocity of flow at the throat (section 2 of the figure) depends on the p_1/p_2 ratio.   If there is a large enough pressure differential between the inside and outside of the tank, sonic velocity will occur at section 2.   From the discussion of Sec. 9.9 it is recognized that supersonic flow is impossible in this situation.

Let us now assume the condition of sonic flow at the throat (that is, $N_{M_2} = 1.0$).   Substituting $N_{M_2} = 1.0$ into Eq. (9.25), we get the *critical pressure ratio*

$$\left(\frac{p_2}{p_1}\right)_c = \left(\frac{2}{k+1}\right)^{k/(k-1)} \tag{9.26}$$

This critical pressure ratio exists whenever the flow through the throat is at sonic velocity.   If the flow through the throat is subsonic, then p_2/p_1 is larger than the ratio given by Eq. (9.26).

The rate of flow through the nozzle of Fig. 9.4 may be found by substituting V_2 from Eq. (9.24) into $G = \gamma_2 A_2 V_2$.   Making use of the

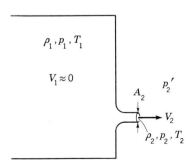

Fig. 9.4.   Flow through converging nozzle.

isentropic relation between the p's and γ's and rearranging, we get

$$G = A_2 \sqrt{2g \frac{k}{k-1} p_1 \gamma_1 \left[\left(\frac{p_2}{p_1}\right)^{2/k} - \left(\frac{p_2}{p_1}\right)^{(k+1)/k} \right]} \qquad (9.27)$$

This expression is applicable so long as $p_2/p_1 < (p_2/p_1)_c$, as given by Eq. (9.26). To determine the maximum flow through the nozzle, we substitute $p_2/p_1 = (p_2/p_1)_c = [2/(k+1)]^{k/(k-1)}$ into Eq. (9.27). The result is

$$G_{\max} = A_2 \sqrt{\frac{2gk}{k-1} p_1 \gamma_1 \left(\frac{2}{k+1}\right)^{2/(k-1)} \frac{k-1}{k+1}} \qquad (9.28)$$

This equation may also be expressed as

$$G_{\max} = \frac{A_2 p_1}{\sqrt{T_1}} \sqrt{\frac{gk}{R} \left(\frac{2}{k+1}\right)^{(k+1)/(k-1)}} \qquad (9.29)$$

In this equation the second term depends only on the properties of the gas. Thus a simple device for metering compressible flows is a converging nozzle at whose throat the sonic velocity is produced.

If the flow through the throat is subsonic, the pressure at the throat is identical with that outside the tank ($p_2 = p_2'$). If the flow through the throat is sonic, the pressure at the throat may be equal to, but is generally greater than, that outside the tank ($p_2 > p_2'$). For air ($k = 1.4$) the value of $(p_2/p_1)_c = 0.528$. Isentropic conditions have been assumed in the preceding equations; hence the flows represent those for an ideal fluid. The flows for real fluids are only slightly less than those given by these equations.

Illustrative example 9.4: Air at 80°F flows from a large tank through a converging nozzle of 2.0-in. exit diameter. The discharge is to an atmospheric pressure of 13.5 psia. Determine the flow through the nozzle for pressures within

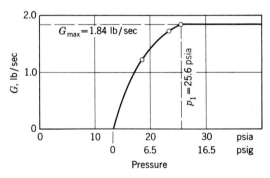

Illustrative Example 9.4

the tank of 5, 10, and 20 psig. Assume isentropic conditions. Plot G as a function of p_1. Assume that the temperature within the tank is 80°F in all cases. From Eq. (9.26) the critical pressure ratio is $(p_2/p_1)_c = 0.528$.

If $\dfrac{p_2'}{p_1} > 0.528$, then subsonic flow will occur at the throat. Sonic flow occurs if

$$\frac{p_2'}{p_1} < 0.528 \quad \text{or} \quad p_1 > \frac{p_2'}{0.528}$$

Since $p_2' = 13.5$ psia, sonic flow occurs if $p_1 > 25.6$ psia (12.1 psig). The maximum flow rate is found from Eq. (9.29) by substituting $p_1 = 25.6$ psia.

$$G_{\max} = \frac{(0.0218)(25.6)(144)}{\sqrt{540}} \sqrt{\frac{32.2(1.4)}{53.3} \left(\frac{2}{2.4}\right)^{2.4/0.4}} = 1.84 \text{ lb/sec}$$

Thus for all values of $p_1 > 12.1$ psig, the flow rate will be 1.84 lb/sec.

To find the flow rate for the conditions where $p_1 < 12.1$ psig (subsonic flow at throat), we use Eq. (9.27). Substituting the appropriate value of p_1 into the equation and noting that for this condition $p_2 = p_2' = 13.5$ psia, we get

For $p_1 = 5$ psig (18.5 psia): $\quad G = 1.20$ lb/sec

For $p_1 = 10$ psig (23.5 psia): $\quad G = 1.69$ lb/sec

The variation of the flow rate with p_1 is shown in the accompanying sketch.

9.11. THE CONVERGING - DIVERGING NOZZLE

If a converging nozzle has attached to it a diverging section, it is possible to attain supersonic velocities in the diverging section. This will happen if sonic flow exists in the throat. In such a case the gas or vapor will continue to expand in the diverging section to lower pressures, and the velocity will continue to increase. The flow through such a converging-diverging nozzle is shown in Fig. 9.5. If there is not enough pressure differential to attain sonic velocity at the throat, the gas or vapor will behave in much the same manner as a liquid, with acceleration in the region up to the throat and deceleration in the diverging section beyond the throat. A plot of the pressure in the flow for such a condition is shown by the dashed lines ABD of Fig. 9.5.

Suppose in Fig. 9.5 that the pressure at (3) continues to decrease, p_1 remaining constant. In such a case the pressure at (2) continues to diminish and the velocity to increase until the limiting acoustic velocity is reached, when the pressure plot is ACE. If the pressure at (3) is further reduced to H, the pressure plot is $ACFGH$, the jump from F to G being a pressure shock, or *normal shock wave*, similar to the hydraulic jump, or standing wave, often seen in open channels conveying water. Through the shock wave the velocity is reduced abruptly from super-

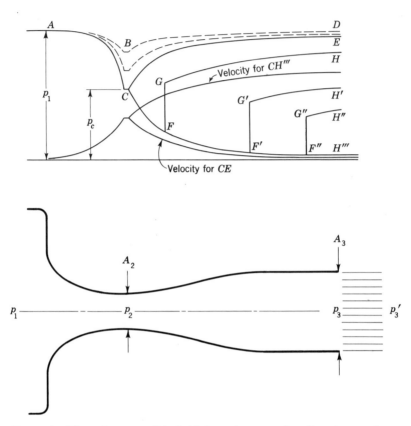

Fig. 9.5.   Flow of compressible fluid through converging-diverging nozzle.

sonic to subsonic, while at the same time the pressure jumps as shown by the lines FG, $F'G'$, and $F''G''$.   The flow through a shock wave is not isentropic, since part of the kinetic energy is converted into heat.   With further reduction of the pressure at (3), the terminal pressure finally becomes H''', so that the pressure history is $ACFH'''$.   In contrast to conditions for flow below sonic velocity, the velocity in the last case continuously increases from (1) to its *maximum* value at (3), which is much *greater* than the sonic velocity, while the pressure *continuously* decreases from (1) to (3).

In Fig. 9.5 the critical pressure at the throat is of course defined by Eq. (9.26), so that $p_c = p_1[2/(k + 1)]^{k/(k-1)}$.   As long as p_1 remains unchanged, the value of p_c remains constant, and thus the rate of discharge through the converging-diverging nozzle is unaffected by any further decrease in the pressure at (3).   When the pressure at (3) is as indicated by H''' in Fig. 9.5, the shock wave will occur in the region downstream of the nozzle outlet.

If p_1 is increased, the sonic velocity may be shown to remain unaltered, but since the density of the gas is increased, the rate of discharge will be greater. The converging nozzle and the converging-diverging nozzle are alike insofar as discharge capacity is concerned. The only difference is that with the converging-diverging nozzle, a supersonic velocity may be attained at discharge from the device, while with the converging nozzle, the sonic velocity is the maximum value possible at any point.

Illustrative example 9.5: Air discharges from a tank through a converging-diverging nozzle with a 2.0-in.-diameter throat. Within the tank the pressure is 50 psia and the temperature is 80°F, while outside the tank the pressure is 13.5 psia. The nozzle is to operate so that the pressure at the outlet (Fig. 9.5, section 3) is 13.5 psia. Find the required diameter of the nozzle outlet. Determine the flow rate and the velocities and temperatures at sections 2 and 3. Assume isentropic flow.

The pressure at the throat will be such that sonic velocity will occur there. Hence $p_2 = p_c = 0.528 p_1 = 26.4$ psia.

The velocity at the outlet may be found from Eq. (9.16).

$$\frac{V_3{}^2}{2g} = RT_1 \frac{k}{k-1} \left[1 - \left(\frac{p_3}{p_1} \right)^{(k-1)/k} \right] = 53.3(540) \frac{1.4}{0.4} \left[1 - \left(\frac{13.5}{50} \right)^{0.4/1.4} \right] = 31,200$$

$$V_3 = 1,420 \text{ fps}$$

The flow rate is computed from Eq. (9.29).

$$G = \frac{0.0218(50 \times 144)}{\sqrt{540}} \sqrt{\frac{32.2(1.4)}{53.3} \left(\frac{2}{2.4} \right)^{2.4/0.4}} = 3.6 \text{ lb/sec}$$

The temperature at (3) may be determined by using Eq. (4.22).

$$\frac{V_3{}^2 - V_1{}^2}{2g} = Jc_p(T_1 - T_3)$$

$$\frac{(1,420)^2}{64.4} = 778(0.24)(540 - T_3)$$

$$T_3 = 372°\text{R} = -88°\text{F}$$

From the perfect-gas law $p_3/\gamma_3 = RT_3$,

$$\gamma_3 = \frac{13.5 \times 144}{53.3(372)} = 0.098 \text{ pcf}$$

Isentropic flow between (2) and (3) may be assumed, since the shock wave does not occur within that region. Thus $p_2/\gamma_2{}^{1.4} = p_3/\gamma_3{}^{1.4}$.

$$\frac{26.4}{\gamma_2{}^{1.4}} = \frac{13.5}{(0.098)^{1.4}}$$

$$\gamma_2 = 0.157 \text{ pcf}$$

The velocity at (2) may now be computed.

$$V_2 = \frac{G}{\gamma_2 A_2} = \frac{3.6}{0.157(0.0218)} = 1{,}050 \text{ fps}$$

The temperature at (2) results from application of Eq. (4.22).

$$\frac{(1{,}420)^2 - (1{,}050)^2}{64.4} = 778(0.24)(T_2 - 372)$$

$$T_2 = 448°\text{R} = -12°\text{F}$$

The area at (3) is computed from

$$A_3 = \frac{G}{\gamma_3 V_3} = \frac{3.6}{0.098(1{,}420)} = 0.0258 \text{ ft}^2$$

Finally, $D_3 = 2.18$ in., required outlet diameter.

9.12. ONE - DIMENSIONAL SHOCK WAVE

In Fig. 9.6 is shown a one-dimensional shock wave where the approaching supersonic flow changes to subsonic flow. This phenomenon is accompanied by a sudden rise in pressure, density, and temperature. Applying the impulse-momentum principle to the fluid in the shock wave, we get

$$\Sigma F_x = p_1 A_1 - p_2 A_2 = \frac{G}{g}(V_2 - V_1) \tag{9.30}$$

Substituting the continuity conditions $(G = \gamma_1 A_1 V_1 = \gamma_2 A_2 V_2)$ and noting that $A_1 = A_2$, we get

$$p_2 - p_1 = \frac{1}{g}(\gamma_1 V_1^2 - \gamma_2 V_2^2) \tag{9.31}$$

which is the pressure jump across the wave.

The energy equation for flow across the shock wave may be expressed as

$$\frac{V_2^2 - V_1^2}{2g} = \frac{k}{k-1}(p_1 v_1 - p_2 v_2) \tag{9.32}$$

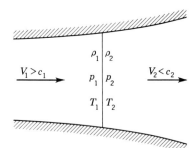

Fig. 9.6.   A one-dimensional normal shock wave.

This is identical with Eq. (4.23). It is suggested that the reader review the development of this equation, in Sec. 4.9.

Equations (9.31) and (9.32) may be solved simultaneously and rearranged algebraically to give some significant relationships. Several such relations are as follows:

$$\frac{p_2}{p_1} = \frac{2kN_{M_1}{}^2 - (k-1)}{k+1} \tag{9.33}$$

$$\frac{V_2}{V_1} = \frac{(k-1)N_{M_1}{}^2 + 2}{(k+1)N_{M_1}{}^2} \tag{9.34}$$

and

$$N_{M_2}{}^2 = \frac{2 + (k-1)N_{M_1}{}^2}{2kN_{M_1}{}^2 - (k-1)} \tag{9.35}$$

These equations permit one to find the physical properties of the flow on the two sides of the one-dimensional shock wave. These equations, of course, are applicable only if $N_{M_1} > 1$; that is, the oncoming flow must be supersonic. It will be seen that the shock wave is analogous to the hydraulic jump in open-channel flow (Sec. 10.18).

9.13. THE OBLIQUE SHOCK WAVE

When the velocity of a body through any fluid, whether a liquid or a gas, exceeds that of a sound wave in the same fluid, the flow conditions are

Fig. 9.7. Schlieren photograph of head wave on 30° (total angle) cone at $N_M = 1.38$. (*Photograph by California Institute of Technology, Guggenheim Aeronautical Laboratory.*)

entirely different from those for all velocities lower than this value. Thus, instead of streamlines such as are shown in Fig. 3.11, the conditions might be as represented in Fig. 9.7, which is a schlieren photograph of supersonic flow past a sharp-nosed model in a wind tunnel. It could also represent a projectile in flight through still air. A conical compression or shock wave extends backward from the tip, as may be seen by the strong density gradient revealed as a bright shadow in the photograph. A streamline in the undisturbed fluid is unaffected by the solid boundary or by a moving projectile until it intersects a shock-wave front, when it is abruptly changed in direction, proceeding roughly parallel to the nose form. Where the conical nose is joined to the cylindrical body of the model, dark shadows may be seen, representing rarefaction waves. The streamlines are again changed in direction through this region, becoming parallel to the main flow again.

The reason why streamlines are unaffected in front of a projectile is that the body travels faster than the disturbance can be transmitted ahead. This will be illustrated by reference to Fig. 9.8. Consider a point source of an infinitesimal disturbance moving at a supersonic velocity V through a fluid. At the instant when this source passes through the point A_0, the disturbance commences to radiate in all directions with the velocity c of a sound wave in this medium. In successive instants the source passes through the points A_1, A_2, and A_3, the last of which may represent the position of the source at the instant of observation. While

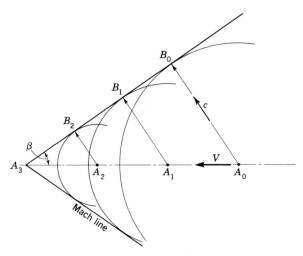

Fig. 9.8. Schematic diagram of disturbance moving with supersonic velocity.

the source has covered the distance $A_0 A_3$ with velocity V, the sound wave, traveling at the slower acoustic velocity c, has progressed only as far as radius $A_0 B_0$. Similar termini of disturbances emanating from A_1 and A_2 form a straight-line envelope, which is the shock wave. The angle β is called the *Mach angle*, and it is seen that

$$\sin \beta = \frac{A_0 B_0}{A_0 A_3} = \frac{c}{V} \tag{9.36}$$

where the dimensionless velocity ratio V/c is the Mach number as derived in Sec. 7.4.

In the case of the finite projectile of Fig. 9.7, the shock wave leaves the tip at an angle with the main flow which exceeds the Mach angle, on account of the conical nose which follows the tip. Appropriate corrections may be applied, however, and the shock-wave angle from such a sharp-nosed object remains an accurate means of measuring supersonic velocities.

9.14. CONCLUDING REMARKS

In this chapter we have seen that in order to solve problems of compressible flow the equation of state of the gas must be combined with the energy equation and the continuity principle. Hence thermodynamics is commonly involved in compressible-flow problems and the expressions relating the various physical parameters are generally quite complicated. In the discussion we have restricted ourselves to one-dimensional flow, and have not considered multidimensional flow, which is of course an extremely important topic, especially when dealing with aircraft and missiles. The intent here was merely to provide an introduction to the flow of compressible fluids. Among the references cited at the end of the book will be found some excellent treatments of compressible flow.

PROBLEMS

9.1. Refer to Illustrative Example 9.1. Find the pressures at sections 100 and 300 ft downstream of the first section. Plot lines equivalent to the hydraulic grade line and the energy line.

9.2. Carbon dioxide flows isothermally at 100°F through a horizontal 6-in.-diameter pipe. The pressure changes from 150.0 to 140.0 psi in a 100-ft length of pipe. Determine the flow rate if the atmospheric pressure is 14.5 psi and ϵ for the pipe is 0.002 ft.

9.3. Refer to Illustrative Example 9.1. How much heat energy must have been added to or subtracted from the flow over the 500-ft length of pipe to maintain the temperature constant?

9.4. Air flows isothermally through a long horizontal pipe of uniform diameter. At a section where the pressure is 100 psia, the velocity is 120 fps. Because of fluid friction the pressure at a distant point is 40 psia. (*a*) What is the increase in kinetic energy per pound of air? (*b*) What is the amount of thermal energy in Btu per pound of air that must be transferred in order to maintain the temperature constant? (*c*) Is this heat transferred to the air in the pipe or removed from it? (*d*) Has the fluid friction in this length of pipe resulted in a loss of total energy or a loss of useful energy?

9.5. If the temperature of air in Prob. 9.4 is 100°F and the diameter of the pipe is 3 in., find the total heat transferred in Btu per hour.

9.6. Air at a pressure of 150 psia and a temperature of 100°F expands in a suitable nozzle to 15 psia. If the flow is frictionless and adiabatic and the initial velocity is negligible, find the final velocity by Eq. (9.16).

9.7. For the case in Prob. 9.6 the final temperature at the end of the expansion will be −170°F, which is the temperature of the air in the jet. Find the jet velocity by Eq. (4.22).

9.8. Derive Eq. (9.16) for isentropic flow by integrating the Euler equation.

9.9. Carbon dioxide flows isentropically. At a point in the flow the velocity is 50 fps and the temperature is 125°F. At a second point on the same streamline the temperature is 80°F. What is the velocity at the second point?

9.10. Refer to Prob. 9.9. If the pressure at the first point were 20 psia, determine the pressure and temperature on the nose of a streamlined object placed in the flow at that point.

9.11. Air flows past an object at 600 fps. The undisturbed air has the physical properties of the standard atmosphere at elevation 10,000 ft (Appendix 3, Table A.3). Find the stagnation pressure by Eqs. (9.19) and (9.20). Note the value of the acoustic (sonic) velocity at this elevation.

9.12. In a high-pressure wind tunnel air at 250 psia is moving at 500 fps at a temperature of 100°F. Find the stagnation pressure and temperature. Note the magnitude of the sonic velocity for the 250-psia 100°F air.

9.13. Show that Eq. (9.20) results from the binomial expansion of Eq. (9.19).

9.14. Determine the acoustic velocity in the atmosphere at sea level and at elevations 5,000, 10,000, 20,000, and 30,000 ft. Assume standard atmosphere (Appendix 3, Table A.3).

9.15. Show in detail the development of Eq. (9.23) from Eqs. (9.21) and (9.22).

9.16. Verify that Eq. (9.26) results from the substitution of N_M at throat equals unity in Eq. (9.25).

9.17. Start with Eq. (9.24) and derive Eq. (9.27).

9.18. Differentiate Eq. (9.27) with respect to p_2/p_1 and set to zero to find the value of p_2/p_1 for which G is a maximum. The answer should correspond to Eq. (9.26).

9.19. Air flows at 150°F from a large tank through a 1.5-in.-diameter converging nozzle. Within the tank the pressure is 85 psia. Calculate the flow rate for external pressures of 10, 30, 50, and 70 psia. Assume isentropic conditions. Plot G as a function of p_2'. Assume that the temperature within the tank is 150°F in all cases. Compute also the temperature at the nozzle outlet for each condition.

9.20. Carbon dioxide within a tank at 40 psia and 80°F discharges through a convergent nozzle into a 14.2-psia atmosphere. Find the velocity, pressure, and temperature at the nozzle outlet. Assume isentropic conditions.

9.21. In Prob. 9.20 if the pressure and temperature within the tank had been 20 psia and 100°F, what would have been the velocity, pressure, and temperature at the nozzle outlet? Assume isentropic conditions.

9.22. Air enters a converging-diverging nozzle at a pressure of 120 psia and a temperature of 90°F. Neglecting the entrance velocity and assuming a frictionless process, find the Mach number at the cross section where the pressure is 35 psia.

9.23. Work Illustrative Example 9.5 with all data the same except for the pressure within the tank, which is 100 rather than 50 psia.

9.24. Air discharges from a large tank through a converging-diverging nozzle. The throat diameter is 3.0 in., and the exit diameter is 4.0 in. Within the tank the air pressure and temperature are 40 psia and 150°F, respectively. Calculate the flow rate for external pressures of 39, 38, 36, and 30 psia. Assume no friction.

9.25. Nitrogen flows from a large tank through a converging-diverging nozzle which has an outlet diameter of 3.0 in. Within the tank the pressure and temperature are 60 psia and 100°F. Outside the tank the pressure is 10.0 psia. Find the maximum possible flow rate through this nozzle, and find the required throat diameter. Assume isentropic flow.

9.26. Air is to flow through a converging-diverging nozzle at 18 lb/sec. At the throat the pressure, temperature, and velocity are to be 20 psia, 100°F, and 500 fps, respectively. At outlet the velocity is to be 200 fps. Determine the throat diameter. Assume isentropic flow.

9.27. Air in a tank under a pressure of 140 psia and 70°F flows out into the atmosphere through a 1.00-in.-diameter converging nozzle. (a) Find the flow rate. (b) If a diverging section (outlet diameter = 1.50 in.) were attached to the converging nozzle, what then would be the flow rate? Neglect friction.

9.28. Repeat Prob. 9.27 for the case where the air within the tank is at 20 psia. Assume all other data to be the same.

9.29. The pressure, velocity, and temperature just upstream of a normal shock wave in air are 10 psia, 2,200 fps, and 23°F. Determine the pressure, velocity, and temperature just downstream of the wave.

9.30. Just downstream of a normal shock wave the pressure, velocity, and temperature are 52 psia, 400 fps, and 120°F. Compute the Mach number upstream of the shock wave. Consider air and carbon dioxide.

9.31. Assuming the tip of the model in Fig. 9.7 to be a point source of infinitesimal disturbance, find the air velocity if the temperature is −60°F and $k = 1.4$. If the actual Mach number is 1.38, what is the percentage error involved in the preceding assumption?

9.32. A schlieren photograph of a bullet shows a Mach angle of 30°. The air is at a pressure of 14 psia and 50°F. Find the approximate speed of the bullet.

TEN

OPEN-CHANNEL FLOW

10.1. OPEN CHANNELS

An open channel is one in which the stream is not completely enclosed by solid boundaries and therefore has a free surface subjected only to atmospheric pressure. The flow in such a channel is caused not by some external head, but rather by the gravity component along the slope of the channel.

The principal types of open channel are natural streams and rivers; artificial canals; and sewers, tunnels, and pipelines not completely filled. Artificial canals may be built to convey water for purposes of water-power development, irrigation or city water supply, and drainage or flood control and for numerous other purposes. While there are examples of open channels carrying liquids other than water, there are few experimental data for such and the numerical coefficients given here apply only to water at natural temperatures.

The accurate solution of problems of flow in open channels is much more difficult than in the case of pressure pipes. Not only are reliable experimental data more difficult to secure, but there is a wider range of conditions than is met with in the case of pipes. Practically all pipes are round, but the cross sections of open channels may be of any shape, from circular to the irregular forms of natural streams. In pipes the degree of roughness ordinarily ranges from that of new smooth metal or wood-stave pipes, on the one hand, to that of old corroded iron or steel pipes, on the other. But with open channels the surfaces vary from that of smooth timber to that of the rough or irregular beds of some rivers. Hence the choice of friction coefficients is attended by greater uncertainty in the case of open channels than in the case of pipes.

Uniform flow was described in Sec. 3.2 as it applies to hydraulic phenomena in general. In the case of open channels uniform flow means that the water cross section and depth remain constant over a certain *reach* of the channel. This requires that the drop in potential energy due to the fall in elevation along the channel be exactly consumed by the energy dissipation through boundary friction and turbulence.

Uniform flow will eventually be established in any channel which continues sufficiently far with a constant slope and cross section. This may be stated in another way, as follows. For any channel of given roughness, cross section, and slope, there exists for a given flow one *and only one* water depth, called y_0, at which the flow will be uniform. Thus, in Fig. 10.1, the flow is accelerating in the reach from A to C, becomes established as uniform flow from C to D, suffers a violent deceleration due to the change of slope between D and E, and finally approaches a new depth of uniform flow somewhere beyond E. There is acceleration in the reach from B to C because the gravity component along the slope is greater than the boundary shear resistance. As the flow accelerates, the boundary

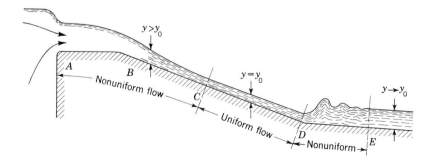

Fig. 10.1. Steady flow down a chute or spillway.

shear increases because of the increase in velocity, until at C the boundary shear resistance becomes equal to the gravity component along the slope. Beyond C there is no acceleration, the velocity is constant, and the flow is uniform. The depth in uniform flow is commonly referred to as the *normal depth* y_0.

Open-channel flow is usually *wholly rough;* hence Reynolds number is not ordinarily of concern. When the occasion calls for it, however, it is usually defined so as to be compatible with that for pipes, or $N_R = 4RV/\nu$, where R is the hydraulic radius (Sec. 8.3).

10.2. HYDRAULIC SLOPE

In open-channel flow we refer to the slope of the *channel bed* S_0, the slope of the *water surface* S_w, and the energy gradient S. It is quite evident that in the case of uniform flow in an open channel the hydraulic grade line coincides with the water surface, for if a piezometer tube is attached to the side of the channel, the water will rise in it until its surface is level with that of the water in the channel. Moreover, in uniform flow the cross section is constant along the channel, and therefore so also is the velocity. Hence the channel bed, water surface (hydraulic grade line), and energy line are all parallel to one another in uniform flow.

The channel-bed slope and water-surface slope are defined as the loss in elevation of channel bed or water surface per unit of horizontal distance along the channel. Thus $S_0 = \tan \theta_0$ and $S_w = \tan \theta_w$, where θ_0 and θ_w are the angles the channel bed and the water surface make with the horizontal, respectively.

The energy gradient (or hydraulic slope) is defined by

$$S = \frac{h_L}{L} \tag{10.1}$$

where h_L is the head loss, and L is the length measured along the channel (not the horizontal). Thus $S = \sin \theta$, where θ is the angle the energy line makes with the horizontal.

In most open channels the bed slope is small, that is, $\theta_0 < 5°$, and thus for uniform flow $\sin \theta \approx \tan \theta$ and $S_0 = S_w \approx S$.

10.3. EQUATION FOR UNIFORM FLOW

In Sec. 8.4 a general equation for frictional resistance in a pressure conduit was developed. The same reasoning may now be applied to uniform flow with a free surface. Consider the short reach of length L between

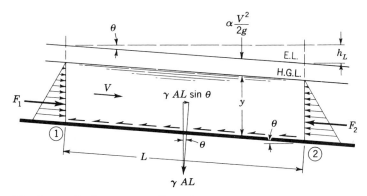

Fig. 10.2. Resistance to uniform flow.

stations (1) and (2) of a channel in uniform flow with area A of the water section (Fig. 10.2). As the flow is neither accelerating nor decelerating, we may consider the body of water contained in the reach in static equilibrium. Summing forces along the channel, the hydrostatic-pressure forces F_1 and F_2 balance each other, since there is no change in the depth y between the stations. The only force in the direction of motion is the gravity component, and this must be resisted by the boundary shear stress τ_0, acting over the area PL, where P is the wetted perimeter of the section. Thus

$$\gamma A L \sin \theta = \tau_0 P L$$

But $\sin \theta = h_L/L = S$. Solving for τ_0, we have

$$\tau_0 = \gamma \frac{A}{P} S = \gamma R S \qquad (10.2)$$

where R is the hydraulic radius, discussed in Sec. 8.3. Substituting the value of τ_0 from Eq. (8.10),

$$\tau_0 = C_f \rho \frac{V^2}{2} = \gamma R S$$

This may be solved for V in terms of either the friction coefficient C_f or the conventional friction factor f to give

$$V = \sqrt{\frac{2g}{C_f} R S} = \sqrt{\frac{8g}{f} R S} \qquad (10.3)$$

10.4. CHÉZY FORMULA

In 1775 Chézy proposed that the velocity in an open channel varied as $\sqrt{RS}$, which led to the formula

$$V = C \sqrt{RS} \qquad (10.4)$$

which is known by his name. It has been widely used both for open channels and for pipes under pressure. Comparing Eqs. (10.4) and (10.3), it is seen that $C = \sqrt{8g/f}$. Despite the simplicity of Eq. (10.4), it has the distinct drawback that C is not a pure number but has the dimensions $L^{1/2}T^{-1}$, requiring that values of C in metric units be converted before being used with English units in the rest of the formula.

As C and f are related, the same considerations that have been presented regarding the determination of a value for f in Chap. 8 apply also to C. For a small open channel with smooth sides, the problem of determining f or C is the same as that in the case of a pipe. But most channels are relatively large compared with pipes, thus giving Reynolds numbers which are higher than those commonly encountered in pipes. Also, open channels are frequently rougher than pipes, especially in the case of natural streams. A study of Fig. 8.10 reveals that, as the Reynolds number and the relative roughness both increase, the value of f becomes practically independent of N_R and depends only on the relative roughness. In 1897 Bazin published his formula for C, which, in view of the foregoing remarks, is not greatly out of line with more modern theory. His formula, expressed in ft-lb-sec units, is

$$C = \frac{157.6}{1 + (m/\sqrt{R})} \qquad (10.5)$$

where m is a measure of the absolute roughness and varies from 0.11 for smooth cement or planed wood to 0.83 for rubble masonry and 2.36 for ordinary earth channels.

10.5. MANNING FORMULA

One of the best as well as one of the most widely used formulas for open-channel flow is that of Robert Manning, who published it in 1890.[1] Manning found from many tests that the value of C varied approximately as $R^{1/6}$, and others observed that the proportionality factor was very close to the reciprocal of n, the coefficient of roughness in the classical Kutter

---

[1] Robert Manning, Flow of Water in Open Channels and Pipes, *Trans. Inst. Civil Engrs. (Ireland)*, vol. 20, 1890.

formula.[1]   This led to the formula which has since spread to all parts of the world.   In metric units, the Manning formula is

$$V = \frac{1}{n} R^{2/3} S^{1/2}$$

The dimensions of n are seen to be $TL^{-1/3}$.*   To avoid converting the numerical value of n for use with English units, the formula itself is changed so as to leave the value of n unaffected.   Thus, in ft-lb-sec units, the Manning formula is

$$V = \frac{1.49}{n} R^{2/3} S^{1/2} \qquad (10.6)$$

where 1.49 is the cube root of 3.28, the number of feet in a meter.   Despite the dimensional difficulties of the Manning formula, which have long plagued those attempting to put all fluid mechanics on a rational dimensionless basis, it continues to be popular because it is simple to use and reasonably accurate.   As n is presumed to vary only with the channel roughness, no trial-and-error solutions are involved in its use.   Representative values of n for various surfaces are given in Table 10.1.

In terms of flow rate Eq. (10.6) may be expressed as

$$Q = AV = \frac{1.49}{n} AR^{2/3} S^{1/2} \qquad (10.7)$$

It was mentioned in Sec. 8.11 that ϵ is a measure of the absolute roughness of the inside of a pipe.   The question naturally arises as to whether ϵ and n may be functionally related to one another.   Such a relation has been proposed by Powell (Fig. 10.3) on the basis of experimental data using the Prandtl-Kármán equation for rough pipes as a guide.   In terms of the hydraulic radius Powell's relation is:

$$\frac{1}{\sqrt{f}} = 2 \log_{10} \left(14.8 \, \frac{R}{\epsilon} \right) \qquad (10.8)$$

[1] The Kutter formula, for many years the most widely used of all open-channel formulas, is now of interest principally for its historical value and as an outstanding example of empirical hydraulics.   This formula, which may be found in several handbooks, included terms to make C a function of S, based on some river-flow data which were later proved in error.   The reader is referred to E. Ganguillet and W. R. Kutter, "Flows of Waters in Rivers and Other Channels," transl. by R. Hering and J. C. Trautwine, Jr., John Wiley & Sons, Inc., New York, 1869.

* As it is unreasonable to suppose that the roughness coefficient should contain the dimension T, the Manning equation is more properly adjusted so as to contain $\sqrt{g}$ in the numerator, thus yielding the dimension of $L^{1/6}$ for n.

Table 10.1   Values of n in Manning's formula
Prepared by R. E. Horton and Others

Nature of surface	n	
	Min	Max
Neat cement surface.....................	0.010	0.013
Wood-stave pipe........................	0.010	0.013
Plank flumes, planed.....................	0.010	0.014
Vitrified sewer pipe.....................	0.010	0.017
Metal flumes, smooth....................	0.011	0.015
Concrete, precast........................	0.011	0.013
Cement mortar surfaces..................	0.011	0.015
Plank flumes, unplaned..................	0.011	0.015
Common-clay drainage tile...............	0.011	0.017
Concrete, monolithic.....................	0.012	0.016
Brick with cement mortar................	0.012	0.017
Cast iron...............................	0.013	0.017
Cement rubble surfaces..................	0.017	0.030
Riveted steel...........................	0.017	0.020
Canals and ditches, smooth earth..........	0.017	0.025
Metal flumes, corrugated.................	0.022	0.030
Canals:		
Dredged in earth, smooth..............	0.025	0.033
In rock cuts, smooth....................	0.025	0.035
Rough beds and weeds on sides.........	0.025	0.040
Rock cuts, jagged and irregular.........	0.035	0.045
Natural streams:		
Smoothest...........................	0.025	0.033
Roughest............................	0.045	0.060
Very weedy..........................	0.075	0.150

The Manning formula may be expressed in terms of $1/\sqrt{f}$ by comparing Eqs. (10.4) and (10.6), from which

$$C = \sqrt{\frac{8g}{f}} = \frac{1.49}{n} R^{\frac{1}{6}}$$

or
$$\frac{1}{\sqrt{f}} = \frac{1.49 R^{\frac{1}{6}}}{n \sqrt{8g}} \tag{10.9}$$

Equating the right-hand sides of Eqs. (10.8) and (10.9) provides the desired correlation between ϵ and n, which is plotted as the solid lines in Fig. 10.3 for three representative values of the hydraulic radius.

The curves of ϵ versus n in Fig. 10.3 must be regarded in the light of the components making up the equation which is plotted. The values of ϵ, for example, were originally determined for artificially roughened pipes

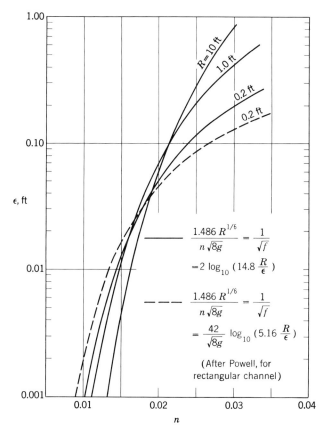

Fig. 10.3. Correlation of n with absolute roughness.

of circular section. We have presumed to extend Eq. (10.8) to open channels of noncircular section with roughness often many times greater than in corresponding pipes. Thus it is not surprising to find a value of n of 0.35, for example, representing a roughness projection in a wide, shallow stream almost equal to the depth. Powell found that Eq. (10.8) did not fit experimental data taken by himself and others on channels of definite roughness.[1] He proposed an equation which, reduced to the form of Eq. (10.8), is shown on Fig. 10.3 and is plotted as a dashed line for a value of $R = 0.2$ ft, which was near the middle of the experimental

[1] R. W. Powell, Resistance to Flow in Rough Channels, *Trans. Am. Geophys. Union*, vol. 31, no. 4, pp. 575–582, 1950; also Flow in a Channel of Definite Roughness, *Trans. ASCE*, vol. 3, pp. 531–566, 1946; see also J. W. Johnson, Rectangular Roughness in Open Channels, *Trans. Am. Geophys. Union*, vol. 25, pt. VI, pp. 906–914, 1944.

range observed.   Powell's equation in this form is valid only for rectangular channels.   Despite the discrepancies in the correlation functions from different sources, the salient feature of the curves is at once apparent.   A *threefold* increase in n (as between the practical values of 0.01 to 0.03) represents something between a *hundred-* and a *thousandfold* increase in ϵ.   That is why the value of ϵ can be in error up to 100 per cent without causing an error of more than a few per cent in the velocity or rate of discharge.

The relationship between n and f as expressed by Eq. (10.9), i.e., $n = \text{constant} \times \sqrt{f}\, R^{\frac{1}{6}}$, indicates that n depends on the conduit size, a fact that is not often appreciated by engineers.   A conduit with $\epsilon = 0.001$ ft, for example, with a hydraulic radius of 1.0 ft will have an n of 0.011 while another conduit with the same surface roughness but with $R = 8.75$ ft will have an n of 0.013.   At small values of ϵ ($\epsilon < 0.03$ ft) the value of n increases with increasing conduit size.[1]   At larger values of ϵ the reverse is true.   That this is so may be seen by inspecting Fig. 10.3.

Illustrative example 10.1:   Find the depth for uniform flow in this channel when the flow rate is 225 cfs if $S_0 = 0.0006$ and n is assumed to be 0.016.   Compute the corresponding value of ϵ.

$$A = (10 + 2y)y$$

and $$R = \frac{A}{P} = \frac{(10 + 2y)y}{10 + 2 \times \sqrt{5}\, y}$$

Thus $$Q = 225 = \frac{1.49}{0.016}(10 + 2y)y\left[\frac{(10 + 2y)y}{10 + 2 \times \sqrt{5}\, y}\right]^{\frac{2}{3}}(0.0006)^{\frac{1}{2}}$$

By trial, $y_0 = 3.4$ ft, uniform flow depth,

$$A = [10 + 2(3.4)]3.4 = 57.0 \text{ ft}^2$$
$$P = 10 + 2 \times \sqrt{5}\,(3.4) = 25.2 \text{ ft}$$
$$R = \frac{A}{P} = \frac{57.0}{25.2} = 2.26 \text{ ft}$$

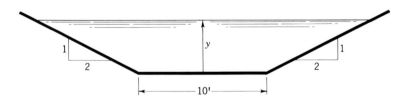

Illustrative Example 10.1

[1] J. B. Franzini and P. S. Chisholm, Current Practice in Hydraulic Design of Conduits, *Water and Sewage Works*, vol. 110, pp. 342-345, Oct., 1963.

Rearranging Eq. (10.9),

$$f = \frac{116n^2}{R^{1/3}} = 0.0227$$

Finally, using Eq. (10.8),

$$\epsilon = 0.0164 \text{ ft}$$

10.6. VELOCITY DISTRIBUTION IN OPEN CHANNELS

Vanoni[1] has demonstrated that the Prandtl universal logarithmic velocity-distribution law for pipes [Eq. (8.28)] also applies to a two-dimensional open channel, i.e., one which is infinitely wide. This equation may be written

$$\frac{u - u_{\max}}{\sqrt{gyS}} = \frac{2.3}{K} \log_{10} \frac{y'}{y}$$

where y = depth of water in channel

u = velocity at a distance y' from channel bed

K = von Kármán constant, having a value of about 0.40 for clear water[2]

This expression can be integrated over the depth to yield the more useful relation

$$u = V + \frac{1}{K} \sqrt{gyS} \left(1 + 2.3 \log_{10} \frac{y'}{y} \right) \qquad (10.10)$$

which expresses the distribution law in terms of the mean velocity V. This equation is plotted in Fig. 10.4, together with velocity measurements that were made on the center line of a rectangular flume 2.77 ft wide and 0.59 ft deep. The filament whose velocity u is equal to V is seen to lie at a distance of $0.632y$ beneath the surface.

Velocity measurements made in a trapezoidal canal, reported by O'Brien,[3] gave the distribution contours shown in Fig. 10.5, with the accompanying values of the correction factors for kinetic energy and momentum. The point of maximum velocity is seen to lie beneath the surface, and the correction factors for kinetic energy and momentum are greater than in the corresponding case of pipe flow. Despite the added importance of these factors, however, the treatment in this chapter follows the earlier procedure of assuming the values of α and β to be

[1] V. A. Vanoni, Velocity Distribution in Open Channels, *Civil Eng.*, vol. 11, pp. 356–357, 1941.

[2] For sediment laden water the value of K may be as low as 0.2.

[3] M. P. O'Brien and J. W. Johnson, Velocity Head Correction for Hydraulic Flow, *Eng. News-Record*, vol. 113, pp. 214–216, 1934.

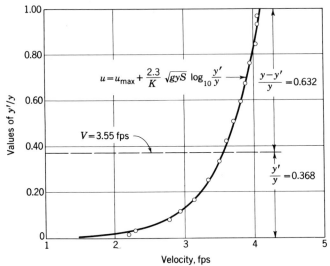

Fig. 10.4. Velocity profile at center of a flume 2.77 ft wide for a flow 0.59 ft deep. (*After Vanoni, Civil Eng., vol.* 11, 1941.)

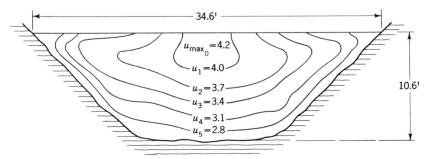

Fig. 10.5. Velocity distribution in trapezoidal canal. $V = 3.32$ fps, $A = 230.5$ ft², $S = 0.000057$, $\alpha = 1.105$, $\beta = 1.048$. (*After O'Brien, Eng. News-Record, vol.* 113, 1934.)

unity, unless stated otherwise. Any thoroughgoing analysis would of course have to take account of their true values.

10.7. MOST EFFICIENT CROSS SECTION

Any of the open-channel formulas given above show that, for a given slope and roughness, the velocity increases with the hydraulic radius. Therefore, for a given area of water cross section, the rate of discharge will be a maximum when R is a maximum, which is to say, when the wetted perimeter is a minimum. Such a section is called the *most efficient cross section* for the given area. Or for a given rate of discharge, the cross-sectional area will be a minimum when the design is such as to make R a maximum (and thus P a minimum). This section would be the most efficient cross section for the given rate of discharge.

Of all geometric figures the circle has the least perimeter for a given area. The hydraulic radius of a semicircle is the same as that of a circle. Hence a semicircular open channel will discharge more water than one of any other shape, assuming that the area, slope, and surface roughness are the same. Semicircular open channels are often built of pressed steel and other forms of metal, but for other types of construction such a shape is impractical. For wooden flumes the rectangular shape is usually employed. Canals excavated in earth must have a trapezoidal cross section, with side slopes less than the *angle of repose* of the bank material. Thus there are other factors besides hydraulic efficiency which determine the best cross section. For given side slopes and area, however, it is possible to determine the shape of the water cross section so that the wetted perimeter, and thus the cost of the channel grading and lining, will be a minimum.

For the trapezoidal channel of Fig. 10.6,

$$A = By + y^2 \tan \phi \qquad \text{and} \qquad P = B + 2y \sec \phi$$

Substituting for B in terms of A gives

$$P = \frac{A}{y} - y \tan \phi + 2y \sec \phi$$

Differentiating with respect to y and equating to zero,

$$\frac{A}{y^2} = \frac{By + y^2 \tan \phi}{y^2} = 2 \sec \phi - \tan \phi$$

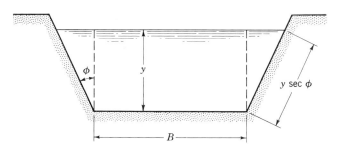

Fig. 10.6

from which $$B = 2y(\sec \phi - \tan \phi) \qquad (10.11)$$

Note that, for the rectangular channel ($\phi = 0$), the most efficient section will have a width of twice the depth.

The hydraulic radius of any cross section of greatest efficiency may now be evaluated from

$$R = \frac{A}{P} = \frac{y^2(2 \sec \phi - \tan \phi)}{2y(2 \sec \phi - \tan \phi)} = \frac{y}{2} \qquad (10.12)$$

To find the side slope giving the greatest possible efficiency for a trapezoidal section, we set P as a function of A (which is constant) and the variable ϕ, then differentiate and equate to zero. From the above relations for most efficient section, $P = 2\sqrt{A(2 \sec \phi - \tan \phi)}$. The differentiation is simpler if we first square P; then

$$\frac{d(P^2)}{d\phi} = 4A(2 \tan \phi \sec \phi - \sec^2 \phi) = 0$$

from which we can see that $\sec \phi = 2 \tan \phi$, $\sin \phi = \frac{1}{2}$, and $\phi = 30°$. The second derivative is positive, indicating that this is a true minimum. This, together with the relation of Eq. (10.11), demonstrates that the most efficient of all trapezoidal sections is the half hexagon.

10.8. CIRCULAR SECTIONS NOT FLOWING FULL

In circular pipes, flow frequently occurs at partial depth. The maximum rate of discharge in such a section occurs at slightly less than full depth, as may be shown by reference to Fig. 10.7. Thus

$$A = \frac{D^2}{4}(\theta - \sin \theta \cos \theta) = \frac{D^2}{4}(\theta - \tfrac{1}{2} \sin 2\theta)$$

$$P = D\theta$$

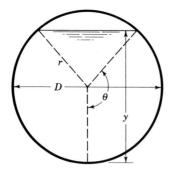

Fig. 10.7.   Circular section not full.

where θ is expressed in radians. This gives

$$R = \frac{A}{P} = \frac{D}{4}\left(1 - \frac{\sin\theta\cos\theta}{\theta}\right) = \frac{D}{4}\left(1 - \frac{\sin 2\theta}{2\theta}\right)$$

For the maximum rate of discharge, the Manning formula indicates that $AR^{2/3}$ must be a maximum. This expression may be established from the preceding relations, then differentiated with respect to θ, set equal to zero, and solved, giving $\theta = 151.15°$. The corresponding value of the depth y is $0.938D$. The maximum velocity will be found to occur at $0.81D$.* Despite the foregoing analysis, circular sections are usually designed to carry the design capacity when flowing full, since the conditions producing maximum flow would frequently include sufficient backwater to place the conduit under slight pressure.

The rectangle, trapezoid, and circle are the simplest geometric shapes from the standpoint of hydraulics, but other forms of cross section are often used, either because they have certain advantages in construction or because they are desirable from other standpoints. Thus oval- or egg-shaped sections are common for sewers and similar channels where there may be large fluctuations in the rate of discharge. It is desirable that the velocity, when a small quantity is flowing, be kept high enough to prevent the deposit of sediment, and when the conduit is full, the velocity should not be so high as to cause excessive wear of the pipe wall.

10.9. SPECIFIC ENERGY AND ALTERNATE DEPTHS OF FLOW—WIDE RECTANGULAR CHANNELS

Totally separate from the concept of energy gradient, or energy difference, between two sections of a stream is the matter of the energy *at a single section* with reference to the channel bed (Fig. 10.8a). This is called the *specific energy* at that section, and its value is given by the following equation:

$$E = y + \frac{V^2}{2g} \tag{10.13}$$

In this section, for simplicity, we shall confine the discussion to very wide rectangular channels.

---

* The above derivation is based upon a roughness coefficient which remains constant as the depth changes. Actually, the value of n has been shown to increase by as much as 28 per cent from the full to about one-quarter full depth, where it appears to be a maximum. This effect causes the actual maximum discharge and velocity to occur at water depths of about 0.97 and 0.83 full depth, respectively. See Design and Construction of Sanitary and Storm Sewers, *ASCE Manual Eng. Practice* 37, pp. 94–95, 1960.

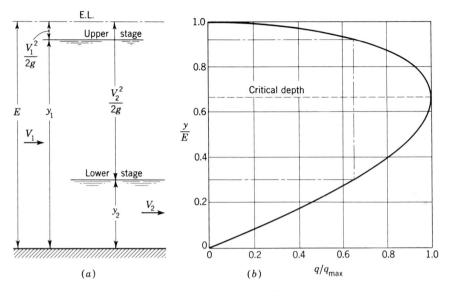

Fig. 10.8.   Depth-discharge curve for constant specific energy.

If q denotes the flow per unit width of a wide rectangular channel, then $V = q/y$ and

$$E = y + \frac{q^2}{2gy^2} \tag{10.14}$$

or
$$q = y \sqrt{2g(E - y)} \tag{10.15}$$

This is the equation of the curve which is shown in dimensionless form in Fig. 10.8b. It is seen that the maximum discharge for a given specific energy occurs when the depth is between $0.6E$ and $0.7E$. This may be established more exactly by differentiating Eq. (10.15) with respect to y and equating to zero. Thus

$$\frac{dq}{dy} = \sqrt{2g} \left(\sqrt{E - y} - \frac{1}{2} \frac{y}{\sqrt{E - y}} \right) = 0$$

from which
$$y_c = \tfrac{2}{3}E \tag{10.16}$$

where y_c is called the *critical depth* for the given specific energy. The maximum rate of discharge for a given specific energy may now be determined by substituting from Eq. (10.16) into Eq. (10.15):

$$q_{max} = \sqrt{g} \, (\tfrac{2}{3}E)^{3/2} = \sqrt{gy_c^3} \tag{10.17}$$

Figure 10.8 shows that any rate of discharge less than the maximum can occur at two different depths for a given value of specific energy. On the upper limb of the curve, the flow is said to be *upper-stage*, or *tranquil,* while on the lower limb it is called *lower-stage,* or *rapid,* flow. The velocity and rate of discharge occurring at the critical depth are termed V_c and $q_c = q_{max}$, the *critical* velocity and flow, respectively. On account of the greater area, the velocity of upper-stage flow is slower than the critical and is called *subcritical* velocity; likewise *supercritical* velocity occurs at lower-stage conditions. Hence the flow is most commonly referred to as subcritical or supercritical.[1] Combining Eqs. (10.16) and (10.13) yields a simple expression for critical velocity,

$$\frac{V_c^2}{2g} = \frac{y_c}{2} \qquad \text{or} \qquad V_c = \sqrt{gy_c} \qquad (10.18)$$

Thus a condition of subcritical or supercritical flow may readily be tested by determining whether the velocity head is less than or greater than half the depth, respectively. This critical velocity bears no relation to the one which separates laminar from turbulent flow. It should be noted that, because of the relationship between velocities and depths, whenever the depth of flow is greater than y_c, the flow is subcritical; also, if the depth is less than y_c, the flow is supercritical.

All the foregoing treatment of alternate depths has been based on a specific energy which has been assumed constant while different depths and rates of discharge were considered. The case may now be put differently, and we may ask about the possible depths corresponding to different specific energies for a *given rate of discharge.* Equation (10.14) is plotted on the specific-energy diagram in Fig. 10.9 for three successively increasing constant rates of discharge per unit width, q, q', and q''. In this diagram the critical depth appears as the depth of minimum specific energy for a given flow. As this has the same meaning as the depth producing maximum discharge for a given specific energy, y_c may be evaluated from Eq. (10.17) for any value of q:

$$y_c = \sqrt[3]{\frac{q^2}{g}} \qquad (10.19)$$

This result may be obtained independently by differentiating Eq. (10.14) with respect to y and equating to zero.

It will be observed in Fig. 10.9 that the depth, while plotted vertically to determine the curve, is also represented by the horizontal distance from the vertical axis to the 45° line. It is also seen that the upper limb of the curve corresponds to subcritical flow, while the lower limb refers to the alternate condition of supercritical flow, as was the case in Fig. 10.8.

We may summarize much of the foregoing discussion as axioms of

[1] It may be shown that, when the Froude number $N_F < 1$, the flow in an open channel is subcritical while if $N_F > 1$, the flow is supercritical.

open-channel flow related to conditions at a given section in a rectangular channel:

1. A flow condition, i.e., a certain rate of discharge flowing at a certain depth, is completely specified by any two of the variables y, q, V, and E, except the combination q and E, which yields in general two alternate stages of flow.

2. For any value of E there exists a critical depth, given by Eq. (10.16), for which the flow is a maximum.

3. For any value of q there exists a critical depth, given by Eq. (10.19), for which the specific energy is a minimum.

4. When flow occurs at critical depth, both Eqs. (10.16) and (10.18) are satisfied and the velocity head is one-half the depth.

5. For any flow condition other than critical, there exists an alternate stage at which the same rate of discharge is carried by the same specific energy. The alternate depth may be found from either the discharge curve (Fig. 10.8) or the specific-energy diagram (Fig. 10.9), by extending a vertical line to the alternate limb of the curve. Analytically, the alternate depth is found by solving Eq. (10.14), which may be reduced from a cubic to a quadratic equation by dividing by $y - y_1$, where y_1 is the alternate depth which is known.

10.10. CHANNEL SLOPE AND ALTERNATE DEPTHS OF FLOW

It will now be emphasized again that uniform flow occurs at a depth which depends only on the rate of discharge, the shape and roughness of the cross section, and the slope of the stream bed. If, for a given roughness and shape, the channel slope is such that the uniform flow is subcritical, the slope is said to be *mild*. If the uniform flow is supercritical, the slope is termed *steep*. Thus the hydraulic steepness of a channel slope is determined by more than its elevation gradient. A steep slope for a channel with a smooth lining could be a mild slope for the same flow in a channel with a rough lining. Even for a given channel, the slope may be mild for a low rate of discharge and steep for a higher one.

The slope of a channel which will just sustain the given rate of discharge in uniform flow at critical depth is termed the *critical* slope S_c. Evidently, for a given cross section and rate of discharge, the uniform flow is upper-stage if $S < S_c$ and lower-stage if $S > S_c$. In Fig. 10.9 it is seen that, when the flow is near critical, a small change in specific energy results in a large change in depth. With flow at or near critical depth there will be an undulating stream surface. Because of this it is undesirable to design channels with slopes near the critical.

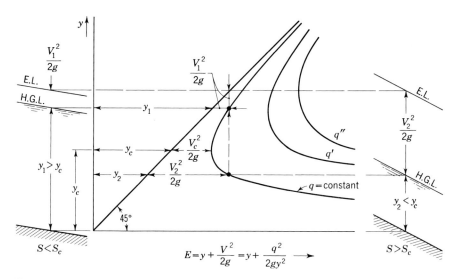

Fig. 10.9. Specific-energy diagram for three constant rates of discharge. (Bottom slopes are greatly exaggerated.)

10.11. CRITICAL DEPTH IN NONRECTANGULAR CHANNELS

For simplicity of explanation, the treatment of critical depth in Sec. 10.9 was confined to wide rectangular channels. We shall now consider an irregular section (Fig. 10.10) of area A carrying a flow Q. Thus Eq. (10.14) becomes

$$E = y + \frac{Q^2}{2gA^2} \qquad (10.20)$$

Differentiating with respect to y,

$$\frac{dE}{dy} = 1 - \frac{Q^2}{2g}\left(\frac{2}{A^3}\frac{dA}{dy}\right)$$

This may now be set equal to zero and solved for the value of the critical depth for the given flow. As A may or may not be a reasonable function of y, it is helpful to observe that $dA = B\,dy$, and thus $dA/dy = B$, the width of the water *surface*. Substituting this in the above expression results in

$$\frac{Q^2}{g} = \left(\frac{A^3}{B}\right)_{y=y_c} \qquad (10.21)$$

as the equation which must be satisfied for critical flow. For a given cross section the right-hand side is a function of y only. A trial-and-error

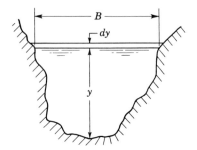

Fig. 10.10

solution is generally required to find the value y_c of y which satisfies Eq. (10.21).

We may next solve for V_c, the critical velocity in the irregular channel, by observing that $Q = A_c V_c$. Substituting this in Eq. (10.21) yields

$$\frac{V_c^2}{g} = \frac{A_c}{B_c} \quad \text{or} \quad V_c = \sqrt{\frac{gA_c}{B_c}} \tag{10.22}$$

If the channel is rectangular, $A_c = B_c y_c$, and the above is seen to reduce to Eq. (10.18).

It has already been pointed out that the cross section most commonly encountered in open-channel hydraulics is not rectangular but trapezoidal. As repeated trial-and-error solutions of Eq. (10.21) become very tedious, the practicing hydraulic engineer avails himself of numerous tables and curves which have been prepared for finding the critical depth in trapezoidal channels of any bottom width and side slopes.[1]

Illustrative example 10.2: In the accompanying figure, water flows uniformly at a steady rate of 14.0 cfs in a very long triangular flume which has side slopes 1:1. The bottom of the flume is on a slope of 0.006, and $n = 0.012$. Is the flow subcritical or supercritical?

$$A = \tfrac{1}{2}(2y)y = y^2$$
$$P = 2\sqrt{2}\,y = 2.83y$$
$$R = \frac{A}{P} = 0.354y$$

From Eq. (10.7),

$$14 = \frac{1.49}{0.012}\,y_0^2(0.354y_0)^{2/3}(0.006)^{1/2}$$

---

[1] S. Kolupaila, Universal Diagram Gives Critical Depth in Trapezoidal Channels, *Civil Eng.*, vol. 20, p. 785, 1950; discussion of this, with simplified single curve, by C. G. Edson in *ibid.*, vol. 21, p. 159, 1951. See also tables 8.1 to 8.3 in H. W. King and E. F. Brater, "Handbook of Hydraulics," 5th ed., McGraw-Hill Book Company, New York, 1963.

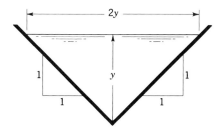

Illustrative Example 10.2

from which $y_0 = 1.495$ ft, uniform flow depth,

$$\frac{Q^2}{g} = \frac{A^3}{b}$$

$$\frac{(14)^2}{32.2} = \frac{(y_c^2)^3}{2y_c}$$

and $y_c = 1.65$ ft

Since y_c is greater than uniform flow depth, the flow is supercritical.

10.12. OCCURRENCE OF CRITICAL DEPTH

When flow changes from subcritical to supercritical or vice versa, the depth must pass through critical depth.   In the former, the phenomenon gives rise to what is known as a *control section*.   In the latter a hydraulic jump (Sec. 10.18) usually occurs.   In Fig. 10.11 is depicted a situation where the flow changes from subcritical to supercritical.   Upstream of the break in slope there is a *mild* slope, the flow is subcritical, and $y_{0_1} > y_c$. Downstream of the break there is a *steep* slope, the flow is supercritical, and $y_{0_2} < y_c$.   At the break in slope the depth passes through critical depth.   This point in the stream is referred to as a control section since the depth at the break controls the depth upstream.   A similar situation occurs when water from a reservoir enters a canal in which the uniform

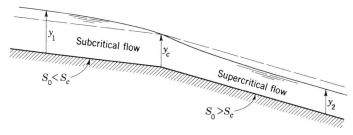

Fig. 10.11.   Change in flow from subcritical to supercritical at a break in the slope.

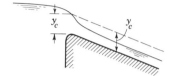

Fig. 10.12.   Hydraulic drop entering steep slope.

depth is less than critical.   In such an instance (Fig. 10.12), the depth
passes through critical depth in the vicinity of the entrance to the canal.
Once again, this section is known as a control section.   By measuring the
depth at a control section, one can compute a reasonably accurate value
of Q by application of Eq. (10.19) for rectangular channels or Eq. (10.22)
for nonrectangular channels.

Another instance where critical depth occurs is that of a free outfall
(Fig. 10.13a) with subcritical flow in the channel prior to the outfall.
Since friction produces a constant diminution in energy in the direction
of flow, it is obvious that at the point of outfall the total energy H must
be less than at any point upstream.   As the critical depth is the value for
which the specific energy is a minimum, this should apparently be the
depth of the stream at this point.   However, the value for the critical
depth is derived on the assumption that the water is flowing in straight
lines.   In the free outfall gravity creates a curvature of the streamlines,
with the result that the depth at the brink is less than critical depth.
It has been found by experiment that the depth at the brink $y_b \approx 0.72 y_c$.
Also, critical depth generally occurs upstream of the brink a distance of

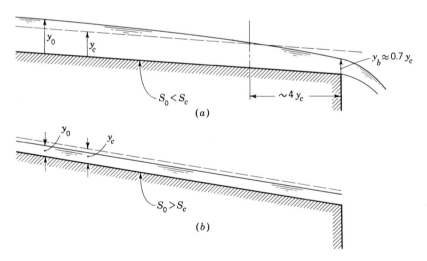

Fig. 10.13.   Free outfall.   (*a*) Mild slope.   (*b*) Steep slope.

somewhere between $3y_c$ and $10y_c$. If the flow is supercritical, there is no drop-down curve (Fig. 10.13b).

Critical depth may occur in a channel if the bottom is humped or if the sidewalls are moved in to form a contracted section. In such cases critical depth will not always occur (Illustrative Example 10.3). Generally, the head loss through such a contraction is very small and may usually be neglected without introducing a sizable error.

Illustrative example 10.3: In the accompanying figure, subcritical uniform flow of water occurs in a 4-ft-wide rectangular flume at a depth of 2.0 ft. A hump of height 0.3 ft is placed in the bottom of the flume. Compute the water depth on the hump if the flow rate is 27 cfs. Neglecting head loss,

$$2.0 + \frac{V_1^2}{2g} = 0.3 + y_2 + \frac{V_2^2}{2g} \qquad (a)$$

By continuity,

$$4 \times 2 \times V_1 = 4y_2V_2$$

and

$$V_2 = \frac{2V_1}{y_2}$$

But

$$V_1 = \frac{27}{4 \times 2} = 3.38 \text{ fps}$$

Hence

$$V_2 = \frac{6.76}{y_2} \qquad (b)$$

Solving Eqs. (a) and (b) simultaneously gives

$$y_2 = 1.6 \text{ ft}$$

From Eq. (10.19),

$$y_c = \sqrt[3]{\frac{q^2}{g}} = \left[\frac{(27/4)^2}{32.2} \right]^{\frac{1}{3}} = 1.12 \text{ ft}$$

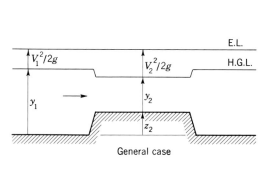

General case

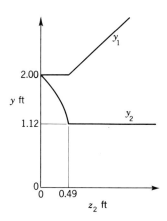

Illustrative Example 10.3

Since $y_2 = 1.6$ ft $> y_c = 1.12$ ft, the flow is subcritical and the depth on the hump is 1.6 ft. Thus, on the hump, there is a drop in the water surface of 0.10 ft.

As a second part of this problem, find how high the hump must be in order for critical depth to occur on it when the flow rate is 27 cfs.

$$2.0 + \frac{V_1^2}{2g} = z_2 + 1.12 + \frac{V_2^2}{2g} \tag{a'}$$

$$V_2 = \frac{27}{4 \times 1.12} = 6.03 \text{ fps} \tag{b'}$$

$$V_1 = \frac{27}{4 \times 2} = 3.38 \text{ fps} \tag{c'}$$

Substituting (b') and (c') in (a') gives

$$z_2 = 0.49 \text{ ft}$$

Thus the minimum-height hump that will produce critical depth on the hump is 0.49 ft. Lesser humps will depress the water surface as shown in the left-hand sketch. Humps higher than 0.49 ft will raise the upstream water level. The higher type of hump is commonly built of concrete and used for flow-measuring purposes. Such structures are discussed under broad-crested weirs, in Sec. 11.23. The right-hand sketch shows the relation between the hump height z_2 and the water depths y_1 and y_2 for the condition where $Q = 27$ cfs.

In the foregoing example the water surface dropped in the vicinity of the hump. However, if the flow had been supercritical, the water surface would have risen. That this is so may be seen by referring to Fig. 10.9. The specific energy is reduced at the hump section by an amount equivalent to the height of the hump. The reduction in specific energy corresponds to an increased depth (Fig. 10.9) on the lower limb (supercritical flow) or a decreased depth on the upper limb (subcritical flow). A similar pattern of reasoning applied to Fig. 10.8 demonstrates that if the channel were contracted laterally, the water surface would drop for subcritical flow or rise for supercritical flow.

10.13. NONUNIFORM OR VARIED, FLOW

As a rule, uniform flow is found only in artificial channels of constant shape and slope, although even under these conditions the flow for some distance may be nonuniform, as shown in Fig. 10.1. But with a natural stream the slope of the bed and the shape and size of the cross section usually vary to such an extent that true uniform flow is rare. Hence the application of the equations given in Secs. 10.3 to 10.5 to natural streams can be expected to yield results that are only approximations to the truth. In order to apply these equations at all, the stream must be divided into lengths within which the conditions are approximately the same.

In the case of artificial channels which are free from the irregularities found in natural streams, it is possible to apply analytical methods to the various problems of nonuniform flow. In many instances, however, the formulas developed are merely approximations, and we must often resort to trial solutions and even purely empirical methods.[1]

In the case of pressure conduits, we have dealt with uniform and nonuniform flow without drawing much distinction between them. This can be done because in a closed pipe the area of the water section, and hence the mean velocity, is fixed at every point. But in an open channel these conditions are not fixed, and the stream adjusts itself to the size of cross section that the slope of the hydraulic gradient requires.

In an open stream on a falling grade the effect of gravity is to tend to produce a flow with a continually increasing velocity along the path, as in the case of a freely falling body. The gravity force is opposed by the frictional resistance. The frictional force increases with velocity, while gravity is constant; so eventually the two will be in balance, and uniform flow will occur. When the two forces are not in balance, the flow is nonuniform.

There are two types of nonuniform flow. In one the changing conditions extend over a long distance, and this may be called *gradually varied flow*. In the other the change may take place very abruptly and the transition is thus confined to a short distance. This may be designated as a *local nonuniform phenomenon*. Gradually varied flow can occur at either subcritical or supercritical flow, but the transition from one stage to the other is ordinarily abrupt, as between D and F in Fig. 10.1. Other cases of local nonuniform flow occur at the entrance and exit of a channel, at changes in cross section, at bends, and at obstructions such as dams, weirs, or bridge piers.

10.14. ENERGY EQUATION FOR GRADUALLY VARIED FLOW

The principal forces involved in flow in an open channel are inertia, gravity, hydrostatic force due to change in depth, and friction. The first three represent the useful kinetic and potential energies of the liquid, while the fourth dissipates useful energy into the useless kinetic energy of turbulence and eventually into heat because of the action of viscosity. Referring to Fig. 10.14, the total energy of the elementary volume of liquid shown is proportional to

$$H = z + y + \alpha \frac{V^2}{2g} \qquad (10.23)$$

[1] For the treatment of many types of flow see Ven Te Chow, "Open-channel Hydraulics," McGraw-Hill Book Company, New York, 1959.

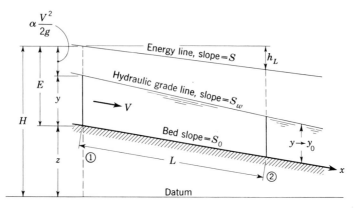

Fig. 10.14. Energy relations for nonuniform flow.

where $z + y$ is the potential energy head above the arbitrary datum, and $\alpha V^2/2g$ is the kinetic energy head, V being the mean velocity in the section. Each term of the equation represents energy in foot-pounds per pound of fluid.

The value of α will generally be found to be higher in open channels than in pipes, as was explained in Sec. 10.6. It may range from 1.05 to 1.40, and in the case of a channel with an obstruction the value of α just upstream, it may be as high as 2.00 or even more. As the value of α is not known unless the velocity distribution is determined, it is often omitted, but an effort should be made to employ it if accuracy is necessary. In the numerical problems in this chapter it is assumed to be unity.

Differentiating Eq. (10.23) with respect to x, the distance along the channel, the rate of energy dissipation is found to be (with $\alpha = 1$)

$$\frac{dH}{dx} = \frac{dz}{dx} + \frac{dy}{dx} + \frac{1}{2g}\frac{d(V^2)}{dx} \tag{10.24}$$

The slope of the energy line is defined as $S = -dH/dx$, while the slope of the channel bed is $S_0 = -dz/dx$, and the slope of the hydraulic grade line or water surface is given by $S_w = -dz/dx - dy/dx$.

The energy equation between two sections (1) and (2) of Fig. 10.14 a distance L apart is

$$z_1 + y_1 + \alpha_1 \frac{V_1^2}{2g} = z_2 + y_2 + \alpha_2 \frac{V_2^2}{2g} + h_L \tag{10.25}$$

As $z_1 - z_2 = S_0 L$ and $h_L = SL$, the energy equation may also be written in the form (with $\alpha_1 = \alpha_2 = 1$)

$$y_1 + \frac{V_1^2}{2g} = y_2 + \frac{V_2^2}{2g} + (S - S_0)L \tag{10.26}$$

The Manning equation (10.6) for uniform flow can be applied to non-uniform flow with an accuracy dependent on the length of the reach taken. Thus a long stream will be divided into several reaches of varying length such that the change in depth is roughly the same within each reach. Then, within a reach, the Manning formula gives

$$S = \left(\frac{n V_m}{1.49 R_m^{2/3}} \right)^2 \tag{10.27}$$

where V_m and R_m are the means of the respective values at the two ends of the reach. With S_0 and n known and the depth and velocity at one end of the reach given, the length L to the end corresponding to the other depth can be computed from Eq. (10.26), rearranged as follows:

$$L = \frac{(y_1 + V_1^2/2g) - (y_2 + V_2^2/2g)}{S - S_0} \tag{10.28}$$

Illustrative example 10.4: At a certain section in a 6-ft-wide rectangular channel the depth is 3.00 ft when the flow rate is 160 cfs. Compute the distance to the section where the depth is 3.20 ft if $S_0 = 0.002$ and $n = 0.012$.

$$Q = \frac{1.49}{n} A R^{2/3} S^{1/2} = \left(\frac{1.49}{0.012} \right) 6 y_0 \left(\frac{6 y_0}{6 + 2 y_0} \right)^{2/3} (0.002)^{1/2} = 160 \text{ cfs}$$

By trial, $\qquad\qquad\qquad y_0 = 3.5$ ft

Critical depth occurs when

$$\frac{Q^2}{g} = \frac{A^3}{b} \qquad \text{or} \qquad \frac{(160)^2}{32.2} = \frac{(6 y_c)^3}{6}$$

from which $y_c = 2.8$ ft. Since $y_0 > y_c$, the flow is subcritical and the depth increases toward normal depth as one proceeds upstream. The calculations are shown in the following table. The total distance is calculated to be 73 ft. The accuracy could be improved by taking more steps. In computing $S - S_0$, a slight error in the calculated value of S will introduce a sizable error in the calculated value of L. Thus it is important that S be calculated as accurately as possible, preferably by use of an electric calculator.

y, ft	A, ft²	P $(6 + 2y)$, ft	R, ft	V, fps	$V^2/2g$, ft	$y + \frac{V^2}{2g}$	Numerator $\Delta \left(y + \frac{V^2}{2g} \right)$	V_{avg}, fps	R_{avg}, ft	S	Denomi-nator $S - S_0$	L, ft
3.00	18.00	12.00	1.500	8.89	1.227	4.227						
							0.022	8.74	1.512	0.00284	0.00084	26
3.10	18.60	12.20	1.525	8.60	1.149	4.249						
							0.029	8.47	1.536	0.00262	0.00062	47
3.20	19.20	12.40	1.548	8.33	1.078	4.278						

$$\Sigma = 73$$

10.15. CRITICAL VELOCITY AND CELERITY OF GRAVITY WAVES

In Sec. 10.9 it was learned that a channel laid on a certain slope will carry a certain rate of discharge at critical velocity in uniform flow. The concepts of critical velocity and depth and alternate stages of flow, however, are of greater significance in cases of nonuniform flow because of the relation between the critical velocity and the *celerity* or velocity of propagation of a gravity wave.

Consider a solitary wave progressing to the left in an open channel with celerity c (Fig. 10.15a). We may replace this situation with the equivalent steady-flow case (Fig. 10.15b) in which the wave stands still while the flow enters at velocity $V_1 = -c$. Writing the energy equation (10.25) between points 1 and 2 (with $z_1 = z_2$, $\alpha_1 = \alpha_2 = 1$, and neglecting friction), we have

$$y_1 + \frac{V_1{}^2}{2g} = y_2 + \frac{V_2{}^2}{2g}$$

By continuity, $y_1 V_1 = y_2 V_2$. Substituting for V_2 and rearranging terms results in

$$\frac{V_1{}^2}{2g} = \frac{y_2 - y_1}{1 - (y_1/y_2)^2}$$

If we now let $y_1 = y$, the undisturbed depth, and $y_2 = y + \Delta y$, where Δy is the wave height, and drop terms of order higher than the first, we have, approximately, for the wave celerity,

$$c = \sqrt{gy}\left(1 + \frac{3}{2}\frac{\Delta y}{y}\right)^{\frac{1}{2}} \approx \sqrt{gy}\left(1 + \frac{3}{4}\frac{\Delta y}{y}\right) \tag{10.29}$$

Equation (10.29) is valid only for waves in shallow water, i.e., for waves of great length and moderate amplitude relative to the depth. For

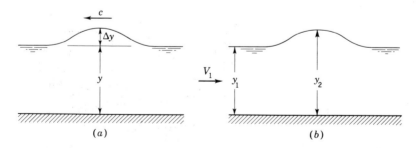

Fig. 10.15. Gravity wave of small amplitude. (*After Rouse (ed.), "Engineering Hydraulics," John Wiley & Sons, Inc., New York, 1950.*)

gravity waves in general, but still presuming small amplitudes, a more accurate equation, where λ is the wavelength from crest to crest, is[1]

$$c = \sqrt{\frac{g\lambda}{2\pi} \tanh \frac{2\pi y}{\lambda}} \qquad (10.30)$$

For deep water, as in the ocean, where y is large compared with the wavelength λ, Eq. (10.30) becomes $c = \sqrt{g\lambda/2\pi}$. As the wave height Δy in Eq. (10.29) becomes small compared with the wavelength λ in Eq. (10.30), either of these equations reduces to

$$c = \sqrt{gy} \qquad (10.31)$$

which is the same as the critical velocity, given by Eq. (10.18) in terms of the critical depth y_c.

From Eq. (10.31) it is seen that the celerity of a wave will increase as the depth of the water increases. But this is the celerity relative to the water. If the water is flowing, the absolute speed of travel will be the resultant of the two velocities. When the stream is flowing at its critical depth y_c, the stream velocity and the wave celerity will be equal. This means that when the surface is disturbed from any cause, the wave so produced *cannot travel upstream.* Quite evidently this also applies to any portion of the stream in supercritical flow, at depth less than y_c. If the disturbance is a permanent one, such as that produced by an obstruction or a change in the channel, the wave remains stationary and is therefore called a *standing* wave.

When the depth is greater than y_c the velocity of flow is less than critical and the wave celerity c is greater than critical velocity. Consequently, under these conditions, any surface disturbance will be able to travel upstream against the flow. Hence the entire stream picture is dependent on whether the stream velocity is smaller or greater than the critical velocity. The situation is analogous to that of the acoustic velocity as described in Sec. 9.9. The standing wave which exists because of a permanent disturbance, when the flow velocity is above the critical, will be at such a direction that $\sin \beta = c/V = \sqrt{gy}/V$, where β is the angle between the direction of flow and the wave front, as shown in Fig. 9.8.[2]

[1] For background of this equation, and further information on waves in open channels, see Hunter Rouse (ed.), "Engineering Hydraulics," pp. 711–768, John Wiley & Sons, Inc., New York, 1950.

[2] A. T. Ippen, Mechanics of Supercritical Flow, *Trans. ASCE*, vol. 116, p. 274, 1951.

10.16. WATER - SURFACE PROFILES IN GRADUALLY VARIED FLOW

As there are some 12 different circumstances giving rise to as many different fundamental types of varied flow, it is helpful to have a logical scheme of type classification. In general, any problem of varied flow, no matter how complex it may appear, with the stream passing over dams, under sluice gates, down steep chutes, on the level, or even on an upgrade, can be broken down into reaches such that the flow within any reach is either uniform or falls within one of the given nonuniform classifications. The stream is then analyzed one reach at a time, proceeding from one to the next until the desired result is obtained.

The following treatment is based, for simplicity, on channels of rectangular section. The section will be considered sufficiently wide and shallow so that we may confine our attention to a section 1 ft wide through which the velocity is essentially uniform. It is important to bear in mind that all the following development is based on a constant value of q, the discharge per unit width, and upon one value of n, the roughness coefficient.

Commencing with Eq. (10.24), we may observe that since $V = q/y$,

$$\frac{1}{2g}\frac{d(V^2)}{dx} = \frac{1}{2g}\frac{d}{dx}\left(\frac{q^2}{y^2}\right) = -\frac{q^2}{g}\frac{1}{y^3}\frac{dy}{dx}$$

Substituting this, plus the S and S_0 terms defined earlier, in Eq. (10.24), yields

$$-S = -S_0 + \frac{dy}{dx}\left(1 - \frac{q^2}{gy^3}\right)$$

or
$$\frac{dy}{dx} = \frac{S_0 - S}{1 - q^2/gy^3} = \frac{S_0 - S}{1 - V^2/gy} \tag{10.32}$$

Evidently, if the value of dy/dx as determined by Eq. (10.32) is positive, the water depth will be increasing along the channel; if negative, it will be decreasing. Looking first at the numerator, S may be considered as the slope [such as would be obtained from Eq. (10.27)] which would carry the given discharge at depth y with uniform flow. Let y_0 denote the depth for uniform flow on the bed slope S_0. Then, by Eq. (10.7), written for the unit-width flow,

$$q = y\frac{1.49}{n}y^{2/3}S^{1/2} \doteq y_0\frac{1.49}{n}y_0^{2/3}S_0^{1/2}$$

This demonstrates that, for constant q and n, $S/S_0 = (y_0/y)^{10/3}$ and, consequently, for $y > y_0$, $S < S_0$, and the numerator is positive. Conversely, for $y < y_0$, $S > S_0$, and the numerator is negative.

To investigate the denominator of Eq. (10.32) we observe that, for critical flow, $y_c = V_c^2/g$ by Eq. (10.18). When the depth is greater than critical, the denominator of Eq. (10.32) is positive. Conversely, when $y < y_c$, the denominator is negative. The term V^2/gy is seen to have the dimensions of a Froude number squared [see Eq. (7.5)]. It is sometimes called the Froude number; also the *kinetic-flow factor*. Evidently, a Froude number greater than 1 corresponds to supercritical flow, while $N_F < 1$ means subcritical flow.

The foregoing analyses have been combined graphically into a series of water-surface profiles (Fig. 10.16). The surface profiles are classified according to slope and depth as follows. If S_0 is positive, the bed slope is termed *mild* (M) when $y_0 > y_c$, *critical* (C) when $y_0 = y_c$, and *steep* (S) when $y_0 < y_c$; if $S_0 = 0$, the channel is *horizontal* (H); and if S_0 is negative, the bed slope is called *adverse* (A). If the stream surface lies above both the normal (uniform flow) and critical depth lines, it is of type 1; if between these lines, it is of type 2; and if below both lines, it is of type 3. The 12 forms of surface curvature are labeled accordingly in Fig. 10.16.

It must be pointed out that the scale of the drawings in Fig. 10.16 is greatly reduced in the horizontal direction. The problems at the end of this chapter demonstrate that gradually varied flow generally extends over many hundreds of feet, and if plotted to an undistorted scale, the rate of change in depth would be scarcely discernible. It may be noted further that, since even a hydraulically steep slope varies but a few degrees from the horizontal, it makes little difference whether the depth y is measured vertically (as shown) or perpendicular to the bed.

It will be observed that some of the curves of Fig. 10-16 are concave upward while others are concave downward. Although the mathematical proof for this is not given, the physical explanation is not hard to find. In the case of the type 1 curves, the surface must approach a horizontal asymptote as the velocity is progressively slowed down because of the increasing depth. Likewise, all curves which approach the normal or uniform depth line must approach it asymptotically, because uniform flow will prevail at sections sufficiently remote from disturbances, as pointed out in Sec. 10.1. The curves which cross the critical-depth line must do so vertically, as the denominator of Eq. (10.32) becomes zero in this case, with a vertical water surface (actually indicating a limiting condition in which the assumptions underlying the theory become invalid). The critical-slope curves, for which $y_0 = y_c$, constitute exceptions to both the foregoing statements, since it is not possible for a curve to be both tangent and perpendicular to the critical-uniform depth line.

To the right of each water-surface profile is shown a representative example of how this particular curve can occur "in nature." Many of the examples show a rapid change from a depth below the critical to a

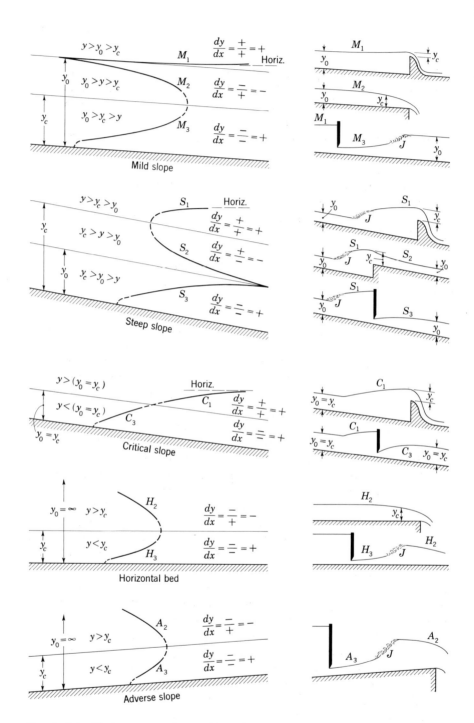

Fig. 10.16. Various types of nonuniform flow.

306

depth above the critical. This is a local phenomenon, known as the hydraulic jump, which is discussed in detail in Sec. 10.18.

The qualitative analysis of water-surface profiles has been restricted to rectangular sections of great width. The curve forms of Fig. 10.16 are, however, applicable to any channel of uniform cross section if y_0 is the depth for uniform flow and y_c is the depth which satisfies Eq. (10.21). The surface profiles can even be used qualitatively in the analysis of natural stream surfaces as well, provided that local variations in slope, shape, and roughness of cross section, etc., are taken into account. The step-by-step method presented in Sec. 10.14 for the solution of nonuniform-flow problems is not restricted to uniform channels and is therefore suited to water-surface-profile computations for any stream whatever.

10.17. EXAMPLES OF WATER - SURFACE PROFILES

The M_1 curve. The most common case of gradually varied flow is where the depth is already above the critical and is increased still further by a dam, as indicated in Fig. 10.17. Referring to the specific-energy diagram of Fig. 10.9, this case is found on the upper limb of the diagram, for here also, as the depth increases, the velocity diminishes without any abrupt transitions, so that a smooth surface curve is obtained. In the case of flow in an artificial channel with a constant bed slope, the water-surface curve would be asymptotic at infinity to the surface for uniform flow, as we noted before. But the problems that are usually of more important interest are those concerned with the effect of a dam on a natural stream and the extent to which it raises the water surface at various points upstream. The resulting water-surface profile in such a case is commonly known as a *backwater curve*.

For an artificial channel where the conditions are uniform, save for the variation in water depth, the problem may be solved by use of Eqs. (10.27) and (10.28). Usually, the solution commences at the dam, where conditions are assumed to be known, and the lengths of successive reaches upstream, corresponding to assumed increments of depth, are

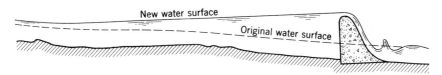

Fig. 10.17.   Backwater curve in natural stream.

computed. A tabular type of solution is the most helpful, with column headings corresponding to the various elements of Eqs. (10.27) and (10.28), the last column being ΣL, which sums up the length from the dam to the point in question. It is important, if accuracy is desired, to keep the depth increment small within any reach; a depth change of 10 per cent or less is fairly satisfactory. The smaller the depth increment used in this step-by-step procedure, the greater the overall distance to some point of specified depth or elevation. When the depth increments are taken infinitesimally small, the effect is that of integrating the equation of nonuniform flow. This has been done numerically, and tables are available which greatly lessen the work of making repeated solutions of backwater curves.[1]

Of course, this type of solution is not restricted to the Manning formula. Equation (10.27) may be replaced with a similar relation based on a constant value of the Chezy C or on a value which varies with R in accordance with Eq. (10.5).

For a natural stream, such as that shown in Fig. 11.11, the solution is not so direct, because the form and dimensions of a cross section cannot be assumed and then the distance to its location computed. As there are various slopes and cross sections at different distances upstream, the value of L in Eq. (10.26) must be assumed, and then the depth of stream at this section can be computed by trial, as in Prob. 10.54.

In view of the fact that for an irregular stream so many approximations must be made as to the actual conditions, the refinements of Eq. (10.26) are not always justified and it is frequently as satisfactory to apply the simple equation for uniform flow, $V = C\sqrt{RS}$. In order to do this, the stream must be divided into various reaches within which the flow may be assumed to be fairly uniform. Then, for each reach, average values, V_m and R_m, are used, and the value of S is determined by trial.

The M_2 curve. This curve, representing accelerated subcritical flow on a slope which is flatter than critical, exists, like the M_1 curve, because of a control condition *downstream*. In this case, however, the control is not an obstruction but the removal of the hydrostatic resistance of the water downstream, as in the case of the free overfall shown in Fig. 10.13a. As in the M_1 curve, the surface will approach the depth for uniform flow at an infinite distance upstream. Practically, because of slight wave action and other irregularities, the distinction between the M_2, or *drop-down*, curve and the curve for uniform flow disappears within a finite distance.

---

[1] M. E. Von Seggern, Integrating the Equation of Nonuniform Flow, *Trans. ASCE*, vol. 115, pp. 71–106, 1950.

The M_3 curve. This occurs because of an upstream control, as the sluice gate shown in Fig. 10.16. The bed slope is not sufficient to sustain lower-stage flow, and at a certain point determined by energy and momentum relations, the surface will pass through a hydraulic jump unless this is made unnecessary by the existence of a free overfall before the M_3 curve reaches critical depth.

The S curves. These may be analyzed in much the same fashion as the M curves, having due regard for downstream control in the case of subcritical flow and for upstream control for supercritical flow. Thus a dam or an obstruction on a steep slope produces an S_1 curve (Fig. 10.16) which approaches the horizontal asymptotically but cannot so approach the uniform depth line, which lies below the critical depth. Therefore this curve must be preceded by a hydraulic jump. The S_2 curve shows accelerated lower-stage flow, smoothly approaching uniform depth. Such a curve will occur whenever a steep channel receives flow at critical depth, as from an obstruction (as shown) or reservoir. The sluice gate on a steep channel will produce the S_3 curve, which also approaches smoothly the uniform depth line.

The C curves. These curves, with the anomalous condition at $y_0 = y_c$, have already been discussed. Needless to say, the critical-slope profiles are not of frequent occurrence.

The H and the A curves. These curves have in common the fact that there is no condition of uniform flow possible. The H_2 and A_2 drop-down curves are similar to the M_2 curve, but even more noticeable. The value of $y_b = 0.7y_c$ given in Sec. 10.12 applies strictly only to the H_2 curve, but is approximately true for the M_2 curve also. The sluice gate on the horizontal and adverse slopes produces H_3 and A_3 curves which are like the M_3 curve, but they do not exist for as great a distance as the M_3 curve before a hydraulic jump occurs. Of course, it is not possible to have a channel of any appreciable length carry water on a horizontal grade, and even less so on an adverse grade.

10.18. THE HYDRAULIC JUMP

By far the most important of the local nonuniform-flow phenomena is that which occurs when the supercritical flow has its velocity reduced to subcritical. We have seen in the surface profiles of Fig. 10.16 that there is no ordinary means of changing from supercritical to subcritical flow with a smooth transition, because theory calls for a vertical slope of the water surface. The result, then, is a marked discontinuity in the surface, characterized by a steep upward slope of the profile, broken throughout with violent turbulence, and known universally as the *hydraulic jump*.

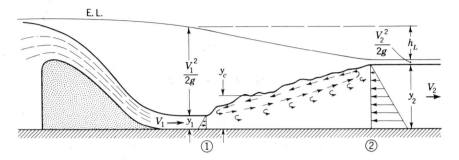

Fig. 10.18. Hydraulic jump on horizontal bed following spillway vertical dimensions to scale for $q = 10.8$ cfs/ft; horizontal scale foreshortened between points (1) and (2) approximately $2\frac{1}{2}:1$.

The specific reason for the occurrence of the hydraulic jump can perhaps best be explained by reference to the M_3 curve of Fig. 10.16. Downstream of the sluice gate the flow decelerates because the slope is not great enough to maintain supercritical flow. The specific energy decreases as the depth increases (proceeding to the left along the lower limb of the specific-energy diagram, Fig. 10.9). Were this condition to progress until the flow reached critical depth, an increase in specific energy would be required as the depth increased from the critical to the uniform flow depth downstream. But this is a physical impossibility. Therefore the jump forms before critical depth is reached.

The hydraulic jump can also occur from an upstream condition of uniform supercritical flow to a nonuniform S_1 curve downstream when there is an obstruction on a steep slope, as illustrated in Fig. 10.16, or again from a nonuniform upstream condition to a nonuniform downstream condition, as illustrated by the H_3, H_2 or the A_3, A_2 combinations. In addition to the foregoing cases, where the channel bed continues at a uniform slope, a jump will form when the slope changes from steep to mild, as on the apron at the base of the spillway, illustrated in Fig. 10.18. This is an excellent example of the jump serving a useful purpose, for it dissipates much of the destructive energy of the high-velocity water, thereby reducing downstream erosion.

The equation relating the depths before and after the hydraulic jump will be derived for the case of a horizontal channel bottom (the H_3, H_2 combination). It is assumed that the friction forces acting are negligible because of the short length of channel involved and because the shock losses are large in comparison. The key to the solution is the law of conservation of momentum, which is that the time rate of change of momentum of a flowing stream must be equal to the components of all forces acting. As the channel is horizontal, the gravity forces will have no component in the direction of flow. Hence we have

$$\frac{\gamma}{g} Q(V_2 - V_1) = \gamma \int_{A_1} h_1 \, dA - \gamma \int_{A_2} h_2 \, dA$$

where h_1 and h_2 are the variable distances vertically from the surface to elements of area in sections (1) and (2) of Fig. 10.18. It is seen that each integral is equal to $h_c A$, the statical moment of the area about an axis lying in the surface, where h_c is the vertical distance from the surface to the centroid of the area. Hence, after rearranging,

$$\frac{\gamma}{g} QV_2 + \gamma h_{c_2} A_2 = \frac{\gamma}{g} QV_1 + \gamma h_{c_1} A_1 \qquad (10.33)$$

That is, the momentum plus the pressure force on the cross-sectional area is constant, or dividing by γ and observing that $V = Q/A$,

$$F_m = \frac{Q^2}{Ag} + A h_c = \text{constant} \qquad (10\text{-}34)$$

In the case of a rectangular channel, this reduces for a unit width to:

$$f_m = \frac{q^2}{y_1 g} + \frac{y_1^2}{2} = \frac{q^2}{y_2 g} + \frac{y_2^2}{2} \qquad (10.35)$$

A curve of values of f_m for different values of y is plotted to the right of the specific-energy diagram shown in Fig. 10.19. Both curves are plotted for the condition of 2 cfs/ft of width. As the loss of energy in the jump does not affect the "force" quantity f_m, the latter is the same after the jump as before, and therefore any vertical line intersecting the f_m curve serves to locate two *conjugate* depths y_1 and y_2. These depths represent possible combinations of depth that could occur before and after the jump.

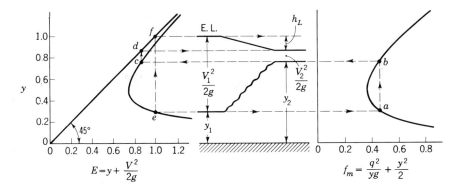

Fig. 10.19. Energy and momentum relations in hydraulic jump.

Thus, in Fig. 10.19, the line for the initial water level y_1 intersects the f_m curve at a as shown, giving the value of f_m, which must be the same after the jump. The vertical line ab then fixes the value of y_2. This depth is then transposed to the specific-energy diagram to determine the value cd of $V_2{}^2/2g$. The value of $V_1{}^2/2g$ is the vertical distance ef, and the head loss h_j caused by the jump is the drop in energy from 1 to 2. Or

$$h_j = \left(y_1 + \frac{V_1{}^2}{2g}\right) - \left(y_2 + \frac{V_2{}^2}{2g}\right) \tag{10.36}$$

When the rate of flow and the depth before or after the jump are given, it is seen that Eq. (10.35) becomes a cubic equation when solving for the other depth. This may readily be reduced to a quadratic, however, by observing that $y_2{}^2 - y_1{}^2 = (y_2 + y_1)(y_2 - y_1)$ and substituting the known depth in the resulting expression:

$$\frac{q^2}{g} = y_1 y_2 \frac{y_1 + y_2}{2} \tag{10.37}$$

This equation can be rearranged to give an explicit expression for the depth after jump as

$$y_2 = \frac{y_1}{2}\left(-1 + \sqrt{1 + \frac{8q^2}{gy_1{}^3}}\right) \tag{10.38}$$

In the case of a hydraulic jump on a sloping channel[1] it is necessary to add the sine component of the weight of the water between sections (1) and (2) of Fig. 10.18 to the general momentum equation.

Although the length of jump is difficult to determine, a good approxi-

Fig. 10.20. Hydraulic jump. (*Photograph by Keck Laboratory of Hydraulics and Water Resources, California Institute of Technology.*)

[1] R. W. Ellms, Computation of the Tailwater Depth of the Hydraulic Jump in Sloping Flumes, *Trans. ASME*, vols. 49–50, HYD-50-5, 1927–1928; Hydraulic Jump in Sloping and Horizontal Flumes, *Trans. ASME*, vol. 54, HYD-54-6, 1932. B. A. Bakhmeteff and E. A. Matzke, The Hydraulic Jump in Sloped Channels, *Trans. ASME*, vol. **60**, pp. 111–118, 1938.

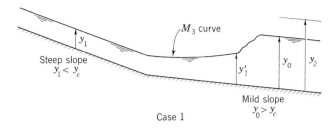

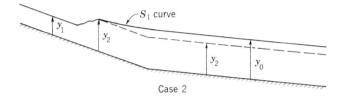

Fig. 10.21. Examples of location of a hydraulic jump. *Note:* y_2 is the conjugate depth of y_1.

mation may be obtained by assuming the jump section to be a trapezoid with bases y_1 and y_2 and altitude of about $6y_2$. This relation may be seen to be approximately true by examination of Fig. 10.20, a photograph of a hydraulic jump in a horizontal channel, caused by a sluice gate upstream.

10.19. LOCATION OF HYDRAULIC JUMP

The problem of determining the location of a hydraulic jump involves a combined application of the principles discussed in Secs. 10.17 and 10.18. Examples of the location of a hydraulic jump are shown in Fig. 10.21. In case (1) the jump occurs downstream of the break in slope, while in case (2) the jump is located upstream of the break. The reasons for this are illustrated by the following example.

Illustrative example 10.5: Analyze the water-surface profile in a long rectangular channel with concrete lining ($n = 0.013$). The channel is 10 ft wide, the flow rate is 400 cfs, and there is an abrupt change in channel slope from 0.0150 to 0.0016. Find also the horsepower loss in the jump.

$$400 = \frac{1.49}{0.013} (10y_0) \left(\frac{10y_0}{10 + 2y_0} \right)^{2\!/\!3} (0.015)^{1\!/\!2}$$

By trial, $\qquad y_0 = 2.17$ ft $\qquad$ (normal depth on upper slope)

Using a similar procedure, the normal depth on the lower slope is found to be 4.80 ft.

$$y_c = \left(\frac{q^2}{g} \right)^{1\!/\!3} = \left[\frac{(400\!/\!10)^2}{32.2} \right]^{1\!/\!3} = 3.68 \text{ ft}$$

Thus flow is supercritical ($y_0 < y_c$) before break in slope and subcritical ($y_0 > y_c$) after break, so a hydraulic jump must occur.

Applying Eq. (10.38) to determine the depth conjugate to the 2.17-ft (upper-slope) normal depth, we get

$$y_2 = \frac{2.17}{2} \left\{ -1 + \left[1 + \frac{8(40)^2}{32.2(2.17)^3} \right]^{1/2} \right\}$$
$$= 5.75 \text{ ft}$$

Therefore the depth conjugate to the upper-slope normal depth of 2.17 ft is 5.75 ft. This jump cannot occur because the normal depth on the lower slope is less than 5.75 ft.

Applying Eq. (10.38) to determine the depth conjugate to the 4.80-ft (lower-slope) normal depth, we get

$$4.8 = \frac{y_1}{2} \left[-1 + \left(1 + \frac{8(40)^2}{32.2 y_1^3} \right)^{1/2} \right]$$
$$y_1 = 2.76 \text{ ft}$$

The lower conjugate depth of 2.76 ft will occur downstream of the break in slope. Thus the condition here is similar to that depicted in Fig. 10.21a. The location of the jump (i.e., its distance below the break in slope) may be found by applying Eq. (10.28):

$$L = \frac{E_1 - E_2}{S - S_0}$$

$$E_1 = 2.17 + \frac{(400/21.7)^2}{64.4} = 7.53 \text{ ft}$$

$$E_2 = 2.76 + \frac{(400/27.6)^2}{64.4} = 6.02 \text{ ft}$$

$$V_m = \frac{1}{2} \left(\frac{400}{21.7} + \frac{400}{27.6} \right) = 16.45 \text{ fps}$$

$$R_m = \frac{1}{2} \left(\frac{21.7}{14.34} + \frac{27.6}{15.52} \right) = 1.645 \text{ ft}$$

$$S = \left[\frac{(0.013)(16.45)}{1.49(1.645)^{2/3}} \right]^2 = 0.0107$$

Finally,
$$L = \frac{7.53 - 6.02}{0.0107 - 0.0016} = 165 \text{ ft}$$

Thus depth on the upper slope is 2.17 ft; downstream of break the depth increases gradually (M_3 curve) to 2.76 ft over a distance of approximately 165 ft; then a hydraulic jump occurs to depth 4.80 ft; downstream of jump the depth remains constant at 4.8 ft.

$$\text{HP loss} = \frac{\gamma Q h_j}{550}$$

$$h_j = E_1 - E_2 = 1.51 \text{ ft}$$

$$\text{HP loss} = \frac{62.4(400)(1.51)}{550} = 68$$

10.20. FLOW AROUND CHANNEL BENDS

The flow around the bend of a channel provides an application of the fundamentals of flow in a curved path, discussed in Sec. 4.16. As there is no torque applied to the fluid, the flow should follow the laws of the free vortex, given in Sec. 4.18, and indeed it would, were it not for the effect of friction on the walls and bottom of the channel. The free-vortex flow of an ideal fluid around a bend is illustrated in the flow net of Fig. 3.9.

In the case of a real liquid in an open channel, it is necessary to differentiate between the behavior at subcritical and supercritical velocities. Subcritical flow in a rectangular channel has been investigated experimentally and has been found to conform fairly well to ideal conditions, especially within the first part of the bend.[1] As the flow continues around the bend, the velocity distribution becomes complicated by the phenomenon of *spiral flow*, which for open channels is analogous to the secondary counterrotating currents found at bends in closed pipes, discussed in Sec. 8.21.

The existence of spiral flow is readily explained by reference to Fig. 10.22. The water surface is superelevated at the outside wall, following approximately the profile given by Eq. (4.45) for the cylindrical free vortex. The element EF is subjected to a centrifugal force mV^2/r which is balanced by an increased hydrostatic force on the left side, due to the superelevation of the water surface at C above that at D. The element GH is subjected to the same net hydrostatic force inward, but the centrifugal force outward is much less because the velocity is decreased by friction near the bottom. This results in a cross flow inward along the bottom of the channel, which is balanced by an outward flow near the water surface; hence the spiral. This spiral flow is largely responsible for the commonly observed erosion of the outside bank of a river bend, with consequent deposition and building of a sand bar near the inside bank.

[1] C. A. Mockmore, Flow around Bends in Stable Channels, *Trans. ASCE*, vol. 109, p. 593, 1944.

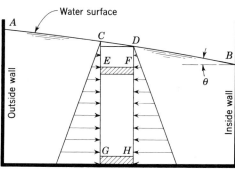

Fig. 10.22. Schematic sketch of flow around a bend in a rectangular channel.

It is generally not possible to perceive the convex surface profile, given by the free-vortex theory and shown in Fig. 10.22.   For most purposes the water surface may be supposed to be a straight line from A to B, raised at the outside wall and depressed at the inside, with the slope given by the ordinary superelevation formula used for highway curves, $\tan \theta = V^2/gr$, where r is the radius of the curve to the center of the channel.

With supercritical flow the complicating factor is the effect of disturbance waves, generated by the very start of the curve.   These waves, one from the outside wall and one from the inside, traverse the channel, making an angle β with the original direction of flow, as discussed in Sec. 10.15.   The water surface along the outside wall will rise from the beginning of the curve, reaching a maximum at the point where the wave from the inside wall reaches the outside wall.   The wave is then reflected back to the inside wall, and the outer surface falls again, and so on around the bend.   The maximum rise is approximately twice the value computed by the free-vortex or superelevation formulas.

Several schemes to lessen the surface rise from wave effect have been investigated.[1]   The bed of the channel may be banked, for instance, so that all elements of the flow are acted upon simultaneously, which is not possible when the turning force comes from the walls only.   As in a banked-railway curve, this requires a transition section preceding the main curve.   Another method is to introduce a counterdisturbance, calculated to offset the disturbance wave caused by the curve.   Such a counterdisturbance can be provided by a section of curved channel of twice the radius of the main section, by a spiral transition curve, or by diagonal sills on the channel bed, all preceding the main curve.

Illustrative example 10.6:   Consider a rectangular flume 15 ft wide, built of unplaned planks ($n = 0.014$), leading from a reservoir in which the water surface is maintained constant at a height of 6 ft above the bed of the flume at entrance

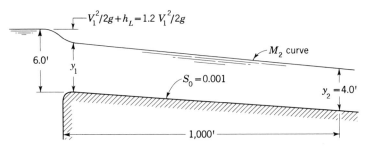

Illustrative Example 10.6.   Mild-slope flume leading from reservoir.

[1] R. T. Knapp, Design of Channel Curves for Supercritical Flow, *Trans. ASCE*, vol. 116, p. 296, 1951.

(see accompanying figure). The flume slopes 1 ft in its length of 1,000 ft, and the depth at the downstream end is held constant at 4 ft by some control farther downstream. The flume is then said to be submerged. Assuming an entrance loss of $0.2V_1^2/2g$, find the capacity.

For a first approximate answer we shall consider the entire flume as one reach. The equations to be satisfied are

Energy at entrance:

$$y_1 + \frac{1.2V_1^2}{2g} = 6.0 \tag{a}$$

Energy equation (10.26) for the entire reach:

$$y_1 + \frac{V_1^2}{2g} = 4.0 + \frac{V_2^2}{2g} + (S - 0.001)L \tag{b}$$

where S is given by Eq. (10.27):

$$S = \left(\frac{nV_m}{1.49R_m^{2/3}}\right)^2 \tag{c}$$

The procedure is to make successive trials of the upstream depth y_1. This determines corresponding values of V_1, q, V_2, V_m, R_m, and S. The trials are repeated until the value of L from Eq. (b) is close to 1,000 ft. The solution is conveniently set in tabular form as follows:

Trial y_1, ft	V_1, Eq. (a), fps	$q = y_1V_1$, cfs	$V_2 = q/4$, fps	V_m, fps	R_1, ft	R_m, ft	S, Eq. (c)	L, Eq. (b)	
5.0	7.32	36.6	9.15	8.24	3.0	2.7	0.00160	890	Increase y_1
5.2	6.55	34.0	8.50	7.52	3.07	2.74	0.00131	2,400	Decrease y_1
5.03	7.20	36.2	9.05	8.13	3.01	2.71	0.00155	1,030	Close enough

The capacity is then $Q = qB$, or $36.2 \times 15 = 543.0$ cfs. A more accurate result can be obtained by dividing the flume into reaches in which the depth change is about 10 per cent of the depth. Thus, commencing at the downstream end, with $q = 36.2$ ft^2/sec, the distance may be calculated to the point where $y = 4.4$ ft, thence to the depth of 4.8 ft, and so on. This procedure will normally lead to a value of ΣL between the assumed end depths which is greater than the length of the flume. The calculated value of y_1 is then decreased, with a consequent increase in the discharge. The approximate procedure shown is seen to be conservative; i.e., the true capacity is greater than that calculated.

PROBLEMS

10.1. For the channel of Illustrative Example 10.1 compute Reynolds number $4RV\rho/\mu$, assuming water at 50°F is flowing. Refer to Fig. 8.10 to verify whether or not the flow is wholly rough. Using this value of N_R and the value of f computed in the illustrative example, determine ϵ by reference to Fig. 8.10. Compare with the ϵ computed in the example.

10.2. Following the method used in Sec. 8.6 in connection with laminar flow in a pipe, derive an expression for laminar flow along a flat plate which may be considered as infinitely wide (see figure). Prove that for a given discharge q per unit width the depth for uniform flow is given by $y_0 = \sqrt[3]{3\nu q/gS}$. (*Note:* The difference between the true vertical and the perpendicular to the channel bed may be neglected here but must sometimes be taken into account.)

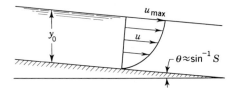

Fig. Prob. 10.2

10.3. Evaluate the friction factor f for the laminar flow of Prob. 10.2 in terms of the Reynolds number, and compare with Eq. (8.20) for pipe flow. (*Note:* Recall from Sec. 8.3 that for a wide channel the hydraulic radius is approximately equal to the depth.)

10.4. Eastern lubricating oil (SAE 30) at 70°F flows down a flat plate 10 ft wide. What is the maximum rate of discharge at which laminar flow may be ensured, assuming that the critical Reynolds number is (as for pipes) 2,000? [*Note:* Whenever pipe data are used for open channels, $4R$ should be substituted for D (Sec. 8.3).] What should be the slope of the plate to secure a depth of 6 in. at this flow rate?

10.5. Assuming the values of f versus N_R and ϵ/D given for pipes in Fig. 8.10 to apply to open channels as well, find the rate of discharge of water at 60°F in a 100-in.-diameter smooth concrete pipe flowing half full, if the pipe is laid on a grade of 2 ft/mile. Note that D should be replaced by $4R$.

10.6. In solving Prob. 10.2, the velocity distribution was found to be $u = (gS/2\nu)y_0^2[1 - (y/y_0)^2]$, where y in this case is the variable distance downward from the surface. Evaluate α, and compare it with the result of Prob. 4.1.

10.7. At what rate (cfs/ft of width) will 60°F water flow in a wide rectangular channel on a slope of 0.00015 if the depth is 0.01 ft? Assume laminar flow and justify this assumption by computing Reynolds number. (*Hint:* Refer to Prob. 10.2.)

10.8. For the channel of Illustrative Example 10.1, compute the flow rate for depths of 1, 3, 5, and 7 ft. Plot a curve of Q versus y.

10.9. The figure shows a cross section of a canal forming a portion of the Colorado River Aqueduct, which is to carry 1,600 cfs. The canal is lined with concrete, for which n is assumed to be 0.014. What must be the grade of the canal, and what will be the drop in elevation per mile?

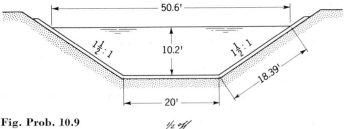

Fig. Prob. 10.9

10.10. In Prob. 10.9 find the corresponding value of ϵ and compare it with values previously given for concrete pipe. Does it fall in the range given? Assuming the solution to Prob. 10.9 to be the true one, evaluate the Bazin m and compare it with range of values given in the text.

10.11. If the flow in the canal of Prob. 10.9 were to decrease to 800 cfs, all other data, including the slope, being the same, what would be the depth of the water?

10.12. What would be the capacity of the canal of Prob. 10.9 if the grade were to be 1.2 ft/mile?

10.13. The figure shows a tunnel section on the Colorado River Aqueduct. The area of the water cross section is 191 ft², and the wetted perimeter is 39.1 ft. The flow is 1,600 cfs. If $n = 0.013$ for a cement lining, find the slope.

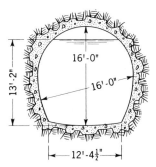

Fig. Prob. 10.13

10.14. A monolithic concrete inverted siphon on the Colorado River Aqueduct is circular in cross section and is 16 ft in diameter. Obviously, it is completely filled with water, unlike the case of Prob. 10.13. If $n = 0.013$, find the slope of the hydraulic grade line for a flow of 1,600 cfs.

10.15. Solve Prob. 10.14, using the methods of Chap. 8 and assuming a mean value of ϵ from Table 8.1 for concrete pipe. Compare the result with that of Prob. 10.14.

10.16. A 30-in.-diameter pipe is known to have a Manning's n of 0.021. What is Manning's n for a 96-in.-diameter pipe having exactly the same ϵ as the smaller pipe?

10.17. Using Eq. (10.10), determine the depth below the surface at which the velocity is equal to the mean velocity. Also find the average of the velocities at 0.2 and 0.8 depths. Let $y = 4$ ft, $S = 0.001$, and $n = 0.025$.

10.18. Work through the derivations of Sec. 10.7 for most efficient cross section, filling in all the missing steps.

10.19. Prove the relations given for maximum discharge in Sec. 10.8. After differentiating, a trial-and-error type of solution will be found most practical here.

10.20. Prove that the most efficient triangular section is that with a right angle at the vertex.

10.21. A rectangular flume of planed timber ($n = 0.012$) slopes 1 ft per 1,000 ft. Compute the rate of discharge if the width is 6 ft and the depth of water is 3 ft. What would be the rate of discharge if the width were 3 ft and the depth of water 6 ft? Which of the two forms would require less lumber?

10.22. A rectangular channel of rubble masonry ($n = 0.017$) is 6 ft wide, the depth of water is 3 ft, and the slope is 1 ft per 1,000 ft. Compute the rate of discharge by the Manning and Bazin formulas, and compare with that of Prob. 10.21.

10.23. A semicircular channel of rubble masonry with a slope of 1 ft per 1,000 ft is to be constructed so as to carry the same flow as the channel of Prob. 10.22. What should be the diameter? Compare the cross-sectional area and amount of lining required with those of Prob. 10.22.

10.24. A circular conduit of concrete ($n = 0.012$) is 10 ft in diameter and slopes 1.6 ft per 1,000 ft. The following table gives values of wetted perimeter and area of water cross section for various depths of water in the conduit. Find the values of V and Q for the various depths in the table, and plot curves of V/V_0 and Q/Q_0 versus depth, where V_0 and Q_0 are velocity and discharge, respectively, when the conduit is full. Such curves are called the *hydraulic elements* of a circular section and are especially useful in the design of sewers. Compare the depth for maximum Q with that given by the theory of Sec. 10.8. At what depth does the maximum velocity occur?

Depth y, ft	Wetted perimeter, ft	Area A, ft²	R, ft	$R^{2/3}$	V, fps	Q, cfs
1.0	6.44	4.09	0.635	0.739	3.66	15.0
3.0	11.59	19.82				
5.0	15.71	39.27				
8.0	22.14	67.36				
9.0	24.98	74.45				
9.5	26.91	77.07				
10.0	31.42	78.54				

10.25. The amount of water to be carried by a canal excavated in smooth earth ($n = 0.030$) is 370 cfs. It has side slopes of 2:1, and the depth of water is to be 5 ft or less (see figure). If the slope is 2.5 ft/mile, what must be the width at the bottom? How does this compare with the most efficient trapezoidal section for these side slopes? (This problem can best be solved by trial.)

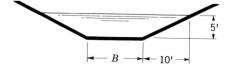

B — 10' — **Fig. Prob. 10.25**

10.26. In Prob. 10.25, if the discharge is to be 200 cfs while the velocity is not to exceed 150 fpm, what must be the width at the bottom and the drop in elevation per mile? Compare this with the bottom width for maximum efficiency.

10.27. Establish the wetted perimeter as a function of the area for the following sections: (*a*) circle; (*b*) semicircle; (*c*) half hexagon; (*d*) half square. Find the side slopes of a trapezoidal section of maximum efficiency which will carry the same flow as a half-square section of the same area.

10.28. Differentiate Eq. (10.13) to obtain the expression for y_c given in Eq. (10.19).

10.29. A rectangular channel 10 ft wide carries a flow of 200 cfs. Find the critical depth and the critical velocity for this flow. Find also the critical slope if $n = 0.020$.

10.30. Using the dimensions of the circular conduit in Prob. 10.24, compute the specific energy for a constant flow of 100 cfs at depths of 1, 3, 5, and 8 ft, assuming $\alpha = 1$. At which depth is E the least, and how does this compare with the critical depth in a rectangular channel of 10-ft width?

10.31. A trapezoidal canal with side slopes of 2:1 has a bottom width of 10 ft and carries a flow of 600 cfs. Find the critical depth and critical velocity.

10.32. If the canal of Prob. 10.31 is lined with brick ($n = 0.015$), find the critical slope for the given rate of discharge.

10.33. Water flows with a velocity of 4 fps and at a depth of 2 ft in a wide rectangular channel. Is the flow subcritical or supercritical? Find the alternate depth for the same discharge and specific energy by two methods: (a) by direct solution of Eq. (10.14); (b) by use of Fig. 10.8.

10.34. Consider a wide rectangular channel on a given slope. With what power of the discharge does the depth vary? With what power of the discharge does the specific energy vary? As the flow increases, does it tend toward subcritical or supercritical conditions? Assume Manning equation, with constant value of n.

10.35. Water flows down a wide rectangular channel of concrete ($n = 0.014$) laid on a slope of 2 ft per 1,000. Find the depth and rate of flow for critical conditions in this channel.

10.36. Water is released from a sluice gate in a rectangular channel 5 ft wide such that the depth is 2 ft and the velocity is 15 fps. Find (a) the critical depth for this specific energy; (b) the critical depth for this rate of discharge; (c) the type of flow and the alternate depth by either direct solution or the discharge curve.

10.37. For the conditions of Prob. 10.36, find the necessary channel slope if the discharge from the sluice gate is to be carried at uniform flow in a rectangular flume 5 ft wide and made of unplaned timber ($n = 0.013$).

10.38. A flow of 10 cfs of water is carried in a 90° triangular flume built of planed timber ($n = 0.011$). Find the critical depth and the critical slope.

10.39. A long straight rectangular channel 10 ft wide is observed to have a wavy surface at a depth of about 6 ft. Estimate the rate of discharge.

10.40. A circular conduit of well-laid brickwork when flowing half full is to carry 400 cfs at a velocity of 10 fps. What will be the necessary fall per mile? Will the flow be subcritical or supercritical?

10.41. A rectangular flume is to be constructed of rough unsized timber. If given a drop of 10 ft/mile, what will be the depth and width for the most economical solution if it is to discharge 40 cfs?

10.42. A flow of 84.7 cfs is to be carried in a rectangular flume made of planed timber, not perfectly true. If the velocity is to be 4 fps, what will be the best dimensions and what will be the drop in 3,000 ft?

10.43. A flow of 100 cfs is carried in a rectangular channel 10 ft wide at a depth of 1.2 ft. If the channel is made of smooth concrete ($n = 0.012$), find the slope necessary to sustain uniform flow at this depth. What change in the roughness coefficient would be required to produce uniform critical flow for the given rate of discharge at this slope?

10.44. This figure depicts the cross section of an open channel for which $S_0 = 0.02$ and $n = 0.015$. The sketch is drawn to the scale shown. When the flow rate is 50 cfs, find (*a*) the depth for uniform flow and (*b*) the critical depth.

Scale:

4'

Fig. Prob. 10.44

10.45. Work both parts of Illustrative Example 10.3 for the case where the flow rate is 16 cfs.

10.46. Work Illustrative Example 10.3 for the case where the flow rate is 50 cfs.

10.47. A rectangular channel 10 ft wide carries 20 cfs in uniform flow at a depth of 0.90 ft. Find the local change in water-surface elevation caused by an obstruction 0.20 ft high on the floor of the channel.

10.48. Suppose that the channel of Prob. 10.47 is so sloped that uniform flow of 20 cfs occurs at a depth of 0.30 ft. Find the local change in water-surface elevation caused by the 0.20-ft-high obstruction.

10.49. A rectangular channel 4 ft wide carries 40 cfs of water in uniform flow at a depth of 2.80 ft. If a bridge pier 1 ft wide is placed in the middle of this channel, find the local change in the water-surface elevation. What is the minimum width of constricted channel which will not cause a rise in water surface upstream?

10.50. Suppose that the depth of uniform flow in the channel of Prob. 10.49 is 0.86 ft. Find the change in water-surface elevation caused by the bridge pier.

10.51. Fifty cubic feet per second of water flows uniformly in a channel of width 6 ft at a depth of 2.5 ft. What is the change in water-surface elevation at a section contracted to a 4-ft width with a 0.2-ft depression in the bottom?

10.52. A rectangular flume of planed timber ($n = 0.012$) is 5 ft wide and carries 60 cfs of water. The bed slope is 0.0006, and at a certain section the depth is 3 ft. Find the distance (in one reach) to the section where the depth is 2.5 ft. Is this distance upstream or downstream?

10.53. Suppose that the slope of the flume in Prob. 10.52 is now changed so that, with the same flow, the depth varies from 4 ft at one section to 3 ft at a section 1,000 ft downstream. Find the new bed slope of the flume. Sketch the flume, the energy grade line, and the water surface to assure that the answer is reasonable.

10.54. Suppose that the slope of the flume in Prob. 10.52 is now increased to 0.01. With the same flow as before, find the depth 1,000 ft downstream from a section where the stream is 1.5 ft deep. Is the flow subcritical or supercritical? [*Note:* In this case it will not be possible to make a direct solution from Eq. (10.26). A trial-and-error solution may best be set in the form of a table with the headings y_2, V_2, V_m, A_2, P_2, R_2, R_m, $R_m^{2/3}$, S, etc.]

10.55. A test on a rectangular glass flume 10 in. wide yielded the following data on a reach of 30-ft length: with still water, $y_2 - y_1 = 0.009$ ft; with a measured flow of 0.1516 cfs, $y_1 = 0.361$, $y_2 = 0.366$ ft. Find the value of the roughness coefficient n.

10.56. For the flume of Prob. 10.44 find the distance between a section where the depth is 3.0 ft to another where the depth is 2.5 ft. Which section is upstream?

10.57. Fill in the missing steps of the derivation leading to Eq. (10.29). As this expression is intended to give no more than the magnitude of c, consider $c = V_1$ instead of $c = -V_1$.

10.58. A thin rod is placed vertically in a stream which is 3 ft deep, and the resulting small disturbance wave is observed to make an angle of about $55°$ with the axis of the stream. Find the approximate velocity of the stream.

10.59. At a point in a shallow lake, the wave from a passing boat is observed to rise 1 ft above the undisturbed water surface. The observed speed of the wave is 10 mph. Find the approximate depth of the lake at this point.

10.60. At a point in the ocean, waves measuring 300 ft from crest to crest are observed to travel at 20 mph. Find the depth of the ocean at this point.

10.61. Classify the water-surface profile of Prob. 10.52 as one of the forms shown in Fig. 10.16. Show all necessary calculations.

10.62. Repeat Prob. 10.61 for the channel of Prob. 10.53.

10.63. The flow in a 15-ft-wide rectangular channel which has a constant bottom slope is 1,400 cfs. A computation using Manning's equation indicates that the normal depth is 6.0 ft. At a certain section the depth of flow in the channel is 2.8 ft. Will the depth increase, decrease, or remain the same as one proceeds downstream from this section? Sketch a physical situation where this type of flow will occur.

10.64. Classify the water-surface profile of Prob. 10.54 as one of the forms shown in Fig. 10.16. Show all necessary calculations.

10.65. Repeat Prob. 10.64 for the channel of Prob. 10.55.

10.66. A wide rectangular channel dredged in earth ($n = 0.035$) is laid on a slope of 10 ft/mile and carries a flow of 100 cfs/ft of width. Find the water depth 2 miles upstream of a section where the depth is 28.9 ft. Compute, using a single reach, and compare the result with that obtained using three reaches.

10.67. The slope of a stream of rectangular cross section is $S_0 = 0.0002$, the width is 160 ft, and the value of the Chézy C is 78.3. Find the depth for a uniform flow of 88.55 cfs per unit width of the stream. If a dam raises the water level so that at a certain distance upstream the increase is 5 ft, how far from this latter section will the increase be only 1 ft?

10.68. When the flow in a certain natural stream is 7,600 cfs, it is required to find the elevation of the water surface at different sections upstream from a certain initial point. A survey of the channel shows that conditions are fairly similar for a length of 1,500 ft upstream from the initial point, and then beyond that there is another stretch of 2,200 ft, and so on. Assuming a rise in the water surface in the distance of 1,500 ft to be 0.20 ft, a study of the stream bed shows the average values of the area and wetted perimeter to be as given in the table below. The computed head loss, based on average velocity and hydraulic radius, is seen to be 0.283 ft, which is greater than that assumed. Hence assume a larger value, and repeat. Complete the following table, and find the probable rise in elevation in the first 1,500 ft. In a similar manner the rises in other lengths may be computed, and the sum of all of them up to the desired point will give the elevation at that point above the initial. Assume $n = 0.036$.

Assumed rise SL, ft	A average, ft^2	P average, ft	R average, ft	V average, fps	Computed $SL = LV^2/C^2R$, ft
0.20	3,100	350	8.86	2.45	0.283
0.25	3,180	359	8.86		
0.26	3,190	360	8.86		
0.27	3,220	363	8.86		
0.28	3,230	364	8.86		

10.69. A rectangular flume 10 ft wide is built of planed timber ($n = 0.012$) on a bed slope of 0.2 ft per 1,000, ending in a free overfall. If the measured depth at the fall is 1.82 ft, find (a) the rate of flow; (b) the distance upstream from the fall to where the depth is 4 ft. (*Note:* Assume that critical depth occurs at a distance of $8y_c$ upstream from the fall, and employ reaches with end depths of 2.7, 3.0, 3.4, and 4.0 ft.)

10.70. A trapezoidal canal dredged in smooth earth ($n = 0.030$) has a bottom width of 15 ft, side slopes of 1:1, and a bed slope $S_0 = 0.0003$. With a flow of 800 cfs, $y_c = 4.05$ ft, and $y_0 = 10.8$ ft. Find the length of M_2 curve extending from a free overfall back to where the depth is 10 ft. Use reaches with end depths of 6, 8, and 10 ft.

10.71. A portion of an outfall sewer is approximately a circular conduit 5 ft in diameter and with a slope of 1 ft in 1,100 ft. It is of brick, for which $n = 0.013$. What would be its maximum capacity for uniform flow? If it discharges 120 cfs with a depth at the end of 3.15 ft, how far back from the end must it become a pressure conduit unless the size or the slope is changed? (*Note:* The solution of Prob. 10.24 shows that the discharge is a maximum when the depth is approximately 0.95 times the diameter, or 4.75 ft in this case.) The values of area and hydraulic radius are given in the following table for depth increments of 0.25 ft

y, ft	A, ft^2	R, ft
3.15	13.1	1.42
3.50	14.7	1.48
3.75	15.8	1.51
4.00	16.9	1.53
4.25	17.8	1.52
4.50	18.6	1.49
4.75	19.3	1.44

(except the first). Proceeding from the mouth upstream, find by tabular solution the lengths of the reaches indicated and the total length to the section where $y = 4.75$ ft.

10.72. In Prob. 10.71 assume the rate of discharge to be 84.3 cfs, and find the depth of water at the section of free outfall and the distance from the mouth at which the depth would equal 4.50 ft. Assume y_c at free outfall.

10.73. In a rectangular channel 10 ft wide with a flow of 200 cfs, the depth is 1 ft. If a hydraulic jump is produced, what will be the depth after it? What will be the loss of energy?

10.74. The hydraulic jump may be used as a crude flowmeter. Suppose that in a horizontal rectangular channel 5 ft wide the observed depths before and after a hydraulic jump are 0.66 and 3.00 ft, respectively. Find the rate of flow and the head loss.

10.75. Repeat Prob. 10.73 for the case where the channel is on a 10 per cent grade. For this slope, jump length $\approx 4y_2$. Assume friction force = 400 lb.

10.76. The tidal bore, which carries the tide into the estuary of a large river, is an example of an abrupt translatory wave, or moving hydraulic jump. Suppose such a bore is observed to rise to a height of 12 ft above the normal low-tide river depth of 8 ft. The speed of travel of the bore upstream is observed to be 15 mph. Find the approximate velocity of the undisturbed river. Does this represent subcritical or supercritical flow? (*Note:* The theory developed in Sec. 10.18 is based on the hydraulic jump in a fixed position. In the case of a moving jump, all kinematic terms must be considered relative to the moving wave as a frame of reference.)

10.77. A hydraulic jump occurs in a triangular flume having side slopes 1:1. The flow rate is 15 cfs, and the depth before jump is 1.0 ft. Find the depth after jump and the horsepower loss in the jump.

10.78. A hydraulic jump occurs in a rectangular channel carrying 200 cfs on a slope of 0.005. The depth after jump is 4.5 ft. What must be the depth before jump?

10.79. A rectangular channel 10 ft wide carries 100 cfs in uniform flow at a depth of 1.67 ft. Suppose that an obstruction such as a submerged weir is placed across the channel, rising to a height of 6 in. above the bottom. Will this obstruction cause a hydraulic jump to form upstream? Why? Find the water depth over the obstruction, and classify the surface profile, if possible, to be found upstream from the weir.

10.80. Suppose that the slope and roughness of the channel in Prob. 10.79 are such that uniform flow of 100 cfs occurs at 1.00 ft. Consider an obstruction rising 4 in. above the bottom of the channel. Will a hydraulic jump form upstream? As in Prob. 10.79, classify the surface profile found just upstream from the obstruction.

10.81. The rectangular flume of planed timber ($n = 0.012$) 20 ft wide, 1,000 ft long, with horizontal bed leads from a reservoir in which the still-water surface is 10 ft above the flume bed. Assume that the depth of the downstream end of the flume is fixed at 8 ft by some control section downstream. Allowing 0.2 velocity head loss at entrance, find the capacity of the flume.

10.82. Suppose that the flume of Prob. 10.81 ends in a free fall, all other conditions remaining the same. The critical depth may be supposed to occur at about $8y_c$ back from the fall. In this case, then, the length of the reach is $1,000 - 8y_c$ where y_c may be given a reasonable value, say,

6 ft, and left constant throughout the trials.   The solution proceeds as in Prob. 10.81, except that y_2 is no longer fixed but becomes y_c, given by Eq. (10.19) for each assumed value of y_1.

10.83. Analyze the water-surface profile in a long rectangular channel ($n = 0.013$). The channel is 10 ft wide, the flow rate is 400 cfs, and there is an abrupt change in slope from 0.0016 to 0.0150.   Refer to Illustrative Example 10.5 for information on normal depths and critical depth.

10.84. Repeat Prob. 10.83 for the case where the flow rate is 150 cfs.

10.85. Repeat Prob. 10.83 for the case where the slope change is from 0.0016 to 0.0006.

10.86. A very wide rectangular channel with bed slope $S_0 = 0.0003$ and roughness $n = 0.020$ carries a steady flow of 50 cfs/ft of width.   If a sluice gate (Fig. 11.38) is so adjusted as to produce a minimum depth of 1.5 ft in the channel, determine whether a hydraulic jump will form downstream, and if so, find the distance from the gate to the jump.

10.87. In a 6-ft-wide rectangular channel ($S = 0.002$, $n = 0.013$) water flows at 250 cfs.   A low dam (broad-crested weir) placed in the channel raises the water to a depth of 8.9 ft.   Analyze the water-surface profile upstream from the dam.

10.88. Solve Prob. 10.87 if the channel slope is 0.0005.   Repeat for $S_0 = 0.0008$.

10.89. A rectangular channel 10 ft wide carries 300 cfs in uniform flow at a depth of 4 ft.   By how much should the outside wall be elevated above the inside wall for a bend of 40-ft radius to the center line of channel?

10.90. Repeat Prob. 10.89 for the same conditions except that the normal depth is 2 ft.

ELEVEN

FLUID MEASUREMENTS

Both the engineer and the scientific investigator are often faced with the problem of measuring various fluid properties such as density, viscosity, and surface tension. Also, measurements are often required of various fluid phenomena, as pressure, velocity, and flow rate. In this chapter only the principles and theory of such measurements will be discussed. Detailed information on the various measuring devices may be found elsewhere in the literature.[1]

11.1. MEASUREMENT OF FLUID PROPERTIES

The measurement of *liquid density* is most commonly determined by weighing a known volume of the liquid. Other techniques include hydrostatic weighing, where an object of known volume is

---

[1] See, for example, "Fluid Meters: Their Theory and Application," 5th ed., American Society of Mechanical Engineers, New York, 1959.

weighed (*a*) in air and then (*b*) in the liquid whose density is to be determined. The *hydrometer* is a variation of this technique. The densities are calculated from fluid statics. Another, though not very accurate, technique of determining liquid density is achieved by placing two immiscible liquids in a U tube, one of known density, the other of unknown density. From fluid statics the unknown density may be found. These various techniques of measuring liquid density are illustrated in Probs. 11.1 to 11.4.

The measurement of *viscosity* is generally made with a device known as a *viscometer*. Various types of viscometers are available. They all depend on the creation of laminar-flow conditions. Since viscosity varies considerably with temperature, it is essential that the fluid be at a constant temperature when a measurement is being made. This is generally accomplished by immersing the device in a constant-temperature bath.

Several types of *rotational viscometers* are available. These generally consist of two concentric cylinders that are rotated with respect to one another. The narrow space between them is filled with liquid whose viscosity is to be measured. The rate of rotation under the influence of a given torque is indicative of the viscosity of the liquid. One difficulty with this type of viscometer is that mechanical friction must be accounted for, and this is difficult to deal with accurately.

The *tube-type viscometer* is perhaps the most reliable. Figure 11.1 shows the Saybolt viscometer. In this device the liquid is originally at *M*, with the bottom of the tube plugged. The plug is removed, and the time required for a certain volume of liquid to pass through the tube

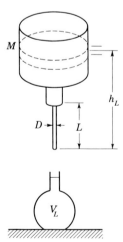

Fig. 11.1.   Tube-type viscometer.

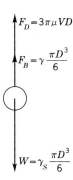

Fig. 11.2. Free-body diagram of sphere falling at terminal velocity.

is a measure of the kinematic viscosity of the liquid.   In this device the flow is unsteady and the tube is of such small diameter that the flow may be assumed to be laminar.   Actually, in many instances the tube may be too short for the establishment of laminar flow.   As an approximation let us apply Eq. (8.19).   From this equation,

$$Q = \frac{\pi D^4 \gamma h_L}{128 \mu L} \tag{11.1}$$

where h_L is the average imposed head on the liquid during the flow period, and $Q \approx V_L/t$, where V_L is the volume of liquid that flows out of the tube in time t.   Substituting $Q = V_L/t$ into Eq. (11.1), we get

$$\nu = \frac{\pi D^4 h_L}{128 V_L L} gt \tag{11.2}$$

Since D, L, V_L, and h_L are constants of the device, $\nu = Kgt$, and the kinematic viscosity is seen to be proportional to the measured time.

There are several other types of tube viscometers, but they are all based on the same principle.   Some come with a set of tubes of various diameters so that measurements can be made on liquids with a wide range of viscosities in a convenient time period.   Because the dimensions of such fine tubes cannot be perfectly duplicated, each tube is individually calibrated by measuring the time for a liquid of known viscosity at a given temperature to discharge the standard volume.

A third type of viscometer is the *falling-sphere* type.   In such a device the liquid is placed in a tall transparent cylinder and a sphere of known weight and diameter is dropped in it.   If the sphere is small enough, Stokes' law (Sec. 13.7) will prevail and the fall velocity of the sphere will be approximately inversely proportional to the absolute viscosity of the liquid.   That this is so may be seen by examining the free-body diagram of such a falling sphere (Fig. 11.2).   The forces acting include gravity, buoyancy, and drag.   Stokes' law states that if $DV/\nu <$

0.1, the drag force on a sphere is given by $F_D = 3\pi\mu VD$, where V is the velocity of the sphere and D is its diameter.   When the sphere is dropped in a liquid, it will quickly accelerate to terminal velocity, at which time $\Sigma F_z = 0$.   Thus

$$W - F_B - F_D = \gamma_s \frac{\pi D^3}{6} - \gamma \frac{\pi D^3}{6} - 3\pi\mu VD = 0$$

where γ_s and γ represent the specific weight of the sphere and liquid, respectively.   Solving the above equation, we get

$$\mu = \frac{D^2(\gamma_s - \gamma)}{18V} \tag{11.3}$$

In the preceding development it was assumed that the sphere was dropped into a liquid of infinite extent.   In actuality, the liquid will be contained in a tube and a *wall effect* will influence the drag force and hence the fall velocity.   It has been found that wall effect[1] can be expressed approximately as

$$\frac{V}{V_t} = 1 + \frac{9D}{4D_t} + \left(\frac{9D}{4D_t}\right)^2 \tag{11.4}$$

where D_t is the tube diameter, and V_t represents the fall velocity in the tube.   Equation (11.4) is applicable only if $D/D_t < 3$.

Other fluid properties such as surface tension, elasticity, vapor pressure, specific heats at constant pressure and constant temperature, and gas constant are commonly determined by physicists, and the techniques for their measurement will not be discussed here.

11.2. MEASUREMENT OF STATIC PRESSURE

To get an accurate measurement of static pressure in a flowing fluid, it is important that the measuring device fit the streamlines perfectly so as to create no disturbance to the flow.   In a straight reach of conduit the static pressure is ordinarily measured by attaching to a piezometer a pressure gage or a U-tube manometer.   The piezometer opening in the side of the conduit should be normal to and flush with the surface. Any projection, such as (c) in Fig. 11.3, will result in error.   Allen and Hopper,[2] for example, found that a projection of 0.10 in. will cause an error equivalent to 16 per cent of the local velocity head.   In this case

[1] J. S. McNown, H. M. Lee, M. B. McPherson, and S. M. Engez, Influence of Boundary Proximity on the Drag of Spheres, *Proc. 7th Intern. Congr. Appl. Mech.,* 1948.

[2] C. M. Allen and L. J. Hopper, Piezometer Investigation, *Trans. ASME,* vol. 54, no. 9, May, 1932.

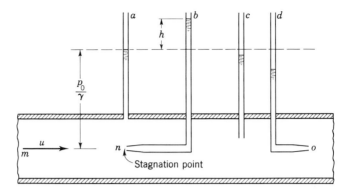

Fig. 11.3

the recorded pressure is depressed below the pressure in the undisturbed fluid because the disturbance of the streamline pattern increases the velocity, hence decreasing the pressure according to the Bernoulli equation.

When measuring the static pressure in a pipe, it is desirable to have two or more openings around the periphery of the section to account for possible imperfections of the wall. For this purpose a *piezometer ring* (Fig. 11.4) is used.

To measure the static pressure in a flow field, the *static tube* (Fig. 11.5) is used. In this device the pressure is transmitted to a gage or manometer through piezometric holes that are evenly spaced around the circumference of the tube. This device will give good results if it is perfectly aligned with the flow. Actually, the mean velocity past the piezometer holes will be slightly larger than that of the undisturbed flow

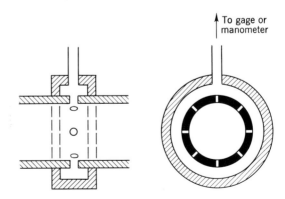

Fig. 11.4. Piezometer ring.

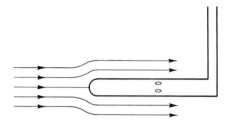

Fig. 11.5.   Static tube.

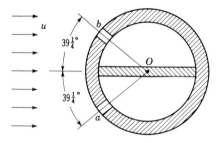

Fig. 11.6.   Direction-finding tube.

field; hence the pressure at the holes will generally be somewhat below the pressure of the undisturbed fluid.   This error can be minimized by making the diameter of the tube as small as possible.   If the direction of the flow is unknown for two-dimensional flows, a *direction-finding tube* (Fig. 11.6) may be used.   This device is a cylindrical tube having two piezometer holes located as shown.   Each piezometer is connected to its own measuring device.   The tube may be rotated until each tube shows the same reading.   Then, from symmetry, one can determine the direction of flow.   It has been found that if the piezometer openings are located as shown, the recorded pressures will correspond to those of the undisturbed flow.

11.3. MEASUREMENT OF VELOCITY WITH PITOT TUBES

One means of measuring the local velocity u in a flowing fluid is the pitot tube, named after Henri Pitot, who used a bent glass tube in 1730 to measure velocities in the River Seine.   In Sec. 4.14 it is shown that the pressure at the forward stagnation point of a stationary body in a flowing fluid is $p_s = p_0 + 1/2\rho u^2$, where p_0 and u are the pressure and velocity, respectively, in the undisturbed flow upstream from the body.   If $p_s - p_0$ can be measured, the velocity at a point is determined by this relation. The stagnation pressure can be measured by a tube facing upstream, such as (b) in Fig. 11.3.   For a jet or open stream with parallel stream-lines only, this single tube is necessary, since the height h to which the liquid rises in the tube above the surrounding free surface is equal to the velocity head in the stream approaching the tip of the tube.

For a closed conduit under pressure it is necessary to measure the static pressure also, as shown by tube (*a*) in Fig. 11.3, and to subtract this from the total pitot reading to secure the differential head *h*. The differential pressure may be measured with any suitable manometer arrangement. The formula for the pitot tube may be derived by writing an energy equation between points *m* and *n* of Fig. 11.3,

$$\frac{p_0}{\gamma} + \frac{u^2}{2g} = \frac{p_s}{\gamma} \tag{11.5}$$

from which

$$u^2 = 2g\left(\frac{p_s}{\gamma} - \frac{p_0}{\gamma}\right)$$

and finally

$$u = \sqrt{2g\left(\frac{p_s}{\gamma} - \frac{p_0}{\gamma}\right)} \tag{11.6}$$

In most cases of flow there is appreciable turbulence in the stream, which means that the velocities of individual particles fluctuate in both direction and magnitude. Hence, in general, the velocities of the particles make varying angles with the axial direction of the channel. The effect of this is to cause the instrument to read a value that is higher than the temporal mean axial component of velocity. Hence Eq. (11.6) must be modified to give

$$u = C_p\sqrt{2g\left(\frac{p_s}{\gamma} - \frac{p_0}{\gamma}\right)} \tag{11.7}$$

where C_p is a pitot-tube coefficient which is slightly less than unity. The value of C_p decreases with increasing turbulence and ranges from 1.0 down to about 0.97. Experimental evidence from a number of sources indicates that a value of between 0.995 and 0.98 will apply to conditions usually encountered.

Where conditions are such that it is impractical to measure static pressure at the wall, a combined *pitot-static tube*, as in Fig. 11.7, may be

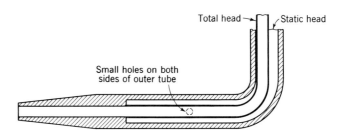

Fig. 11.7. Pitot-static tube.

used. The static pressure is measured through two or more holes drilled through an outer tube into an annular space, and it is assumed that the flow follows along the outside of the tube in such a way that the true static pressure is obtained.

Another instrument, the *pitotmeter*, consists of two tubes, one pointing upstream and the other downstream, such as tubes (*b*) and (*d*) of Fig. 11.3. The reading for tube (*d*) will be considerably below the level of the static head. The equation applicable to a pitotmeter is

$$u = C_I \sqrt{2g \left(\frac{p_s}{\gamma} - \frac{p'}{\gamma} \right)} \qquad (11.8)$$

where C_I, the coefficient of the instrument, is usually determined by experiment, and p'/γ is the pressure head at point *o* just downstream of the tip of the downstream pitot tube.

Equation (11.8) is also applicable to a pitot-static tube, for with this device rarely are the piezometer holes located in precisely the correct position to indicate the true value of p_0/γ. The Prandtl-type pitot-static tube (Fig. 11.8) has been found to give excellent results with $C_I = 1.0$. The pressure distribution along such a tube drops from the stagnation pressure to something less than the static pressure as the flow rounds the nose of the tube. The pressure rises back up and becomes higher than the static pressure near the vertical stem. A feature of the Prandtl tube is that, even when it is not placed exactly in line with the flow, the errors in the static and stagnation values balance each other so that correct velocity heads will be read for deviations up to $\pm 15°$.

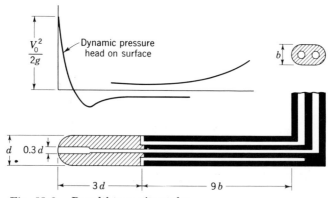

Fig. 11.8. Prandtl-type pitot tube.

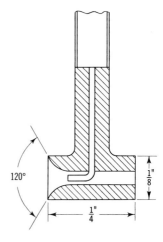

Fig. 11.9.   Kiel probe.

Still greater insensitivity to angularity may be obtained by guiding the flow past the pitot tube by means of a shroud, as shown in Fig. 11.9. Such an arrangement, called a *Kiel probe*, is used extensively in aeronautics. The stagnation-pressure measurement with this device is accurate to within 1 per cent of the dynamic pressure for yaw angles up to $\pm 54°$. A disadvantage is that the static pressure must be measured independently with a wall piezometer, a static tube, or the static portion of a Prandtl tube.

The direction-finding tube (Fig. 11.6) may be used to determine velocity. The procedure is to orient it properly so that both piezometers give the same reading. This reading is the static head. Then turn the tube through $39\frac{1}{4}°$ to obtain the stagnation pressure head. The difference in the two readings is the velocity head. This device has been used extensively in wind tunnels and in the investigation of hydraulic machinery.

11.4. MEASUREMENT OF VELOCITY BY OTHER METHODS

Other methods for measuring local velocity will be discussed in this section.

Hot-wire anemometer. The hot-wire anemometer is a device useful not only for indicating the velocity at a point but for measuring the fluctuation velocity, as in Fig. 3.6, as it responds rapidly to any change. Its operation depends upon the fact that the electrical resistance of a wire depends upon its temperature; that the temperature, in turn, depends upon the heat transfer to the surrounding fluid; and that the coefficient of heat transfer increases with increasing velocity. The hot wire, which is generally of platinum or tungsten, can be connected through a suitable circuit either to carry a constant current, in which case the voltage is a measure of the velocity, or to hold a constant voltage, the resulting current then being a function of the velocity.

Current meter and rotating anemometer. These two instruments, which are the same in principle, determine the velocity as a function of the speed at which a series of cups or vanes rotate about an axis either parallel to or normal to the flow. The instrument used in water is called a *current meter*, and when designed for use in air, it is called an *anemometer*. As the force exerted depends upon the density of the fluid as well as upon its velocity, the anemometer must be so made as to operate with less friction than the current meter.

If the meter is made with cups which move in a circular path about an axis perpendicular to the flow, it always rotates in the same direction and at the same rate regardless of the direction of the velocity, whether positive or negative, and it even rotates when the velocity is at right angles to its plane of rotation. Thus this type is not suitable where there are eddies or other irregularities in the flow. If the meter is constructed of vanes rotating about an axis parallel to the flow, resembling a propeller, it will register the component of velocity along its axis, especially if it is surrounded by a shielding cylinder. It will rotate in an opposite direction for negative flow and is thus a more dependable type of meter.

Photographic methods. The camera is one of the most valuable tools in a fluid-mechanics research laboratory. In studying the motion of water, for example, a series of small spheres consisting of a mixture of benzene and carbon tetrachloride adjusted to the same specific gravity as the water can be introduced into the flow through suitable nozzles. When illuminated from the direction of the camera, these spheres will stand out in a picture. If successive exposures are taken on the same film, the velocities and the accelerations of the particles can be determined.

In the study of compressible fluids many techniques have been devised to measure optically the change in density, as given by the *interferometer*, or the *rate* at which density changes in space, as determined in the *shadowgraph* and *schlieren* methods.[1] From such measurements of density and density gradient it is possible to locate shock waves. Although of great importance, these photographic methods are too complex to warrant further description here.

---

[1] For an excellent discussion of optical methods used in the study of fluid flow, see Irving Shames, "Mechanics of Fluids," appendix A.7, pp. 528–535, McGraw-Hill Book Company, New York, 1962. Another good reference is H. Liepmann and A. Roshko, "Elements of Gas Dynamics," pp. 153–170, John Wiley & Sons, Inc., New York, 1957.

11.5. MEASUREMENT OF DISCHARGE

There are various ways of measuring discharge. In a pipe, for example, the velocity may be determined at various radii using a pitot-static tube or a pitot tube in combination with a wall piezometer. The cross section of the pipe may then be considered as a series of concentric rings, each with a known velocity. The flow through these rings is summed up, as in Fig. 11.10, to determine the total flow rate.

To determine the flow in a river or stream, a similar technique is used. The stream is divided into a number of convenient sections, and the average velocity in each section is measured. A pitot tube could be used for such measurements, but a current meter is more commonly used. It has been found that the average velocity occurs at about 0.6 × depth (Sec. 10.6), so the velocity is generally measured at that level. Another widely used method is to take the average of the velocities at 0.2 × depth and 0.8 × depth. The procedure for determining stream discharge is shown in Fig. 11.11.

Other techniques for measuring flow rate include the *salt-velocity* method. In this method a charge of concentrated salt is injected into the flow at an upstream station. Its arrival at a downstream station is detected from conductivity measurements. In flowing between the two stations, the salt disperses and its arrival at the downstream station is spread out over a considerable period of time. The time of travel between the two stations is taken as the time from the instant of injection at the upstream station to the time at which the centroid of the conductivity-time curve passes the downstream station. Knowing the

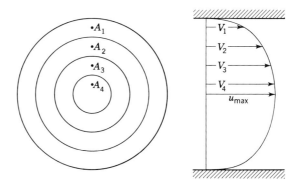

Fig. 11.10. Determination of pipe discharge.
$Q = \Sigma A_i V_i = A_1 V_1 + A_2 V_2 + \cdots$.

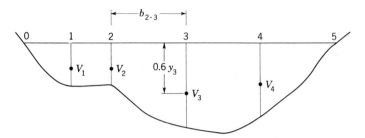

Fig. 11.11.   Determination of discharge in a stream.

$$Q_{2-3} = \left(\frac{y_2 + y_3}{2}\right) b_{2-3} \frac{V_2 + V_3}{2}$$

$$Q_{total} = \Sigma Q$$

travel time and the distance, the velocity may be determined, and then by multiplying by the cross-sectional area, we get the flow rate.

Devices for the direct measurement of discharge can be divided into two categories, those which measure by weight or positive displacement a certain quantity of fluid and those which employ some aspect of fluid mechanics. An example of the first type of device is the household water meter in which a nutating disk oscillates in a chamber. On each oscillation a known amount of water passes through the meter. The second type of flow-measuring device, dependent on basic principles of fluid mechanics in combination with empirical data, will be discussed in the following sections.

11.6. ORIFICES, NOZZLES, AND TUBES

Among the devices used for the measurement of discharge are orifices and nozzles. Tubes are rarely so used but are included here because their theory is the same, and experiments upon tubes provide information as to entrance losses from reservoirs into pipelines.

An *orifice* is an opening in the wall of a tank or in a plate normal to the axis of a pipe, the plate being either at the end of the pipe or in some intermediate location. An orifice is characterized by the fact that the thickness of the wall or plate is very small relative to the size of the opening. A *standard orifice* is one with a sharp edge as in Fig. 11.12a or an absolutely square shoulder as in Fig. 11.12b so that there is only a line contact with the fluid. Those shown in Fig. 11.12c and d are not standard because the flow through them is affected by the thickness of the plate, the roughness of the surface, and for (d), the radius of curvature. Hence such orifices should be calibrated if high accuracy is desired.

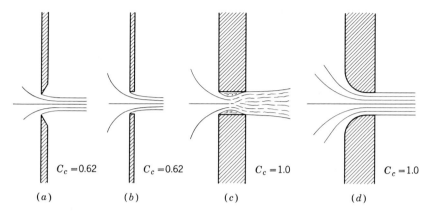

$C_c = 0.62$ $C_c = 0.62$ $C_c = 1.0$ $C_c = 1.0$

(a)   (b)   (c)   (d)

Fig. 11.12.   Types of orifice.

A *nozzle* is a converging tube, as in Fig. 11.13, if it is used for liquids; but for a gas or a vapor a nozzle may first converge and then diverge again (Sec. 9.11) to produce supersonic flow.   A nozzle has other important uses, such as providing a high-velocity stream for fire fighting or for power in a steam turbine or a Pelton water wheel.

A *tube* is a short pipe whose length is not more than two or three diameters.   There is no sharp distinction between a tube and the thick-walled orifices of Fig. 11.12c and d.   A tube may be of uniform diameter, or it may diverge.

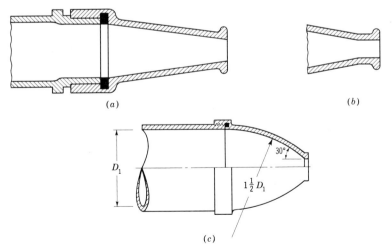

(a)   (b)

D_1 $30°$

$1\frac{1}{2} D_1$

(c)

Fig. 11.13.   Nozzles.   (a) Conical nozzle.   (b) Straight-tip nozzle.   (c) Fire nozzle.

11.7. CHARACTERISTICS OF FLUID JETS

A jet is a stream issuing from an orifice, nozzle, or tube. It is not enclosed by solid boundary walls, but is surrounded by a fluid whose velocity is less than its own. The two fluids may be different, or they may be of the same kind. A *free* jet is a stream of liquid surrounded by a gas and is therefore directly under the influence of gravity. A *submerged* jet is a stream of any fluid surrounded by a fluid of the same kind. As it is buoyed up by this surrounding fluid, it is not directly under the action of gravity.

Jet contraction.   Where the streamlines converge in approaching an orifice, as shown in Fig. 11.14, they continue to converge beyond the orifice until they reach the section xy, where they become parallel. For the ideal case, this location is an infinite distance away, but in reality, because of friction between the jet and the surrounding fluid, this section is usually found very close to the orifice. Commonly, it is about $0.5D_o$ from the opening, where D_o is the diameter of the orifice. For a free jet with a high velocity or a submerged jet with any velocity, the friction with the surroundings is such that the jet slows down and diverges beyond xy. The section xy is then a section of minimum area and is called the *vena contracta*.[1]

By *jet velocity* is meant the value of the average velocity at the vena contracta. The velocity profile for a jet is shown in Fig. 11.15, where it is seen to be nearly constant except for a small annular ring around the outside. The average velocity V is thus only slightly less than the center, or maximum, velocity u_c. As the streamlines are straight at the section xy, it follows that at the vena contracta the pressure is

---

[1] Of course, if a free jet is discharged vertically downward, the acceleration due to gravity will cause its velocity to increase and the area to decrease continuously, so that there may be no apparent section of minimum area. In such special cases, the vena contracta should be taken as the place where marked contraction ceases and before the place where gravity has increased the velocity to any appreciable extent above the true jet velocity.

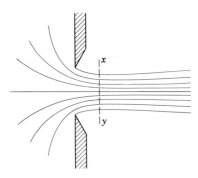

Fig. 11.14.   Jet contraction.

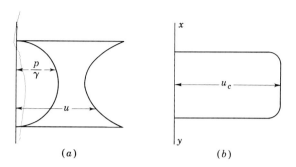

Fig. 11.15. Pressure and velocity variation in jet. (*a*) At orifice. (*b*) At vena contracta.

constant across the diameter and except for a very small increase due to surface tension, this pressure must be equal to that in the medium surrounding the jet.[1]

In the plane of the orifice the cross-sectional area is greater than at xy, and hence the average velocity must be less. As the streamlines at this point are curved, centrifugal action will cause the pressure to increase from the edge of the orifice to the center, in accordance with Sec. 4.16. Thus the pressure across the diameter will vary somewhat as shown in Fig. 11.15, and consequently, from the flow equation, the velocity u must also vary in the manner shown.

As the contraction of the jet is due to the converging of the approaching streamlines, it may be prevented altogether by causing the particles of fluid to approach in an axial direction solely, as in the free discharge from the end of a straight pipe or by a construction such as in (*c*) or (*d*) of Fig. 11.12. Also, if an orifice is placed near a corner of a tank, the streamlines are partially prevented from converging and the contraction is thus diminished. Roughness of the surface around the orifice reduces the velocity of the fluid approaching from the side and thereby also reduces the contraction.

11.8. JET COEFFICIENTS

Coefficient of velocity C_v. The velocity that would be attained at the vena contracta if friction did not exist may be termed the *ideal velocity* V_i.* It is practically the value of u_c in Fig. 11.15. Because of

---

[1] The pressure within a jet is totally different from the *force* that the jet is capable of exerting upon some object that it may *strike*.

* This is frequently called *theoretical velocity*, but the authors feel this is a misuse of the word *theoretical*. Any correct theory should allow for the fact that friction exists and affects the result. Otherwise it is not correct theory, but merely an incorrect hypothesis.

friction, the actual average velocity V is less than the ideal velocity, and the ratio V/V_i is called the *coefficient of velocity*.   Thus $V = C_v V_i$.

Coefficient of contraction C_c.   The ratio of the area of a jet, A, at the vena contracta to the area of the orifice or other opening, A_o, is called the *coefficient of contraction*.   Thus $A = C_c A_o$.

Coefficient of discharge C_d.   The ratio of the actual rate of discharge Q to the ideal rate of discharge Q_i, if there were no friction and no contraction, may be defined as the *coefficient of discharge*.   Thus $Q = C_d Q_i$.   By observing that $Q = AV$ and $Q_i = A_o V_i$, it is seen that $C_d = C_c \times C_v$.

Other coefficients which are sometimes more convenient to use will be defined in specific cases as they occur in later sections of the text.

The average velocity V of a free jet may be determined by a velocity traverse of the jet with a fine pitot tube, or it may be obtained by measuring the flow rate and dividing by the cross-sectional area of the jet.   The velocity may also be computed approximately from the coordinates of the trajectory of the jet, as discussed in Sec. 4.15.   The ideal velocity V_i is computed by the Bernoulli theorem.   Thus C_v for an orifice, nozzle, or tube may be computed by dividing V by V_i.

The coefficient of discharge is the one that can most readily be obtained and with a high degree of accuracy.   It is also the one that is of the most practical value.   For a liquid the actual Q can be determined by some standard method such as a volume or a weight measurement over a known time.   For a gas one can note the change in pressure and temperature in a container of known volume from which the gas may flow.   Obviously, if any two of the coefficients are measured, the third can be computed from them.

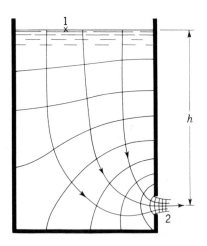

Fig. 11.16.   Free jet.

11.9. JET WITH NO VELOCITY OF APPROACH

The velocity of a fluid approaching an orifice or nozzle or similar device is called the *velocity of approach*. In Fig. 11.16 it is assumed that the area of the tank is so large relative to that of the orifice that the velocity at (1) is negligible. Let the Bernoulli theorem [Eq. (4.9)] be written between point (1) at the surface and point (2) in the jet, assuming the pressure is the same at both points. Then $0 + h + 0 = 0 + 0 + V_i^2/2g$, from which

$$V_i = \sqrt{2gh} \tag{11.9}$$

This was one of the earliest rational laws of hydraulics (1643), known as Torricelli's theorem from its discoverer, who was a student of Galileo.

According to the definitions just given, the actual velocity of the jet is

$$V = C_v \sqrt{2gh} \tag{11.10}$$

and the actual discharge is

$$Q = AV = C_c A_o (C_v \sqrt{2gh}) = C_d A_o \sqrt{2gh} \tag{11.11}$$

In case the pressures are not the same at (1) and (2), then in place of h in the preceding equations we should have $h + p_1/\gamma - p_2/\gamma$.

11.10. SUBMERGED ORIFICE

For a submerged orifice, as shown in Fig. 11.17, the equation is written between points (1) and (2), realizing that the pressure head on the jet at (2) is equal to y. Thus

$$0 + (h + y) + 0 = y + 0 + \frac{V_i^2}{2g}$$

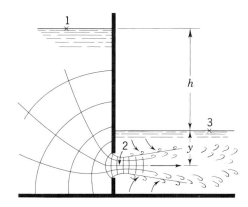

Fig. 11.17. Submerged jet.

and as the y term cancels, the result is the same as in the preceding case. Thus the actual velocity is $V = C_v \sqrt{2gh}$.

For a submerged orifice the coefficients are practically the same as for a free jet, except that, for heads less than 10 ft and for very small orifices, the discharge coefficient may be slightly less. It is of interest to observe that if the energy equation is written between (1) and (3), the result is $h_L = H_1 - H_3 = h$. Therefore this is one instance where it is impossible to assume no friction loss. Actually, the head loss in this case is that of a submerged discharge, as described in Sec. 8.17.

11.11. JET WITH VELOCITY OF APPROACH

In case the velocity of approach is not negligible, as was assumed in the preceding discussion, it is necessary to consider the velocity head at point (1). Thus, in Fig. 11.18, writing the Bernoulli equation between points (1) and (2) and then introducing the velocity coefficient, the actual jet velocity is

$$V_2 = C_v \sqrt{2g \left(\frac{p_1}{\gamma} + \frac{V_1^2}{2g} \right)} \tag{11.12}$$

This is seen to be similar in form to Eq. (11.10), and if the velocity at (1) could be determined in some way, the value of the jet velocity could be computed directly. If Q were measured, then $V_1 = Q/A_1$ or V_1 might be determined by a pitot-tube traverse. But even if V_1 is known only approximately, the error in using such a value cannot be great, as $V_1^2/2g$ is usually small compared with p_1/γ. However, V_1 can be eliminated by the continuity equation since

$$V_1 = A_2 V_2 / A_1 = C_c A_o V_2 / A_1 = C_c (D_o / D_1)^2 V_2$$

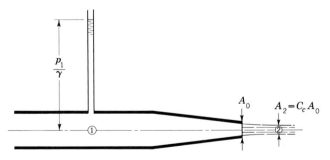

Fig. 11.18

Substituting this value of V_1 in Eq. (11.12), the actual jet velocity is

$$V_2 = \frac{C_v}{\sqrt{1 - C_c^2(D_o/D_1)^4}} \sqrt{2g \frac{p_1}{\gamma}} \qquad (11.13)$$

Comparing this with Eq. (11.10), we see that the divisor is the factor that corrects for the velocity of approach where D_o and D_1 are the diameters of the orifice or nozzle tip and the approach pipe, respectively, and h is replaced by p_1/γ.

Multiplying the jet velocity by the jet area, which is $A_2 = C_c A_o$, the rate of discharge is

$$Q = \frac{C_c C_v A_o}{\sqrt{1 - C_c^2(D_o/D_1)^4}} \sqrt{2g \frac{p_1}{\gamma}} \qquad (11.14)$$

Although this formula is strictly logical, it is more convenient to employ a coefficient C, so that

$$Q = \frac{CA_o}{\sqrt{1 - (D_o/D_1)^4}} \sqrt{2g \frac{p_1}{\gamma}} \qquad (11.15)$$

It is seen that $C_c C_v$ and C are identical in numerical value only when $D_o/D_1 = 0$ but they are very nearly the same in value when D_o/D_1 is small, as less than 0.4. It is even more convenient to replace Eqs. (11.14) and (11.15) by

$$Q = KA_o \sqrt{2g \frac{p_1}{\gamma}} \qquad (11.16)$$

where K is a *flow coefficient*, determined experimentally for a given ratio of D_o/D_1.

11.12. ENERGY LOSS AND NOZZLE EFFICIENCY

The loss of head in friction in an orifice, nozzle, or tube may be determined by writing the energy equation between some point upstream and the vena contracta of the jet. Letting H now represent the *total* head upstream while $V_2^2/2g$ is the velocity head in the jet, the equation is $H - h_L = V_2^2/2g$. But as $V_2 = C_v \sqrt{2gH}$ and $V_2^2/2g = C_v^2 H$, the substitution of this last expression in the preceding energy equation results in two equivalent expressions for the loss of head through a nozzle,

$$h_L = (1 - C_v^2)H = \left(\frac{1}{C_v^2} - 1\right)\frac{V_2^2}{2g} \qquad (11.17)$$

It should be noted that the contraction coefficient is merely the relation between the area of a jet and the orifice and is not involved at all in friction loss.

As the jet from a nozzle is frequently employed for power purposes in a steam turbine or a Pelton wheel, its energy efficiency is of interest. The efficiency of a nozzle is defined as the ratio of the power in the jet to the power passing a section in the pipe at the base of the nozzle. Since the discharge is the same for the two points, the efficiency is merely the ratio of the heads at these two sections. Thus, referring to Fig. 11.18, $e = H_2/H_1$. But $H_2 = V^2/2g$, and $H_1 = p_1/\gamma + V_1^2/2g$, and so from Eq. (11.12) it follows that $H_2 = C_v^2 H_1$. Hence the nozzle efficiency is

$$e = C_v^2 \tag{11.18}$$

Because the velocity in the jet is not uniform across a diameter, the true kinetic energy in the jet is slightly greater than that given by $V^2/2g$, as was shown in Sec. 4.1. Thus, for a good nozzle, the true efficiency of a nozzle may be about 1 per cent greater than the value given by Eq. (11.18). For most nozzles $C_v \approx 0.98$; hence $h_L \approx 0.04 V_2^2/2g$.

Illustrative example 11.1: A 2-in. circular orifice (not standard) in the end of a 3-in.-diameter pipe discharges a measured flow of 0.60 cfs of water when the pressure in the pipe is 10.0 psi. If the jet velocity is determined by the pitot tube to be 39.2 fps, find the values of the coefficients C_v, C_c, C_d, C, and K.

$$\frac{p_1}{\gamma} = 10 \left(\frac{144}{62.4}\right) = 23.1 \text{ ft}$$

$$V_1 = \frac{Q}{A_1} = \frac{0.60}{0.0491} = 12.23 \text{ fps} \qquad \frac{V_1^2}{2g} = 2.32 \text{ ft}$$

From Eq. (11.12),

$$C_v = \frac{V}{V_i} = \frac{39.2}{\sqrt{2g(23.1 + 2.32)}} = 0.97$$

$$\text{Area of jet} = \frac{Q}{V} = \frac{0.60}{39.2} = 0.0153 \text{ ft}^2$$

Then

$$C_c = \frac{A_j}{A_o} = \frac{0.0153}{0.0218} = 0.702$$

From $C_d = C_v C_c$, $C_d = 0.970 \times 0.702 = 0.680$ [this value could also have been obtained from Eq. (11.14)].

From Eq. (11.15), $C = 0.640$

From Eq. (11.16), $K = 0.715$

11.13. VALUES OF COEFFICIENTS

Velocity coefficient. The coefficient of velocity is a measure of the extent to which friction retards the jet velocity of a real fluid. For

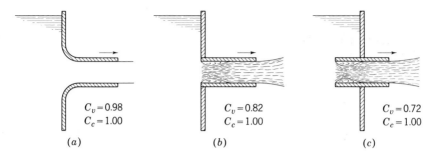

Fig. 11.19. Coefficients for tubes.

sharp-edged circular orifices the velocity coefficient may range from about 0.95 to 0.994. The smaller values are found with small orifices and low heads. For good nozzles with smooth walls the velocity coefficient is usually from 0.97 to 0.99. For certain tubes and other devices the velocity coefficients may be much lower, as may be observed in Fig. 11.19b and c. Such tubes have considerable friction loss, not because of the initial contraction of the entering stream, but because of its subsequent reexpansion as it fills the tube. Rounding the entrance, as in Fig. 11.19a, greatly reduces the friction.

Contraction coefficient. Coefficients of contraction range from approximately 0.50 to 1.00. For ideal flow through a rectangular sharp-edged orifice classical hydrodynamics yields a value for C_c of

$$\frac{\pi}{\pi + 2} = 0.611^*$$

and this is also practically the value for standard sharp-edged circular orifices, such as those shown in Fig. 11.12a and b, for orifices 2.5 in. in diameter or larger and for heads above about 3 ft. For very small orifices and for heads as low as a few inches, the effects of adhesion, surface tension, and capillarity will increase the coefficient of contraction up to 0.72, and even more in extreme cases.

Any device that provides a uniform diameter for a short distance before exit, such as the tubes in Fig. 11.19 or the nozzle tip in Fig. 11.13b, will usually eliminate any contraction, and thus $C_c = 1.00$. While this increases the size of the jet from a given area, it also tends to produce more friction. The contraction coefficient is very sensitive to small changes in the edge of the orifice or in the upstream face of the plate. Thus slightly rounding the edge of the orifice in Fig. 11.12b, instead of

* Horace Lamb, "Hydrodynamics," 6th ed., pp. 98–99, Dover Publications, New York, 1945.

maintaining a perfectly square corner, will increase the contraction coefficient materially.

Tubes (b) and (c) in Fig. 11.19 are shown as flowing full, and because of the turbulence, the jets issuing from them will have a "broomy" appearance. Because of the contraction of the jet at entrance to these tubes the local velocity in the central portion of the stream will be higher than that at exit from the tubes, and hence the pressure will be lower. If the pressure is lowered to that of the vapor pressure of the fluid, the streamlines will then no longer follow the walls. In such a case tube (b) becomes equivalent to orifice (b) in Fig. 11.12, while tube (c) behaves as shown in Fig. 11.20. If its length is less than its diameter, the reentrant tube is called a *Borda mouthpiece*. Because of the greater curvature of the streamlines for a reentrant tube, the contraction coefficient is lower than for any other type and the velocity coefficient is also lower. But if the jet springs clear as in Fig. 11.20, the velocity coefficient is as high as for a sharp-edged orifice.

The Borda mouthpiece is of interest because it is one device for which the contraction coefficient can be very simply calculated. For all other orifices and tubes there is a reduction of the pressure on the walls adjacent to the opening, but the exact pressure values are unknown. But for the reentrant tube, the velocity along the wall of the tank is almost zero at all points, and hence the pressure is essentially hydrostatic. The only unbalanced pressure is that on an equal area opposite to the tube, and its value is $\gamma h A_o$. The time rate of change of momentum due to the flow out of the tube is $\rho Q V = \gamma A V^2/g$, where A is the area of the jet.

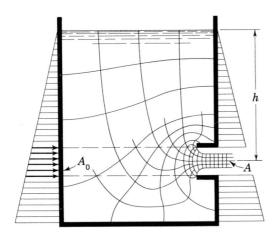

Fig. 11.20. Borda tube.

Equating force to time rate of change of momentum, $\gamma h A_o = \gamma A V^2/g$, and thus, $V^2 = gh A_o/A$. Ideally, $V^2 = 2gh$, and thus, ideally, $C_c = A/A_o = 0.5$. If it be assumed that $C_v = 0.98$, the actual values will be $C_c = 0.52$ and $C_d = 0.51$.

It is not easy to compute contraction coefficients in other cases, but they can be determined reasonably well by means of flow nets. However, without taking this much trouble, a little judgment will enable one to make a fair estimate of the contraction.

Discharge coefficient. If this coefficient has to be estimated in a particular case, it is usually better to assume velocity and contraction coefficients separately and calculate the discharge coefficient from them. Thus it is known that the velocity coefficient for a standard orifice is about 0.98 and its contraction coefficient is 0.62; hence $C_d = 0.98 \times 0.62 = 0.61$ approximately. For some devices the velocity coefficient is the determining factor, while for others it is the contraction coefficient that governs.

Although numerous experiments have been made and their results published, there is as yet no general agreement on precise values for discharge coefficients for orifices and nozzles, so that calibration is desirable if high accuracy is desired. For standard sharp-edged circular orifices the range of values for C_d is generally from 0.60 to 0.66, the lower values occurring at higher heads because of increased contraction. For nozzles the coefficients of discharge depend mostly on the shape of the nozzle. The coefficients of discharge for the nozzles of Fig. 11.13 are 0.92, 0.98, and 0.82, respectively.

11.14. VENTURI TUBE

The converging tube is an efficient device for converting pressure head to velocity head, while the diverging tube converts velocity head to pressure head. The two may be combined to form a venturi tube, named after Venturi, an Italian, who investigated its principle about 1791. It was applied to the measurement of water by Clemens Herschel in 1886. As shown in Fig. 11.21, it consists of a tube with a constricted *throat* which produces an increased velocity accompanied by a reduction in pressure, followed by a gradually diverging portion in which the velocity is transformed back into pressure with slight friction loss. As there is a definite relation between the pressure differential and the rate of flow, the tube may be made to serve as a metering device.

The Herschel type of *venturi meter* has a converging cone with the proportions shown in Fig. 11.21. In Fig. 11.22 is shown a *venturi nozzle*, with a converging section which is believed to have a coefficient less sensitive to changes in the smoothness of the surface. The venturi

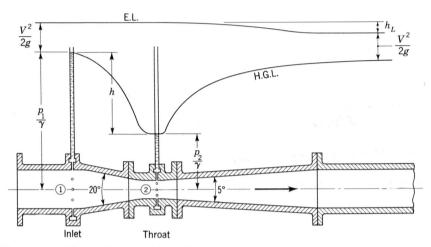

Fig. 11.21.   Venturi meter with conical entrance.

meter is used for measuring the rate of flow of both compressible and incompressible fluids.   In this section we shall consider the application of the venturi meter to incompressible fluids.   In Sec. 11.18 the application of the venturi meter to compressible fluids will be discussed.

Writing the Bernoulli equation between (1) and (2), we have, for the ideal case,

$$\frac{p_1}{\gamma} + z_1 + \frac{V_1{}^2}{2g} = \frac{p_2}{\gamma} + z_2 + \frac{V_2{}^2}{2g}$$

Substituting the continuity equation, $V_1 = (A_2/A_1)V_2$, we get for the ideal throat velocity

$$(V_2)_{\text{ideal}} = \sqrt{\frac{1}{1 - (A_2/A_1)^2}} \sqrt{2g\left(\frac{p_1}{\gamma} + z_1 - \frac{p_2}{\gamma} - z_2\right)}$$

As there is some friction loss between (1) and (2), the true velocity is slightly less than the value given by this expression.   Hence we may introduce a discharge coefficient C, so that the flow is given by

$$Q = A_2 V_2 = \frac{CA_2}{\sqrt{1 - (D_2/D_1)^4}} \sqrt{2g\left(\frac{p_1}{\gamma} + z_1 - \frac{p_2}{\gamma} - z_2\right)} \quad (11.19)$$

which is equivalent to Eq. (11.15).   For a given meter the dimensions are known and constant.   Although C varies with the rate of flow, the variation is very small and, if an average value is assumed, the equation for a particular meter reduces to

$$Q = M \sqrt{\frac{p_1}{\gamma} + z_1 - \frac{p_2}{\gamma} - z_2} \qquad (11.20)$$

In the preceding equations it should be noted by reference to Eq. (2.12) that if a differential manometer is used with piezometric connections at sections (1) and (2),

$$\frac{p_1}{\gamma} + z_1 - \frac{p_2}{\gamma} - z_2 = \frac{MR}{12}\left(\frac{s_m}{s_f} - 1\right) \qquad (11.21)$$

where MR is the manometer reading in inches, and s_m and s_f are the specific gravities of the manometer and flowing fluids, respectively.

The venturi tube is an accurate device for flow measurement and is most valuable for large flows in pipelines. With a suitable recording device the flow rate can be integrated so as to give the total quantity of flow. Aside from the installation cost, the only disadvantage of the venturi meter is that it introduces a permanent frictional resistance in the pipeline. This loss is practically all in the diverging part from (2) to (3) (Fig. 4.9) and is ordinarily from $0.1h$ to $0.2h$.

Values of D_2/D_1 may vary from $\frac{1}{4}$ to $\frac{3}{4}$, but a common ratio is $\frac{1}{2}$. A small ratio gives increased accuracy of the gage reading, but is accompanied by a higher friction loss and may produce an undesirably low pressure at the throat, sufficient in some cases to cause liberation of dissolved air or even vaporization of the liquid at this point. This phenomenon, called *cavitation*, has been described in Sec. 4.8.

The angles of convergence and divergence in the original Herschel meter are 20 and 5°, respectively, as in Fig. 11.21, but in other tubes these angles have been increased to as much as 30 and 14°, respectively. It is believed that a minimum friction loss is obtained for an angle of 5° in the diffuser, but a larger angle will reduce the length and cost of the tube.

For accuracy in use, the venturi meter should be preceded by a straight

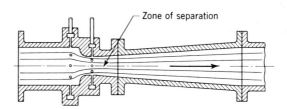

Fig. 11.22. Venturi meter with entrance profile that is the standard nozzle of the Society of German Engineers.

pipe whose length is at least 5 to 10 pipe diameters.   The approach section becomes more important as the diameter ratio increases, and the required length of straight pipe depends on the conditions preceding it. Thus the vortex formed from two short-radius elbows in planes at right angles, for example, is not eliminated within 30 pipe diameters.   Such a condition can be alleviated by the installation of straightening vanes preceding the meter.[1]

The pressure differential should be obtained from piezometer rings (Fig. 11.4) surrounding the pipe, with a number of suitable openings in the two sections.   In fact, these openings may sometimes be replaced by very narrow slots extending all the way around the circumference.   A pulsating flow gives a differential which is proportional to the square of the instantaneous velocities, and thus a mean velocity computed from the square root of the mean manometer reading will result in a measured flow slightly greater than the actual flow.[2]

11.15. VENTURI - METER COEFFICIENTS

Unless specific information is available for a given venturi tube, the value of C may be assumed to be about 0.99 for large tubes and about 0.97 or 0.98 for small ones, provided the flow is such as to give reasonably high Reynolds numbers.   A roughening of the surface of the converging section from age or scale deposit will reduce the coefficient slightly.   Venturi tubes in service for many years have shown a decrease in C of the order of 1 to 2 per cent.[3]

Dimensional analysis of a venturi tube indicates that the coefficient C should be a function of Reynolds number and of the geometric parameters D_1 and D_2.   Values of venturi-tube coefficients are shown in Fig. 11.23.[4]   This diagram is for a diameter ratio of $D_2/D_1 = 0.5$ only, but it

---

[1] W. S. Pardoe, The Effect of Installation on the Coefficients of Venturi Meters, *Trans. ASME*, vol. 65, p. 337, 1945.

[2] S. R. Beitler, The Effect of Pulsation on Orifice Meters, *Trans. ASME*, vol. 61, p. 309, 1939.

[3] C. M. Allen and L. J. Hooper, Venturi and Weir Measurements, *Mech. Eng.*, June, 1935, p. 369.   W. S. Pardoe, *Mech. Eng.*, January, 1936, p. 60.

[4] Figure 11.23 is adapted from a similar graph by W. S. Pardoe, The Coefficients of Herschel-type Cast-iron Venturi Meters, *Trans. ASME*, vol. 67, p. 339, July, 1945. Note that N_R is computed for conditions at the throat.   To determine the Reynolds number, it is often convenient to use a "hybrid" set of units and compensate with a correction factor.   Thus

$$N_R = \frac{15.28Q}{D\nu} = \frac{22,740G}{D \times \text{centipoises}}$$

where D is the diameter in inches, ν is kinematic viscosity in square feet per second, and Q and G are expressed in cubic feet per second and pounds per second, respectively.   This last form is especially convenient in the case of gases.

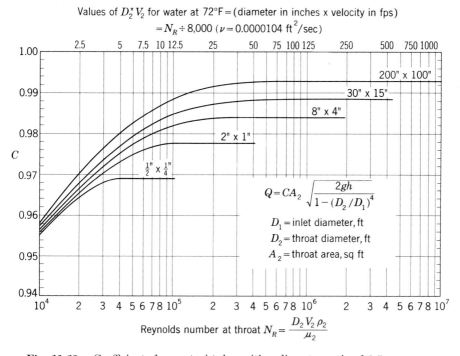

Fig. 11.23. Coefficients for venturi tubes with a diameter ratio of 0.5.

is reasonably valid for smaller ratios also. For larger ratios C decreases slightly. Thus for $D_2/D_1 = 0.75$ the values are about 1 per cent less than shown in Fig. 11.23. Although this diagram is based on venturi tubes of the type shown in Fig. 11.21, the coefficients will be accurate within 1 per cent for similar devices, such as the venturi nozzle of Fig. 11.22.

Occasionally, the precise calibration of a venturi tube has given a value of C greater than 1. Such an abnormal result is sometimes due to improper piezometer openings. But another explanation is that the α's at sections (1) and (2) are such that this is so.

11.16. FLOW NOZZLE

If the discharge cone of a venturi nozzle is omitted, the result is a *flow nozzle* of the type shown in Fig. 11.24. This is simpler than the venturi tube and can be installed between the flanges of a pipeline. It will answer the same purpose, though at the expense of an increased friction loss in the pipe. Although the venturi-meter equation [Eq. (11.19)] can be employed for the flow nozzle, it is more convenient and customary to

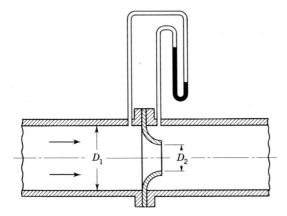

Fig. 11.24.   Flow nozzle.

include the correction for velocity of approach with the coefficient of discharge, as in Eq. (11.16), so that

$$Q = KA_2 \sqrt{2g \left(\frac{p_1}{\gamma} + z_1 - \frac{p_2}{\gamma} - z_2 \right)} \qquad (11.22)$$

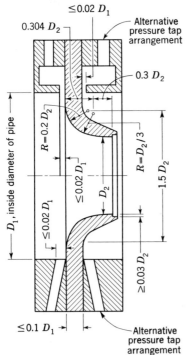

Fig. 11.25.   ISA flow nozzle.

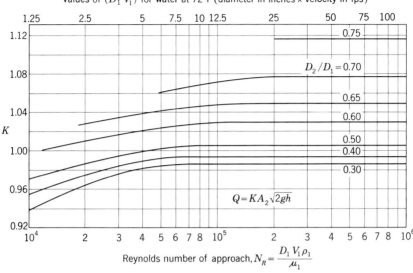

Fig. 11.26. Flow coefficients for ISA nozzle. (*Adapted from ASME Flow Measurement*, 1959.)

where K is called the *flow coefficient*, and A_2 is the area of the nozzle throat. Comparison with Eq. (11.19) establishes the relation

$$K = \frac{C}{\sqrt{1 - (D_2/D_1)^4}} \tag{11.23}$$

Although there are many designs of flow nozzles, the ISA (International Standards Association) nozzle (Fig. 11.25) has become an accepted standard form in many countries. Values of K for various diameter ratios of the ISA nozzle are shown in Fig. 11.26 as a function of Reynolds number. Note that in this case the Reynolds number is computed for the approach pipe rather than for the nozzle throat, which is a convenience since N_R in the pipe is frequently needed for other computations also.

As shown in Fig. 11.26, many of the values of K are greater than unity, which is a result of including the correction for approach velocity with the conventional coefficient of discharge. There have been many attempts to design a nozzle for which the velocity-of-approach correction would just cancel the discharge coefficient, leaving a value of the flow coefficient equal to unity. Detailed information on these so-called *long-radius* nozzles may be found in the ASME publications on fluid meters and flow measurement.[1]

---

[1] Flow Measurement by Means of Standardized Nozzles and Orifice Plates, pt. 5, chap. 4, in *ASME Power Test Codes on Instruments and Apparatus*, 1959.

As in the case of the venturi meter, the flow nozzle should be preceded by at least 10 diameters of straight pipe for accurate measurement.
Two alternative locations for the pressure taps are shown in Fig. 11.25.
The head loss across an ISA flow nozzle is shown in Fig. 11.28 as a percentage of the differential head $(p_1/\gamma + z_1 - p_2/\gamma - z_2)$.

11.17. ORIFICE METER

An orifice in a pipeline, as in Fig. 11.27, may be used as a meter in the
same manner as the venturi tube or the flow nozzle. It may also be
placed on the end of the pipe so as to discharge a free jet. The coefficients are practically identical in the two cases. The difference between
the orifice in the present discussion and that in the earlier sections of
this chapter is that here the pipe walls are nearer to the edge of the
orifice so that there is less contraction of the jet, resulting in a higher
value of C_c, and also there is a much larger value of the velocity of
approach. For the numerical values of the coefficients mentioned in Sec.
11.13 to apply, the ratio D_o/D_1 should be less than $\frac{1}{5}$, where D_o and D_1
are the diameters of the orifice and the approach pipe, respectively.
Typical values of C_c and C_d for an orifice meter versus D_o/D_1 ratio are
shown in Fig. 11.28.

For an orifice meter, instead of using Eq. (11.14), it is more convenient to use Eq. (11.15), as explained in Sec. 11.11. For ease of ref-

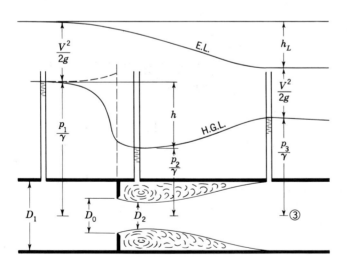

Fig. 11.27. Thin-plate orifice in a pipe.

erence this is given here as

$$Q = \frac{CA_o}{\sqrt{1 - (D_o/D_1)^4}} \sqrt{2g\left(\frac{p_1}{\gamma} + z_1 - \frac{p_2}{\gamma} - z_2\right)} \qquad (11.24)$$

This equation has the additional advantage that C varies little for diameter ratios up to 0.85 as shown in Fig. 11.28. As it is not satisfactory to use higher ratios, the marked variation beyond that point is of no importance.

It will be observed that this equation is the same as that for the venturi meter and differs from it only in the numerical value of C. As given here the equation differs from the form given in Sec. 11.11 in that $p_1/\gamma + z_1 - p_2/\gamma - z_2$ replaces p_1/γ, but Eqs. (11.15), (11.19), and (11.24) are really identical.

As in the case of the nozzle of Sec. 11.11 and the flow nozzle of Sec. 11.16, it is convenient to reduce the equation to

$$Q = KA_o \sqrt{2g\left(\frac{p_1}{\gamma} + z_1 - \frac{p_2}{\gamma} - z_2\right)} \qquad (11.25)$$

Although all three forms of the orifice equation will be found in use, the present trend is toward Eq. (11.25) because of the simplified computation. The relation between C_d, C, and K is shown in Fig. 11.28.[1] If the value of any one of these coefficients is known for a given diameter ratio, corresponding values of the other three may be computed or read from Fig. 11.28.

The difference between an orifice meter and a venturi meter or flow nozzle is that for both of the latter there is no contraction, so that A_2 is also the area of the throat and is fixed, while for the orifice, A_2 is the area of the jet and is a variable and is less than A_o, the area of the orifice. For the venturi tube or flow nozzle the discharge coefficient is practically a velocity coefficient, while for the orifice the value of C or K is much more affected by C_c than it is by C_v.

Thus the coefficient C for an orifice meter is much less than it is for a venturi or a flow nozzle, and it also varies in a different manner with Reynolds number, as may be seen by comparing Figs. 11.23 and 11.29.

Figure 11.27 shows that the pressure drops to a minimum at the vena contracta at (2) and then gradually rises to (3), which is four to eight pipe

[1] The curves shown in Fig. 11.28 were calculated from data given by the following: S. R. Beitler and Paul Bucher, The Flow of Fluids through Orifices in 6-inch Pipes, *Trans. ASME*, vol. 52, no. 30, 1930. Ed S. Smith, Jr., Quantity-rate Fluid Meters, *ibid.*, vol. 52, no. 30, 1930. H. S. Bean, E. Buckingham, and P. S. Murphy, Discharge Coefficients of Square-edged Orifices for Measuring the Flow of Air, *Natl. Bur. Std. (U.S.), Res. Paper* 49. *ASME Fluid Meters Rept.*, 1931.

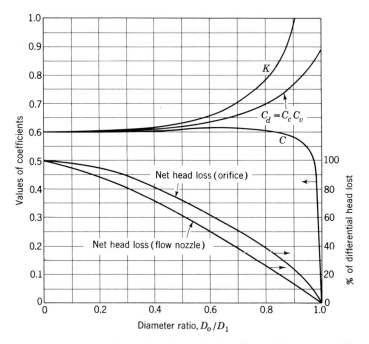

Fig. 11.28. Coefficients for sharp-edged orifice with pressure differential measured either at the flanges or at the vena contracta. Also head loss across orifice and flow nozzle. All curves are for $N_R(D_1 V_1 \rho_1/\mu) > 10^5$.

diameters downstream, after which it slowly diminishes because of normal pipe friction. The drop in pressure between (1) and (2) is due to the acceleration given the stream in passing through the orifice, while the pressure drop between (1) and (3) is due to the loss of head. A considerable portion of the kinetic energy of the jet is transformed into kinetic energy of rotation in vortices which are formed as the jet expands to fill the pipe. This kinetic energy of rotation is not converted into pressure, but is eventually dissipated by viscosity effects and converted into heat.

The pressure differential may be measured between (1), which is about one pipe diameter upstream, and the vena contracta (2), which is approximately one-half the pipe diameter downstream. The distance to the vena contracta is not a constant, but decreases as D_o/D_1 increases. The differential can also be measured between the two corners on each side of the orifice plate. These *flange taps* have the advantage that the orifice meter is self-contained; the plate may be slipped into a pipeline without the necessity of making piezometer connections in the pipe. The hydraulic grade line in Fig. 11.27 indicates the pressure variation at the center of the stream. In the corner where the orifice joins the pipe, the pressure is a little higher than in the center, because of the stagnation effect. For a similar reason the pressure on the downstream corner is a little higher than that at the vena contracta, and hence the differential pressure measured with flange taps is not materially different from that obtained with *vena contracta taps* as described above. For precise work, however, there exist curves of the flow coefficient obtained with each of these two schemes of measuring the pressure differential.

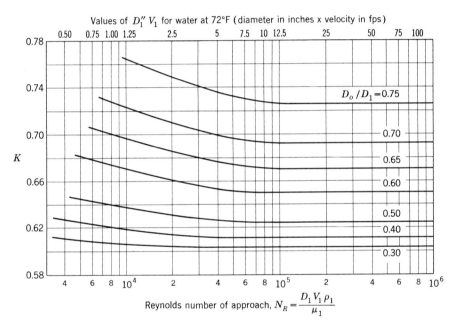

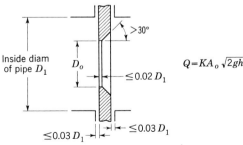

Fig. 11.29. VDI orifice meter and flow coefficients for flange taps. (*Adapted from NACA Tech. Mem. 952.*)

The orifice as a measuring device has the merit that it may be installed in a pipeline with a minimum of trouble and expense.   Its principal disadvantage is the greater frictional resistance offered by it as compared with the venturi tube.[1]

Illustrative example 11.2:   A 2-in. ISA flow nozzle is installed in a 3-in. pipe carrying water at 72°F.   If a water-air manometer shows a differential of 2 in., find the flow.

This is a trial-and-error type of solution.   First assume a reasonable value of K. From Fig. 11.26, for $D_2/D_1 = 0.67$, for the level part of the curve, $K = 1.06$.   Then from Eq. (11.22),

$$Q = KA_2 \sqrt{2g \left(\frac{p_1}{\gamma} + z_1 - \frac{p_2}{\gamma} - z_2 \right)}$$

where

$$A_2 = \frac{\pi}{4} \times \frac{2^2}{144} = 0.0218 \text{ ft}^2$$

and

$$\Delta \left(\frac{p}{\gamma} + z \right) = \frac{2}{12} = 0.167 \text{ ft}$$

Thus $Q = 1.06 \times 0.0218 \times 8.02 \times \sqrt{0.167} = 0.0757$ cfs

With this first determination of Q,

$$V_1 = \frac{Q}{A} = \frac{0.0757}{0.0492} = 1.54 \text{ fps}$$

Then $D_1'' V_1 = 3 \times 1.54 = 4.62$

From Fig. 11.26, $K = 1.04$ and

$$Q = \frac{1.04}{1.06} \times 0.0757 = 0.0743 \text{ cfs}$$

No further correction is necessary.

11.18. FLOW MEASUREMENT OF COMPRESSIBLE FLUIDS

Strictly speaking, most of the equations that have been presented in the preceding part of this chapter apply only to incompressible fluids, but practically, they may be used for all liquids and even for gases and vapors where the pressure differential is small relative to the total pressure.   As this is the condition usually encountered in the metering of all fluids, even compressible ones, the preceding treatment has extensive application. However, there are conditions in metering fluids where compressibility must be considered.

As in the case of incompressible fluids, equations may be derived for ideal frictionless flow and then a coefficient introduced to obtain a correct result.   The ideal conditions that will be imposed for a compressible

[1] For further information on orifices, see "Flow Meters: Their Theory and Application," 5th ed., American Society of Mechanical Engineers, New York, 1959.

fluid are that it is frictionless and that there is to be no transfer of heat; i.e., the flow is adiabatic. This last is practically true for metering devices, as the time for the fluid to pass through is so short that very little heat transfer can take place.

Because of the variation in density with both pressure and temperature, it is necessary to express the rate of discharge of a compressible fluid in terms of weight rather than volume. Also, the continuity equation must now be

$$G = \gamma_1 A_1 V_1 = \gamma_2 A_2 V_2$$

Applying Eq. (4.20) to a fluid meter,

$$V_2 = C_v \sqrt{\frac{2gJ(E_1 - E_2)}{1 - (\gamma_2 A_2/\gamma_1 A_1)^2}} \tag{11.26}$$

and the rate of discharge is

$$G = C\gamma_2 A_2 \sqrt{\frac{2gJ(E_1 - E_2)}{1 - (\gamma_2 A_2/\gamma_1 A_1)^2}} \tag{11.27}$$

In these equations E_2 is the value of enthalpy after a frictionless adiabatic expansion from p_1 to p_2. It may be obtained from vapor tables or charts and is very convenient for vapors. The discussion of such tables and their use is outside the scope of this text, and is in the field of thermodynamics, but for a gas $E_1 - E_2 = c_p(T_1 - T_2)$, where $T_2 = T_1(p_2/p_1)^{(k-1)/k}$. For compressible fluids, p must be absolute pressure.

However, Eqs. (11.26) and (11.27) can be replaced by equations involving pressures directly, and in these forms they can be used for either gases or vapors by the selection of the appropriate value of k. From Eq. (9.16) and the continuity equation we obtain

$$V_2 = C_v \sqrt{2g \frac{k}{k-1} p_1 v_1 \frac{1 - (p_2/p_1)^{(k-1)/k}}{1 - (A_2/A_1)^2 (p_2/p_1)^{2/k}}} \tag{11.28}$$

and multiplying this by $\gamma_2 A_2$ and replacing γ_2 in terms of γ_1, the rate of discharge is

$$G = CA_2 \sqrt{2g \frac{k}{k-1} p_1 \gamma_1 \left(\frac{p_2}{p_1}\right)^{2/k} \frac{1 - (p_2/p_1)^{(k-1)/k}}{1 - (A_2/A_1)^2 (p_2/p_1)^{2/k}}} \tag{11.29}$$

where γ_1 may be replaced by p_1/RT_1 if desired.

Inasmuch as this equation is too complex for convenient use in metering, it is replaced by the simpler equation for an incompressible fluid, but with the insertion of an expansion factor Y.

From Eq. (11.19) the weight rate of flow G' of an incompressible fluid through a venturi meter is

$$G' = \gamma Q' = \frac{\gamma C A_2}{\sqrt{1 - (D_2/D_1)^4}} \sqrt{2g\left(\frac{p_1}{\gamma} + z_1 - \frac{p_2}{\gamma} - z_2\right)} \quad (11.30)$$

Neglecting the z terms, Eq. (11.30) may be written as

$$G' = C A_2 \sqrt{2g\gamma \frac{p_1 - p_2}{1 - (D_2/D_1)^4}} \quad (11.31)$$

If the fluid is compressible, the specific weight will decrease from γ_1 to γ_2 as the pressure drops from p_1 to p_2 and the value of G' determined by Eq. (11.31) will be larger than the true value G as given by Eq. (11.29). Therefore we use an expansion factor Y such that $G = YG'$. Therefore the true flow rate for a compressible fluid is[1]

$$G = C Y A_2 \sqrt{2g\gamma_1 \frac{p_1 - p_2}{1 - (D_2/D_1)^4}} \quad (11.32)$$

where C has the same value as for an incompressible fluid at the same Reynolds number.

Values of Y may be found by experiment or by computing the value of G by Eq. (11.29) and finding the relation between it and G' for a variety of conditions. The values so determined may then be used for all future work. The value of Y may be plotted for any one value of k as a simple function of the ratio p_2/p_1. Such a chart is shown in Fig. 11.30.[2]

For other values of k, similar charts could be constructed, but if no such chart is available, it will be necessary to use Eq. (11.29). However, it will be found that Y does not vary a great deal with different values of k. Thus, for $p_2/p_1 = 0.90$ and $D_2/D_1 = 0.65$, values of Y for $k = 1.4, 1.3,$ and 1.2 are $0.9309, 0.9259,$ and 0.9201, respectively. For smaller values of p_2/p_1 and D_2/D_1 the differences will be greater.

In Fig. 11.30 it may be observed that for the venturi meter no values for Y are shown for p_2/p_1 ratios less than 0.528. This is so because, for air and other gases having an adiabatic constant $k = 1.4$, the p_2/p_1 ratio will always be greater than 0.528 if the flow is subsonic, as was pointed out in Sec. 9.10.

---

[1] Equations (11.29) to (11.32) seem to be inconsistent in that they use the throat area A_2 with the specific weight γ_1 in the pipe or inlet. The practical reason is that the diameter of the throat is more accurately known than the diameter of the pipe and the pressure and temperature in the pipe are more generally known than those in the throat. Note that γ_1 may be replaced by p_1/RT_1.

[2] For a venturi or nozzle throat where $C_c = 1$,

$$Y = \sqrt{\frac{[k/(k-1)](p_2/p_1)^{2/k}[1 - (p_2/p_1)^{(k-1)/k}]}{1 - (p_2/p_1)}} \sqrt{\frac{1 - (D_2/D_1)^4}{1 - (D_2/D_1)^4(p_2/p_1)^{2/k}}}$$

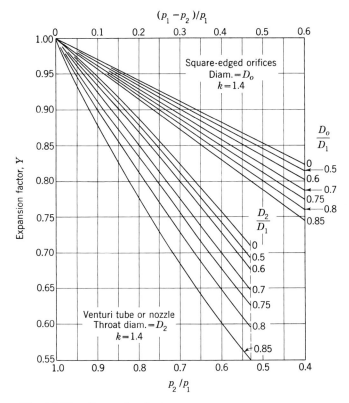

Fig. 11.30. Expansion factors.

Equation (11.32) is directly applicable to the flow of compressible fluids through venturi meters and flow nozzles where $C_c = 1.0$, provided the flow is subsonic. For orifice meters the A_2 of Eq. (11.32) must be replaced with $C_c A_o$, where A_o is the cross-sectional area of the orifice opening. For compressible fluids the C_c of an orifice meter depends on the p_2/p_1 ratio; hence Y varies in a different manner than in the case of a venturi meter. Values of Y for orifice meters are shown in Fig. 11.30. In the case of an orifice meter the maximum jet velocity is the acoustic velocity c, but this does not impose a limit on the rate of discharge because the jet area continues to increase with decreasing values of p_2/p_1. For this reason the values of Y for the orifice are extended in Fig. 11.30 to lower values of p_2/p_1.

It has been found by experiment that the flow through an orifice meter increases continuously as the pressure ratio decreases. Perry experimented with air with a negligible velocity of approach and carried

p_2 down to a value as low as $0.05p_1$, at which pressure the flow was 13.7 per cent more than at the critical pressure. His formula for the orifice is

$$G = 0.465 \frac{A_o p_1}{\sqrt{T_1}} \sqrt{1 - \left(\frac{p_2}{p_1}\right)^2}$$

where A_o and p_1 can both involve either square feet or square inches.[1]

Any converging or converging-diverging nozzle in which acoustic velocity occurs at the throat can serve as a metering device. In Sec. 9.10 the critical pressure at the throat of a nozzle was shown to be

$$p_c = p_1 \left(\frac{2}{k+1}\right)^{k/(k-1)} \tag{11.33}$$

This expression applies when the velocity of approach is negligible.[2] An empirical expression involving velocity of approach in a very simple manner and one which is also surprisingly accurate has been presented by W. H. Church. It is

$$\frac{p_c}{p_1} = \left(\frac{2}{k+1}\right)^{k/(k-1)} + \frac{(D_2/D_1)^5}{5} \tag{11.34}$$

For venturi tubes and nozzles where the velocity in the throat is the acoustic velocity, G may be found by substituting p_c for p_2 in Eq. (11.32) and employing the value of Y for $p_2/p_1 = p_c/p_1$, if Y is known for the particular k value. If Y is not available for the particular k concerned, Eq. (11.29) may be used by inserting the numerical value of p_c for p_2.

If the velocity of approach is negligible, $A_2/A_1 = 0$. Inserting the expression for p_c of Eq. (11.33) for p_2 in Eq. (11.28), the latter reduces to

$$V_2 = c = \sqrt{2g \frac{k}{k+1} p_1 v_1} \tag{11.35}$$

for an ideal frictionless flow. In reality there is a slight discrepancy here, for fluid friction does require that a velocity coefficient be introduced, and this in turn would make V_2 less than the acoustic velocity. The fact is that the velocity is not uniform across the throat diameter, and if the velocity in the main portion of the stream is acoustic, the small portion of the flow near the wall does not reach the acoustic value until a short dis-

---

[1] J. A. Perry, Jr., *Trans. ASME*, vol. 71, p. 757, 1949.

[2] By the same steps used in deriving Eq. (11.33), an exact expression including velocity V_1 may be found to be $p_c^{(k-1)/k} = \dfrac{2}{k+1} p_1^{(k-1)/k} + \dfrac{k-1}{k+1} \left(\dfrac{A_2}{A_1}\right)^2 \dfrac{p_c^{(k+1)/k}}{p_1^{2/k}}$, which can be solved by trial.

tance downstream.   However, this discrepancy is minor and is covered by the numerical value of C used in computing G, which is the quantity we are really interested in evaluating.

Equation (11.35) gives the ideal velocity at a venturi throat where the pressure is p_c and the specific volume is v_c.   The flow is obtained by multiplying by a coefficient C, the throat area A_2, and specific weight γ_c, or preferably dividing by specific volume $v_c = v_1(p_1/p_c)^{1/k}$ and replacing p_c in terms of p_1 by Eq. (11.33).   The flow is then

$$G = CA_2 \sqrt{2g \frac{p_1}{v_1} \frac{k}{k+1} \left(\frac{2}{k+1} \right)^{2/(k-1)}} \tag{11.36}$$

where C is a coefficient with the same value as for an incompressible fluid at the same Reynolds number and is normally of the order of 0.98.

It can be shown that for a perfect gas the acoustic velocity is independent of the pressure and depends only upon the absolute temperature.   Thus, at the throat, the value of c is $\sqrt{gkRT_2}$, or from Eq. (11.35), is $\sqrt{2g[k/(k+1)]RT_1}$, from which, when the throat velocity is acoustic, $T_2 = T_1 2/(k+1)$.   But Eq. (11.36) shows that the rate of discharge is proportional to the initial pressure p_1 inasmuch as $p_1/v_1 = p_1^2/RT_1$.

It is obvious that for any specific gas with a given value of k, Eq. (11.36) may be greatly simplified.   Thus, if $k = 1.4$, for example, the equation reduces to

$$G = C \frac{3.88 A_2 p_1}{\sqrt{RT_1}} \tag{11.37}$$

and furthermore, for air with $R = 53.3$ ft/°F,

$$G = C \frac{0.53 A_2 p_1}{\sqrt{T_1}} \tag{11.38}$$

In these last two equations the area units for both A_2 and p_1 must be the same and can be square inches and pounds per square inch, respectively, or they can both involve square feet.   If these last three equations are used for an orifice, then the orifice area A_o replaces A_2, and an appropriate value of C must be used.

It must be remembered that Eqs. (11.35) to (11.38) are to be used only when the velocity of approach is negligible and when p_2 at the throat of a venturi tube or converging-diverging nozzle is reduced to the value p_c as obtained from Eq. (11.33).   For an orifice p_2 is the pressure in the space into which the jet issues, no matter how low this pressure may become.

11.19. WEIRS

The weir has long been a standard device for the measurement of water in an open channel. In its simplest form the water flows over the top of a plate as shown in Fig. 11.31. The rate of flow is determined by measuring the height H (head), relative to the crest, at a distance upstream from the crest at least four times the maximum head that is to be employed. The amount of drawdown at the crest is typically about $0.15H$.

The upstream face of the weir plate should be smooth, and the plate should be strictly vertical. The crest should have a sharp, square upstream edge, a top width of $\frac{1}{16}$ to $\frac{1}{8}$ in., and a bevel on the downstream side, so that the nappe springs clear, making a line contact for all but the very lowest heads. If it does not spring clear, the flow cannot be considered as true weir flow and the experimentally determined coefficients do not apply. The velocity at any point in the nappe is related to the energy line as shown in Fig. 11.31. The approach channel should be long enough so that normal velocity distribution exists and the surface should be free of waves. It may sometimes be necessary to install baffles to ensure a quiet flow of approach. All deviations from proper weir construction increase the flow over the computed value.

The value of H is measured by a head gage, two forms of which are shown in Fig. 11.32. The *hook gage* is brought up to the surface from below until its point just pierces the water surface, when the scale is read. From this reading must be subtracted the reading when the point is level with the weir crest. The *point gage* is lowered to the water surface from above, and the scale is read just as the point touches the surface. The point gage may be connected into an electric circuit so that a small light shows when contact is made with the water. Both gages may be

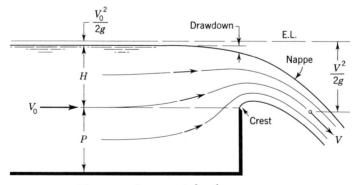

Fig. 11.31. Flow over sharp-crested weir.

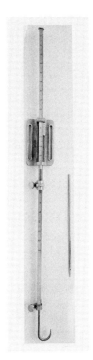

Fig. 11.32. Hook gage and point gage. *(Courtesy of W. & L. E. Gurley Co.)*

used in an open stream, but it is better if they are used in a stilling well at one side of the channel.

Suppressed rectangular weir. This type of weir is as wide as the channel, and the width of the nappe is the same as the length of the crest. As there are no contractions of the stream at the sides, it is said that end contractions are *suppressed*. It is essential that the sides of the channel upstream be smooth and regular. It is common to extend the sides of the channel downstream beyond the crest so that the nappe is confined laterally. The flowing water tends to entrain air from this enclosed space under the nappe, and unless this space is adequately ventilated, there will be a partial vacuum and perhaps all the air may eventually be swept out. The water will then cling to the downstream face of the plate, and the discharge will be greater for a given head than when the space is vented. Therefore venting of a suppressed weir is necessary if the standard formulas are to be applied.

Weir with end contractions. When the length B of the crest of a rectangular weir is less than the width of the channel, there will be a lateral contraction of the nappe so that its width is less than B. It is believed that end contractions are a source of error, and so this type of

weir is not considered as accurate as the preceding. Its chief virtue is
that the approach channel need not be of uniform cross section or have
smooth sides.

   Triangular, or V-notch, weir. For relatively small flows the
rectangular weir must be very narrow and thus of limited maximum
capacity, or else the value of H will be so small that the nappe will not
spring clear but will cling to the plate. For such a case the triangular
weir has the advantage that it can function for a very small flow and
also measure reasonably large flows as well. The vertex angle is usually
between 10 and 90° but rarely larger.

11.20. RECTANGULAR - WEIR FORMULAS

To derive the flow equation for a rectangular weir, consider an elementary
area $dA = B\,dh$ in the plane of the crest, as shown in Fig. 11.33, and
assume the velocity through this area to be equal to $\sqrt{2gh}$. The apparent flow through this area is

$$dQ = B\,dh\,\sqrt{2gh} = B\,\sqrt{2g}\,h^{\frac{1}{2}}\,dh$$

and this is to be integrated over the whole area, i.e., from $h = 0$ to $h = H$.
   Performing this integration, we obtain an ideal Q_i which is

$$Q_i = \sqrt{2g}\,B\int_0^H h^{\frac{1}{2}}\,dh = \tfrac{2}{3}\,\sqrt{2g}\,BH^{\frac{3}{2}}$$

But this ideal flow will be decreased slightly by fluid friction and decreased
much more by other factors. Thus, considering Figs. 11.31 and 11.33,
which show sections at right angles to each other, it is apparent that the
area of the stream in the plane of the crest is much less than BH, because
of the drawdown at the top and the crest contraction below. As h is
never as small as zero, there is no zero velocity at the top of the nappe,

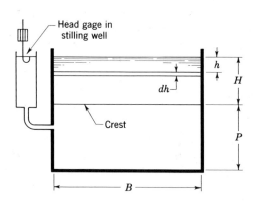

Fig. 11.33. Rectangular sharp-
crested weir without end contractions.

and furthermore the streamlines in general are not normal to the plane of the area. To correct for these discrepancies, it is necessary to introduce an experimental coefficient of discharge C_d. This, then, gives us the basic formula for a *suppressed rectangular weir*, which is

$$Q = C_d \, \tfrac{2}{3} \, \sqrt{2g} \, BH^{3/2} \tag{11.39}$$

For a given rectangular weir, this equation can be reduced to $Q = C_w BH^{3/2}$ where C_w is the *weir coefficient*. Neither C_d nor C_w are constant, though they do not vary a great deal.

If V_0, the velocity of approach at the section where H is measured, is appreciable, the limits of integration should then be $H + V_0^2/2g$ and $V_0^2/2g$; so the resulting fundamental equation is

$$Q = C_d \, \tfrac{2}{3} \, \sqrt{2g} \, B \left[\left(H + \frac{V_0^2}{2g} \right)^{3/2} - \left(\frac{V_0^2}{2g} \right)^{3/2} \right] \tag{11.40}$$

To be strictly correct, the velocity head should be multiplied by α to correct for the nonuniformity of the velocity, as explained in Sec. 4.1. To do this precisely, it would be necessary to measure local velocities over the area, but this is not usually practicable, and so α is usually assumed to be 1.0.

Small-scale but precise experiments covering a wide range of conditions led Rehbock[1] of the Karlsruhe Hydraulic Laboratory in Germany to the following expression for C_d in Eqs. (11.39) and (11.40):

$$C_d = 0.605 + \frac{1}{305H} + 0.08 \frac{H}{P} \tag{11.41}$$

This equation was obtained by fitting a curve to the plotted values of C_d for a great many experiments and is purely empirical. Capillarity is accounted for by the second term, while velocity of approach (assumed to be uniform) is responsible for the last term. Rehbock's formula has been found to be accurate within 0.5 per cent for values of P of 0.33 to 3.3 ft and for values of H of 0.08 to 2.0 ft with the ratio H/P not greater than 1.0. It is even valid for greater ratios than 1.0 if the bottom of the discharge channel is lower than that of the approach channel so that backwater does not affect the head.

Equation (11.40) with C_d as given by Eq. (11.41) must be solved by trial. An approximate value of Q may be first obtained by applying Eq. (11.39). Then the effect of V_0 can be accounted for to obtain a refined value of Q.

[1] T. Rehbock, in discussion of E. W. Schoder and K. B. Turner, Precise Weir Measurements, *Trans. ASCE*, vol. 93, p. 1143, 1929.

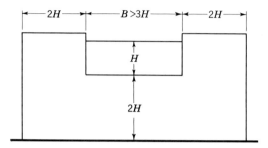

Fig. 11.34. Limiting proportions of standard contracted weirs.

Dimensional analysis of weir flow leads to some interesting conclusions that provide a basis for an understanding of the factors that influence the coefficient of discharge. The physical variables that influence the flow Q over the weir of Figs. 11.31 and 11.33 include B, H, P, g, μ, σ, and ρ. Using the Buckingham II theorem (Sec. 7.7), and without going into the details, the following results:

$$Q = \varphi \left(N_W, N_R, \frac{P}{H} \right) B \sqrt{g}\, H^{3/2}$$

Thus, comparing this expression with Eq. (11.39), we conclude that C_d depends on N_W, N_R, and P/H. It has been found that P/H is the most important of these (Probs. 11.62 and 11.70). The Weber number N_W, which accounts for surface-tension effects, is important only at low heads. In the flow of water over weirs the Reynolds number is generally quite high, so viscous effects are generally insignificant. If one were to calibrate a weir for the flow of oil, however, N_R would undoubtedly affect C_d substantially.

11.21. WEIR WITH END CONTRACTIONS

When the width B of a rectangular weir is less than that of the channel, Francis[1] concluded that the effect of each side contraction is to reduce the width of the nappe by $0.1H$. The usual contracted weir will have a contraction at each side, but occasionally a weir is placed against one sidewall, so that the contraction on one side is suppressed. If $n =$ the number of contractions, which may be 2, 1, or 0, the Francis formula, based on Eq. (11.39), with $C_d = 0.622$, is

$$Q = 3.33(B - 0.1nH)H^{3/2} \tag{11.42}$$

[1] James B. Francis, "Lowell Hydraulic Experiments," 5th ed., D. Van Nostrand Company, Inc., Princeton, N.J., 1909.

This formula is an excellent illustration of the limitations of an empirical formula. It is accurate within the limits of the experiments on which it was based. But it is seen that if H is large enough relative to B, the formula would indicate zero flow, and for an even larger value of H, the computed result would be negative. If this equation is to be used, the minimum proportions allowable are as shown in Fig. 11.34, but still larger ratios are desirable. Even with such limitations, it may yield results that are up to 3 per cent too high.

Cipolletti weir. In order to avoid correcting for end contractions, the sides of the Cipolletti weir are given a $\frac{1}{4}$:1 batter, which is supposed to add enough to the effective width of the stream to offset the lateral contraction. Thus, if B is the width or length of the crest,

$$Q = 3.367BH^{3/2} \tag{11.43}$$

11.22. TRIANGULAR, OR V - NOTCH, WEIR

In Fig. 11.35 is a triangular weir with a vertex angle θ. The rate of discharge through an elementary area dA is $dQ = C_d \sqrt{2gh}\, dA$. Now $dA = 2x\, dh$, and $x/(H - h) = \tan \theta/2$. Substituting in the foregoing, the following result is obtained for the entire notch:

$$Q = C_d 2 \sqrt{2g} \tan \frac{\theta}{2} \int_0^H (H - h)h^{1/2}\, dh$$

Integrating between limits and reducing, the fundamental equation for all triangular weirs is obtained:

$$Q = C_d \frac{8}{15} \sqrt{2g} \tan \frac{\theta}{2} H^{5/2} \tag{11.44}$$

For a given angle θ and assuming C_d is constant, this may be reduced to

$$Q = KH^{5/2} \tag{11.45}$$

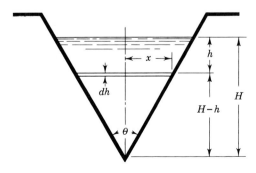

Fig. 11.35. Triangular weir.

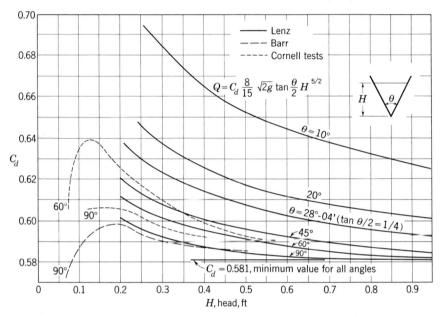

Fig. 11.36.   Coefficients for triangular weirs.

In Fig. 11.36 are presented experimental values of C_d for water flowing over V-notch weirs with central angles varying from 10 to 90°. The solid lines represent tests by Lenz;[1] the dotted lines are from data taken at Cornell University;[2] the dashed line represents a 90° weir with a fine sharp edge, reported by Barr.[3]   The rise in C_d at heads less than 0.5 ft is due to incomplete contraction.   At lower heads the frictional effects reduce the coefficient.   At very low heads, when the nappe clings to the weir plate, the phenomenon can no longer be classed as weir flow and Eq. (11.44) is inapplicable.

11.23. BROAD - CRESTED WEIR

Another type of weir is the broad-crested weir (Fig. 11.37), which is usually built of concrete.   One of its advantages is that it is rugged and can stand up well under field conditions.

[1] Arno T. Lenz, Viscosity and Surface Tension Effects on V-notch Weir Coefficients, *Trans. ASCE*, vol. 108, pp. 759–802, 1943.

[2] *Eng. News*, vol. 73, p. 636, 1915.

[3] James Barr, Experiments upon the Flow of Water over Triangular Notches, *Engineering*, Apr. 8–15, 1910.

The broad-crested weir, as mentioned in Illustrative Example 10.3, is a critical-depth meter; that is, critical depth occurs on the crest of the weir. In Eq. (10.16) it was shown that, for a rectangular channel, $E = \frac{3}{2}y_c$, while Eq. (10.19) stated that $y_c = (q^2/g)^{1/3}$. Employing these relations, we can write for the flow over a broad-crested weir:

$$Q = B \sqrt{gy_c{}^3} = B \sqrt{g(\tfrac{2}{3}E)^3} = B(\tfrac{2}{3})^{3/2} \sqrt{g}\, E^{3/2} \qquad (11.46)$$

Let us now substitute this expression into Eq. (11.39), which is applicable to broad-crested weirs as well as sharp-crested ones, since both have rectangular flow cross sections. This yields

$$C_W = \frac{1}{\sqrt{3}} \left(\frac{E}{H}\right)^{3/2} \qquad (11.47)$$

For very high weirs (that is, P/H large) the velocity of approach becomes small, so that $H \to E$, and thus $C_W \to 1/\sqrt{3} = 0.577$. Hence it is seen that C_W depends on the P/H ratio. When P/H is small, C_W is large, and vice versa.

11.24. SLUICE GATE

The sluice gate shown in Fig. 11.38 is a device used to control the passage of water in an open channel. When properly calibrated, it may also serve as a means of flow measurement. As the lower edge of the gate opening is flush with the floor of the channel, contraction of the bottom side of the issuing stream is entirely suppressed. Side contractions will of course depend on the extent to which the opening spans the width of the channel. The complete contraction on the top side, however, because of the larger velocity components parallel to the face of the gate, will offset the suppressed bottom contraction, resulting in a coefficient of

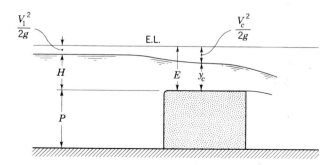

Fig. 11.37.   Broad-crested weir.

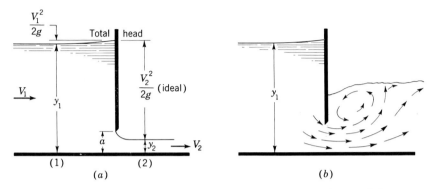

Fig. 11.38. Flow through sluice gate. (*a*) Free flow. (*b*) Submerged flow.

contraction nearly the same as for a slot with contractions at top and bottom.

Flow through a sluice gate differs fundamentally from flow through a slot in that the jet is not free but guided by a horizontal floor. Consequently, the final jet pressure is not atmospheric, but distributed hydrostatically in the vertical section. Writing the Bernoulli theorem with respect to the stream bed as datum from point 1 to point 2 in the free-flow case (Fig. 11.38*a*),

$$\frac{V_1{}^2}{2g} + y_1 = \frac{V_2{}^2}{2g} + y_2$$

from which, introducing a velocity coefficient,

$$V_2 = C_v \sqrt{2g\left(y_1 + \frac{V_1{}^2}{2g} - y_2\right)}$$

Following the customary definition of the coefficient of discharge, $C_d = C_c C_v$, there results

$$Q = C_d A \sqrt{2g(y_1 - y_2) + V_1{}^2} \qquad (11.48)$$

where $A = aB$ is the area of the gate opening. As in the case of the flow nozzle and the orifice meter, it is convenient to absorb the velocity of approach into an experimental flow coefficient and to include also in this coefficient the effect of downstream depth. The simple discharge equation for flow under a sluice gate results:

$$Q = K_s A \sqrt{2g y_1} \qquad (11.49)$$

where K_s is defined as the *sluice coefficient*.

Values of K_s fall between 0.55 and 0.60 for free flow, but are materially reduced when the flow conditions downstream are such as to produce submerged flow, as shown in Fig. 11.38b.[1]

11.25. OTHER METHODS OF MEASURING DISCHARGE

In addition to the foregoing "standard" devices for measuring the flow of fluids, there are a number of supplementary devices less amenable to exact theoretical analysis but worthy of brief mention. One of the simplest for measuring flow in a pipeline is the *elbow meter*, which consists of nothing more than piezometer taps at the inner and outer walls of a 90° elbow in the line. The pressure difference, due to the centrifugal effects at the bend, will vary approximately as the velocity head in the pipe. Like other meters, the elbow should have sections of straight pipe upstream and downstream and should be calibrated in place.[2]

The *rotameter* (Fig. 11.39) consists of a vertical glass tube that is slightly tapered, in which the metering *float* is suspended by the upward motion of the fluid around it. Directional notches cut in the float keep it rotating and thus free of wall friction. The rate of flow determines the equilibrium height of the float, and the tube is graduated to read the flow directly. The rotameter is also used for gas flow, but the weight of the float and the graduation must be changed accordingly.

---

[1] Values of discharge coefficients for sluice and other types of gates may be found in Hunter Rouse (ed.), "Engineering Hydraulics," pp. 536–543, John Wiley & Sons, Inc., New York, 1950.

[2] W. M. Lansford, The Use of an Elbow in a Pipe Line for Determining the Rate of Flow in the Pipe, *Univ. Ill. Eng. Expt. Sta. Bull.* 289, December, 1936.

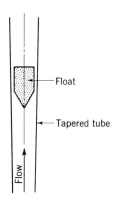

Fig. 11.39.   Rotameter.

PROBLEMS

11.1. A small object weighs 1.32 lb in air and 1.02 lb in a liquid.   The volume of this object is known to be 0.0060 ft³.   What is the density of the liquid?

11.2. A hydrometer is made in the form of a ¼-in.-diameter cylinder of length 10 in.   Attached to the end of the cylinder is a 1-in.-diameter sphere. The entire device weighs 14.0 g.   What range of specific gravities can be measured with this device?

11.3. To what depth will the hydrometer of Prob. 11.2 sink when placed in a liquid having a density of 1.74 slugs/ft³?

11.4. Carbon tetrachloride ($s = 1.59$) is placed in an open U tube.   A liquid is poured into one of the legs of the tube.   A liquid column 15.4 in. high balances a carbon tetrachloride column 10.0 in. high.   What is the specific weight of the liquid?   The text states that this method will give only approximate values.   Why is this so?

11.5. A rotational viscometer is constructed of two concentric cylinders of height 10.0 in.   The OD of the inner cylinder is 3.950 in., and the ID of the outer cylinder is 4.050 in.   When a torque of 5.0 ft-lb is applied to the outer cylinder, it was found to rotate at 1 revolution per 3.5 sec.   Find the viscosity of the fluid.   Neglect mechanical friction.

11.6. A tube viscometer similar to the one of Fig. 11.1 has a tube diameter of 0.0422 in. and a tube length of 3.05 in.   The vertical distance from the liquid surface in the reservoir to the tube outlet changed from 9.50 to 9.00 in. during a run.   The flow volume was 50 cm³, and the time was 126.4 sec.   Find the kinematic viscosity of the liquid.

11.7. Fifty cubic centimeters of water at 80°F flows through a tube-type viscometer in 50.5 sec.   An equal volume of oil at 60°F flows through the same viscometer in 800 sec.   Find the absolute viscosity of the oil if $s = 0.86$.

11.8. Water at 50°F flows through a tube-type viscometer in 100.0 sec.   How long will it take 90°F water to pass through the same viscometer?

11.9. A 0.25-in.-diameter lead sphere ($s = 11.4$) falls through an oil ($s = 0.86$) at a constant velocity of 0.150 fps.   The oil is contained in a 2.25-in.-diameter tube.   Find the viscosity of the oil.   Check N_R to see if it is less than 0.10.

11.10. A 4-in.-diameter tube contains oil ($s = 0.9$) having a viscosity of 0.005 lb-sec/ft².   Find the maximum size of steel sphere ($s = 7.8$) that will satisfy Stokes' law.   What will be the fall velocity of this sphere?

11.11. A 0.10-in.-diameter sphere has a fall velocity of 0.005 fps when a certain liquid is contained in a 1.0-in.-diameter tube.   Compute the fall velocities in tubes of diameter 0.50, 2.0, 4.0, and 10.0 in.   Plot fall velocity vs. tube diameter.

11.12. In the figure, pressure gage A reads 10.0 psi, while pressure gage B reads 11.0 psi.   Find the velocity if 50°F air is flowing.   Atmospheric pressure is 26.8 in. Hg.   Assume $C_p = 1.0$ and neglect compressibility effects.

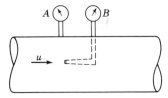

Fig. Prob. 11.12

11.13. In Prob. 11.12, if the two pressure gages were replaced by a differential manometer containing water, what would be the reading on the manometer?

11.14. The pitotmeter in the figure is connected to a mercury manometer, and the reading is 4.0 in. The velocity is known to be 11.8 fps. If carbon tetrachloride ($s = 1.59$) is flowing, what is C_I for the instrument?

Fig. Prob. 11.14

11.15. A pitot tube is placed in a pipe carrying water at 60°F. The pitot tube and a wall piezometer tube are connected to a water-mercury manometer which registers a differential of 3 in. Assuming $C_p = 0.99$, what is the velocity approaching the tube?

11.16. Suppose that the fluids of Prob. 11.15 are reversed so that mercury is flowing in the pipe and water is the gage fluid (with the manometer now inverted). With the same gage differential, what would be the velocity of the mercury?

11.17. A Prandtl tube is placed on the center line of a smooth 12-in.-diameter pipe in which 80°F water is flowing. The reading on a differential manometer attached to this Prandtl tube is 10 in. of carbon tetrachloride ($s = 1.59$). Find the flow rate.

11.18. A pitot-static tube for which $C_I = 0.98$ is connected to an inverted U tube containing oil ($s = 0.85$). Water is flowing. What is the velocity if the manometer reading is 4.0 in.?

11.19. In the figure, with uniform flow in the open channel, $a = 2.80$ ft. Find b if $n = 0.020$.

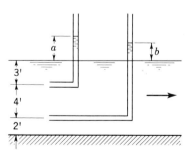

Fig. Prob. 11.19

11.20. In Fig. 11.10 let the pipe diameter be 24 in. and suppose the flow is laminar, that is, $u = u_{max} - kr^2$. Divide the circle into concentric rings with radii 3, 6, 9, and 12 in., and compute the flow rate by the method of Fig. 11.10 by taking the velocities at radii of 1.5, 4.5, 7.5, and 10.5 in.

as representative of the rings.   Use a value of 10 fps for u_{max}.   Compare the result with that obtained by integration.

11.21. Water issues from a circular orifice under a head of 40 ft.   The diameter of the orifice is 4 in.   If the discharge is found to be 479 ft³ in 3 min, what is the coefficient of discharge?   If the diameter at the vena contracta is measured to be 3.15 in., what is the coefficient of contraction and what is the coefficient of velocity?

11.22. A jet discharges from an orifice in a vertical plane under a head of 12 ft. The diameter of the orifice is 1.5 in., and the measured discharge is 0.206 cfs.   The coordinates of the center line of the jet are 11.54 ft horizontally from the vena contracta and 3.0 ft below the center of the orifice. Find the coefficients of discharge, velocity, and contraction.

11.23. The velocity of water in a pipe 4 in. in diameter is 10 fps.   At the end of the pipe is a nozzle whose velocity coefficient is 0.98.   If the pressure in the pipe is 8 psi, what is the velocity in the jet?   What is the diameter of the jet?   What is the rate of discharge?   What is the head loss?

11.24. A jet of water 3 in. in diameter is discharged through a nozzle whose velocity coefficient is 0.96.   If the pressure in the pipe is 12 psi and the pipe diameter is 8 in. and if it is assumed that there is no contraction of the jet, what is the velocity in the nozzle?   What is the rate of discharge?

11.25. The nozzle in the figure throws a stream of water vertically upward such that the power available in the jet at point (2) is 3.42 hp.   If the pressure at the base of the nozzle, point (1), is 21.0 psi, find (*a*) the theoretical height to which the jet will rise; (*b*) the coefficient of velocity; (*c*) the head loss between (1) and (2); (*d*) the theoretical diameter of the jet at a point 20 ft above (2).

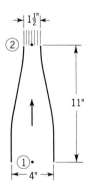

Fig. Prob. 11.25

11.26. The loss of head due to friction in an orifice, nozzle, or tube may be expressed as $h_L = kV^2/2g$, where V is the actual velocity of the jet. (*a*) Compute k for the three tubes in Fig. 11.19.   (*b*) If the tubes discharge water under a head of 5 ft, compute the loss of head in each case.

11.27. The diverging tube shown in the figure discharges water when $h = 5$ ft. The area A is twice area A_o. Neglecting all friction losses, find (a) velocity at throat; (b) pressure head at throat.

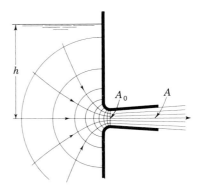

Fig. Prob. 11.27

11.28. If the barometer pressure is 14.7 psia and the water temperature is 80°F, what is the maximum value of h at which the tube will flow full, all other data being the same as in Prob. 11.27? What will happen if the value of h is made greater than this?

11.29. For a rounded entrance and tube flowing full as in the sketch for Prob. 11.27, $C_c = 1.0$ both for the throat and the exit, and thus $C_v = C_d$ for both sections. For the throat, assume the value of C_v as given for (a) in Fig. 11.19, and assume that for the tube as a whole the discharge coefficient applied to the exit end is 0.70. If $h = 5$ ft, find the velocity at the throat and the pressure head at the throat, and compare with Prob. 11.27.

11.30. Find the maximum theoretical head at which the Borda tube of Fig. 11.20 will flow full if the liquid is water at 80°F and the barometer reads 28.4 in. Hg. Assume $C_d = 0.72$ for the tube flowing full.

11.31. In the figure, the pitot tube in a water jet at elevation 60 ft registers a pressure of 16.5 psi. The orifice at the bottom of the large open tank

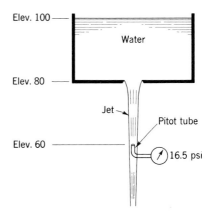

Fig. Prob. 11.31

has a diameter of 1.00 in. Find C_c and C_v of the orifice. Neglect air resistance. The flow rate is 0.12 cfs.

11.32. Determine the value of M for a 9- by 3-in. venturi tube, assuming $C = 0.983$.

11.33. If the venturi tube of Prob. 11.32 were situated vertically, as shown in the figure, with a differential manometer between inlet and throat, and if h were replaced by y in. Hg differential, find the equivalent value of M if the fluid is (a) water at 60°F; (b) oil with a specific weight of 53 pcf.

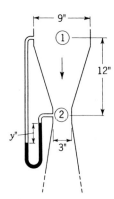

Fig. Prob. 11.33

11.34. Suppose the meter of Prob. 11.32 were to be used for a flow of 2.5 cfs. Find (a) the differential pressure in feet of the liquid; (b) the head loss from inlet to throat; (c) the probable head loss across the entire meter.

11.35. Solve parts (a) and (c) of Prob. 11.34 for the case where the throat is enlarged to a 4.5-in. diameter (assuming no change in C). What is the percentage reduction in sensitivity and in head loss?

11.36. An 8- by 4-in. venturi meter is to deliver 5 cfs of water at 60°F. What will be the value of M?

11.37. Solve Prob. 11.36 for the case of a 6- by 4-in. meter. What is the percentage change in sensitivity?

11.38. Suppose that the tube of Prob. 11.36 were to be used for an oil whose kinematic viscosity is 0.0005 ft²/sec. What would be the differential for a flow of 3.5 cfs?

11.39. Suppose that a 4-in. VDI orifice were used in an 8-in. pipe to measure a flow of 0.5 cfs of water at 72°F. What would be the differential?

11.40. Suppose that the fluid in Prob. 11.39 is changed to a crude oil ($s = 0.925$), other conditions remaining the same. What would be the differential in feet of oil and in pounds per square inch (Fig. 1.2)?

11.41. A 6-in. VDI orifice is used in an 8-in. pipe to measure the flow of crude oil ($s = 0.855$) at 15°F. If an oil-mercury differential gage shows a reading of 3.56 in., what is the flow?

11.42. An 8-in. nonstandard orifice is installed in a 10-in. pipe carrying water. At a flow of 3.5 cfs, a water-mercury differential gage reads 1.7 in. Compute the values of the coefficients C_d, C, and K.

11.43. A 6-in. pipe carries 1.5 cfs of water at 72°F. Find the differential head and head loss across the following types of meters: (a) a 6- by 3-in. VDI orifice; (b) a 6- by 3-in. ISA flow nozzle; (c) a 6- by 3-in. venturi meter.

11.44. Assume that air at 70°F and 100 psia flows through a venturi meter and that the pressure at the throat is 60 psia. The inlet area is 0.60 ft², and the throat area is 0.15 ft². The tube coefficient is 0.98, and k for air is 1.4. (a) Find the rate of discharge by direct computation in Eq. (11.29). (b) Evaluate Y from Fig. 11.30, and use it to find the rate of discharge.

11.45. What would be the value of Y and the rate of discharge for a square-edged orifice for the same data as in Prob. 11.44, assuming $C = 0.60$ for a liquid?

11.46. What is the value of the throat velocity in Prob. 11.44?

11.47. Natural gas, for which $k = 1.3$ and $R = 96$ ft/°F, flows through a venturi meter with pipe and throat diameters of 12 and 6 in., respectively. The initial pressure of the gas is 150 psia, and its temperature is 60°F. If the meter coefficient is 0.98, find the rate of flow for a throat pressure of 100 psia.

11.48. Helium, for which $k = 1.66$ and $R = 386$ ft/°F, is in a tank under a pressure of 50 psia and a temperature of 80°F. It flows out through an orifice ½ in. in diameter. For such an orifice, $C_v = 0.98$, and $C_c = 0.62$ for liquids. Find the rate of flow if the pressure into which the gas discharges is 40 psia. Assume $Y = 0.95$.

11.49. Air is in a tank under a pressure of 200 psia and at a temperature of 100°F. It flows out through an orifice having an area of 1.5 in.² into a space where the pressure is 80 psia. Compute the rate of discharge by Eq. (11.32) and the Perry equation, assuming $C = 0.60$ for the orifice for air.

11.50. Using the same data as in Prob. 11.49, what would be the flow if the air discharged into a space where the pressure is 15 psia?

11.51. Employing Perry's equation for the flow of air through an orifice, by what percentage would the flow into a perfect vacuum be increased over the flow into a space where the pressure $p_2 = p_c$?

11.52. Suppose the air at the initial pressure and temperature of 20 psia and 70°F were flowing with a velocity one-half that of a sound wave in the medium. What would be the dynamic pressure?

11.53. Find the critical pressure ratios p_c/p_1 for the natural gas of Prob. 11.47 and the helium of Prob. 11.48.

11.54. For the data in Prob. 11.48 find the rate of discharge if $p_2 = p_c$.

11.55. Air in a tank under a pressure of 140 psia and a temperature of 70°F flows out into the atmosphere, where the barometer pressure is 14 psia through an orifice ¼ in. in diameter. Find the rate of discharge.

11.56. For air at $p_1 = 100$ psia and a temperature of 70°F, find the critical pressure and the corresponding throat velocity in a suitable nozzle, neglecting the velocity of approach. What will the values be if $D_2/D_1 = 0.80$?

11.57. Find the critical pressure and the acoustic velocity for wet steam flowing through an orifice with an initial pressure of 100 psia, neglecting velocity of approach and any friction losses. (Steam tables give $v_c = 7.0$ ft³/lb for steam that is initially slightly wet.) $k = 1.13$.

11.58. Superheated steam initially at a pressure of 100 psia and a temperature of 450°F expands without friction and with a negligible velocity of approach. Find the critical pressure and the acoustic velocity. (For this case $v_c = 8.35$ ft^3/lb.) $k = 1.3$.

11.59. A rectangular sharp-crested weir 3.0 ft high extends across a rectangular channel which is 8 ft wide. When the head is 1.200 ft, find the rate of discharge (a) by neglecting the velocity of approach; (b) by trial, including velocity of approach. Find also the percentage change from (a).

11.60. Suppose the rectangular weir of Prob. 11.59 is contracted at both ends. Find the rate of discharge for a head of 1.200 ft by the Francis formula. What would be the maximum value of H for which the Francis formula could be used?

11.61. A stream flows with a velocity of 3 fps at a depth of 1 ft in a rectangular channel. What height of sharp-crested suppressed weir must be installed to raise the upstream depth to 4 ft?

11.62. Plot a family of curves of C_d versus P/H with H as a parameter. Use the Rehbock formula. These curves give a complete picture of the variation of C_d for sharp-crested rectangular weirs.

11.63. (a) What is the rate of discharge of water over a 45° triangular weir when the head is 0.5 ft? (b) With the same head, what would be the increase in discharge obtained by doubling the notch angle, i.e., for a 90° weir? (Use curves of C_d versus H.) (c) What would be the head for discharge of 2.0 cfs of water over a 60° triangular weir?

11.64. For the Cipolletti weir, derive the expression for the slope $\frac{1}{4}$:1 of the sides of the trapezoid by setting the reduction in discharge due to contraction equal to the increase in discharge due to the triangular area added.

11.65. All the weir crests discussed in this chapter produce flow rates which vary as the head to some power greater than 1. In certain cases, such as in the outlet of a constant-velocity sedimentation chamber, it is desirable to employ a weir form in which Q varies directly with H. The *proportional-flow weir* is set flush with the bottom of the channel, as shown in the figure, while the sides taper inward, following the hyperbola $x\sqrt{y} = k$, a constant. Commencing with the head $h = H - y$, on the element of area $dA = 2x\,dy = 2(k/\sqrt{y})\,dy$, prove that the discharge equation for such a weir may be written as $Q = C_d\pi k \sqrt{2g}\,H$, and evaluate k in terms of the width B and the velocity V in the rectangular approach channel.

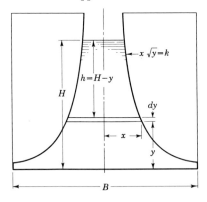

Fig. Prob. 11.65

11.66. Develop in general terms an expression for the per cent of error in Q over a triangular weir if there is a small error in the measurement of the vertex angle. Assume there is no error in the weir coefficient. Compute the per cent error in Q if there is a 2° error in the measurement of the total vertex angle of a triangular weir having a total vertex angle of 75°.

11.67. A 60° V-notch weir and a rectangular weir with end contractions having a crest length of 2 ft are both used to measure a flow rate of approximately 0.25 cfs. Assuming C_d is known precisely for both weirs, compute the percentage of error in Q that would result from an error of 0.02 ft in the respective head measurements.

11.68. A broad-crested weir rises 1.0 ft above the bottom of a horizontal channel. With a measured head of 2.0 ft above the crest, what is the rate of discharge per unit width?

11.69. A broad-crested weir of height 2.00 ft in a channel 5.00 ft wide has a flow over it of 9.50 cfs. What is the water depth just upstream of the weir?

11.70. Using Eq. (11.47), plot C_W versus P/H for broad-crested weirs. Select a suitable parameter so that an entire family of curves can be plotted.

11.71. A rectangular channel 6 ft wide contains a sluice gate which extends across the width of the channel. If the gate produces free flow when it is opened 0.4 ft with an upstream water depth of 3.5 ft, find the rate of discharge, assuming $C_d = 0.60$ and $C_c = 0.62$. Evaluate K_s.

11.72. Refer to Illustrative Example 4.6. If $C_v = 0.98$, what is the flow rate? If $C_c = 0.62$, what is the height of the opening? Find K_s.

TWELVE

UNSTEADY-FLOW PROBLEMS

12.1. INTRODUCTION

This text deals mostly with steady flow, since the majority of cases of engineering interest are of this nature. However, there are a few cases of unsteady flow that are very important, some of which are discussed in this chapter. It has been explained that turbulent flow is unsteady in the strictest sense of the word, but if the mean temporal values are constant over a period of time, it is called mean steady flow. Attention is here directed to cases where the mean temporal values continuously vary.

There are two main types of unsteady flow to be considered. The first is where the water level in a reservoir or pressure tank is steadily rising or falling, so that the rate of flow varies continuously, but where change takes place slowly. The second is where the velocity in a pipeline is changed rapidly by the fast closing or opening of a valve.

In the first case, of slow change, the flow is subject to the same forces as have previously been considered. Fast changes, of the second type, require the consideration of elastic forces.

Unsteady flow also includes such topics as oscillations in connected reservoirs and in U tubes and such phenomena as tidal motion and flood waves. Likewise, the field of machinery regulation by servomechanisms is intimately connected with unsteady motion. However, none of these topics will be considered here.

12.2. DISCHARGE WITH VARYING HEAD

When flow occurs under varying head, the rate of discharge will continuously vary; then the problem may be either to find the total change in volume in a given time interval or to find the length of time necessary for a certain change in level.

Let V_L = total volume under consideration in Fig. 12.1, while into it there is an inflow at the rate Q_1 and an outflow at the rate Q_2. It follows that in any time dt the total change in volume is

$$dV_L = Q_1 \, dt - Q_2 \, dt$$

If A_s = area of the surface of the volume while dz is the change in level of the surface, then $dV_L = A_s \, dz$. Equating these two expressions for dV_L,

$$A_s \, dz = Q_1 \, dt - Q_2 \, dt \tag{12.1}$$

Either Q_1 or Q_2 or both may be variable and functions of z or one of the two may be either constant or zero. For example, if liquid is discharged through an orifice or a pipe of area A under a differential head z, $Q_2 = C_d A \sqrt{2gz}$, where C_d is a numerical discharge coefficient and z is a variable. If the liquid flows out over a weir or a spillway of length B, $Q_2 = CBz^{3/2}$, where C is the appropriate coefficient. (For steady flow z would be the constant H.) In either case z is the variable height of the

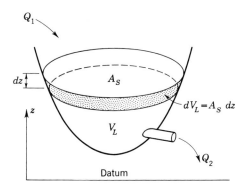

Fig. 12.1

liquid surface above an appropriate datum.   In like manner Q_1 may
be some function of z though it is more commonly expressible as a function
of t.   Such problems will not be considered here.

Equation (12.1) is general, and if it is possible to express A_s, Q_1,
and Q_2 as functions of z, the time t may be found by

$$t = \int_{z_1}^{z_2} \frac{A_s\, dz}{Q_1 - Q_2} \tag{12.2}$$

In many practical cases of natural reservoirs, the surface area is not a
simple mathematical function of z but values of it may be known for
various values of z.   In such a case, Eq. (12.2) may be solved graphically
by plotting values of $A_s/(Q_1 - Q_2)$ against simultaneous values of z.
The area under such a curve to some scale is the numerical value of the
integral.

It may be observed that instantaneous values for Q have been
expressed in the same manner as for steady flow.   This is not strictly
correct, since for unsteady flow the energy equation should also include
an acceleration head.   The introduction of such a term renders the solution much more difficult.   In cases where the value of z does not vary
rapidly, no appreciable error will result if this acceleration term is disregarded.   Therefore the equations will be written as for steady flow.

Illustrative example 12.1:   The open wedge-shaped tank in the accompanying
figure has a length of 15 ft perpendicular to the sketch.   It is drained with a 3-in.-
diameter pipe of length 10 ft whose discharge end is at elevation zero.   The coefficient
of loss at pipe entrance is 0.50, the total of the bend loss coefficients is 0.20, and f for
the pipe is 0.018.   Find the time required to lower the water surface in the tank
from elevation 8 to 5 ft.   Neglect the possible change of f with N_R, and assume that
the acceleration effects in the pipe are negligible.

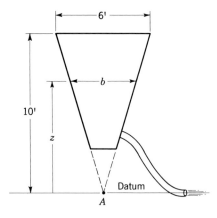

Illustrative Example 12.1

Energy equation from water surface to jet at discharge:

$$z - \left[0.5 + 0.2 + 0.018 \left(\frac{10}{0.25} \right) \right] \frac{V^2}{2g} = \frac{V^2}{2g}$$

$$z - 1.42 \frac{V^2}{2g} = \frac{V^2}{2g}$$

$$V = 5.16z^{1/2}$$

$$Q_2 = AV = \frac{\pi}{4}(0.25)^2 5.16z^{1/2} = 0.254z^{1/2}$$

The area of the water surface may be expressed as

$$A_s = 15b = 15Kz$$

At the top of the tank, $A_s = 15 \times 6 = 15K(10)$, $K = 0.6$. Thus

$$A_s = 15(0.6)z = 9z$$

Applying Eq. (12.2),

$$t = \int_8^5 \frac{9z \, dz}{0 - 0.254z^{1/2}} = -\frac{9}{0.254} \int_8^5 z^{1/2} \, dz$$

$$= -35.4[\tfrac{2}{3}z^{3/2}]_8^5 = 270 \text{ sec}$$

Note that if the pipe had discharged at an elevation other than zero, the integral would have been different, because the head on the pipe would then have been $z + h$, where h is the vertical distance of the discharge end of the pipe below or above point A of the figure.

12.3. UNSTEADY FLOW OF INCOMPRESSIBLE FLUIDS IN PIPES

When the flow in a pipe is unsteady, the energy equation has a term, the *accelerative head* $\dfrac{L}{g} \dfrac{dV}{dt}$, which accounts for the effect of the acceleration of the fluid. That this is so may be seen by examining Fig. 12.2, in which is shown the simple case of unsteady flow of an incompressible fluid in a horizontal pipe. The left-hand sketch shows the steady-flow case, while unsteady flow is depicted in the two right-hand sketches. The analysis below the sketches indicates that, with the same instantaneous flow rates, the pressure is depressed at section (2) if the acceleration is positive or increased if it is negative.

Equation (a) in Fig. 12.2 is recognized as being identical with Eq. (8.5), while Eqs. (b) and (c) are special cases of Eq. (5.28), with the effect of head loss added. For the case where the pipe is not necessarily horizontal, the energy equation generally applicable to unsteady incompressible fluid flow in a uniform pipe is

$$\left(z_1 + \frac{p_1}{\gamma} + \frac{V_1^2}{2g} \right) - \left(z_2 + \frac{p_2}{\gamma} + \frac{V_2^2}{2g} \right) - h_L = \frac{L}{g} \frac{dV}{dt}$$

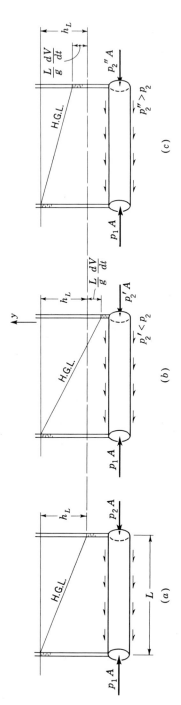

Fig. 12.2. Steady and unsteady flow of incompressible fluid in a horizontal pipe. (Flow is instantaneously equal in all three pipes.) (a) Steady flow; $(dV/dt = 0)$. (b) Unsteady flow; $(dV/dt$ is positive). (c) Unsteady flow; $(dV/dt$ is negative).

$$\Sigma F = ma = 0$$

$$p_1A - p_2A - \tau_0 PL = 0$$

$$\frac{p_1}{\gamma} - \frac{p_2}{\gamma} = \frac{\tau_0 PL}{\gamma A}$$

$$h_{L_{1-2}} = \frac{\tau_0 L}{\gamma R}$$

$$(a)$$

$$\Sigma F = ma \neq 0$$

$$p_1A - p_2'A - \tau_0 PL = \frac{\gamma A L}{g}\frac{dV}{dt}$$

$$\frac{p_1}{\gamma} - \frac{p_2'}{\gamma} = \frac{\tau_0 PL}{\gamma A} + \frac{L}{g}\frac{dV}{dt}$$

$$\frac{p_1}{\gamma} = \frac{p_2'}{\gamma} + h_L + \frac{L}{g}\frac{dV}{dt}$$

$$\frac{p_1}{\gamma} - \frac{p_2'}{\gamma} = h_L + \frac{L}{g}\frac{dV}{dt}$$

$$(b)$$

$$\frac{p_1}{\gamma} - \frac{p_2''}{\gamma} = h_L + \frac{L}{g}\frac{dV}{dt}$$

where dV/dt is negative

$$(c)$$

P = wetted perimeter; R = hydraulic radius.

Since $V_1 = V_2$ for a uniform pipe, we may write

$$\left(z_1 + \frac{p_1}{\gamma}\right) - \left(z_2 + \frac{p_2}{\gamma}\right) = h_L + \frac{L}{g}\frac{dV}{dt} \tag{12.3}$$

In this equation h_L represents the head loss between sections (1) and (2) while L is the distance between the sections. It is presumed that the head loss at any instant is equal to the steady-flow head loss for the flow rate at that instant. Experimental evidence indicates that this presumption is reasonably valid.

Illustrative example 12.2: When the centrifugal pump in the accompanying figure is rotating at 1,650 rpm, the steady-flow rate is 1,600 gpm. If the pump speed is increased instantaneously to 2,000 rpm, determine the flow rate as a function of time. Assume that the head developed by the pump is proportional to the square of the rotative speed. Writing the unsteady-flow energy equation,

$$50 - 0.5\frac{V_1{}^2}{2g} - f_1\frac{L_1}{D_1}\frac{V_1{}^2}{2g} + h_p - f_2\frac{L_2}{D_2}\frac{V_2{}^2}{2g} = \frac{V_2{}^2}{2g} + \frac{L_1}{g}\frac{dV_1}{dt} + \frac{L_2}{g}\frac{dV_2}{dt}$$

where the subscripts 1 and 2 refer to the 10- and 6-in.-diameter pipes, respectively. Note that the accelerative head for each pipe depends on the respective L and dV/dt values.

From continuity,

$$V_1 = \frac{A_2 V_2}{A_1} = \left(\frac{6}{10}\right)^2 V_2 = 0.36 V_2$$

Hence

$$\frac{dV_1}{dt} = \frac{A_2}{A_1}\frac{dV_2}{dt} = 0.36\frac{dV_2}{dt}$$

Thus

$$50 - 0.5\frac{(0.36V_2)^2}{2g} - 0.030\left(\frac{200}{10/12}\right)\frac{(0.36V_2)^2}{2g} + h_p - 0.020\left(\frac{750}{6/12}\right)\frac{V_2{}^2}{2g}$$
$$= \frac{V_2{}^2}{2g} + \frac{200}{g}(0.36)\frac{dV_2}{dt} + \frac{750}{dt}\frac{dV_2}{dt}$$

Evaluating and combining terms,

$$50 + h_p = 32.0\frac{V_2{}^2}{2g} + \frac{822}{g}\frac{dV_2}{dt} \tag{a}$$

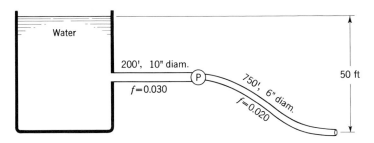

Illustrative Example 12.2

With the original steady-flow conditions ($dV/dt = 0$),

$$V_2 = \frac{Q}{A_2} = \frac{1,600/449}{0.196} = 18.2 \text{ fps}$$

and

$$h_p = 32 \frac{V_2{}^2}{2g} - 50 = 115 \text{ ft}$$

After the speed is increased to 2,000 rpm,

$$h_p = 115(2,000/1,650)^2 = 169 \text{ ft}$$

Substituting into (a),

$$50 + 169 = 32 \frac{V_2{}^2}{2g} + \frac{822}{g} \frac{dV_2}{dt}$$

Expressing the foregoing in terms of Q,

$$219 = 12.9Q^2 + 130 \frac{dQ}{dt} \tag{b}$$

Solving for dt and integrating, noting that at $t = 0$, $Q = 3.56$ cfs,

$$\int_0^t dt = 130 \int_{3.56}^Q \frac{dQ}{219 - 12.9Q^2}$$

$$t = 122 \ln \frac{14.8 + 3.6Q}{14.8 - 3.6Q} - 320$$

$$e^{0.0082t + 2.62} = \frac{14.8 + 3.6Q}{14.8 - 3.6Q}$$

Finally,

$$Q = 4.10 \frac{e^{0.0082t + 2.62} - 1}{e^{0.0082t + 2.62} + 1}$$

Note that as $t \to \infty$, $Q \to 4.10$ cfs, the steady-state flow rate for the condition where $h_p = 169$ ft. It should also be noted that the speed of a pump cannot be changed instantaneously from one value to another, as was assumed in this example.

12.4. VELOCITY OF PRESSURE WAVE IN PIPES

Unsteady phenomena, with rapid changes taking place, frequently involve the transmission of pressure in waves or surges. As shown in Appendix 2, the velocity of a pressure wave is

$$c = \sqrt{\frac{g}{\gamma} E_v} = \sqrt{\frac{E_v}{\rho}} \tag{12.4}$$

where E_v is the volume modulus of the medium. For water, a typical value of E_v is $144 \times 300,000$ psf, and thus the velocity of a pressure wave in water is $c = 4,720$ fps. But for water in an elastic pipe, this value is modified by the stretching of the pipe walls, and as shown in Appendix 2, E_v is replaced by K, such that

$$K = \frac{E_v}{1 + (D/t)(E_v/E)}$$

where D and t are the diameter and wall thickness of the pipe, respectively, and E is the modulus of elasticity of the pipe material. As the ratios D/t and E_v/E are dimensionless, any consistent units may be used in each.

The velocity of a pressure wave in water ($E_v = 300,000$ psi) in an elastic pipe is then

$$
c_P = \sqrt{\frac{g}{\gamma} K} = \frac{4,720}{\sqrt{1 + \dfrac{D}{t}\dfrac{300,000}{E}}} \tag{12.5}
$$

Values of the modulus of elasticity for steel, cast iron, and concrete are about 30,000,000, 15,000,000 and 3,000,000 psi, respectively. Values of the volume modulus E_v for various liquids are given in Appendix Three, Table A.5.

For normal pipe dimensions the velocity of a pressure wave in a pipe usually ranges between 2,000 and 4,000 fps, but it will always be less than 4,720 fps.

12.5. WATER HAMMER

In the preceding unsteady-flow cases in this chapter, the changes of velocity were presumed to take place slowly. But if the velocity of a liquid in a pipeline is abruptly decreased by a valve movement, the phenomenon encountered is called *water hammer*. This is a very important problem in the case of hydroelectric plants, where the flow of water must be rapidly varied in proportion to the load changes on the turbine. Water hammer occurs in liquid-flow pressure systems whenever a valve is closed. The terminology water hammer is perhaps misleading since the phenomenon can occur in any liquid.

Instantaneous closure. Although it is physically impossible to close a valve instantaneously, such a concept is useful as an introduction to the study of real cases. Assume that the valve at N in Fig. 12.3a is closed instantaneously. The lamina of liquid next to the valve will be compressed by the rest of the column of liquid flowing against it. At the same time the walls of the pipe surrounding this lamina will be stretched by the excess pressure produced. The next upstream lamina will then be brought to rest, and so on. It is seen that the volume of liquid in the pipe does not behave as a rigid incompressible body but that the phenomenon is affected by the elasticity of both the liquid and the pipe. Thus the cessation of flow and the resulting pressure increase move along the pipe as a wave with the velocity c_P as given by Eq. (12.5).

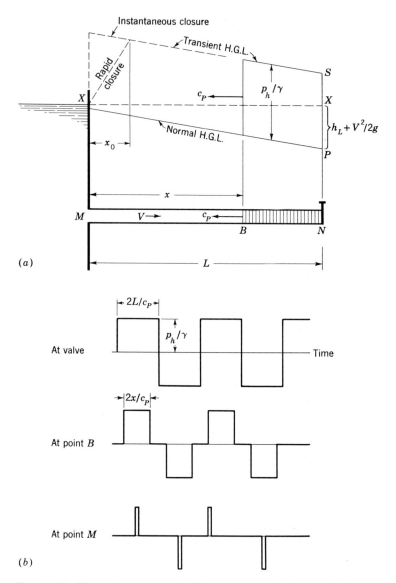

Fig. 12.3. Water hammer. (*a*) Valve at end of pipeline. (*b*) Water-hammer pressures with instantaneous valve closure. Pipe friction and damping neglected.

After a short interval of time the volume of liquid BN will have been brought to rest, while the liquid in the length MB will still be flowing with its initial velocity and initial pressure. When the pressure wave reaches the inlet at M, the entire mass in the length L will be at rest but will be under an excess pressure throughout. There will be a transient hydraulic grade line parallel to the original hydraulic grade line, but at a height p_h/γ above it.

It is impossible for a pressure to exist at M that is greater than that due to depth MX, and so when the pressure wave arrives at M, the pressure at M drops instantly to the value it would have for zero flow. But the entire pipe is now under an excess pressure; so the liquid in it is compressed, and the pipe walls are stretched. Then some liquid starts to flow back into the reservoir, and a wave of pressure unloading travels along the pipe from M to N. At the instant this unloading wave reaches N, the entire mass of liquid will be under the static pressure indicated by the line XX. But the liquid is still flowing back into the reservoir, and this reverse velocity must now be stopped. This will produce a drop in pressure at N that ideally will be as far below the static pressure as the pressure an instant before was above it. Then a wave of rarefaction travels back up the pipe from N to M. Ideally, there would be a series of pressure waves traveling back and forth over the length of the pipe and alternating equally between high and low pressures about the value for zero flow.

The time for a round trip of the pressure wave from N to M and back again is

$$T_r = 2\,\frac{L}{c_P} \tag{12.6}$$

where L is the length of pipe, and so for an instantaneous valve closure the excess pressure remains constant for this length of time, before it is affected by the return of the unloading pressure wave; and in like manner the pressure defect during the period of rarefaction remains constant for the same length of time. At a distance x from the inlet, such as at B, the time for a round trip of a pressure wave is only $2x/c_P$, and hence at that point the time duration of the excess or deficient pressure will be $2x/c_P$, as shown in Fig. 12.3b. At the inlet M, where $x = 0$, the excess pressure occurs for only an instant.

In Fig. 12.4 is shown a close-up in the vicinity of the valve. If the valve is closed abruptly, a pressure wave travels up the pipe with a celerity c_P. In a short interval of time dt an element of liquid of length $c_P\,dt$ is brought to rest. Applying Newton's second law, $F\,dt = M\,dV$,

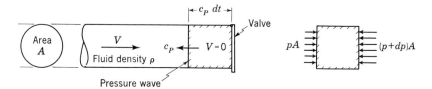

Fig. 12.4. Definition sketch for analysis of water hammer in pipes.

and neglecting friction,

$$[pA - (p + dp)A]\,dt = (\rho A c_P\,dt)\,dV$$
$$- dp = \rho c_P\,dV$$

Since the velocity is reduced to zero, $dV = -V$; dp represents the increase in pressure due to valve closure, and hence $dp = p_h$, the water-hammer pressure. Thus

$$p_h = \rho c_P V \tag{12.7}$$

It will be observed that the pressure increase is independent of the length of the pipe and depends solely upon the celerity of the pressure wave in the pipe and the change in the velocity of the water. The total pressure at the valve immediately after closure is $p_h + p$, where p is the pressure in the pipe just upstream of the valve prior to closure.

Consider now conditions at the valve as affected by both pipe friction and damping. In Fig. 12.3a, when the pressure wave from N has reached B, the water in BN will be at rest and for zero flow the hydraulic grade line should be a horizontal line. There is thus a tendency for the grade line to flatten out for the portion BN. Hence, instead of the transient gradient having the slope imposed by friction, as shown in the figure, it will approach a horizontal line starting from the transient value at B. Thus the pressure head at N will be raised to a slightly higher value than NS shortly after the valve closure.

This slight increase in pressure head at the valve over the theoretical

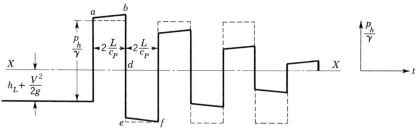

Fig. 12.5. Pressure history at valve with instantaneous closure, considering pipe friction and damping.

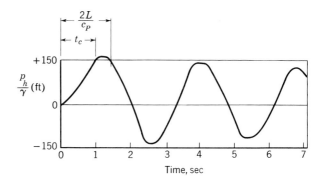

Fig. 12.6. Rapid valve closure in time t_c less than $2L/c_P$. Actual measurement of pressure changes at valve.

value Vc_P/g has been borne out by tests. In Fig. 12.5 the line ab is shown as sloping upward because of this adverse pressure gradient, and for the same reason ef may slope slightly downward, as all conditions are now reversed. Also, because of damping, the drop de will be less than bd, and the waves will be of decreasing amplitude about the line of zero flow until the final equilibrium pressure is reached.

All the preceding analysis assumes that the wave of rarefaction will not cause the minimum pressure at any point to drop down to or below the vapor pressure. If it should do so, the water would separate and produce a discontinuity.

Rapid closure. It is physically impossible for a valve to be closed instantaneously; so we shall now consider the real case where the valve is closed in a finite time t' which is more than zero but less than $2L/c_P$. In Fig. 12.6 are shown actual pressure recordings for such a case. The shape of the curve during the time t_c depends entirely upon the operation of the valve and its varying effect upon the velocity in the pipe. But the maximum pressure rise is still the same as for instantaneous closure. The only differences are that it endures for a shorter period of time and the vertical lines of Fig. 12.5 are changed to the sloping lines of Fig. 12.6. If the time of valve closure were exactly $2L/c_P$, the maximum pressure rise at the valve would still be the same but the curves in Fig. 12.6 would all end in sharp points for both maximum and minimum values, since the time of duration would be reduced to zero.[1]

---

[1] Figures 12.6 and 12.7 are from water-hammer studies made by the Southern California Edison Co. on an experimental pipe with the following data: $L = 3{,}060$ ft, internal diameter $= 2.06$ in., $c_P = 4{,}371$ fps, $V = 1.11$ fps, $Vc_P/g = 151$ ft, $2L/c_P = 1.40$ sec, static head $= 306.7$ ft, head before valve closure $= 301.6$ ft, $h_L = 5.1$ ft. In Fig. 12.6 the time of closure $= 1$ sec, and it will be noted that the actual rise in pressure head is slightly more than 151 ft. In Fig. 12.7 the time of closure $= 3$ sec.

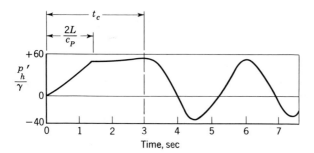

Fig. 12.7. Slow valve closure in time t_c greater than $2L/c_P$. Actual measurement of pressure changes at valve.

No matter how rapid the valve closure may be, so long as it is not the idealized instantaneous case, there will be some distance from the intake, such as x_0, within which the valve closure time is more than $2x_0/c_P$. Thus, in any real case, the maximum pressure rise cannot extend all the way to the reservoir intake. In the actual case, the maximum pressure rise will be constant at the instantaneous value p_h for a distance from the valve up to this point a distance x_0 from the intake. From this point the excess pressure will diminish to zero at the intake. This is shown as a uniform rate of decrease in Fig. 12.3a.

Slow closure. The preceding discussion has assumed a closure so rapid (or a pipe so long) that there is an insufficient time for a pressure wave to make the round trip before the valve is closed. Slow closure will be defined as one in which the time of valve movement is greater than $2L/c_P$. In this case the maximum pressure rise will be less than in the preceding because the wave of pressure unloading will reach the valve before the movement is completed and will thus stop any further increase in pressure.

Thus in Fig. 12.7 the pressure would continue to rise if it were not for the fact that at a time $2L/c_P$ a return unloading pressure wave reaches the valve and stops the pressure rise at a value of about 53 ft as contrasted with about three times that value in Fig. 12.6. Subsequent pressure changes as elastic waves travel back and forth are very complex and require a detailed step-by-step analysis that is beyond the scope of this text. In brief, the method consists in assuming the valve movement to take place in a series of steps each of which produces a pressure $\Delta p'$ proportional to each ΔV.*

* For details of computing successive pressures for slow valve closure and for further explanation of much of this condensed treatment, see John Parmakian, "Waterhammer Analysis," Prentice-Hall, Inc., Englewood Cliffs, N.J., 1955.

Tests have shown that for slow valve closure, i.e., in a time greater than $2L/c_P$, the excess pressure produced decreases uniformly from the value at the valve to zero at the intake. The water-hammer pressure p_h' developed by gradual closure of a valve when $t_c > 2L/c_P$ is given approximately by

$$p_h' \approx \frac{2L/c_P}{t_c} p_h = \frac{2Lp_h}{c_P t_c} = \frac{2LV\rho}{t_c} \tag{12.8}$$

where t_c is the time of closure.

Illustrative example 12.3: In Fig. 12.3a the elasticity and dimensions of the pipe are such that the celerity of the pressure wave is 3,200 fps. Suppose the pipe has a length of 2,000 ft and a diameter of 4 ft. The flow rate is initially 30 cfs. Water is flowing. Find (a) the water-hammer pressure for instantaneous valve closure; (b) the approximate water-hammer pressure at the valve if it were closed in 4.0 sec; (c) the water-hammer pressure at the valve if it is manipulated so that the flow rate drops almost instantly from 30 to 10 cfs; (d) the maximum water-hammer pressure at a point in the pipe 300 ft from the reservoir if a 1.0-sec valve closure reduces the flow rate from 10 cfs to zero.

$$V = \frac{Q}{A} = \frac{30}{\pi 2^2} = 2.38 \text{ fps}$$

(a) $p_h = \rho c_P V = 1.94(3,200)(2.38) = 14,800 \text{ psf} = 102.6 \text{ psi}$

(b) $p_h' \approx \dfrac{4,000/3,200}{4.0} p_h = \dfrac{1.25}{4.00}(102.6) = 32.1 \text{ psi}$

(c) For this case of partial closure Eq. (12.7) may be written as $\Delta p_h = \rho c_P(\Delta V)$.

$$\Delta V = \frac{30-10}{\pi 2^2} = 1.59 \text{ fps}$$

$$\Delta p_h = 1.94(3,200)(1.59) = 9,900 \text{ psf} = 68.5 \text{ psi}$$

(d) If $2x_0/c_P = 1.0$ sec, $x_0 = 1,600$ ft, so that full water-hammer pressure will be developed in the pipe only in the region that is farther than 1,600 ft from the reservoir.

For this case, at valve

$$p_h = 1.94(3,200) \frac{2.38}{3} = 4,920 \text{ psf} = 34.2 \text{ psi}$$

At point 300 ft from reservoir:

$$p_h = 34.2(300/1,600) = 6.4 \text{ psi}$$

12.6. SURGE CHAMBERS

In a hydroelectric plant the flow of water to a turbine must be decreased very rapidly whenever there is a sudden drop in load. This rapid decrease in flow will result in high water-hammer pressures and may result in the need for a very strong and hence expensive pipe. There are several ways

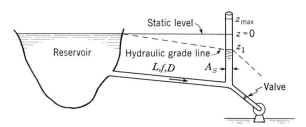

Fig. 12.8.   Definition sketch for surge-chamber analysis.

to handle a situation of this sort; one is by use of a *surge tank*, or *surge chamber*. A simple surge chamber is a vertical standpipe connected to the pipeline as shown in Fig. 12.8. With steady flow in the pipe, the water level z_1 in the surge chamber is below the static level ($z = 0$). When the valve is suddenly closed, water rises in the surge chamber. The water surface in the tank will then fluctuate up and down until damped out by fluid friction. The section of pipe upstream of the surge tank is in effect afforded protection from the high water-hammer pressures that would exist on valve closure if there were no chamber.

An approximate analysis for this simple surge tank may be acquired by writing the energy equation for unsteady flow between the surface of the reservoir and the water surface in the surge chamber. Neglecting fluid friction, velocity head, and inertial effects in the chamber and neglecting pipe and surge chamber entrance losses, we get

$$0 - f\frac{L}{D}\frac{V^2}{2g} = z + \frac{L}{g}\frac{dV}{dz}\frac{dz}{dt} \qquad (12.9)$$

In this equation z represents the level of the water surface in the surge chamber measured positively upward from the static level where $z = 0$.

With the valve completely closed, the continuity equation is

$$AV = A_s\frac{dz}{dt} \qquad \cdot \quad (12.10)$$

where A and A_s are the cross-sectional areas of the pipe and chamber, respectively. Combining these two equations, integrating, and solving for V yields

$$V^2 = \frac{2gAD^2}{LA_sf^2}\left(1 - \frac{fA_s}{AD}z\right) - Ce^{-(fA_s/AD)z} \qquad (12.11)$$

which expresses the relation between velocity in the pipe and water-surface level in the tank over the interval from valve closure to the top of the first surge. Equation (12.11) may be used to estimate the maximum height of surge z_{max} by finding the constant of integration C for steady-state conditions at the instant of closure ($z = z_1$) and then solving for z_{max} when $V = 0$. Since the derivation neglected fluid friction, velocity head, and entrance losses and assumed instantaneous valve closure, the value of z_{max} as computed by Eq. (12.11) will be too large and thus the results provide a conservative estimate for preliminary design of simple surge tanks.

Surge chambers are usually open at the top and of sufficient height so that they will not overflow. In some instances they are permitted to overflow if no damage will result. There are many types of surge chambers. Some have a restriction at entry; others have a closed top so that there is an air cushion within the tank during operation.

The surge chamber, in addition to providing protection against water-hammer pressures, fulfills another desirable function. That is, in the event of a sudden demand for increased flow, it can provide some excess water, while the entire mass of water in a long pipeline is being accelerated. The acceleration of masses of liquids in pipelines is discussed in the next section.

12.7. VALVE OPENING

When a valve at the end of a pipe is quickly opened, elastic waves travel back and forth until damping produces an equilibrium condition, similar to that in valve closure. The analysis is similar to that for closure, except that the signs are reversed. Thus the initial pressure wave is one of rarefaction. Also, the pressure drop is limited to the difference between the initial values on the two sides of the valve and can have no such magnitude as is possible in the case of water hammer. A further difference is that, with valve closure, the velocity of flow changes very rapidly and is accompanied by rapid and large pressure changes; with valve opening, the pressures remain constant at both ends of the pipe and the velocity of flow changes gradually.

In view of the foregoing, a very close approximation to the phenomenon of valve opening may be had by assuming an incompressible liquid in a rigid pipe, thus neglecting wave phenomena. Such an assumption for instantaneous closure of a valve would indicate an infinite pressure rise, but no such result is possible for an instantaneous opening.

Assume a pipe of length L, as in Fig. 12.3a, and let the head NX be denoted by h. Consider the friction loss in the pipe to be represented as $h_L = kV^2/2g$, where k is assumed to be constant, although actually it may vary with the velocity unless the pipe is very rough. With these assumptions the energy equation of unsteady flow [Eq. (12.3)] written between X and N of Fig. 12.3a becomes

$$h - k\frac{V^2}{2g} = \frac{V^2}{2g} + \frac{L}{g}\frac{dV}{dt}$$

Let us define the steady-flow velocity by V_0 and note that

$$(1 + k)V_0{}^2 = 2gh$$

Inserting this in the preceding equation after multiplying by $2g$, we get

$$dt = \frac{2L}{1 + k}\frac{dV}{V_0{}^2 - V^2}$$

from which
$$t = \frac{L}{(1 + k)V_0}\ln\frac{V_0 + V}{V_0 - V} \tag{12.12}$$

This equation indicates that equilibrium will be attained only after an infinite time, but it will be found that the equilibrium value will be approached very closely within a short time. It must be remembered that this is an idealized case. In reality there will be elastic waves and damping, so that true equilibrium will be reached in a finite time.

PROBLEMS

12.1. Suppose a ship lock has vertical sides and that water enters or discharges through a conduit area A such that $Q = C_d A \sqrt{2gz}$, where z is the variable difference in level between the surface of the lock and that outside. Prove that for the water level in the lock to change from z_1 to z_2 the time is

$$t = \left(\frac{2A_s}{C_d A \sqrt{2g}}\right)(z_1{}^{1/2} - z_2{}^{1/2})$$

(*Note:* If the lock is being filled, the signs must be reversed.)

12.2. Suppose a reservoir has vertical sides and that initially there is a steady flow into it such that the height of the surface above the level of the spillway is z_1. If the inflow is suddenly cut off, prove that the time required for the water level to fall from z_1 to z_2 is $t = (2A_s/CB)(1/\sqrt{z_2} - 1/\sqrt{z_1})$. How long will it take theoretically for the outflow to cease entirely?

12.3. Suppose a ship lock is of uniform rectangular cross section and is 300 ft long by 90 ft wide. Suppose the water enters the lock through a conduit for which the discharge coefficient is 0.50. If the water surface in the lock is initially 36 ft below the level of the surface of the water upstream, how large must the conduit be if the lock is to be filled in 5 min?

12.4. The spillway of a reservoir is 100 ft long, and the value of C is 3.45. Suppose that for the range of levels here considered the area of the water surface is constant and is 700,000 ft². Initially, there is a flow into the reservoir at such a rate that the height of the surface above that of the spillway crest is 3 ft, and then the inflow is suddenly diverted. Find the length of time for the water surface to fall to a height of 1 ft above the level of the spillway. How long, theoretically, will it take for the outflow to reduce to zero?

12.5. The spillway of a reservoir is 40 ft long, and the value of C is 3.50. The area of the water surface is assumed constant at 600,000 ft² for the range of heights here considered. Initially, the water surface is 3 ft below the level of the spillway crest. If suddenly there is turned into this reservoir a flow of 500 cfs, what will be the height of water in the reservoir for equilibrium? How long a time will be required for this height to be reached? How long a time will be required for the water surface to reach a height of 2 ft above the level of the spillway? (*Note:* This last can be solved by integration after substituting x^3 for $z^{3/2}$ and consulting integral tables. However, it will be easier to solve it graphically either by plotting and actually measuring the area or by computing the latter by some method, such as Simpson's rule.)

12.6. Water enters a reservoir at such a rate that the height of water above the level of the spillway crest is 3 ft. The spillway is 100 ft long, and the value of C is 3.45. The area of the water surface for various water levels is as follows:

z, ft	A_s, ft²
3.00	860,000
2.50	830,000
2.00	720,000
1.50	590,000
1.25	535,000
1.00	480,000

If the inflow is suddenly reduced to 150 cfs, what will be the height of water for equilibrium? How long will it take, theoretically, for equilibrium to be attained? How long will it take for the level to drop from 3 to 1 ft above that of the spillway?

12.7. The figure shows a tank with vertical sides containing a liquid with a surface area A_s. The liquid discharges through an orifice under a head z which varies from the initial height h to 0 as the tank empties down to the orifice level. Neglecting friction losses, what is the total kinetic energy of the jet during the time required for the liquid surface to drop from h to 0? How does this kinetic-energy summation compare with the total energy of the mass of fluid initially in the tank above the orifice level?

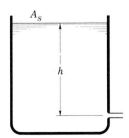

Fig. Prob. 12.7

12.8. Suppose that in Prob. 12.7 the value of A_s is 10 ft², h is 16 ft, and the jet diameter is 4 in. (*a*) How long will it take the tank to empty down to the orifice level? (*b*) If the liquid is water, what will be the total kinetic energy of the jet during that time?

12.9. The figure shows the frustum of a cone with an orifice in the bottom of 2-ft² area. Assume $C_d = 1.0$. If the water level outside is constant at (2), how long will it take the level in the cone to drop from (1) to (2)? (*Note:* Diameter $= Ky$, and $y = z + h_2$, where z is the variable distance between surface levels.)

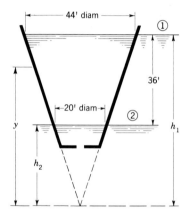

Fig. Prob. 12.9

12.10. If in the figure for Prob. 12.9 the water surface is constant at (1) and the cone is initially empty, how long will it take for the level in the cone to rise from (2) to (1)?

12.11. The tank in the figure has vertical sides and is 5 ft in the dimension normal to the plane of the paper. It is divided by a vertical plate in which is a submerged orifice 0.5 ft² in area. Assume $C_d = 1.0$. How long a time will be required for the two water surfaces to equalize?

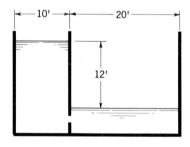

Fig. Prob. 12.11

12.12. A 1-in.-diameter smooth brass pipe 1,000 ft long drains an open cylindrical tank which contains oil ($\rho = 1.8$ slugs/ft³, $\mu = 0.0006$ lb-sec/ft²). The pipe discharges at elevation 100 ft. Find the time required for the oil level to drop from elevation 120 to elevation 108 ft if the tank is 4 ft in diameter.

12.13. Verify that the neglect of the $(L/g)(dV/dt)$ term was justified in Illustrative Example 12.1 by finding its value when $z = 5$ ft.

12.14. A large reservoir is being drained with a pipe system as shown in the figure. Initially, when the pump is rotating at 200 rpm, the flow rate is 6.3 cfs. If the pump speed is increased instantaneously to 250 rpm, determine the flow rate as a function of time. Assume that the head h_p developed by the pump is proportional to the square of the rotative speed; that is, $h_p \propto n^2$.

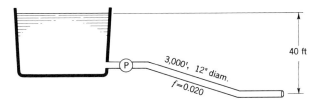

Fig. Prob. 12.14

12.15. Refer to Illustrative Example 12.2 and make a plot of flow rate vs. time.

12.16. Suppose that in Illustrative Example 12.2 the pump speed had been reduced instantaneously from 1,650 to 1,150 rpm. What then would have been the rate of deceleration of the flow immediately after the change in pump speed?

12.17. Attached to the tank in the figure is a flexible 1-in.-diameter hose ($f = 0.015$) of length 200 ft. The tank is hoisted in such a manner that $h = 20 + 3t$, where h is the head in feet and t is the time in seconds. (a) Find as accurately as you can the flow rate at $t = 10$ sec. (b) Suppose h were decreasing at the same rate. What, then, would be the flow rate when $h = 50$ ft?

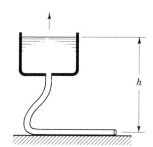

Fig. Prob. 12.17

12.18. In Prob. 12.17 suppose h were changed instantaneously from 20 to 50 ft. Under these conditions find the flow rate at $t = 10$ sec.

12.19. Find the celerity of a pressure wave in benzene (Appendix 3, Table A.5) contained in a 6-in.-diameter steel pipe having a wall thickness of 0.285 in.

12.20. For the situation depicted in Illustrative Example 12.3 find the water-hammer pressure at the valve if a flow of 80 cfs is reduced to 25 cfs in

3.0 sec.   Under these conditions, what would be the maximum water-hammer pressures at points 500 and 1,500 ft from the reservoir?

12.21. What is the celerity of a pressure wave in a water pipe 5 ft in diameter if it is (*a*) steel with a thickness of 0.5 in.; (*b*) concrete with a thickness of 4 in.?

12.22. If the steel pipe in Prob. 12.21 is 4,000 ft long, what is the time required for a pressure wave to make the round trip from the valve? If the initial water velocity is 8 fps, what will be the rise in pressure at the valve if the time of closure is less than the time of a round trip?

12.23. If the valve in Prob. 12.22 is closed at such a rate that the velocity in the pipe decreases uniformly with respect to time and closure is completed in a time $t_c = 5L/c_P$, what will be the pressure at the valve when the first pressure unloading wave reaches the valve?

12.24. In the figure, the total length of pipe is 10,000 ft, its diameter is 36 in., and its thickness is $\frac{3}{4}$ in.   Assume $E = 30,000,000$ psi and $E_v = 300,000$ psi.   If the initial velocity for steady flow is 10 fps and the valve at G is partially closed so as to reduce the flow to half of the initial velocity in 4 sec, find (*a*) maximum pressure rise from the water hammer; (*b*) point of maximum total pressure.

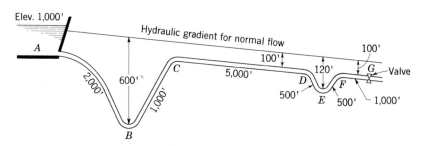

Fig. Prob. 12.24

12.25. Derive Eq. (12.11).

12.26. A 36-in. steel pipe 3,000 ft long supplies water to a small power plant. What height would be required for a simple surge tank 6 ft in diameter situated 50 ft upstream from the valve at a point where the center line of the pipe is 120 ft below the water surface in the reservoir if the tank is to protect against instantaneous closure of a valve at the plant?   The valve is 150 ft below reservoir level, and the discharge is 150 cfs.   Take $f = 0.015$.   There is a bell-mouthed entrance to the pipe from the reservoir.   The surge tank is not to overflow.

12.27. Repeat Prob. 12.26 for the case where the surge tank is to have a diameter of 10 ft.

12.28. Using the data of Prob. 12.26, find the diameter of surge tank that will produce a surge requiring a tank height of 175 ft.

12.29. A 4-in.-diameter pipe of length 3,000 ft drains a reservoir.   The elevation difference between the reservoir water surface and the pipe outlet is 100 ft.   Initially, there is no flow since there is a plug at the pipe outlet. The plug is then removed.   Plot Q versus t, assuming $f = 0.020$.

12.30. Repeat Prob. 12.29 for the case where the pipe length is 300 ft rather than 3,000 ft.

12.31. A 10-in.-diameter pipe ($f = 0.020$) of length 300 ft is connected to a reservoir. At the discharge end of the pipe is a nozzle that produces a 4-in.-diameter jet. The elevation difference between the jet and the water surface in the reservoir is 40 ft. The nozzle has a coefficient of velocity of 0.95. Initially, there is a tight-fitting plug in the nozzle, which is then removed. For this situation derive an equation similar to Eq. (12.12) and plot flow rate vs. time. Assume that the liquid level in the reservoir does not drop.

12.32. A large water reservoir is drained by a pipeline that consists of 200 ft of 6-in.-diameter pipe ($f = 0.030$) followed by 500 ft of 10-in.-diameter pipe ($f = 0.020$). The point of discharge is 100 ft below the elevation of the reservoir water surface. A valve at the discharge end of the pipe is initially closed. It is then quickly opened. Derive an equation similar to Eq. (12.12) applicable to this situation, and plot flow rate vs. time. Neglect minor losses.

12.33. An open tank containing oil ($s = 0.85$, $\mu = 0.0005$ lb-sec/ft^2) is connected to a 2-in.-diameter smooth pipe of length 3,000 ft. The elevation drop from liquid surface in tank to point of discharge is 15 ft. A valve on the discharge end of the pipe, initially closed, was then opened. Plot the ensuing flow rate vs. time.

12.34. A vertical 1-in.-diameter pipe 10 ft long is full of oil of specific gravity 0.88 and viscosity 0.004 lb-sec/ft^2. Find the time required to drain the pipe after a plug is removed from the lower end. Assume that the head loss is given by the equation of established laminar flow and that surface-tension effects are negligible.

THIRTEEN

FORCES ON IMMERSED BODIES[1]

13.1. INTRODUCTION

A body which is wholly immersed in a homogeneous fluid may be
subject to two kinds of forces arising from relative motion between
the body and the fluid. These forces are termed the *drag* and the
lift, depending on whether the force is parallel to the motion or at
right angles to it, respectively. Fluid mechanics draws no distinction between two cases giving rise to relative motion, namely,
when a body moves rectilinearly at constant speed through a
stationary fluid or when a fluid travels at constant velocity past
a stationary body. Thus it is possible to test airplane models in
wind tunnels and torpedo models in water tunnels and predict
with confidence the behavior of their prototypes when moving
through still fluid. For instructional purposes it is somewhat
simpler to fix our ideas on the stationary body in the moving
fluid, while the practical result desired is more frequently associated with a body moving through still fluid.

[1] Dr. Alfred C. Ingersoll is largely responsible for the writing of this
chapter.

406

In this chapter we shall first consider the drag, or resistance, forces. As we shall not be concerned with wave action at a free surface, gravity does not enter the problem and the forces involved are those due to inertia and viscosity.[1] The effect of the former is known as *form*, or *pressure, drag* F_p and is equal to the integration of the components in the direction of the motion of all the normal pressure forces exerted on the surface of the body. The Newtonian law of resistance states that the pressure drag is given by the dynamic pressure [from Eq. (4.33)] acting on the projected area A of the body *normal to the flow* times a coefficient C_p which must be determined by experiment. Thus

$$F_p = C_p \rho \, \frac{V^2}{2} \, A \qquad (13.1)$$

The effect of viscosity, producing resistance by the sliding of the fluid layers one upon another, is termed the *friction*, or *surface, drag* F_f. As in the case of laminar flow in pipes, the frictional resistance is proportional to the fluid viscosity, to V, and to the area of the wetted surface *parallel to the flow*. For convenience, however, it is customary to set this equation in the same general form as Eq. (13.1):

$$F_f = C_f \rho \, \frac{V^2}{2} \, BL \qquad (13.2)$$

where C_f = friction-drag coefficient, dependent on viscosity, among other factors

L = length of surface parallel to flow

B = transverse width, conveniently approximated for irregular shapes by dividing total surface area by L

It is important to note that for a body such as a plate with both sides immersed in the fluid, Eq. (13.2) gives the drag for *one side* only.

From our experience with pipe flow we should expect that the friction drag would be more amenable to a theoretical approach than pressure drag. This is not necessarily the case. In previous chapters the *boundary layer* was described as a very thin layer of fluid adjacent to a surface, in which viscosity is important, while outside of this layer the fluid can be considered as frictionless or ideal. This concept, originated by Prandtl, is one of the important advances in modern fluid mechanics.

---

[1] Actually, without viscosity there could be no drag force at all. The flow of a frictionless fluid about any body, as constructed mathematically or by the flow-net technique of Chap. 3, produces opposing stagnation points at the nose and tail of the body. The pressure distribution, as computed from the Bernoulli theorem and integrated over the entire body, always adds up to zero in the direction of the flow. This situation is known as *D'Alembert's paradox*.

It means that the mathematical theory of ideal fluid flow, including the flow-net method studied in Chap. 3, can actually be used to determine the streamlines in the real fluid at a short distance away from a solid wall. The Bernoulli theorem may then be used to determine the normal pressures on the surface, for such pressures are practically the same as those outside of this thin layer.

The boundary layer may be entirely laminar, or it may be primarily turbulent with a laminar sublayer, as in Fig. 8.6. The boundary layer increases in thickness with distance from the leading edge of a surface, as shown in both Figs. 8.4 and 8.6. The important difference between the case at hand and that of pipe flow, however, is that in pipe flow the boundary layers from the opposite walls of the pipe merge together after a certain distance and the flow becomes "all boundary layer," while with airplanes, submarines, trains, etc., the boundary layer, even though it may reach a thickness of several inches, is still small compared with the dimensions of the ideal fluid. By "ideal" fluid we refer not to the great mass of air or water totally unaffected by the passing object, but to the fluid region outside of the boundary layer in which the streamlines are determined by the presence of the body.

13.2. FRICTION DRAG OF BOUNDARY LAYER

We may derive the friction drag produced by a boundary layer by examining the change in momentum of the fluid which is slowed down by the layer. Let us consider the boundary layer and drag force on one side of a smooth, flat plate of width B, placed parallel to the undisturbed velocity U, as shown in Fig. 13.1. At a distance x from the leading edge the velocity u in the boundary layer will vary from zero at the plate to U at

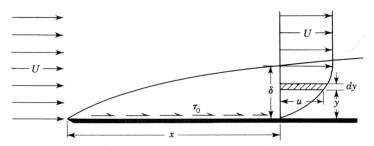

Fig. 13.1. Growth of laminar boundary layer along a smooth plate (vertical scale exaggerated).

the outer limit of the layer in a fashion somewhat as shown.[1]   Now consider an element of area $B\,dy$ normal to the flow, at a distance y from the plate, through which the velocity is u.

$$\text{Mass rate of flow through element} = \rho u B\,dy$$
$$\text{Momentum rate of this flow} = \rho u^2 B\,dy$$
$$\text{Original momentum rate of same flow} = \rho u U B\,dy$$
$$\text{Change in momentum rate of this flow} = \rho u B(U - u)\,dy$$

By Newton's second law, the rate of change of momentum (which is the same as change in momentum rate) is equal to the app'ied force, and this force must come from the surface resistance.   Thus, integrating over the thickness δ of the layer, assuming incompressible flow,

$$F_x = \rho B \int_0^\delta u(U - u)\,dy \tag{13.3}$$

where F_x is the total friction drag on the plate *from the leading edge up to* x.

It will now be assumed that the velocity profiles at various distances along the plate are similar to each other:

$$\frac{u}{U} = f\left(\frac{y}{\delta}\right) = f(\eta) \qquad \eta = \frac{y}{\delta}$$

There is experimental evidence that this assumption is valid if there is no pressure gradient along the surface and if the boundary layer does not change from laminar to turbulent within the region considered.   Then, substituting for u in Eq. (13.3) and changing the variable y to the dimensionless η, $dy = \delta\,d\eta$, and the limits become 0 to 1, giving

$$F_x = \rho B U^2 \delta \int_0^1 f(\eta)[1 - f(\eta)]\,d\eta$$

which, for convenience, may be written

$$F_x = \rho B U^2 \delta\alpha \tag{13.4}$$

where α is a function of the boundary-layer velocity distribution only and is given by the indicated integral (not to be confused with the kinetic-energy factor α discussed in Chap. 4).

---

[1] The thickness of the boundary layer is conventionally defined to be the distance from the solid wall to the point at which the velocity is within 1 per cent of the undisturbed velocity, but in this analysis the velocity of the outer filament will be assumed *equal* to U.

We next investigate the local wall shear stress τ_0 at distance x from the leading edge.   From the definition of surface resistance, $dF_x = \tau_0 B\, dx$, or

$$\tau_0 = \frac{1}{B}\frac{dF_x}{dx} = \frac{1}{B}\frac{d}{dx}(\rho B U^2\, \delta\alpha)$$

and as all the expression for F_x is constant save δ,

$$\tau_0 = \rho U^2 \alpha \frac{d\delta}{dx} \tag{13.5}$$

This expression for the shear stress is valid for either laminar or turbulent flow in the boundary layer, but in this form it is not useful until the quantities α and $d\delta/dx$ are evaluated.   As α is a function of the area under the velocity-distribution curve, its value is relatively insensitive to the detailed form of this curve and in fact varies by only 50 per cent between the two extreme cases of laminar and turbulent boundary layer. To proceed further, we must examine the two forms of boundary layer separately.

13.3. LAMINAR BOUNDARY LAYER

As in the case of laminar flow in pipes, we may examine the shear stress at the plate wall by aid of the velocity gradient and the definition of viscosity,

$$\tau_0 = \mu\left(\frac{du}{dy}\right)_{y=0} = \frac{\mu}{\delta}\left(\frac{du}{d\eta}\right)_{\eta=0} = \frac{\mu U}{\delta}\left[\frac{df(\eta)}{d\eta}\right]_{\eta=0}$$

which may be abbreviated to

$$\tau_0 = \frac{\mu U \beta}{\delta} \tag{13.6}$$

where β, like α, is a dimensionless function of the velocity-distribution curve and is given by the expression in brackets.

Equations (13.5) and (13.6) are two independent expressions for τ_0. Equating them to one another results in a simple differential equation,

$$\delta\, d\delta = \frac{\mu\beta}{\rho U \alpha}\, dx$$

with solution

$$\frac{\delta^2}{2} = \frac{\mu\beta}{\rho U \alpha}\, x + C$$

where $C = 0$, since $\delta = 0$ at $x = 0$.   Therefore

$$\delta = \sqrt{\frac{2\mu\beta x}{\rho U \alpha}} = \sqrt{\frac{2\beta}{\alpha}}\,\frac{x}{\sqrt{N_{Rx}}} \tag{13.7}$$

where $N_{Rx} = xU\rho/\mu$ may be called the *local* Reynolds number. It should be noted that N_{Rx} increases linearly in the downstream direction. We have shown that the thickness of the laminar boundary layer increases with distance from the leading edge, while the shear stress, as given by Eq. (13.6), decreases as the layer grows along the plate.

To evaluate Eq. (13.7), we must know or assume the velocity profile in the laminar boundary layer. In Prob. 10.2 the uniform laminar flow of a liquid with a free surface over a flat plate was examined and the velocity distribution was found to be a parabola with the vertex at the free surface. The flow in the boundary layer is like free surface flow in that the shear stress is essentially zero at the outer edge of the layer, but it differs in that the boundary layer is continuously growing in thickness and is therefore a case of nonuniform laminar flow along a plate. Nevertheless the velocity distribution may be closely represented by a parabola, as shown in Fig. 13.2. In dimensionless terms this curve becomes

$$\frac{u}{U} = f(\eta) = 2\eta - \eta^2 \tag{13.8}$$

The other velocity profile in Fig. 13.2 was derived by Blasius from the fundamental equations of viscous flow, with all factors considered, and

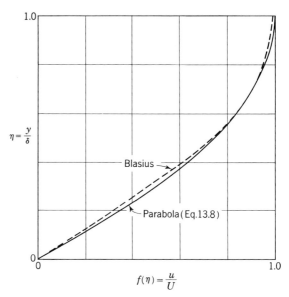

Fig. 13.2. Velocity distribution in laminar boundary layer on flat plate. (*Blasius curve adapted from NACA Tech. Mem. 1217, Fig. 30, 1949.*)

has been closely checked by experiment.[1] This curve is based on the thickness δ being defined as that for which $u = 0.99U$.

As can be demonstrated by Prob. 13.2, the parabolic distribution will give numerical values for α and β of 0.133 and 2.0, respectively.   The Blasius curve yields $\alpha = 0.135$ and $\beta = 1.63$, the principal difference lying in the milder slope of the velocity gradient at the wall.   With the Blasius values substituted in Eq. (13.7) we obtain

$$\frac{\delta}{x} = \sqrt{\frac{2 \times 1.63}{0.135}} \frac{1}{\sqrt{N_{Rx}}} = \frac{4.91}{\sqrt{N_{Rx}}} \tag{13.9}$$

If the value of δ from Eq. (13.9) is substituted in Eq. (13.6) with $\beta = 1.63$, there results for the shear stress

$$\tau_0 = 0.332 \frac{\mu U}{x} \sqrt{N_{Rx}} \tag{13.10}$$

But we have another expression for shear stress, given in Eq. (8.10), $\tau_0 = c_f \rho U^2/2$.*   Setting this equal to Eq. (13.10) allows a determination of the local friction coefficient

$$c_f = \frac{0.332 \mu U \sqrt{N_{Rx}}}{\rho x U^2/2} = \frac{0.664}{\sqrt{N_{Rx}}} \tag{13.11}$$

If the boundary layer remains laminar over the length of L of the plate, the total friction drag on one side of the plate is given by integrating Eq. (13.10):

$$F_f = B \int_0^L \tau_0 \, dx = 0.332B \sqrt{\rho \mu U^3} \int_0^L x^{-\frac{1}{2}} \, dx$$

$$= 0.664B \sqrt{\rho \mu L U^3} \tag{13.12}$$

Comparing Eq. (13.12) with the standard friction-drag equation (13.2), and substituting U for the more general velocity V, it may be seen that

$$C_f = 1.328 \sqrt{\frac{\mu}{\rho L U}} = \frac{1.328}{\sqrt{N_R}} \tag{13.13}$$

where it is noted that N_R is based on the characteristic length of the whole plate.   The laminar boundary layer will remain laminar if undisturbed,

---

[1] See H. Schlichting, "Boundary Layer Theory," 4th ed., pp. 116–125, McGraw-Hill, 1960.

* The reader will observe an apparent inconsistency between the notation used here and that used in Chap. 8.   Thus, in pipe flow, the significant reference velocity is the mean velocity V in the pipe, while in flow over a plate, it is the *uniform* velocity U of the undisturbed fluid.   Likewise, C_f has been employed in Chap. 8 to denote a friction coefficient for the fully developed boundary layer in a pipe, while c_f is used here to denote the local friction coefficient of the growing layer.

up to a value of N_{Rx} of between 300,000 and 500,000.   In this region the layer becomes turbulent, increasing noticeably in thickness and displaying a marked change in velocity distribution.

Illustrative example 13.1:   Find the friction drag on one side of a plate 6 in. wide and 18 in. long, placed longitudinally in a stream of crude oil ($s = 0.925$) at 60°F, flowing with undisturbed velocity of 2 fps.

From Fig. 1.2, $\nu = 0.001$ ft²/sec

Then $N_R = \dfrac{LU}{\nu} = \dfrac{1.5 \times 2}{0.001} = 3{,}000$

well within the laminar range.

From Eq. (13.13), $C_f = \dfrac{1.328}{\sqrt{N_R}} = \dfrac{1.328}{\sqrt{3{,}000}} = 0.0242$

From Eq. (13.2), $F_f = 0.0242 \times 0.925 \times 1.938 \dfrac{2^2}{2} \dfrac{6 \times 18}{144} = 0.065$ lb

Find the thickness of the boundary layer and the shear stress at the trailing edge of the plate.

From Eq. (13.9), $\dfrac{\delta}{x} = \dfrac{4.91}{\sqrt{3{,}000}} = 0.0898$

$\delta = 0.0898 \times 1.5 = 0.1348$ ft $= 1.62$ in.

From Eq. (13.10), $\tau_0 = 0.332 \times \dfrac{0.00179 \times 2}{1.5} \sqrt{3{,}000} = 0.0434$ psf

13.4. TURBULENT BOUNDARY LAYER

Comparing the laminar and turbulent boundary layers in Fig. 13.3, the velocity distribution in the turbulent boundary layer shows a much

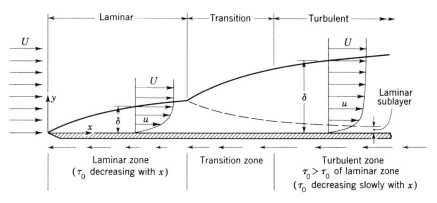

Fig. 13.3.   Laminar and turbulent boundary layers along a flat plate (vertical scale greatly exaggerated).

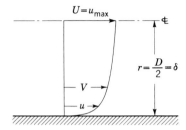

Fig. 13.4. Flow in a pipe as a turbulent boundary layer.

steeper gradient near the wall and a flatter gradient throughout the remainder of the layer. As would be expected, then, the wall shear stress is greater in the turbulent boundary layer than in the laminar layer at the same Reynolds number. In this case, however, it is not practical to proceed along the lines of Eqs. (13.5) and (13.6), determining the shear stress from the velocity gradient at the wall. We turn instead to turbulent flow in a circular pipe because of the wealth of experimental information in that field compared with that of flow in a turbulent boundary layer. We learned in Eq. (8.15) that the shear stress at the wall of a pipe is given by

$$\tau_0 = f\rho \frac{V^2}{8} \tag{13.14}$$

where V again denotes the average velocity in the pipe. Now we shall assume that the turbulent boundary layer occupies all the region between the wall and the center line of the pipe as in Fig. 13.4. The radius of the pipe then becomes the thickness of the boundary layer, and by analogy, the velocity at the center of the pipe, here denoted by U, corresponds to the undisturbed velocity at the outer edge of the boundary layer. We may obtain a relation between V and U by use of the pipe-factor equation (8.30). Taking a middle value of $f = 0.028$ and allowing for the 1 per cent difference in velocity between the edge of the boundary layer and the free stream, we have

$$U = 1.235V \tag{13.15}$$

To proceed further, we need a simple relation between f and N_R for turbulent pipe flow. The Blasius equation (8.34) provides a useful relationship. Substituting Eqs. (8.34) and (13.15) into (13.14) gives

$$\tau_0 = \frac{0.316}{\left(\dfrac{DV}{\nu}\right)^{1/4}} \frac{\rho V^2}{8} = \frac{0.316}{\left(\dfrac{2\delta}{\nu}\dfrac{U}{1.235}\right)^{1/4}} \frac{\rho}{8} \left(\frac{U}{1.235}\right)^2 = \frac{0.023\rho U^2}{\left(\dfrac{\delta U}{\nu}\right)^{1/4}} \tag{13.16}$$

If we now equate the two expressions for τ_0 [(13.5) and (13.16)], there results

$$\rho U^2 \alpha \frac{d\delta}{dx} = \frac{0.023\rho U^2}{(\delta U/\nu)^{1/4}} \tag{13.17}$$

Upon integrating this expression (with the condition $\delta = 0$ at $x = 0$), there results

$$\delta = \left(\frac{0.0287}{\alpha}\right)^{4/5} \left(\frac{\nu}{Ux}\right)^{1/5} x \tag{13.18}$$

If we can evaluate α, all the other unknowns are readily determined from the foregoing equations. To do this requires that we know or assume the velocity distribution in the turbulent boundary layer. Of the many formulas for this distribution that have been proposed, the most convenient for our purpose is Eq. (8.35), the seventh-root law, which can be expressed as

$$u = Uf(\eta) = U\eta^{1/7} \tag{13.19}$$

Recalling the integral definition of α from Eq. (13.4), this yields $\alpha = 0.0972$. Substituting this value in Eq. (13.18) gives

$$\frac{\delta}{x} = \frac{0.377}{N_{Rx}^{1/5}} \tag{13.20}$$

while substituting this value of δ in Eq. (13.16) yields

$$\tau_0 = 0.0587\rho \frac{U^2}{2} \left(\frac{\nu}{Ux}\right)^{1/5} \tag{13.21}$$

or

$$c_f = \frac{0.0587}{N_{Rx}^{1/5}} \tag{13.22}$$

With this value for c_f the total friction drag on one side of the plate becomes

$$F_f = B \int_0^L \tau_0 \, dx = 0.0735\rho \frac{U^2}{2} \left(\frac{\nu}{UL}\right)^{1/5} BL \tag{13.23}$$

or in Eq. (13.2) the friction-drag coefficient is

$$C_f = \frac{0.0735}{N_R^{1/5}} \qquad \text{for } N_R < 10^7 \tag{13.24}$$

where it is again noted that the characteristic length in N_R is L, the total length of the plate parallel to the flow. For Reynolds numbers above 10^7, Schlichting has proposed a modification of Eq. (13.24) which agrees better with experimental results,[1]

$$C_f = \frac{0.455}{(\log_{10} N_R)^{2.58}} \qquad \text{for } N_R > 10^7 \qquad (13.25)$$

Illustrative example 13.2: Find the surface resistance on the top and sides of a semitrailer 8 ft wide, 10 ft high, and 35 ft long, traveling at 60 mph through air ($\gamma = 0.0725$ pcf) at 50°F. Assume that the front end of the trailer is sufficiently rough so that the surface resistance may be expected to rise entirely from the turbulent boundary layer, starting directly at the leading edge.

From Fig. 1.2, for air at 50°F, $\nu = 0.00015$ ft²/sec. Then

$$N_R = \frac{LU}{\nu} = \frac{35 \times 88}{0.00015} = 20,550,000$$

As $N_R > 10^7$, use Eq. (13.25):

$$C_f = \frac{0.455}{(7.31)^{2.58}} = 0.00268$$

Then, by Eq. (13.2),

$$F_f = 0.00268 \times \frac{0.0725}{32.2} \times \frac{(88)^2}{2} \times (10 + 8 + 10)35 = 22.9 \text{ lb}$$

Find the thickness of the boundary layer and the shear stress at the trailing edge. By Eq. (13.20),

$$\delta = \frac{35 \times 0.377}{(205.5)^{1/5} \times 10} = 0.455 \text{ ft}$$

By Eq. (13.22), $\qquad c_f = \dfrac{0.0587}{(20.55)^{1/5} \times 10} = 0.00202$

and $\qquad \tau_0 = 0.00202 \times \dfrac{0.0725}{32.2} \times \dfrac{(88)^2}{2} = 0.176 \text{ psf}$

13.5. FRICTION DRAG IN TRANSITION REGIME

In the two preceding sections we have treated separately the resistance due to laminar and turbulent boundary layers on a flat plate. When the plate is of such length that there is a transition from the laminar to the turbulent boundary layer on the plate surface, the friction drag may be computed as follows.

Let x_c in Fig. 13.5 be the distance from the leading edge to the point where the boundary layer becomes turbulent, which will normally occur at a value of N_{Rx} of between 300,000 and 500,000. The drag of the turbulent portion of the boundary layer may be approximated as the drag which would occur if a turbulent boundary layer extended along the whole plate, less the drag of a fictitious turbulent layer from the leading

[1] H. Schlichting, Boundary Layer Theory, Part II, *NACA Tech. Mem.* 1218, p. 39, 1949.

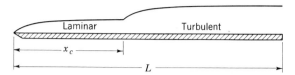

Fig. 13.5. Boundary layers along a plate of finite length.

edge to x_c. Thus

$$F_\text{turb} = F_\text{total turb} - F_\text{turb to } x_c$$

When the drag from the laminar boundary layer up to x_c is added, we have, from Eqs. (13.13), (13.24), and (13.25), for the total drag, assuming the plate is long enough so that $N_R > 10^7$,

$$F_f = \rho \frac{U^2}{2} B \left[\frac{1.328 x_c}{\sqrt{N_{Rc}}} + \frac{0.455 L}{(\log_{10} N_R)^{2.58}} - \frac{0.0735 x_c}{N_{Rc}^{1/5}} \right]$$

where N_{Rc} is based on the length x_c to the point of transition, while N_R is based on the total length L of the plate, as before.   Next we observe that

$$\frac{N_{Rc}}{N_R} = \frac{x_c}{L} \qquad \text{or} \qquad x_c = \frac{N_{Rc}}{N_R} L$$

and thus

$$F_f = \rho \frac{U^2}{2} BL \left[1.328 \frac{\sqrt{N_{Rc}}}{N_R} + \frac{0.455}{(\log_{10} N_R)^{2.58}} - \frac{0.0735 N_{Rc}^{4/5}}{N_R} \right]$$

which, for $N_{Rc} = 500{,}000$, reduces to

$$C_f = \frac{0.455}{(\log_{10} N_R)^{2.58}} - \frac{1{,}700}{N_R} \tag{13.26}$$

Equations (13.13), (13.25), and (13.26) are plotted in Fig. 13.6, together with some comparison measurements and indicated ranges of applicability.

All the treatment of laminar and turbulent boundary layers has so far been based upon the surface of the immersed body being smooth.   The laminar layer can be "tripped" into becoming a turbulent layer by a local region of excessive roughness.   The height of this *critical roughness* is

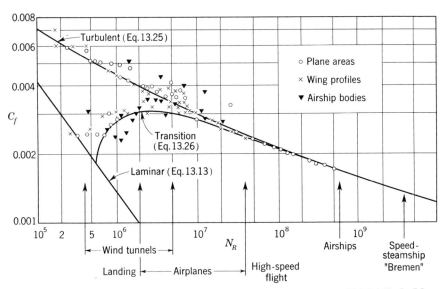

Fig. 13.6. Drag coefficients for a smooth plate. (*Adapted from NACA Tech. Mem. 1218, p. 117, 1949.*)

given approximately by[1]

$$\epsilon_c = \frac{15\nu}{\sqrt{\tau_0/\rho}} = 26\frac{\nu}{U} N_{Rx}{}^{\frac{1}{4}} \tag{13.27}$$

where τ_0 is determined by Eq. (13.10).

We see that the height of the critical roughness depends on the distance from the leading edge.   As the boundary layer grows along the plate, the roughness must be greater in order to upset the stability of the layer. It must be recalled that when N_{Rx} reaches a value in the neighborhood of 400,000, the laminar layer of itself becomes unstable, however smooth the surface, and changes to a turbulent boundary layer with a thin laminar sublayer lying close to the surface.   As in the case of flow in pipes, the surface is considered hydraulically smooth if the roughness points do not project through this sublayer.

The thickness of the laminar sublayer is not a clearly determinable quantity, but it appears to be well agreed that the thickness of the strictly laminar region is given approximately by [see Eq. (8.26) for pipe flow]

$$\delta_s = \frac{5\nu}{\sqrt{\tau_0/\rho}} \tag{13.28}$$

[1] I. Tani, J. Hama, and S. Mituisi, On the Permissible Roughness in the Laminar Boundary Layer, *Aeronaut. Res. Inst., Tokyo Imp. Univ., Rept.* 15, p. 419, 1940.

while a transition layer extends to

$$\delta_t = \frac{30\nu}{\sqrt{\tau_0/\rho}} \qquad (13.29)$$

In both these equations τ_0/ρ may be obtained from Eq. (13.21). If the roughness height is only of the order of δ_s and a little greater, the surface may still be considered smooth, but if the roughness height is greater than δ_t, the surface is truly rough and the drag is materially increased.

It may be remarked finally that a plate or wing which is to incur minimum drag must be very smooth near the leading edge, where the laminar layer or sublayer is thinnest, while greater roughness may be tolerated near the trailing edge. Since the wall shear is so much greater in a turbulent boundary layer than in a laminar one, anything that can be done to delay the breakdown of the laminar boundary layer will greatly reduce the frictional drag force on a body. The *laminar flow wing* for aircraft is one for which suction slots along the leading edge of the wing help to maintain a favorable pressure gradient (Sec. 13.6) along the upper surface of the wing. This delays the breakdown of the laminar boundary layer, and thus such wings have much less drag than conventional ones.

Illustrative example 13.3: A submarine, which may be supposed to approximate a cylinder 10 ft in diameter and 50 ft long, travels submerged at 3 knots (5.06 fps) in sea water at 40°F. Find the friction drag.

From Fig. 1.2, by interpolation $\nu = 0.000018$ ft^2/sec. Then

$$N_R = \frac{5.06 \times 50}{0.000018} = 1.406 \times 10^7$$

From Eq. 13.26 or Fig. 13.6,

$$C_f = 0.00272$$

and

$$F_f = 0.00272 \times \frac{64}{32.2} \times \frac{(5.06)^2}{2} \times \pi \times 10 \times 50 = 109 \text{ lb}$$

Find the value of the critical roughness for a point 1 ft from the nose of the submarine.

At $x = 1$ ft:

$$N_{Rx} = \frac{5.06 \times 1}{0.000018} = 281,000$$

By Eq. (13.27),

$$\epsilon_c = \frac{26 \times 0.000018}{5.06} (281,000)^{1/4} = 0.00214 \text{ ft}$$

Find the height of roughness at the mid-section of the submarine which would class the surface as truly rough.

At $x = 25$ ft:

$$N_{Rx} = \frac{5.06 \times 25}{0.000018} = 7.03 \times 10^6$$

By Eq. (13.21),

$$\tau_0/\rho = 0.0587 \times \frac{(5.06)^2}{2} \frac{1}{(70.3 \times 10^5)^{1/5}} = 0.0322 \text{ ft}^2/\text{sec}^2$$

Then, by Eq. (13.29), $$\delta_t = \frac{30 \times 0.000018}{\sqrt{0.0322}} = 0.003 \text{ ft}$$

13.6. BOUNDARY - LAYER SEPARATION AND PRESSURE DRAG

The motion of a thin stratum of fluid lying wholly inside the boundary layer is determined by three forces:

1. The forward pull of the outer free-moving fluid, transmitted through the laminar boundary layer by viscous shear and through the turbulent boundary layer by momentum transfer (Sec. 8.8).
2. The viscous retarding of the solid boundary which must, by definition, hold the first stratum adjacent to it at rest.
3. The pressure gradient along the boundary.   The stratum is accelerated by a pressure gradient with the pressure decreasing in the direction of flow and retarded by an adverse gradient.

The treatment of fluid resistance in the foregoing sections has been restricted to the drag of the boundary layer along a flat plate, that is to say, in the *absence of a pressure gradient*.   In the presence of a favorable pressure gradient the boundary layer is "held" in place.   This is what occurs in the accelerated flow around the *forebody*, or upstream portion, of a cylinder, sphere, or other object, such as that of Fig. 3.11.   If a particle enters the boundary layer near the forward stagnation point with a low velocity and high pressure, its velocity will increase as it flows into the lower pressure region along the side of the body.   But there will be some retardation from wall friction (force 2 above) so that its total useful energy will be reduced by a corresponding conversion into thermal energy.

What happens next may best be explained by reference to Fig. 13.7. Let A represent a point in the region of accelerated flow, with a normal velocity distribution in the boundary layer (either laminar or turbulent), while B, C, D, and E are points downstream on the curved surface along

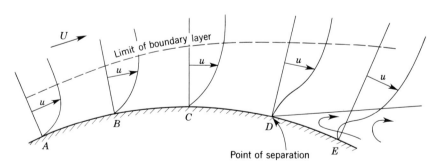

Fig. 13.7.   Growth and separation of boundary layer due to increasing pressure gradient.

which the pressure is increasing in accordance with ideal-flow theory. When the particle in the boundary layer passes the point of minimum pressure and maximum velocity (B), it cannot regain its original pressure and velocity values because of the energy it has converted into heat. The velocity of the layer close to the wall is reduced at C and finally brought to a stop at D. Now the increasing pressure calls for further retardation; but this is impossible, and so the boundary layer actually *separates* from the wall. At E there is a backflow next to the wall, driven in the direction of decreasing pressure—upstream in this case—and feeding fluid into the boundary layer which has left the wall at D.

Downstream from the point of separation the flow is characterized by irregular turbulent eddies, formed as the separated boundary layer becomes rolled up in the reversed flow. This condition generally extends for some distance downstream until the eddies are worn away by viscous attrition. The whole disturbed region is called the *turbulent wake* of the body.

Because the eddies cannot convert their kinetic energy of rotation into an increased pressure, as the ideal-fluid theory would dictate, the pressure within the wake remains close to that at the separation point. Since this is always less than the pressure at the forward stagnation point, there results a net pressure difference tending to move the body with the flow, and this force is the *pressure*, or *form*, drag.

Although the laminar and turbulent boundary layers behave in essentially the same manner at a point of separation, the *location* of the separation point on a given curved surface will be very different for the two cases. In the laminar layer the transfer of momentum from the rapidly moving outer strata through the viscous-shear process to the inner strata is slow and ineffective. Consequently, the laminar boundary layer is "weak" and cannot long stick to the wall against an adverse pressure gradient. The transition to a turbulent boundary layer, on the other hand, brings a violent mixing of the faster-moving outer strata into the slower-moving inner strata, and vice versa. The mean velocity close to the boundary is greatly increased, as shown in Fig. 13.3. This added energy enables the boundary layer better to withstand the adverse pressure gradient, with the result that with a turbulent boundary layer the point of separation is moved downstream to a region of higher pressure.

13.7. DRAG OF THREE - DIMENSIONAL BODIES

The total drag on a body is principally the sum of the friction drag and the pressure drag.

$$F_D = F_f + F_p$$

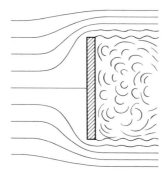

Fig. 13.8. Turbulent wake behind a flat plate held normal to the flow.

In the case of a well-streamlined body, such as an airplane wing or the hull of a submarine, the friction drag is the major part of the total and may be determined by the methods of the preceding articles on the boundary layer. Only rarely is it desired to compute the pressure drag separately from the friction drag. Usually, when the wake resistance becomes significant, one is interested in the total drag only. Indeed, it is customary to employ a single equation which gives the total drag,[1]

$$F_D = C_D\rho \frac{V^2}{2} A \tag{13.30}$$

in terms of an overall drag coefficient C_D, with the other quantities the same as in Eq. (13.1), except that in the case of the lifting vane (as an airplane wing) the area A is defined as the product of the span and the mean chord (Figs. 13.14 and 13.20). In such a case the area is neither strictly parallel to nor normal to the flow.

In the case of a body with sharp corners, such as the plate of Fig. 13.8 set normal to the flow, separation always occurs at the same point, and the wake extends across the full projected width of the body. This results in a relatively constant value of C_D, as may be seen from the plot for the flat disk in Fig. 13.9. If the body has curved sides, however, the location of the separation point will be determined by whether the boundary layer is laminar or turbulent. This location in turn determines the size of the wake and the amount of the pressure drag.

The foregoing principles are vividly illustrated in the case of the flow around a sphere. For very low Reynolds numbers ($DV/\nu < 1$, in which D is the diameter of the sphere) the flow about the sphere is completely

---

[1] In the equations for the drag on three-dimensional bodies, we revert to the use of V to designate a general reference velocity, but not necessarily the uniform velocity U of the preceding sections.

viscous and the friction drag is given by Stokes' law,

$$F_D = 3\pi\mu V D \qquad (13.31)$$

Equating this equation to Eq. (13.30), where A is defined as $\pi D^2/4$, the frontal area of the projected sphere, gives the result that $C_D = 24/N_R$. The similarity between this case and the value of the friction factor for laminar flow in pipes is at once apparent. This regime of the flow about a sphere is shown as the straight line at the left of the plot of C_D versus N_R in Fig. 13.9.

As N_R is increased beyond 1, the laminar boundary layer separates from the surface of the sphere, beginning first at the rear stagnation point, where the adverse pressure gradient is the strongest. The curve of C_D in Fig. 13.9 begins to level off as the pressure drag becomes of increasing importance and the drag becomes more proportional to V^2. With further increase in N_R, the point of separation moves forward on the sphere, increasing the size of the turbulent wake and consequently the proportion of form resistance, until at $N_R \approx 1,000$ the point of separation remains fairly stable at about 80° from the forward stagnation point.

For a considerable range of Reynolds numbers conditions remain fairly stable, the laminar boundary layer separating from the forward half of the sphere and C_D remaining fairly constant at about 0.45. At a value of N_R of about 350,000 for the smooth sphere, however, the drag coefficient is suddenly reduced by about 50 per cent, as may be seen in Fig. 13.9. The reason for this lies in a change from laminar to turbulent boundary layer on the sphere. The point of separation is moved back to something like 115°, from the stagnation point, with a consequent decrease in the size of the wake and the pressure drag.

If the "level" of turbulence in the free stream is high, the transition from laminar to turbulent boundary layer will take place at lower Reynolds numbers. Because this phenomenon of shift in separation point is so well defined, the sphere is often used as a turbulence indicator. The Reynolds number producing a value of C_D of 0.3—which lies in the middle of the rapid-drop range—becomes an accurate measure of the turbulence.

As was mentioned previously, the transition from laminar to turbulent boundary layer may also be prematurely induced by artificially roughening the surface over a local region. The two pictures of Fig. 13.10 clearly show the effectiveness of this procedure. By roughening the nose of the sphere the boundary layer is made turbulent and the separation point moved back. The added roughness and turbulent boundary layer cause an increase in friction drag, to be sure, but this is of secondary importance compared with the marked decrease in the size and effect of

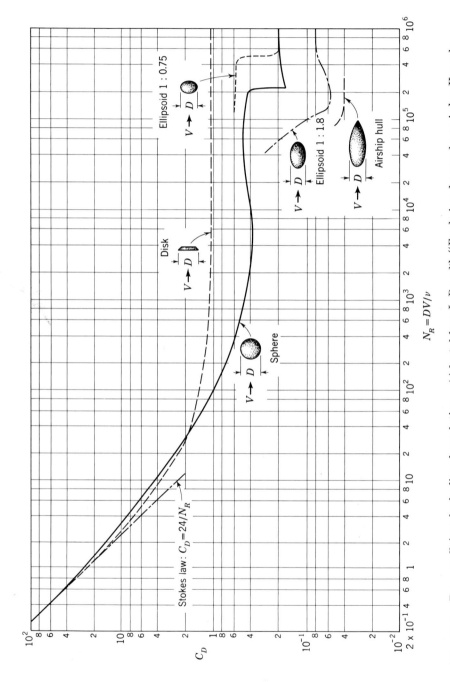

Fig. 13.9. Drag coefficient for bodies of revolution. (*Adapted from L. Prandtl, "Ergebnisse der aerodynamischen Versuchsanstalt zu Göttingen," p. 29, R. Oldenbourg KG, Munich, 1923, and F. Eisner, Das Widerstandsproblem, Proc. 3d Intern. Congr. Appl. Mech., 1930, p. 32.*)

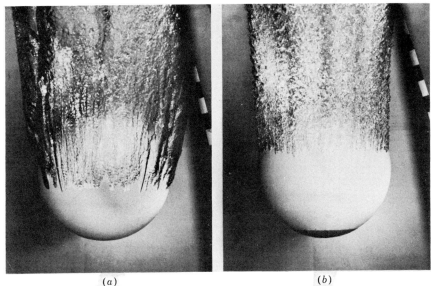

(a) (b)

Fig. 13.10.   Bowling ball 8.5 in. in diameter, at velocity of approximately 25 fps in water.   (a) Smooth surface.   (b) 4-in.-diameter patch of sand grains cemented to nose.   Note the shift in point of separation as the boundary layer is made turbulent. (*Photograph by U.S. Naval Ordnance Test Station, Pasadena Annex.*)

the wake.   This explains the main reason why the surface of a golf ball is perforated.   A smooth-surfaced ball would have greater overall drag and would not travel as far when driven.

Plots of C_D versus N_R for various other three-dimensional shapes are also shown in Fig. 13.9.   It may be pointed out here that the object of *streamlining* a body is to move the point of separation as far back as possible and thus to produce the minimum size of turbulent wake.   This decreases the pressure drag, but by making the body longer so as to promote a gradual increase in pressure, the friction drag is increased.   The optimum amount of streamlining, then, is that for which the sum of the friction and pressure drag is a minimum.   Quite evidently, from what we have learned, the first attention in streamlining must be given the rear end, or downstream part, of a body.   The shape of the forebody is important principally to the extent that it governs the location of the separation point(s) on the afterbody.   A rounded nose produces the least disturbance in the streamlines and is therefore the best form for incompressible or compressible flow at subsonic velocities.

Illustrative example 13.4:   A sphere with a diameter of 1 ft is held in an air stream which flows with a velocity of 200 fps.   If the air is at 59°F and 14.7 psi, find the Reynolds number, the drag coefficient, and the drag.

From Appendix 3, Table A.2, this is seen to be the standard atmosphere at sea level.   From this table or from Fig. 1.2, $\nu = 1.564 \times 10^{-4}$ ft²/sec, and

$$N_R = \frac{DV}{\nu} = \frac{1 \times 200}{1.564 \times 10^{-4}} = 1.28 \times 10^6$$

From Fig. 13.9 (extrapolated), $C_D = 0.209$.
    From Eq. (13.30),

$$F_D = C_D \rho \frac{V^2}{2} A = 0.209 \times 0.002378 \times \frac{(200)^2}{2} \pi \frac{1^2}{4} = 7.82 \text{ lb}$$

Notice that if the sphere had been streamlined in the fashion of the airship hull shown in Fig. 13.9, the drag coefficient would have been reduced to about 0.04, giving $F_D = 1.5$ lb, a reduction in resistance of 81 per cent.

13.8. DRAG OF TWO - DIMENSIONAL BODIES

Two-dimensional bodies are also subject to friction and form drag.   However, the flow about a two-dimensional body exhibits some peculiar properties which are not ordinarily found in the three-dimensional case of flow around a sphere.   For example, with Reynolds numbers less than 1, the flow around a cylinder is completely viscous and the drag coefficient is given by the straight-line part of the curve at the left of Fig. 13.11.   As the Reynolds number increases from 2 to about 30, the boundary layer separates symmetrically from the two sides of the cylinder and two weak, symmetrical standing eddies are formed.   The equilibrium of the standing eddies is maintained by the flow from the separated boundary layer, and the eddies increase in length with increase in velocity in order to dissipate their rotational energy to the free-streaming fluid.

At some limiting Reynolds number, depending on the shape of the cylinder (not necessarily circular), the width of the confining channel, and the turbulence in the stream, the eddies break off, having become too long to hang on, and wash downstream.   This gives rise to the beginning of the celebrated *Kármán vortex trail*.   Above this critical N_R, and visibly up to a value of about 120, the vortices are shed first from one side of the cylinder and then from the other.   The result is a staggered double row of vortices in the wake of the object.   Von Kármán analyzed the vortex trail as a problem in ideal fluid flow with separated vortices and found only one spacing of the vortices which would be stable, i.e., such that any slight disturbance would tend to restore the pattern rather than destroy it.   This he determined as

$$\sinh \frac{\pi a}{b} = 1 \qquad \text{or} \qquad \frac{a}{b} = 0.281 \qquad (13.32)$$

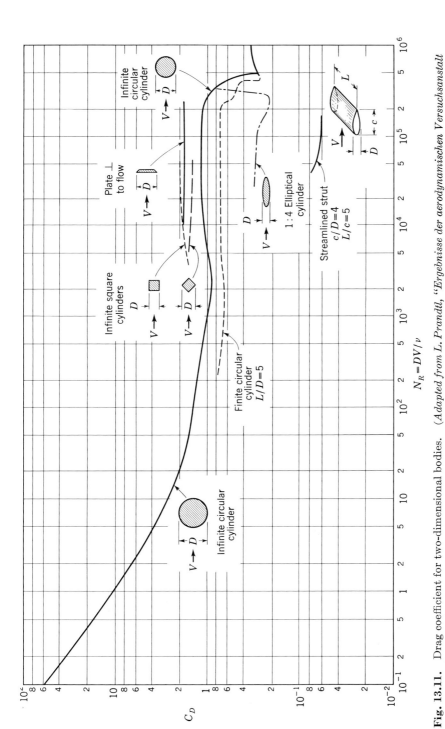

$N_R = DV/\nu$

Fig. 13.11. Drag coefficient for two-dimensional bodies. (*Adapted from L. Prandtl, "Ergebnisse der aerodynamischen Versuchsanstalt zu Göttingen," p. 24, R. Oldenbourg KG, Munich, 1923; F. Eisner, Das Widerstandsproblem, Proc. 3d Intern. Congr. Appl. Mech., p. 32, 1930; A. F. Zahm, R. H. Smith, and G. C. Hill, Point Drag and Total Drag of Navy Struts No. 1 Modified, NACA Rept. 137, p. 14, 1922; and W. F. Lindsey, Drag of Cylinders of Simple Shapes, NACA Rept. 619, pp. 4–5, 1938.*)

427

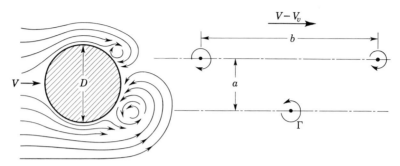

Fig. 13.12.   The Kármán vortex trail following a cylinder.

where a and b are as given in Fig. 13.12.   This spacing is confirmed by experiment.

The entire vortex system moves with respect to the fluid at a velocity V_v which varies as the strength of the vortices and inversely as the spacing b between them.   The velocity of the vortex trail downstream with respect to the cylinder will then be $V - V_v$.   This enables us to write an expression for the frequency with which vortices are shed from one side of the cylinder.

$$f = \frac{V - V_v}{b} \tag{13.33}$$

The frequency has been given by G. F. Taylor and substantiated by Lord Rayleigh to be about

$$f = 0.198 \frac{V}{D}\left(1 - \frac{19.7}{N_R}\right) \tag{13.34}$$

It is this alternating shedding of vortices and the accompanying forces that gives rise to the phenomenon of aerodynamic instability, of such importance in suspension bridges.   It is also understood to account for the "singing" of wind blowing across wires.

For Reynolds numbers above 120 or so it is difficult to perceive the vortex trail, but the eddies continue to be shed alternately from each side up to a value of N_R of about 20,000.   Beyond this the viscous forces become negligible, and it is not possible to say how the eddies form and leave the cylinder.   As in the case of the sphere, the boundary layer becomes turbulent at a value of N_R of about 350,000.   The corresponding sharp drop in C_D may be seen in Fig. 13.11.

Values of C_D for various other two-dimensional shapes are given in Fig. 13.11.   As may be noted from the curve for the finite cylinder, the resistance is decreased if three-dimensional flow can take place around the ends.

13.9. EFFECTS OF GRAVITY AND COMPRESSIBILITY

All the treatment of drag so far has been restricted to the relation between forces of inertia and viscosity. When the body is not completely immersed in a single fluid but rather breaks the surface between two fluids of different densities, the effect of gravity must be included. This is the case with a ship which floats on the surface between water and air. The resistance to the motion of a ship is the sum of friction drag on the hull, pressure drag from the wake, and wave-making resistance at the prow. The use of a ship model, tested at the same Froude number as the prototype, to aid in predicting the total drag on the full-sized ship was discussed in Sec. 7.4.

At near-sonic velocities in compressible fluids the drag characteristics change rapidly because of the radical change in the form of the compression waves emanating from the body. It will be observed in Fig. 3.11 that, for velocities less than sonic, the compression wave or signal reaches ahead of the body and causes the streamlines to be diverted around it. In supersonic flow a conical shock wave extends back from the tip of the body, an example of which may be seen in Fig. 9.7. Sharp changes in velocity and pressure occur across this shock wave. The drag coefficient for a given body rises steeply as the Mach number (Sec. 7.4) approaches and passes 1.0, then falls gradually, and approaches a constant value

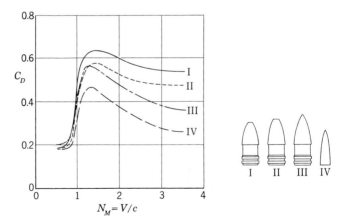

Fig. 13.13. Drag coefficients for projectiles as a function of Mach number. (*From L. Prandtl, "Abriss der Strömungslehre," Friedr. Vieweg & Sohn, Brunswick, Germany, 1935.*)

asymptotically. This is illustrated in the curves of Fig. 13.13, which show curves of C_D versus N_M for several projectile shapes.

Fortunately, by the time the velocity is high enough for compressibility effects to become important, it is so high that viscous effects are altogether negligible and Reynolds number does not enter the picture. We mentioned earlier that for streamlining against ordinary subsonic flow a rounded nose form and a long tapered afterbody generally result in the minimum form and total drag. In supersonic flow the best nose form is a sharp point. This produces the minimum extent of the shock wave. The wake resistance is evidently not so important a feature, because the low pressure within the wake is limited to absolute zero.

Illustrative example 13.5: An 8-in.-diameter projectile the shape of No. III in Fig. 13.13 travels at 2,000 fps through standard atmosphere at an altitude of 20,000 ft. Find the resistance.

From Appendix 2, the acoustic velocity is given by $c = \sqrt{gkRT}$. From Appendix 3, Table A.2, the temperature is $-12.28°F$, or $459.6 - 12.28 = 447.3°A$. Then, with $k = 1.4$ for air and with $g = 32.2$ ft/sec² approximately,

$$c = \sqrt{32.2 \times 1.4 \times 53.34 \times 447.3} = 1{,}035 \text{ fps}$$

and so
$$N_M = 2{,}000/1{,}035 = 1.932$$

From Fig. 13.13,
$$C_D = 0.48$$

Then
$$F_D = 0.48 \times 0.001267 \times \frac{(2{,}000)^2}{2} \times \frac{\pi 8^2}{4 \times 144} = 425 \text{ lb}$$

13.10. LIFT AND CIRCULATION

At the start of this chapter we briefly mentioned the lift as a force which acts on an immersed body normal to the relative motion between the fluid and the body. The most commonly observed example of lift is that of the airplane wing suspended in the air by this force. The elementary explanation for such a lift force is that the air velocity over the top of the wing is faster than the mean velocity, while that along the underside is slower than the mean (Fig. 13.14a). The Bernoulli theorem then shows a lower pressure on the top and a higher pressure on the bottom (Fig. 13.14b), resulting in a net upward lift.

The increased velocity over the top of the wing of Fig. 13.14a and the decreased velocity around the bottom of the wing can be explained by noting that a *circulation* (Sec. 5.3) is induced as the wing moves relative to the flow field. The strength of the circulation depends, in the real case, on the shape of the wing and its velocity and orientation with respect to the flow field. A schematic diagram of the situation is presented in Fig. 13.15.

The relationship between lift and circulation is one that has been

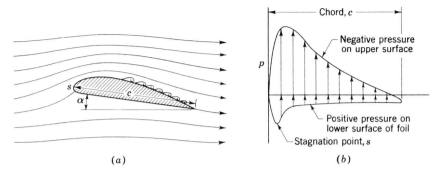

Fig. 13.14. Streamlines and pressure distribution about a cambered airfoil, at angle of attack $\alpha = 8.6°$. (*Data from L. Prandtl, "Ergebnisse der aerodynamischen Versuchsanstalt zu Göttingen," R. Oldenbourg, KG, Munich, 1923.*)

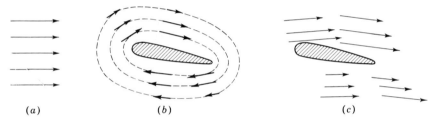

Fig. 13.15. Schematic superposition of circulation on uniform rectilinear flow field. (*a*) Uniform rectilinear flow field.   (*b*) Circulation.   (*c*) Net effect.

studied exhaustively for years by many investigators. An understanding of this relationship is essential to the analysis of various aerodynamic and hydrodynamic problems. To illustrate the theory of lift, we shall consider the flow of an ideal fluid past a cylinder and assume that a circulation about the cylinder is imposed on the flow. First, though, let us consider the velocity field surrounding a free vortex (Fig. 13.16). The equation for this field was given in Sec. 4.18 as $vr = C$, a constant. The circulation can be readily computed by application of Eq. (5.8) if we choose the closed path as the circular streamline L_1 concentric with the center of the vortex. The velocity is evidently around this path and tangent to it ($\cos \beta = 1$), and the line integral of dL is simply the circumference of the circle. Applying the same treatment to another concentric circle L_2, we get

$$\Gamma = v \oint_L dL = v_1(2\pi r_1) = v_2(2\pi r_2)$$

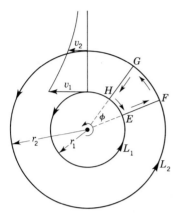

Fig. 13.16. Circulation about a vortex center.

But from the vortex velocity field $v_1 r_1 = v_2 r_2 = C$, and hence

$$\Gamma = 2\pi C \qquad (13.35)$$

which demonstrates that the circulation around two different curves, each completely enclosing the vortex center, is the same. It may be proved more rigorously that the circulation around *any path enclosing the vortex center* is given by $\Gamma = 2\pi C$. The circulation is seen to depend only on the vortex constant C, which is called the *strength* of the vortex.

A corollary states that the circulation around a path *not enclosing* the vortex center is zero. Let us take the path *EFGH* of Fig. 13.16. Along the two radial lines *EF* and *GH*, $\cos \beta = 0$, while along the two circular arc segments, $\Gamma_{FG} = v_2 \phi r_2$ and $\Gamma_{HE} = -v_1 \phi r_1$, resulting in a net circulation of $\phi(v_2 r_2 - v_1 r_1) = 0$.

13.11. FLOW ABOUT A CYLINDER

Let us now consider the flow of an ideal fluid about a cylinder infinitely long. From classical hydrodynamics it has been shown that with steady flow of uniform velocity U (Fig. 13.17a) the velocity around the periphery of the cylinder is given by

$$v = 2U \sin \theta \qquad (13.36)$$

The pressure distribution on the cylinder may be computed by writing the Bernoulli theorem between a point at infinity in the free-streaming fluid and a point on the cylinder wall. Since the pressure distribution is completely symmetrical about the cylinder, there is no net lift or drag for this ideal case.

Putting this uniform flow aside for the moment, we next suppose a circulatory flow about the cylinder (Fig. 13.17b). Adopting the positive clockwise direction of circulation customary in fluid mechanics, the peripheral velocity V on the surface of the cylinder due to circulation may be expressed as

$$V = \frac{\Gamma}{2\pi R} \tag{13.37}$$

In the flow field outside the cylinder $v = \Gamma/2\pi r$. This velocity distribution produces a pressure variation which is radially symmetrical, in accordance with the free-vortex theory. We see that the solid cylinder has replaced the vortex center in the circulation theory. If the reader wishes an explanation for the existence of the circulation, it may be supposed to arise from rotating the cylinder, which indeed may be demonstrated in a real fluid.

Next let us *superpose* the circulatory flow onto the uniform motion, to form the unsymmetrical flow of Fig. 13.17c. The velocity at the periphery is the sum of the two contributions, or

$$v = 2U \sin \theta + \frac{\Gamma}{2\pi R} \tag{13.38}$$

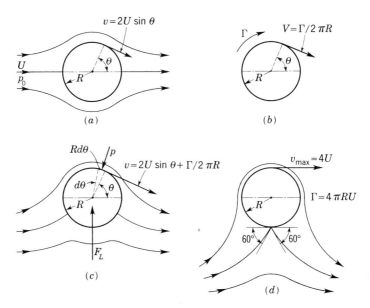

Fig. 13.17. Circulation and lift from unsymmetrical flow about a cylinder.

The general equation for the pressure p at any point on the circumference is obtained as follows:

$$\frac{p_0}{\gamma} + \frac{U^2}{2g} = \frac{p}{\gamma} + \frac{v^2}{2g}$$

where p_0 is the pressure at some distance away where the velocity is uniform. From these two equations

$$p - p_0 = \frac{\rho}{2} \left[U^2 - \left(2U \sin \theta + \frac{\Gamma}{2\pi R} \right)^2 \right]$$

Since the elementary area per unit of length of the cylinder is $R\, d\theta$ and the lift F_L is the summation of all the components normal to the direction of U, the resulting value of F_L is obtained from

$$F_L = -B \int_0^{2\pi} (p - p_0)R \sin \theta\, d\theta$$

Substituting the expression for $p - p_0$ and integrating, this reduces to

$$F_L = \rho B U \Gamma \qquad\qquad (13.39)$$

where F_L is the lift force and B is the length of the cylinder.

The existence of this transverse force on a rotating cylinder is known as the *Magnus effect*, after the man who first observed it in 1852. Equation (13.39)—the *Kutta-Joukowski theorem*—is known by the name of the two men who pioneered the quantitative investigation of the lift force shortly after the turn of the century. The great importance of this theorem is that it applies not only to the circular cylinder but to a cylinder of any shape, including in particular the lifting vane, or *airfoil*, as shown in Fig. 13.14.

It is clear from Fig. 13.17c that the stagnation points have shifted downward from the horizontal axis, but they are still symmetrical about the vertical axis. At the point of stagnation on the cylinder, v in Eq. (13.38) will be zero. Thus we have

$$-2U \sin \theta = \frac{\Gamma}{2\pi R}$$

This shows that if we can measure the angle to the stagnation point and know the free-stream velocity, we may obtain the circulation from

$$\Gamma = -4\pi R U \sin \theta \qquad\qquad (13.40)$$

Figure 13.17c illustrates a case where $\Gamma < 4\pi R U$, that is, where $|\sin \theta| < 1$. For the case of $\Gamma = 4\pi R U$, $\sin \theta = -1$, and the two stagnation points meet together at the bottom of the cylinder as shown in Fig. 13.17d. The two streamlines make angles of $60°$ with the tangent to the cylinder.

The maximum peripheral velocity for this case occurs at the top and amounts to

$$v_{\max} = 2U + \frac{4\pi R U}{2\pi R} = 4U$$

This condition of coincident stagnation points may be obtained by rotating a cylinder so that its peripheral velocity is about four times the free-stream velocity.[1] If the cylinder is rotated at still greater speed, the stagnation point is removed entirely from the cylinder surface, and a ring of fluid is dragged around with the cylinder.

Illustrative example 13.6: A cylinder 4 ft in diameter and 25 ft long rotates at 90 rpm with its axis perpendicular to an airstream with a wind velocity of 120 fps (81.8 mph). The specific weight of the air is 0.0765 pcf. Assuming no slip between the cylinder and the circulatory flow, find (a) the value of the circulation; (b) the transverse or lift force; and (c) the position of the stagnation points.

(a) Peripheral velocity:

$$V = \frac{2\pi R n}{60} = 2\pi \times 2 \times {}^{90}\!/_{60} = 18.84 \text{ fps}$$

From Eq. (13.35),

$$\Gamma = 2\pi R V = 2\pi \times 2 \times 18.84 = 237 \text{ ft}^2/\text{sec}$$

(b) From Eq. (13.39),

$$F_L = \rho B U \Gamma = \frac{0.0765}{32.2} \times 25 \times 120 \times 237 = 1{,}685 \text{ lb}$$

(c) From Eq. (13.40),

$$\sin \theta = -\frac{\Gamma}{4\pi R U} = -\frac{237}{4\pi 2 \times 120} = 0.0786$$

Therefore
$$\theta = -4.5° \text{ from either stagnation point}$$

Actually, the real circulation produced by surface drag of the rotating cylinder would be only about half that obtained above for the no-slip assumption.

13.12. LIFT OF THE AIRFOIL

The reader may well ask why so much attention is given to the flow about a cylinder when it is obvious that there are few practical applications of the lift on a cylinder.[2] The answer is that one of the most remarkable

[1] The ideal-fluid theory, from Eq. (13.37), would call for only half this speed of rotation to give the required circulation, but the viscosity of the real fluid requires that every point of the cylinder be moving as fast as or faster than the adjacent fluid if this effective circulation is to be obtained.

[2] In the early 1920s A. Flettner developed the "rotorship," which substituted motor-driven cylindrical rotors for sails. The ship was then driven by the Magnus effect but still required wind. A few trans-Atlantic crossings were made, but the rotorship was ultimately found to be uneconomical. See A. Flettner, "The Story of the Rotor," Willhoft, New York, 1926.

applications of mathematics to engineering is *conformal transformation*,[1] by which the flow about one body may be mapped into the flow about a body of different (though mathematically related) shape.   Certain quantities, notably the circulation and relative position of the stagnation points, remain unchanged in the mapping.   The importance of the circular cylinder, then, is that it can be mapped into a perfectly workable airfoil by the so-called *Joukowski transformation*.   The position of the stagnation points is determined from the physical requirements of the flow about the airfoil, and these stagnation points, mapped back onto the cylinder, determine the circulation, by Eq. (13.40), and the lift, by Eq. (13.39).[2]

Let us examine the airfoil of Fig. 13.18.   As fluid flows past the foil, there will be a tendency for stagnation points to form at the points of the foil, corresponding to the 0 and 180° points of the corresponding cylinder (Fig. 13.17a).   Just where these points occur on the foil depends on the *angle of attack* α, or the attitude of the foil with respect to the oncoming flow, as shown in the figure.   We shall assume a positive angle of attack in Fig. 13.18a, with corresponding initial stagnation points *a* and *b*. While the location of these stagnation points involves no difficulty in the case of the ideal fluid, we see at once that the condition at the trailing edge—with the air from the underside trying to flow around the sharp cusp of the foil—becomes a point of violent separation in real fluid flow.

This condition lasts no more than an instant, however, for stagnation point *b* is soon swept back to the trailing edge of the foil (Fig. 13.18b), where it stays.   This stable position of the point *b* is necessary, according to the so-called *stagnation hypothesis* of N. Joukowski, in order to avoid an infinite velocity around the sharp cusp of the foil.   Now this shift in the rear stagnation point of the foil corresponds to a shift in the rear stagnation point of the related cylinder to a negative angle, somewhat as

[1] For an excellent discussion of conformal transformation see H. R. Vallentine, "Applied Hydrodynamics," Butterworth & Co. (Publishers), Ltd., London, 1959.

[2] It must be understood that while the Joukowski profile is a workable lifting vane, the modern airfoil has undergone many modifications to improve its performance for various special purposes.   The mapping theory described here applies exactly to the Joukowski foil and in principle to any lifting vane.

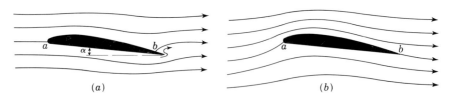

Fig. 13.18.   Adjustment of stagnation points to avoid infinite velocity at trailing edge.

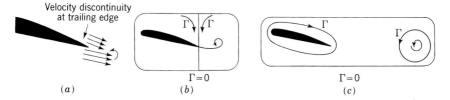

Fig. 13.19. Life history of the starting vortex.

shown in Fig. 13.17c. Vertical symmetry of the flow about the cylinder requires that the forward stagnation point move downward by the same angle. This in turn maps a new location of the forward stagnation point on the airfoil, and such a shift also takes place in the real flow. We see, then, that a circulation has become established about the airfoil, the magnitude of which is determined by the location of the stagnation points on the corresponding cylinder. The lift may then be determined analytically by Eq. (13.39).

Although the Joukowski hypothesis appears perfectly reasonable, we must investigate whether or not nature will actually perform this adjustment of the stagnation point to the cusp of the airfoil profile. Our acceptance of this hypothesis is complicated by the perfectly valid theorem of Thomson (Lord Kelvin), which states that "the circulation around a closed curve in the fluid does not change with time if one moves with the fluid." How is a circulation created around the airfoil where none existed before? The answer was first suggested by Prandtl and has been well substantiated with photographs. He showed that the initial separation point at the cusp caused a *starting vortex* to form, as shown in Fig. 13.19a. In order to satisfy Thomson's theorem, an equal and opposite circulation must automatically be generated around the foil (Fig. 13.19b). After this circulation has been established, the starting vortex breaks off and is left behind as the airplane moves forward, but just to satisfy Thomson's theorem, the starting vortex keeps whirling around until it dies out from viscous effects (Fig. 13.19c). The net circulation around a curve including the profile and this vortex is still zero. When the airfoil comes to a stop or changes its angle of attack, new vortices are formed to effect the necessary change in circulation.[1]

13.13. INDUCED DRAG ON AIRFOIL OF FINITE LENGTH

The discussion of lift has so far been limited to strictly two-dimensional flow. When the foil or lifting vane is of finite length in a free fluid, how-

[1] For photographs and further details, see L. Prandtl and O. G. Tietjens, "Applied Hydro- and Aeromechanics," p. 160, McGraw-Hill Book Company, New York, 1934.

ever, there are end conditions which affect both the lift and the drag. Since the pressure on the underside of the vane is greater than that on the upper side, fluid will escape around the ends of the vane and there will be a general flow outward from the center to the ends along the bottom of the vane and inward from the ends to the center along the top. The movement of the fluid upward around the ends of the vane results in small tip vortices which are cast off from the wing tips. In theory, the Thomson theorem still holds, for the tip vortices are of equal and opposite magnitude. If the circulation is computed about a hypothetical path passing through the foil and along the axes of the tip and starting vortices, as shown in Fig. 13.20, it will still add up to zero. Practically, of course, the circulation about the foil continues to exist, but the tip and starting vortices soon die out from viscous resistance.

The closed path consisting of the finite wing, the tip vortices, and the starting vortices of Fig. 13.20 constitutes a large vortex ring (actually a horseshoe when the starting vortices have died out) inside of which there is a downward velocity induced by the vortices. Prandtl showed this induced, or *downwash*, velocity U_i to be a constant if the wing is so constructed as to produce an elliptical distribution of lift over a given span. The downwash changes the attitude of the foil in the stream, decreasing the effective angle of attack by $\epsilon = \arctan{(U_i/U)}$, as shown in Fig. 13.21.

The wing may now be analyzed on the basis of a foil of infinite length set in a stream of uniform velocity U_0, at angle of attack $\alpha_0 = \alpha - \epsilon$. The lift F_{L0} generated from the circulation about the infinite foil must be normal to U_0. This force is seen to be resolved into two components, the true lift F_L normal to U and a component parallel to U called the *induced drag* F_{Di}. In conformity with our other drag terms, we represent the

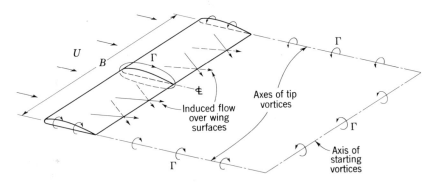

Fig. 13.20. Wing of finite span.

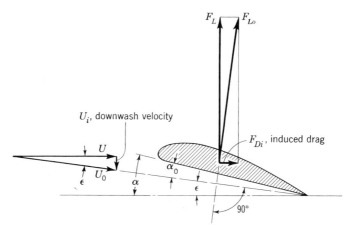

Fig. 13.21.   Definition sketch for induced drag.

induced drag in the standard form

$$F_{Di} = C_{Di}\rho \frac{V^2}{2} A \qquad (13.41)$$

It is now necessary to distinguish between the two- and three-dimensional cases of drag.   The skin friction and pressure drag discussed earlier in this chapter will be lumped into the *profile drag* F_{D0}, which includes all drag forces acting on the profile of infinite length.   The total drag on the finite span is then the sum of the profile and induced drags, or

$$F_D = F_{D0} + F_{Di} \qquad (13.42)$$

As the angle ϵ is small,

$$U_0 \approx U \qquad F_{L0} \approx F_L \qquad F_{Di} \approx \epsilon F_L$$

It should be noted at this point that in addition to expressing the lift force by Eq. (13.39), it is convenient to express it as

$$F_L = C_L\rho \frac{V^2}{2} A \qquad (13.43)$$

where C_L is the lift coefficient, and A is the projected area of the airfoil or body normal to the lift vector.

The computations for the elliptical distribution of lift are too complex to appear here, but they result in the simple relation

$$\frac{U_i}{U} = \epsilon\text{(radians)} = \frac{C_L}{\pi(B/c)} \qquad (13.44)$$

where B is the span, and c is the mean chord.   From Eqs. (13.41), (13.43), and (13.44), together with the above expression for F_{Di}, we have

$$C_{Di} = \frac{C_L{}^2}{\pi(B/c)} \qquad (13.45)$$

and finally, for the coefficient of total drag on a foil of finite length,

$$C_D = C_{Do} + \frac{C_L{}^2}{\pi(B/c)} \qquad (13.46)$$

As would be expected, C_{Di} is seen to depend on the lift coefficient, i.e., the angle of attack and the *aspect ratio* B/c. For zero lift or infinite aspect ratio the induced drag would be zero. These equations are important in comparing data for an airfoil tested at one aspect ratio with data for another foil at a different aspect ratio.

It remains to explain how the induced drag, occurring as it does in the ideal-fluid theory, fits into the D'Alembert paradox, which states that there is no drag on a body in ideal flow. The work done against the flow by the induced drag is conserved in the kinetic energy of the tip vortices cast from the ends of the foil. In real fluid, evidence of the tip vortices may frequently be seen in the form of *vapor trails* extending for miles across the sky. The decreased temperature caused by the decreased pressure at the center of the vortex causes condensation of the moisture in the air.

13.14. LIFT AND DRAG DIAGRAMS

A wealth of data on the lift and drag of various airfoils has been obtained from wind-tunnel tests. The results of such tests may be presented graphically as plots of the lift and drag coefficients vs. the angle of attack. Since the efficiency of the airfoil is measured by the ratio of lift to drag, the value of C_L/C_D is generally plotted also. These three curves can be combined neatly into a single curve, suggested by Prandtl, known as a *polar diagram* (Fig. 13.22).

The coordinates of the polar diagram are the lift and drag coefficients, while the angles of attack are represented by different points along the curve. The ratio of lift to drag is the slope of the line from the origin to the curve at any point. Evidently, the maximum value of the ratio occurs when this line is tangent to the curve. The lift is seen to increase with the angle of attack up to the *point of stall*. Beyond this point the boundary layer along the upper surface of the foil separates and creates a deep turbulent wake.

The polar diagram is notably instructive with regard to the drag coefficient, consisting of the coefficients of profile and induced drag as

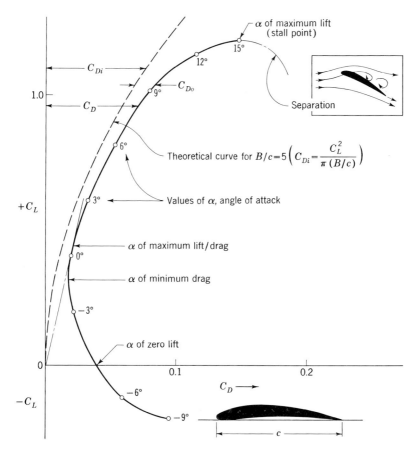

Fig. 13.22. Polar diagram for wing of aspect ratio 5. (*Curve from L. Prandtl and O. G. Tietjens, "Applied Hydro- and Aeromechanics," p. 152, McGraw-Hill Book Company, New York, 1934.*)

shown in Eq. (13.46). The dashed line in Fig. 13.22 is the parabola of Eq. (13.45). For an aspect ratio of 5, as shown, the induced drag is a major part of the total drag. For greater aspect ratios the parabola remains closer to the vertical axis, and the total drag is correspondingly decreased.

The polar diagram of a Clark Y airfoil, rectangular in plan, 6-ft chord by 36-ft span, is shown in Fig. 13.23. It will be observed that the angle of attack is read from a geometric reference which has little meaning by itself. The important reference angle is the angle of attack for zero lift, in this case $-5.6°$. In general, this is also the angle for minimum drag.

The lift coefficient can be shown theoretically to be given by

$$C_L = 2\pi\eta\alpha_0'$$ (13.47)

where α_0' is the angle of attack (for the airfoil of infinite span) measured in radians from the attitude of no lift, and η is a correction factor for frictional effects, having a value of about 0.9 for modern airfoil sections.

It will be recalled from Sec. 13.13 that the induced-drag theory assumed an elliptical distribution of lift over the span of the finite airfoil. For the rectangular airfoil the expressions for induced angle of attack

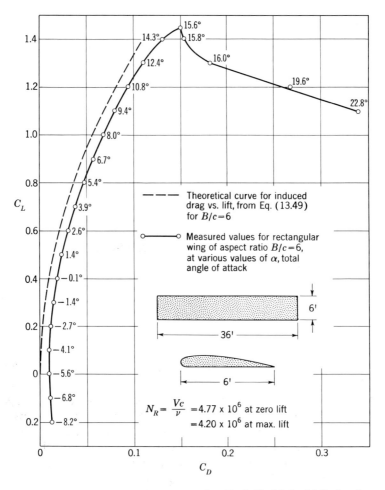

Fig. 13.23. Polar diagram for rectangular Clark Y airfoil of 6-ft chord by 36-ft span. (*Data from A. Silverstein, NACA Rept. 502, p. 15, 1934.*)

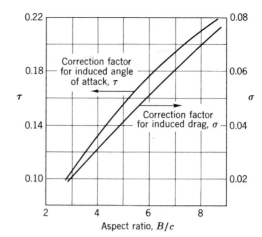

Fig. 13.24. Correction factors for transforming rectangular airfoils from finite to infinite aspect ratio. (*From A. Silverstein, NACA Rept. 502, Fig. 7, 1934.*)

and induced-drag coefficient given in Eqs. (13.44) and (13.45) must be corrected as follows:

$$\epsilon(\text{radians}) = \frac{C_L}{\pi(B/c)}(1 + \tau) \tag{13.48}$$

and
$$C_{Di} = \frac{C_L{}^2}{\pi(B/c)}(1 + \sigma) \tag{13.49}$$

where τ and σ are correction factors given in Fig. 13.24.

Illustrative example 13.7: For a rectangular Clark Y airfoil of 6-ft chord by 36-ft span, find the value of the friction coefficient η if the angle of attack $\alpha = 5.4°$ when the wing is moving at 300 fps through standard atmosphere at altitude 10,000 ft. Find the weight which the wing will carry and the horsepower required to drive it.

From Fig. 13.23, with $\alpha = 5.4°$, $C_L = 0.8$, $C_D = 0.047$. From Fig. 13.24, for $B/c = 6$, $\tau = 0.175$.

From Eq. (13.48),

$$\epsilon = \frac{0.8}{\pi(36/6)}(1 + 0.175) = 0.0498 \text{ rad} = 2.85°$$

From Fig. 13.21, $\alpha_0 = \alpha - \epsilon = 5.40 - 2.85 = 2.55°$. Since angle of zero lift is $-5.6°$,

$$\alpha_0' = 2.55 + 5.6 = 8.15° = 0.1424 \text{ rad}$$

From Eq. (13.47),

$$\eta = \frac{C_L}{2\pi\alpha_0'} = \frac{0.8}{2\pi \times 0.1424} = 0.894$$

The wing will support a weight equal to the lift force,

$$F_L = C_L\rho\frac{V^2}{2}Bc$$

From Appendix 3, Table A.2, at 10,000 ft, $\rho = 0.001756$ slug/ft^3.

$$F_L = 0.8 \times 0.001756 \times \frac{(300)^2}{2} \times 36 \times 6 = 13,680 \text{ lb}$$

while

$$F_D = \frac{0.047}{0.8} \times 13,680 = 803 \text{ lb}$$

$$\text{Horsepower required} = \frac{803 \times 300}{550} = 438 \text{ hp}$$

PROBLEMS

13.1. Commencing with the general equation for a parabola $u = ay^2 + by + c$, derive the velocity distribution of Eq. (13.8) in the dimensionless form shown.

13.2. For the parabolic velocity distribution of Eq. (13.8), derive the numerical values of α and β of 0.133 and 2.0, respectively.

13.3. Derive Eq. (13.18) along the lines suggested in the text.

13.4. For the Prandtl seventh-root law given in Eq. (13.19) derive the value of $\alpha = 0.0972$ for the turbulent boundary layer.

13.5. Derive Eq. (13.21) from the information given.

13.6. Demonstrate the equality of the two expressions of Eq. (13.27).

13.7. A smooth, flat plate 12 ft wide and 2.5 ft long (parallel to the flow) is immersed in water at 60°F flowing at an undisturbed velocity of 2 fps. Find the thickness of the boundary layer and the shear stress (a) at the center and (b) at the trailing edge of the plate, assuming a laminar boundary layer over the whole plate. Also, find the total friction drag on one side of the plate.

13.8. Assume that the boundary layer of Prob. 13.7 is disturbed near the leading edge. Compute the corresponding quantities for the turbulent boundary layer covering the whole plate, and compare the results.

13.9. For the critical Reynolds number of 350,000 for transition from laminar to turbulent flow in the boundary layer, find the corresponding critical Reynolds number for flow in a circular pipe. How does this compare with the value given in Chap. 8? (*Hint:* Consider the boundary-layer thickness to correspond to the radius of the pipe in laminar flow, while the undisturbed velocity U of the boundary-layer theory represents the centerline velocity u_{max} of the pipe flow.)

13.10. A streamlined train is 300 ft long, with sides 9 ft high and the top 9 ft wide. Assuming the skin-friction drag on sides and top to be equal to that on one side of a flat plate 27 ft wide and 300 ft long, compute the horsepower required to overcome the skin-friction drag when the train is traveling at 100 mph through standard atmosphere air at sea level.

13.11. A smooth, thin, flat plate with sharpened edges is 10 by 2 ft and is submerged in water the temperature of which is 60°F. If it moves through the water with a velocity of 1.22 fps in the direction of the 10-ft length, what is the total drag?

13.12. A harpoon is $\frac{3}{4}$ in. in diameter and 5 ft long, with a sharp tip. If this harpoon is launched in the water at 60°F at a speed of 25 fps, find the friction drag. What will be the maximum thickness of the boundary layer?

13.13. An airplane wing having a chord length parallel to the flow of 6.5 ft moves through standard atmospheric air at an altitude of 10,000 ft and a speed of 250 mph. Find the critical roughness for a point one-tenth the chord length back from the leading edge. Find the surface drag on a section of this wing of 20 ft span.

13.14. It is well known that when one is at the beach one can lie down to get out of the wind. Suppose the wind velocity 6 ft above the beach is 20 fps. Approximately what would be the velocity at 0.5 ft and at 1.0 ft above ground level?

13.15. Compare the values of C_f as computed by Eqs. (13.24) and (13.25) for $N_R = 10^7$.

13.16. A flat plate 20 ft long is towed at 6 fps through a liquid ($\gamma = 50$ pcf, $\mu = 0.00026$ lb-sec/ft^2). Determine the drag on the plate. Plot the boundary-layer profile, showing its thickness along the plate. Plot the local shear stress τ_0 as a function of x, and determine the area under this curve. Compare this value with the computed value of the drag. Assume that the boundary-layer changes from laminar to turbulent at a Reynolds number of 300,000.

13.17. Refer to the harpoon of Prob. 13.12. Determine the drag on the harpoon for various velocities from 0 to 50 fps. Consider movement through (a) 60°F water; (b) 60°F air at sea level; and (c) 60°F air at elevation 5,000 ft. Plot curves of drag vs. velocity.

13.18. Refer to the plate of Prob. 13.16. Make the necessary calculations to plot drag vs. velocity for velocities ranging from 0 to 50 fps.

13.19. A steel sphere ($s = 7.8$) of diameter 0.25 in. is released in a tank of oil ($\gamma = 52$ pcf). The sphere is observed to have a terminal velocity of 2.0 fpm. What is the viscosity of the oil?

13.20. What will be the terminal velocity of the sphere of Prob. 13.19 in 100°F water? Assume negligible wall effect.

13.21. Compute the drag on a 15-in.-diameter sphere from wind under sea-level conditions. Plot drag vs. velocity for a range of velocities from 0 to 100 fps.

13.22. Repeat Prob. 13.21 for wind at 10,000-ft elevation.

13.23. A metal ball of diameter 1.0 ft and weight 90 lb is dropped from a boat into the ocean. Determine the maximum velocity the ball will achieve as it falls through the water. Properties of ocean water: $\rho = 2.0$ slugs/ft^3, $\mu = 3.3 \times 10^{-5}$ lb-sec/ft^2.

13.24. Suppose a well-streamlined automobile has a body form corresponding roughly to the airship hull of Fig. 13.9, while a poorly streamlined car has a body approximating the 1:0.75 oblate ellipsoid, each with a diameter of 6 ft. Find the horsepower required to overcome air resistance in each of the two cases if the velocity is 60 mph through standard air at sea level (Appendix 3, Table A.2).

13.25. It is desired to calculate approximately the pressure drag on the streamlined train of Prob. 13.10. As a rough approximation, assume that the nose and tail of the train are of the shape of the two halves of the prolate ellipsoid of Fig. 13.9, of 9 ft diameter. Find the drag on the ellipsoid (pressure drag on the train), and compare with the skin-friction drag on the train determined earlier.

13.26. Suppose that the 10- by 2-ft flat plate of Prob. 13.11 is dragged through the water at the same velocity as before, but with the flat side normal to the direction of motion. What is the approximate drag force, and by what per cent is it increased over the result of Prob. 13.11? [*Hint:* Assume that the drag coefficient for the plate of finite length is in the same ratio to the coefficient for the infinite plate as is the ratio of coefficients for the finite cylinder ($L/D = 5$) and the infinite cylinder of Fig. 13.11, for the same Reynolds number.]

13.27. Compare the velocity of a 0.1-in.-diameter bubble of air rising through water with that of a 0.1-in. drop of water falling through air. Assume standard air at sea level and water at the same temperature.

13.28. The drag coefficient for a hemispherical shell with the concave side upstream is approximately 1.33 if $N_R > 10^3$. Find the diameter of parachute required to provide a fall velocity no greater than that caused by jumping from an 8-ft height, if the total load is 200 lb. Assume standard air at sea level.

13.29. Find the rate of fall of a particle of sand ($s = 2.56$) in water at 60°F if the particle may be assumed spherical in shape and the diameter is (*a*) 0.1 mm; (*b*) 1.0 mm; (*c*) 10 mm.

13.30. Particles of sediment are removed from water supplies by continuous-flow settling basins so designed that the particles fall to the bottom while they are detained in the basin. To settle the 1-mm particle of Prob. 13.29, what should be the ratio of depth to detention time, in feet per second? Show that this quantity is exactly the same as the rate of discharge through the basin divided by its surface area. (*Note:* This quantity is called the *overflow rate* and is the first criterion in the design of any settling basin.)

13.31. A regulation football is approximately 6.78 in. in diameter and weighs 14.5 oz. Its shape is not greatly different from the prolate ellipsoid of Fig. 13.9. Find the resistance when the ball is passed through still air (14.7 psia and 80°F) at a velocity of 40 fps. What is the deceleration at the beginning of the trajectory? Assuming no change in drag coefficient, find the percentage change in resistance if the air temperature is 20°F.

13.32. An eight-oar racing shell is traveling through the water at a mean velocity of 12 mph. Assume each oar is 9 ft long, with a length of 6 ft from the oarlock to the center of the "spoon," which may be supposed to have a projected area of 120 in.² and a drag coefficient equal to that of a disk. If the "stroke" is 32 cycles/min and if each oarsman sweeps a right angle in one-fourth of his rowing cycle, what is the maximum thrust of the oars? It must be assumed that the shell moves at something less (say, 20 per cent) than its mean velocity when the oars are in the water. The maximum velocity occurs during the backstroke when the oarsmen shift their weight toward the stern. Why?

13.33. Referring to Prob. 13.32, the oarsman on his backstroke moves at half the angular velocity of his forward stroke, while the shell moves at perhaps 10 per cent above its mean velocity. Find the drag resulting from a "feathered" oar vs. an unfeathered one, in percentage of the forward thrust from Prob. 13.32.

13.34. Find the bending moment at the base of a cylindrical radio antenna 0.30 in. in diameter extended to 6 ft in length on an automobile traveling through standard air at 80 mph.

13.35. What frequency of oscillation is produced by a 60-mph wind of standard air blowing across a ⅛-in.-diameter wire?

13.36. If each of the projectile forms I and IV of Fig. 13.13 represents a 1,000-lb bomb having a diameter of 20 in., find the terminal velocities of each form in standard air at sea level, and compare the two.

13.37. With the aid of Fig. 13.17c, and commencing with Eq. (13.38), derive the equations and fill in the steps leading to Eq. (13.39). Take care to account for all changes in sign.

13.38. Calculate the value of the lift coefficient for the rotating cylinder in Illustrative Example 13.6, assuming the effective circulation to be half the theoretical. If the drag coefficient may be assumed to be unchanged by the rotation of the cylinder, find the total force of the wind on the rotor and its direction.

13.39. Assume the rotor of Illustrative Example 13.6 to be installed upright on a ship which is proceeding due north at 30 fps. The wind has an *absolute* velocity of 50 fps due east. If the drag coefficient of the cylinder is 1.0 and the "lines" of stagnation are separated by 120° on the rotor, find approximately the component of the total air force on the rotor in the direction of the ship's motion. Assume standard air.

13.40. Consider a cylinder of radius a in a stream of ideal fluid in which the undisturbed velocity and pressure are V and p_0 and the density is ρ. Utilizing Eq. (13.36) and the Bernoulli theorem, evaluate the dimensionless pressure coefficient $(p - p_0)/(\rho V^2/2)$ for every 10° over the surface of one quadrant of the cylinder, and plot to scale, measuring the pressure radially from the cylinder surface. What is the actual pressure in pounds per square inch on the surface of a cylinder 1 ft in diameter, 70° from the forward stagnation point, if the cylinder is 20 ft under the free surface of a stream of water at 60°F, flowing at 10 fps?

13.41. Suppose a circulation of 20 ft²/sec to be superposed about the cylinder of Prob. 13.40. Find the location of the stagnation points and the lift for a length of 30 ft.

13.42. A double stagnation point is observed to occur on a cylinder 3 ft in diameter, rotating in a stream of standard air (sea level) having a velocity of 50 fps. Find the lift force per foot of the cylinder. What is the lift coefficient?

13.43. There have often been arguments over the validity and extent of the curve of a pitched baseball. According to tests (*Life*, July 27, 1953), a pitched baseball was found to rotate at 1,400 rpm while traveling at 43 mph. The horizontal projection of the trajectory revealed a smooth curve of about 800 ft radius. If the ball were 9 in. in circumference and weighed 5 oz, find the transverse force required to produce the observed curvature. Assuming the shape of the ball to be roughly that of a cylinder having a diameter equal to the ball's diameter and a length of two-thirds its diameter, find the value of the circulation that would be required to produce the transverse force. Compare this with that obtained by assuming no slip at the equator of the ball. Assume standard air at sea level.

13.44. An airplane having a Clark Y airfoil wing of 6-ft chord by 36-ft span, with polar diagram given in Fig. 13.23, weighs 1,500 lb. Neglecting the aerodynamic forces on the fuselage and tail, find the speed required to get the airplane off the ground.   Find the horsepower required.   Find the circulation about the wing and the strength of the starting vortex. Assume standard air at sea level and angle of attack for maximum ratio of lift to drag.

13.45. A wing of 40-ft span and 320 ft² "plan-form" area moves horizontally through standard atmosphere at 10,000 ft with a velocity of 200 fps.   If the wing supports 3,000 lb, find (a) the required value of the lift coefficient; (b) the downwash velocity, assuming an elliptical distribution of lift over the span; (c) the induced drag.

13.46. If the plan form of the wing in Prob. 13.45 were rectangular, what would be the proper values of the induced angle of attack and induced drag?

13.47. For the Clark Y airfoil of Fig. 13.23, evaluate the friction coefficient η of Eq. (13.47) for values of C_L of 0.2, 0.6, 1.0, and 1.4.

13.48. A kite has a shape corresponding roughly to a rectangular airfoil of 2-ft chord and 4-ft span.   When rigged as shown in the figure, the guideline exerts a tension of 11 lb when the wind velocity is 30 mph in standard air at 1,000 ft altitude.   Evaluate C_L, C_{D0}, and the friction coefficient η.

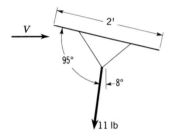

Fig. Prob. 13.48

13.49. A sailplane weighing 400 lb including its load has a 4-ft-chord by 24-ft-span wing of the Clark Y section.   Assuming that its characteristics are the same as those for the larger wing of the same aspect ratio shown in Fig. 13.23, find the angle of glide through standard air at 2,000 ft which will produce the greatest horizontal distance range.   Neglect air forces on the fuselage and tail.   (*Note:* The aspect ratio of 6 is here chosen for convenience in working the problem with the available data.   Actually, the sailplane may be constructed with an aspect ratio of about twice this, so as to reduce the induced drag to an absolute minimum.)

13.50. At what angle of glide will the sailplane of Prob. 13.49 reach a minimum velocity of descent; in other words, at what angle will it remain in the air the longest time?   Compare angles and velocities with those obtained in Prob. 13.49.   (*Note:* A trial-and-error type of solution will be required here.)

FOURTEEN

SIMILARITY LAWS AND FACTORS FOR TURBOMACHINES

14.1. TURBOMACHINES

In this text the only hydraulic machines considered are those to which the principles of Chap. 6 may be applied. In all such cases fluid velocity *relative* to the vanes or blades is essential to the action. Such devices are known as *turbomachines*. Another definition is that a turbomachine is one in which there is a change in whirl or angular momentum of the fluid. Such equipment may include turbines of all types: centrifugal and axial-flow pumps for liquids or corresponding compressors for air or other gas; blowers (which develop low pressures only); fans (which move air or other gas with very small pressure change); ship and airplane propellers; fluid couplings; and even windmills. However, limitations of space prevent a complete treatment of all these items.

It will be observed that all the foregoing are devices which rotate. Rotary engines, rotary pumps, and rotary compressors also rotate, but they are all positive-displacement machines with operating characteristics similar to those of reciprocating machines, such as those with a piston in a cylinder. Relative motion of the fluid is not an essential factor in their operation, and they will not be treated in this text.

14.2. EFFICIENCY DEFINITIONS

Turbine. For a turbine of any type, whether steam or hydraulic, the hydraulic efficiency is the ratio of the power delivered to the shaft to the available power of the fluid flowing through the runner, or rotor. The difference between these two powers is the hydraulic friction loss in the machine plus the loss at exit. It was shown in Sec. 6.12 that the work or power delivered to the shaft per unit weight or flow rate, respectively, often called the head utilized, is $h'' = (u_1 V_1 \cos \alpha_1 - u_2 V_2 \cos \alpha_2)/g$. If h is defined as the head available, then the *hydraulic efficiency* is

$$e_h = \frac{h''}{h} \tag{14.1}$$

For the hydraulic turbine h is the gross head for the plant minus the pipe friction.

The mechanical efficiency is the ratio of the power delivered by the machine (at the coupling if one exists) to that delivered by the fluid to the shaft. The difference between these two is equal to the power consumed in mechanical friction in bearings and stuffing boxes and also in disk friction. The latter is the friction between the sides of the rotor and the fluid in the adjacent casing. It is entirely separate from the fluid friction due to flow through the rotor, and is not a function of such flow. If the mechanical losses are represented by fhp (friction horsepower) while the power delivered is bhp (brake horsepower), the *mechanical efficiency* is

$$e_m = \frac{\text{bhp}}{\text{bhp} + \text{fhp}} \tag{14.2}$$

It may be observed that bhp + fhp is analogous to indicated horsepower in a reciprocating engine. For a hydraulic turbine the mechanical efficiency is usually relatively high, such as from 95 to 98 per cent.

In many machines some fluid flows around the outside of the rotor and hence does no work. This leakage thus represents a loss of energy proportional to that available from the total flow. If Q_L represents this leakage, while Q represents the total flow, the *volumetric efficiency* may be defined as

$$e_v = \frac{Q - Q_L}{Q} \tag{14.3}$$

Ordinarily, this leakage loss is a very small percentage and for some machines does not exist, but under unfavorable conditions it is occasionally an important item.

The *total*, or *overall*, *efficiency* of a turbine is

$$e = e_h \times e_m \times e_v = \frac{\text{bhp} \times 550}{Gh} \tag{14.4}$$

The quantity $Gh/550$, which represents the available power input to the turbine, is sometimes designated as *water horsepower*. The total flow is $G = \gamma Q$, but if there is leakage of water which does not flow through the runner, the actual power delivered to the shaft is $\gamma(Q - Q_L)h''$ in foot-pounds per second.

Pump. For a pump, compressor, blower, or fan the efficiencies are analogous to those for a turbine but are inverted. Thus the *hydraulic efficiency* is

$$e_h = \frac{h}{h''} \tag{14.5}$$

where h is the actual head developed by or delivered by the machine, while h'' is the head delivered by the vanes to the fluid. The latter represents the unit work, or power, transmitted through the shaft to the pump.

The *mechanical efficiency* is

$$e_m = \frac{\text{bhp} - \text{fhp}}{\text{bhp}} \tag{14.6}$$

where bhp is the power delivered to the pump shaft at the coupling. This is called *brake horsepower* because it is the brake horsepower of the motor or prime mover which drives the machine. (It is sometimes called *shaft horsepower*.)

If there is any leakage loss from the high-pressure side to the low-pressure side, this represents a loss of power because work has been done upon this fluid. Hence the *volumetric efficiency* is

$$e_v = \frac{Q}{Q + Q_L} \tag{14.7}$$

where Q represents the flow actually delivered.

The *total*, or *overall*, *efficiency*, commonly designated merely as *efficiency*, is

$$e = e_h \times e_m \times e_v = \frac{Gh}{\text{bhp} \times 550} \tag{14.8}$$

Again, $Gh/550$ is called water horsepower. These same definitions apply to compressors, blowers, or fans, but if there is an appreciable change in the density of the fluid, some modifications may be necessary.

14.3. SIMILARITY LAWS

This term is applied to certain general laws of proportionality or similarity. They are useful laws in that they enable us to predict the performance of a given machine under different conditions of operation from those under which it may have been tested. Also, they enable us to predict the performance of a series of *homologous machines* of different sizes from the known performance of any one of the series. Homologous machines are those which are geometrically similar so that one is merely an enlargement or reduction of the other.

Turbine. In Fig. 14.1 is shown a profile of a turbine runner, and in Fig. 6.11 is shown a section in another plane. A turbine runner may be regarded as a special form of orifice in that the flow through it is proportional to an area times a velocity and the latter is some function of $\sqrt{2gh}$. The net circumferential area is $A_c = f\pi DB$, where f is the fractional part of the area that is free space, the vanes taking up the rest. The value of f is of the order of 0.95. For a series of homologous runners $B/D = m = $ constant, and therefore $A_c = f\pi mD^2$.

The radial component of the velocity entering the runner is (Fig. 6.11) $V_r = V_1 \sin \alpha_1 = C_r \sqrt{2gh}$, where C_r is a factor determined by test and influenced by the type of runner, though it is substantially constant for a series of homologous runners. As

$$Q = A_c V_r = (f\pi m C_r \sqrt{2g}) D^2 \sqrt{h}$$

the expression within the parentheses may be replaced by K_q so that

$$Q = K_q D^2 \sqrt{h} \qquad (14.9)$$

where K_q is a constant for a series of homologous runners. Note that K_q has the same dimensions as $\sqrt{g}$.

From Eq. (6.18) torque is a function of ρQ, r_1, r_2, V_1, and V_2. Now r_1 and r_2 are proportional to D, and V_1 and V_2 are both functions of $\sqrt{h}$. Hence torque is proportional to $\rho(D^2 \sqrt{h})D \sqrt{h}$, or

$$T = K_t \gamma D^3 h \qquad (14.10)$$

The rotative speed is $\omega = u/r$, where ω is expressed in radians per second, though for practical engineering purposes it is customary to use

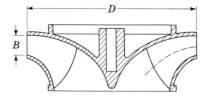

Fig. 14.1. Profile of turbine runner or pump impeller.

revolutions per minute for most hydraulic machinery.   As

$$n = \frac{60\omega}{2\pi} = \frac{60u_1}{\pi D}$$

and u_1 is proportional to $\sqrt{h}$,

$$n = K_n \frac{\sqrt{h}}{D} \tag{14.11}$$

Power $= T\omega$, and as $\omega = 2\pi n/60$, it follows that

$$\text{bhp} = K_p \gamma D^2 h^{3/2} \tag{14.12}$$

Since bhp $= e\gamma Qh/550$, Eq. (14.12) could also have been obtained by inserting in this expression the value of Q from Eq. (14.9).

Pump.   The same Fig. 14.1 will serve to illustrate the case of a pump, but for the centrifugal pump the flow is outward.[1]   There is, however, a practical difference in usage.   For a turbine we are usually interested in its operation under a certain head which is fixed by nature.   For a pump we are usually interested in its operation at a certain rotative speed, determined by the motor which drives it.   For this reason, when dealing with pumps, it is convenient to have n in the equations.

From Eq. (14.11),

$$h = K_1 D^2 n^2 \tag{14.13}$$

and substituting this expression for h in Eq. (14.13), we obtain

$$Q = K_2 D^3 n \tag{14.14}$$

$$T = K_3 \gamma D^5 n^2 \tag{14.15}$$

$$hp = K_4 \gamma D^5 n^3 \tag{14.16}$$

For any one design of a turbine or a pump these constants can be evaluated, preferably from test data, and then used for a series of different sizes, provided they are all homologous.

14.4. PERIPHERAL - VELOCITY FACTOR

For a turbine runner or a pump impeller the ratio of its peripheral velocity to $\sqrt{2gh}$ is almost universally denoted by ϕ.   Thus, for a turbine,

$$u_1 = \phi \sqrt{2gh} \tag{14.17}$$

---

[1] For the sake of brevity the term *pump* will be used, though the similarity laws apply not only to centrifugal and axial-flow pumps but also to blowers and fans of different types and even to centrifugal and axial-flow compressors, with due allowance for the variation in fluid density where there is a material change in pressure within the machine.

while for a centrifugal pump,

$$u_2 = \phi \sqrt{2gh} \qquad \text{or} \qquad h = \frac{1}{\phi^2} \frac{u_2^2}{2g} \qquad\qquad (14.18)$$

inasmuch as u_1 and u_2 are the designations of the peripheral speeds of these respective machines. (For an axial-flow machine the vane-tip speed will be designated as u_t and the factor as ϕ_t.) Omitting subscripts,

$$\omega = \frac{u}{r} = \frac{\phi \sqrt{2gh}}{r}$$

but for practical engineering use,

$$n = \frac{60u}{\pi D} = \frac{60\phi \sqrt{2gh}}{\pi D} \qquad\qquad (14.19)$$

which may be reduced to the convenient form

$$nD = 153.2\phi \sqrt{h} \qquad\qquad (14.20)$$

For any machine its peripheral velocity might be any value from zero up to some maximum under a given head, and ϕ would consequently vary through as wide a range. But the speed which is of the most practical significance is that at which the efficiency is a maximum. The value of this dimensionless factor for this particular speed may be designated as ϕ_e, but frequently the subscript is omitted. It is the numerical value of ϕ_e that would usually be inserted into Eq. (14.20).

The numerical value of ϕ_e depends upon the type of the machine, but for a series of homologous machines it is a constant. Its numerical value in a specific case may be estimated by theory, but practically it is determined by test.

14.5. DIMENSIONLESS RELATIONS

It has already been stated that the radial component of velocity of the fluid might be expressed as

$$V_r = C_r \sqrt{2gh}$$

where C_r is a dimensionless factor the value of which depends upon the design of the machine in question. In similar manner we may write

$$V_1 = C_1 \sqrt{2gh} \qquad \text{and} \qquad V_2 = C_2 \sqrt{2gh} \qquad\qquad (14.21)$$

where V_1 and V_2 represent the absolute velocities of the water at entrance to and exit from the rotor. In the case of the Pelton waterwheel $C_1 = C_v$, the velocity coefficient of the nozzle, but for other machines its value would be entirely different.   It not only varies with the type of machine, but for a given machine its value varies with the relation between peripheral velocity and head.   The same comments might be made of C_2.   As in the case of ϕ, there is one value corresponding to the point of maximum efficiency, which might be distinguished as C_e.

For a turbine the hydraulic efficiency has been defined as

$$e_h = \frac{h''}{h} = \frac{u_1 V_1 \cos \alpha_1 - u_2 V_2 \cos \alpha_2}{gh}$$

so that if these various velocities are replaced by the relations just given, the hydraulic efficiency may be expressed as

$$e_h = 2\phi \left(C_1 \cos \alpha_1 - \frac{r_2}{r_1} C_2 \cos \alpha_2 \right) \tag{14.22}$$

which shows that the hydraulic efficiency of a turbine is independent of the head.   This is a very important practical deduction.   Both the mechanical-friction and leakage losses are relatively small, so that a considerable variation in their values has but slight effect upon the total efficiency.

As a very close approximation it may therefore be stated that the efficiency is constant for any constant value of ϕ inasmuch as C_1, C_2, and α_2 are all related to ϕ in some definite manner for any one design.   This means that for any set of homologous machines, so long as the ϕ's are the same, the shapes of the velocity triangles at entrance and discharge are the same, regardless of the size of the machines or the heads under which they operate.   Thus, for any *one* value of ϕ, there are *corresponding values for all the other quantities or factors as determined by the similarity laws.* There is one value of ϕ for which the efficiency is a maximum.   This is commonly designated as ϕ_e.   For maximum efficiency of any one type of machine there is only *one shape* of the velocity triangle at entrance and only one for that at exit, and similarly, there are *unique values for all other quantities or factors.*

The hydraulic efficiency. is independent of the head, because the hydraulic losses all vary at the same rate as does the water-horsepower input.   But the mechanical-friction losses do not increase at as fast a rate with increasing head and speed.   Thus, in reality, there is a slight increase in total efficiency as the head increases.   The change cannot be great since the mechanical-friction losses are rarely more than about 2 per cent.

A similar analysis applied to the pump shows that its hydraulic efficiency is also independent of the head or speed so long as ϕ is constant. For any one value of ϕ, both the hydraulic losses and the water horsepower vary as n^3, but the mechanical losses vary approximately as n^2.   Hence there is a slight increase in total efficiency with higher speeds of the same machine. There is a limit to this, however, since with higher fluid velocities there will be a lower pressure at intake for the same setting, and eventually cavitation will cause the efficiency to drop. This can be offset only by installing the pump at a lower elevation relative to the source.

14.6. RESTRICTION ON USE OF SIMILARITY LAWS

Similarity laws are of great practical value and are also reliable, but they are restricted to certain conditions in their application. Thus, in comparing two machines of different sizes, the two must be homologous, as has been stated previously. But even for the same machine there is a restriction, which will now be explained.

Consider Fig. 14.2, which may represent the rate of discharge through a hydraulic turbine at different rotative speeds under a constant head, which we shall assume to be h_2. There is no simple or accurate theory which will determine this relationship, and so the curve shown must be established by test. There is thus no theoretical relation between any two points on the *same* curve. But suppose we have the complete curve from experiment and we wish to compute the corresponding curve for some other head, such as h_1. This may be done by the use of Eqs. (14.9) and (14.11) together, but not by one of them alone. Thus, if we use the former equation to give $Q_1 = Q_2 \sqrt{h_1/h_2}$, this value will be found only at a speed $n_1 = n_2 \sqrt{h_1/h_2}$. As both Q and n are seen to vary as $\sqrt{h}$, it follows that corresponding points are on straight lines through the origin.

If n varies as $\sqrt{h}$, Eq. (14.20) shows that ϕ must be constant, and this is the limitation that must be imposed on use of the similarity laws. If corresponding points on the two curves are thus related, there is also a definite relation between any other coordinates, such as horsepower or other values, but in any case the two values are for the same value of ϕ.

As a further illustration of this principle, consider Fig. 14.3, which

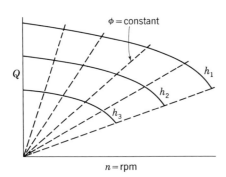

Fig. 14.2. Performance at various constant heads.

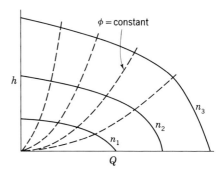

Fig. 14.3. Performance at various constant speeds.

shows the relation between h and Q for a centrifugal pump running at some constant speed n_1. Again, this curve is one which cannot be calculated by any simple or accurate theory and is determined experimentally. At some other speed n_2, Eq. (14.13) gives us $h_2 = h_1(n_2/n_1)^2$, but at the same time Eq. (14.14) gives $Q_2 = Q_1(n_2/n_1)$. Thus corresponding values for h and Q at the same value of ϕ lie along parabolas through the origin. Hence, for the similarity laws to apply, ϕ must in every case be the same for the two points, but the nature of the constant ϕ-lines on any diagram depends upon the particular coordinates.

14.7. SPECIFIC SPEED

Turbines. A most useful practical factor for turbines is the expression commonly known as *specific speed*. Using the expression for Q from Sec. 14.3,

$$\text{bhp} = \frac{e\gamma Qh}{550} = \left(\frac{e\gamma f\pi \sqrt{2g}}{550} mC_r \right) D^2 h^{3/2}$$

Substituting in this equation the value of D^2 as obtained from Eq. (14.19), we obtain

$$\text{bhp} = \left[\frac{e\gamma f(2g)^{3/2}(60)^2}{550\pi} \phi^2 mC_r \right] \frac{h^{5/2}}{n^2}$$

It is seen that, in addition to numerical constants, the expression in brackets contains certain design factors. If the expression within the brackets is represented by n_s^2, then, taking the square root of this equation and rearranging, we obtain the *specific speed*, which is

$$n_s = \frac{n\sqrt{\text{bhp}}}{h^{5/4}} \tag{14.23}$$

Although under a given head any value of rotative speed and corresponding brake horsepower might be used, the only ones that will yield a significant value for n_s are those for which the efficiency is a maximum. Hence the value of n to be used should be the most efficient speed for the given head, and the brake horsepower should be that for maximum efficiency at that speed.

The only justification for the term specific speed is that if the turbine is made of such a size as to develop 1 bhp under 1 ft head, then n_s would be the revolutions per minute, but the dimensions of n_s are really $F^{½}L^{-¾}T^{-³⁄₂}$. An inspection of the terms in the brackets will show that n_s is a function of the design factors $\phi \sqrt{mC_r}$, and therefore its value depends on the design of the turbine. In fact, it might better be called *type characteristic*, or some similar name, because it does indicate the type of the turbine.

Pumps. A specific-speed factor is equally useful for pumps, blowers, and fans, but it will appear in a different form. In the case of a turbine, we are primarily interested in the power it will deliver, whereas in the case of a pump or similar machine, we are primarily interested in the quantity rate at which it will deliver fluid. Substituting the value of D^2 from Eq. (14.19) in the expression for Q in Sec. 14.3, we obtain

$$Q = \left[\frac{f(2g)^{³⁄₂}(60)^2}{\pi} \phi^2 m C_r \right] \frac{h^{³⁄₂}}{n^2}$$

As in the case of the turbine, the expression in brackets contains not only numerical constants but also design factors, and if this expression is represented by n_s^2, we obtain the *specific speed*

$$n_s = \frac{n \sqrt{Q}}{h^{¾}} \tag{14.24}$$

For a given pump this expression might have any value from zero at no flow to infinity at maximum Q and zero head, but the only value that is significant is that at the point of maximum efficiency.

In the case of fans, it is customary to express their capacities in terms of cubic feet per minute, while for pumps handling liquids, it is customary to use cubic feet per second for large flows and to use gallons per minute for most usual capacities. Employing this common unit,

$$N_s = \frac{n \sqrt{\text{gpm}}}{h^{¾}} \tag{14.25}$$

where $N_s = 21.2n_s$. Similarly to the turbine, the specific speed for a pump is the revolutions per minute for a pump of such a size as to deliver unit volume of fluid per unit time at a head of 1 ft, although the actual dimensions are $L^{¾}T^{-³⁄₂}$. The real value of the expression is that it indicates the type of pump (or fan) for any given conditions.

For a multistage pump the value of h to be used in computing specific speed is the head per stage. For a double-suction pump the specific speed is sometimes based on the total capacity, but in general it is preferable to compute it by using one-half of the total capacity on the basis that a double-suction impeller is the equivalent of two single-suction impellers placed back to back.

PROBLEMS

14.1. At a hydroelectric plant the difference in elevation between the surface of the water at intake and at the tailrace is 600 ft. When the flow is 80 cfs, the friction loss in the penstock is 60 ft and the head utilized by the turbine is 460 ft. The mechanical friction in the turbine is 100 hp, and the leakage loss is 3 cfs. Find (a) hydraulic efficiency; (b) volumetric efficiency; (c) power delivered to shaft; (d) brake horsepower; (e) mechanical efficiency; (f) overall efficiency.

14.2. A turbine runs at 150 rpm, discharges 200 cfs, and develops 1,600 bhp under a net head of 81 ft. (a) What is its efficiency? (b) What would be the revolutions per minute, Q, and brake horsepower of the same turbine under a net head of 162 ft for homologous conditions?

14.3. If a homologous turbine to that in Prob. 14.2 has a runner of twice the diameter, what would be the revolutions per minute, Q, and brake horsepower under the same head of 81 ft?

14.4. What are the values of the torque exerted by the runners in Probs. 14.2 and 14.3? What is the specific speed for the runners of Probs. 14.2 and 14.3?

14.5. If ϕ for the runner in Prob. 14.2 is 0.72, what is the diameter of the runner? What, then, are the values of K_q, K_t, K_n, and K_p for that series?

14.6. A centrifugal-pump runner 18 in. in diameter discharges 25 cfs at a head of 100 ft when running at 1,200 rpm. If its efficiency is 85 per cent, what is the brake horsepower? If the same pump were run at 1,800 rpm, what would be h, Q, and brake horsepower for homologous conditions?

14.7. For the pump in Prob. 14.6, what are the values of K_1, K_2, and K_4? What is the specific speed?

14.8. (a) A Pelton waterwheel under a net head of 2,350 ft runs at 450 rpm and delivers 17,500 bhp. What is its specific speed? (b) A reaction turbine under a head of 92 ft runs at 100 rpm and delivers 35,000 bhp. What is its specific speed? (c) If $\phi = 0.46$ for the former and 0.75 for the latter, what is the diameter of each runner?

14.9. A model centrifugal pump is made with a scale ratio of 1:10. The model was tested at 3,600 rpm and delivered 3 cfs at a head of 125 ft with an efficiency of 90 per cent. Assuming the prototype to have an efficiency of 91 per cent and to develop the same head, what will be its speed, capacity, and horsepower required? Liquid pumped is water.

14.10. All dimensions of pump A are one-third as large as the corresponding dimensions of pump B. When operating at 300 rpm, B delivers 100 gpm of water against a head of 50 ft. What must be the rotative speed of A if it is to deliver 100 gpm against a head of 50 ft?

FIFTEEN

IMPULSE TURBINES

15.1. DEFINITION

An impulse turbine, whether for water, steam, or gas, is one in which the total drop in pressure of the fluid takes place in one or more stationary nozzles and there is no change in pressure of the fluid as it flows through the rotating wheel. As there is no pressure variation in flow over the buckets or vanes, the fluid does not fill the passageway between one bucket or vane and the next. Customarily, only a portion of the circumference of the wheel is acted upon by the fluid at any one instant.

The energy of the fluid entering the rotor is in the form of kinetic energy of the jets. In flow over the buckets or vanes of the runner this kinetic energy is absorbed by transformation into the mechanical work delivered to the shaft, a part is dissipated in fluid friction, and there is some residual kinetic energy of the fluid leaving the rotor.

The foregoing statements and the theory presented in this

text apply to all types of turbine, but steam and gas turbines involve thermodynamic principles in addition, and so their complete theory is outside the scope of this book. Because of practical features, the mechanical construction of hydraulic turbines differs widely from that of steam or gas turbines, and physically they bear little resemblance to each other. In this text the descriptive material will be confined to the hydraulic turbine.

15.2. THE HYDRAULIC IMPULSE TURBINE

Several types of hydraulic impulse turbines have been produced in the past, but the only one that has survived is the Pelton wheel (Fig. 15.1), so called in honor of Lester A. Pelton (1829–1908), who contributed much to its development in the early gold-mining days in California. Pelton was granted a patent in 1880 on an improved type of bucket, its principal feature being a *splitter* in the middle, since previously the buckets were merely cups. Later, W. A. Doble brought out the *ellipsoidal* bucket, which is the basis of the modern forms.[1]

15.3. SETTINGS

Impulse turbines are usually set with the shaft horizontal, and there is usually only one jet on a wheel. If an electric generator is driven by one wheel, the generator is mounted between two bearings, with the wheel outside. It is then called a *single-overhung* unit. Often a single generator is driven by two wheels, as in Fig. 15.1, and this is a double-overhung unit.

---

[1] The term *Pelton* is commonly used to designate a type and does not necessarily imply that the wheel has been built by the company bearing that name. In fact, it is the designation commonly used by all European manufacturers.

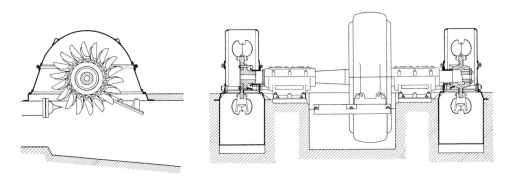

Fig. 15.1. Double-overhung impulse wheel.

Fig. 15.2. Vertical-shaft impulse turbine with six nozzles at the Bridge River plant in British Columbia. Gross head = 1,226 ft, net head = 1,118 ft, 62,000 hp, n = 300 rpm, pitch diameter = 95 in. (*Courtesy of Pelton Water Wheel Co.*)

Occasionally, two or more jets may be employed on one wheel to increase the power of a horizontal-shaft wheel, but more commonly the multijet arrangement is used with a vertical-shaft turbine, as in Fig. 15.2.

15.4. HEAD ON IMPULSE TURBINE

The gross head for a power plant is the difference in elevation between headwater and tailwater, or $Y + z$ in Fig. 15.3. The pressure within the case of an impulse wheel is atmospheric, and consequently this is the pressure at which the jet is discharged. Thus the portion z is unavailable; so the gross head on the wheel itself is Y only. This is also called the *static* head. It is impractical to set the wheel too near the surface of the tailwater because it might then be submerged with any rise in level of the latter. However, as Pelton wheels are usually installed under high heads, the percentage loss due to this setting is small. Thus, if the head is 2,000 ft and z is 10 ft, the loss is only 0.5 per cent.

The net, or effective, head on the wheel is the static head minus the pipe friction losses. Since the nozzle is an integral part of the turbine, the head is that at B in Fig. 15.3; so the effective, or net, head is

$$h = \frac{p_B}{\gamma} + \frac{V_B{}^2}{2g} \tag{15.1}$$

The energy, or head, supplied at the nozzle is expended in four ways. A small amount is lost in fluid friction in the nozzle, a portion is expended in fluid friction over the buckets, kinetic energy is carried away in the water discharged from the buckets, and the rest is delivered to the buckets. Thus

$$h = \left(\frac{1}{C_v{}^2} - 1\right)\frac{V_1{}^2}{2g} + k\frac{v_2{}^2}{2g} + \frac{V_2{}^2}{2g} + h'' \qquad (15.2)$$

where V_1 = jet velocity
$\quad\;\; v_2$ = relative velocity
$\quad\;\; V_2$ = absolute velocity leaving the buckets

The greater part of the mechanical energy delivered to the buckets is transferred to the shaft, but some of it is used in overcoming mechanical friction in the bearings and in windage loss.

15.5. NOZZLES

In any turbine it is necessary that the flow rate be varied in proportion to the load on the machine; and for the impulse wheel this is done by varying the size of the jet, but with as little change in jet velocity as possible. This is accomplished by varying the position of the needle in the needle nozzle of Fig. 15.4. The shape of both nozzle tip and needle should be such as to cause a minimum friction loss for all positions of the needle and also such as to avoid cavitation damage to the needle at any position.

An important feature in attaining high efficiency in an impulse wheel is that the jet be uniform, the ideal being to have all particles of water moving in parallel lines with equal velocities and with no spreading out of the jet. Air friction retards the water on the outside of the jet, and

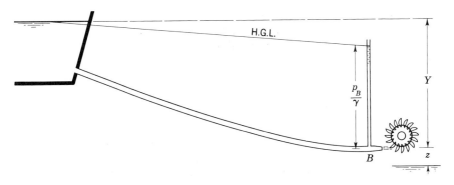

Fig. 15.3

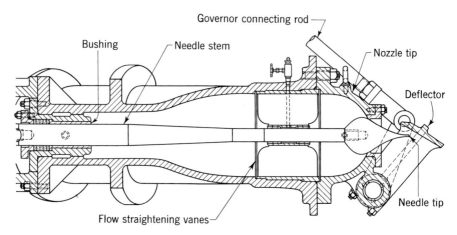

Fig. 15.4.   Needle nozzle with jet deflector.

the needle causes the velocity in the center to be slightly reduced.   Careful design of both nozzle tip and needle will minimize these effects, and a gain in turbine efficiency of several per cent has been made by improved nozzle design producing better jets.

When a needle nozzle has been opened to its maximum amount, the tip of the needle still projects beyond the plane of the orifice, as shown in Fig. 15.8.   Hence the net area of the nozzle opening is less than that of the nozzle tip and should be measured normal to the streamlines.   The jet area at the vena contracta is less than this net area, but as the needle is moved to reduce the nozzle opening, the ratio of jet area to net nozzle area increases.

When the needle nozzle is opened to give the maximum size of jet, the velocity coefficient is usually about 0.98 to 0.99 or even higher.   Thus the nozzle efficiency, as defined in Sec. 11.12, may be 96 to 98 per cent or even more.   As the needle is moved to decrease the nozzle opening, the nozzle efficiency decreases, but it is still above 90 per cent for capacities down to one-half of the maximum flow.   Thus it is a very efficient load-regulating device.

15.6. SPEED REGULATION

It is necessary that the flow of water to a turbine be varied as rapidly as the load changes in order to maintain the speed constant.   In the event of a sudden decrease in load, there must then be an equally abrupt decrease in the quantity of water supplied to the machine.   As impulse wheels are usually installed only in high-head plants, there is necessarily a long pipe, and dangerous water hammer would result if there were a rapid reduction of velocity within it. This may be avoided in several ways.

One means of solving this problem is the use of a jet deflector, as shown in Fig. 15.4. This is a plate which can be moved rapidly by the governor to deflect a portion of the jet so that a decreased amount of water actually hits the buckets. Then the needle can be slowly moved to decrease the flow in the pipe gradually. As this is being done, the deflector is simultaneously withdrawn from the jet.

Another means is the use of an auxiliary needle nozzle below the main one. As the governor rapidly moves the needle to reduce the flow of water to the buckets, at the same time it opens the auxiliary nozzle, which discharges a jet that misses the wheel altogether. Thus there need be no change in flow in the pipe. However, to save wasting water, a delaying mechanism will slowly close the auxiliary nozzle.

Still a third arrangement is the deflecting needle nozzle, where the entire nozzle is movable about a ball-and-socket joint at its base. The governor can then swing the nozzle so that the jet is directed downward from the horizontal, only a portion of it striking the buckets. The nozzle is restored to its initial position as the needle is slowly closed.

It is seen that all these governing arrangements are such as to reduce the flow of water to the impulse wheel rapidly and yet bring about a reduction of flow in the pipeline more slowly and with a minimum waste of water. However, in case of a sudden demand for more power, the governor will move the needle rapidly to provide a bigger nozzle opening, but it will take time for the flow in a long pipe to be accelerated. The only possible aid in this case is to have a big surge chamber (Sec. 12.6) located as close to the power plant as topography permits. Fortunately, while there may be sudden decreases in load, as when a circuit breaker opens, increases in load usually come on more gradually.

15.7. WHEEL CONSTRUCTION

Figure 15.5 shows an impulse runner for a horizontal shaft, while Fig. 15.6 gives the runner for the vertical-shaft unit of Fig. 15.2. In most cases buckets are bolted to a rim, as shown in these two illustrations, but runners are also cast in one piece, as shown in Fig. 15.7.

The three illustrated have been built by the same company. Buckets made by other manufacturers, though differing slightly in detail, are much the same. In all cases there is a notch to permit the bucket to attain a position more nearly tangent to the direction of the jet before the bucket lip intercepts the jet. The jet then strikes a splitter, which divides it so

Fig. 15.5. Runner at Big Creek-2A plant of Southern California Edison Co. Static head = 2,418 ft, net head = 2,200 ft, n = 250 rpm, pitch diameter = 162 in. (This was one of the original runners for 50-cycle generation. All have been replaced by 300-rpm runners for 60-cycle generation.) (*Courtesy of Pelton Water Wheel Co.*)

that equal quantities flow out each side, thus eliminating end thrust on the shaft.

The faces of the buckets are surfaces of double curvature more or less ellipsoidal in shape and are smooth-ground. The buckets are made of bronze or steel. The height and width of the bucket should each be 2.5 to 4 times the jet diameter; otherwise bucket efficiency will suffer. The exact proportions depend upon the ratio of wheel diameter to jet diameter.

15.8. ACTION OF JET

In Fig. 15.8 it is seen that the bucket intercepts the jet at a and, as the bucket moves to b, the particles of water intercepted at a have reached x.

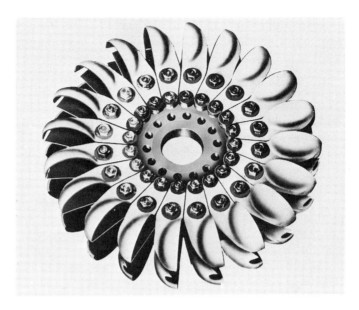

Fig. 15.6. Runner of Fig. 15.2. (*Courtesy of Pelton Water Wheel Co.*)

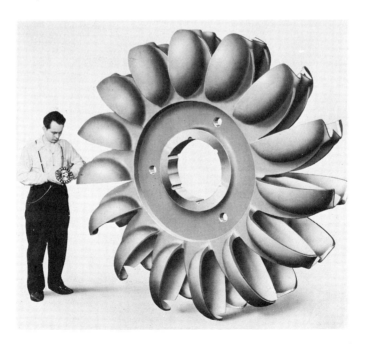

Fig. 15.7. Integral cast runner. (*Courtesy of Pelton Water Wheel Co.*)

In similar fashion, other streamlines are cut off as the bucket moves from a to b, and when the bucket is in position c, the *profile* of the water acting upon it is bx. The last bit of the water to "catch up" with a bucket will be when the bucket is somewhere between c and e. Thus at first the direction of u, the bucket velocity, is downward relative to the direction of the jet; when the bucket splitter is directly below the axis of rotation, u and V_1 will be in the same straight line, and subsequently the direction of u will be upward relative to the direction of the jet. In other words, u varies in direction during the time when the water is entering the bucket, and the angle α varies from α' to α''. Hence, to construct a single triangle for the entrance velocities, it is necessary to use an angle α_1, which is an average value. The average value of this angle will also decrease as the wheel speed increases from zero. The triangle shown in Fig. 15.8 is for average entrance relations when the wheel is running at the proper speed for maximum efficiency.

Although the last particle of water may have overtaken the bucket when the latter has reached the position indicated by α'', water continues to flow over the bucket and be discharged from the side of the latter beyond that location. Thus water will be discharging from the bucket in position e. This is not shown in Fig. 15.8 but can be seen in the instantaneous photograph of Fig. 15.9. If all the water from the nozzle is to be used by the wheel, it is necessary for the last drop to leave the bucket before the latter passes beyond position f. The attainment of this result

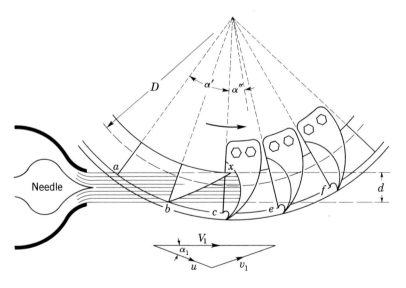

Fig. 15.8

Fig. 15.9. Instantaneous photograph of a 12-in. Pelton wheel at 1,125 rpm, $\phi = 0.8$. (*California Institute of Technology, Mechanical Engineering Laboratory.*)

depends upon the relation between u and V_1 and also upon the ratio of the diameter of the wheel to the diameter of the jet and upon the bucket spacing.

It may be seen from the drawing in Fig. 15.8 and the photograph in Fig. 15.9 that the water is acting upon several buckets at the same time. Thus, although the amount of water per unit time striking a single moving bucket is G', as in Sec. 6.9, the total discharge from the nozzle G acts upon the wheel as a unit, because, unlike the single object, the wheel as a whole is not moving away from the nozzle. However, if the wheel runs at a speed that is in excess of the proper speed, some of the water may go straight through without ever catching up with a bucket before the latter swings up above the line of action.

The velocity relations at discharge, as shown in Fig. 15.10, must also represent average values. The view here shown is that in a plane at right angles to that of Fig. 15.8 and represents the case where the bucket is directly below the axis of rotation and the bucket velocity u and the jet velocity V_1 are in the same straight line.

Inspection of Fig. 15.8 shows that, when the bucket is entering the jet,

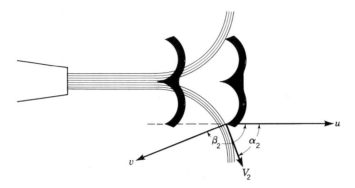

Fig. 15.10.   Velocity relations at discharge.

the radius of the wheel at which the water enters is greater than that at which it leaves, whereas, when the bucket has traveled to the point where it is moving upward, the water is leaving the bucket at a maximum radius. Hence initially r_1 is greater than r_2, and later it is just the reverse.   As an average it may be assumed that $r_1 = r_2$, which is a close approximation to reality.

15.9. WHEEL DIAMETER

The diameter D that is used in equations and calculations for the impulse wheel is the diameter of the pitch circle.   This, as shown in Fig. 15.8, is the circle to which the center line of the jet is tangent.

The ratio of the pitch diameter to the diameter of the jet may be very large, and there is no theoretical upper limit.   An extreme case in practice is that of a Pelton wheel which was direct-connected to a reciprocating air compressor.   Because of the high head, the bucket velocity was 138.5 fps, but the compressor required a rotative speed as low as 80 rpm. Thus the diameter of the wheel was 33 ft.   The exact size of the jet is not known to the authors, but since the buckets were only 5 by 7 in., the diameter of the jet could not have been very far from 1.5 in.   Thus $D/d = 264$. In Valais, Switzerland, are some Pelton wheels 11.67 ft in diameter with jets 1.5 in. in diameter, giving a ratio of 93.4.

On the other hand, there are limiting minimum values of this ratio, which depend in part upon the spacing of the buckets.   For good efficiency with bolted buckets a ratio of 12 is very good; this means that the diameter of the wheel in feet equals the diameter of the jet in inches. However, with some sacrifice in efficiency, a value as low as 9 seems to be the practical lower limit for bolted buckets, but a ratio as low as 6 may be used for the integral type of Fig. 15.7.

15.10. TORQUE AND POWER FOR IDEAL CASES

Case 1. The ideal case first considered will be obtained by assuming $\alpha_1 = 0°$ and $\beta_2 = 180°$, although such values are physically impossible in a real wheel. However, these assumptions permit a convenient analysis, for all velocities are in the same straight line, and it is not necessary to solve velocity triangles. Assume, further, that $r_1 = r_2 = D/2$, that there is no fluid friction in flow over the buckets, and that all the water discharged by the nozzle acts upon the buckets. For these ideal conditions the simple relations are $v_1 = V_1 - u$, $v_2 = v_1$, $V_2 = u - v_2 = 2u - V_1$, and

$$\Delta V = V_1 - V_2 = 2(V_1 - u)$$

Hence the tangential force acting upon the wheel in this ideal case is

$$F_u = \rho Q \Delta V = \rho Q 2(V_1 - u) \tag{15.3}$$

This is the equation of a straight line, as in Fig. 15.11, and shows that the

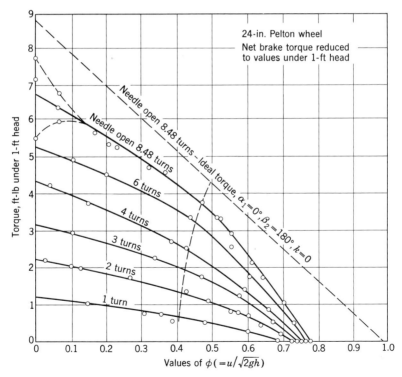

Fig. 15.11. Relation between torque and speed at constant head. (*From tests made by F. G. Switzer and R. L. Daugherty.*)

torque $F_u \times D/2$ is a maximum at zero wheel speed and decreases to zero when $u = V_1$ or $\phi = C_v$, where $\phi = \mu/\sqrt{2gh}$ (Eq. 14.17).

Instead of plotting either revolutions per minute or peripheral velocity, the dimensionless factor ϕ is used to express the speed, since the numerical values of this factor will apply with only slight variations for any size of wheel under any head. Dimensionless factors might also be used in Fig. 15.11 for torque and power, but it is more convenient to reduce these values for the 24-in. wheel to their values for 1 ft head. The similarity laws then enable values to be computed from these for any size of homologous wheel under any head.

An equation for power is obtained by multiplying F_u by u; this is the equation of a parabola, such as shown in Fig. 15.12. The power will be zero when the wheel speed is zero and also when the torque is zero. In this ideal case the only loss is that due to the kinetic energy at discharge from the buckets. As $V_2 = 2u - V_1$, it is seen that this kinetic energy is zero when $u = V_1/2$. Hence, for this speed ratio, as also when $\phi = C_v/2$,

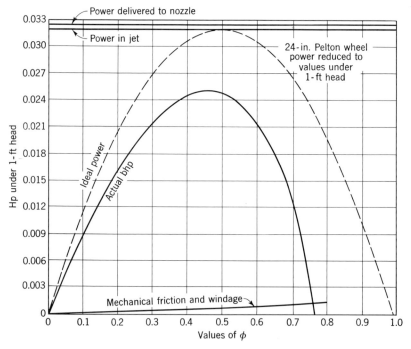

Fig. 15.12. Relation between power and speed at constant head with maximum nozzle opening. (*From tests made by F. G. Switzer and R. L. Daugherty.*)

the power of the wheel is a maximum and for this idealized case is then equal to the power of the jet.

Inasmuch as the power input to the wheel is independent of the wheel speed and is therefore constant, the efficiency curve is the same as the power curve, but to some suitable scale.

Case 2.   A closer approach to reality may be realized by using the factor k to take account of friction loss in flow through the buckets, as in Eq. (6.21), and also considering the true bucket angle β_2, which is of the order of 165°.   Then $V_2 \cos \alpha_2 = u + v_2 \cos \beta_2 = u + v_1 \cos \beta_2 / \sqrt{1 + k}$, from which is obtained

$$F_u = \rho Q \left(1 - \frac{\cos \beta_2}{\sqrt{1 + k}}\right)(V_1 - u) \qquad (15.4)$$

which is still the equation of a straight line if k is considered as constant. This approach is still somewhat idealized since α_1 is taken as zero along with other simplifying assumptions.   However, the value of the torque at all speeds is lower than that given by application of Eq. (15.3) and is thus nearer to the true value.

For this case the power and efficiency curves are still parabolas, with their maximum values at $u = V_1/2$ or $\phi = C_v/2$, but both these maximum values will be lower than in case 1, because fluid friction in flow over the buckets is now being considered.

Although α_1 is not zero, as here assumed, an approximate expression for hydraulic efficiency may be obtained by multiplying Eq. (15.4) by u and dividing by $\gamma Q h$.   If V_1 and u are replaced by $C_v \sqrt{2gh}$ and $\phi \sqrt{2gh}$, respectively, the result is

$$e_h = 2 \left(1 - \frac{\cos \beta_2}{\sqrt{1 + k}}\right)(C_v - \phi)\phi \qquad (15.5)$$

The special significance of this equation is that it confirms an earlier statement that the hydraulic efficiency is independent of the head and depends only upon dimensionless quantities.

Illustrative example 15.1:   Assume an ideal case of an impulse wheel with $\alpha_1 = 0°$, $\beta_2 = 160°$, $k = 0.44$, $C_v = 0.98$, a jet diameter of 10 in., and a pitch diameter of 10 ft.   For operation under the purely artificial value of 1 ft net head, $u = \phi \sqrt{2g} = 8.02\phi$, $V_1 = 0.98 \sqrt{2g} = 7.86$ fps, and

$$\gamma Q = 62.4 \times 0.545 \times 7.86 = 267 \text{ lb/sec}$$

Hence, using Eq. (15.4), the expression for torque will be

$$T = 5 \left(\frac{267}{32.2}\right)\left(1 + \frac{0.940}{1.2}\right) 8.02(C_v - \phi)$$

If $\phi = 0.49$, $T = 291$ ft-lb.   The power is

$$F_u u = T\omega = T\frac{u}{r} = 291\left(\frac{3.93}{5}\right) = 228.5 \text{ ft-lb/sec} = 0.415 \text{ hp}$$

The power input $= \gamma Qh/550 = (267 \times 1)/550 = 0.487$ hp.   The hydraulic efficiency is $0.415/0.487 = 0.855$.   This last could have been determined directly by Eq. (15.5).

Under 1 ft head, $v_1 = 7.86 - 3.93 = 3.93$ fps and $v_2 = 3.93/\sqrt{1.44} = 3.27$ fps. Hence the head loss in bucket friction is $0.44(3.27)^2/2g = 0.0732$ ft, or 7.32 per cent. $V_2 \cos \alpha_2 = 3.93 + 3.27 \cos 160° = 3.93 - 3.07 = 0.86$ fps,

$$V_2 \sin \alpha_2 = v_2 \sin \beta_2 = 3.27 \sin 160° = 3.27 \times 0.342 = 1.12 \text{ fps}$$

Hence $\cot \alpha_2 = 0.86/1.12 = 0.768$, or $\alpha_2 = 52.5°$, and $V_2 = 1.41$ fps, from which the discharge loss is $(1.4)^2/2g = 0.031$ ft, or 3.10 per cent.   The head lost in the nozzle is 4 per cent; so the total hydraulic loss is 14.42 per cent, which is a close check on the computed efficiency of 85.5 per cent.

15.11. ACTUAL TORQUE AND POWER

In Fig. 15.11 are shown the brake-torque curves for a Pelton wheel with different nozzle openings, the maximum being when the needle, the position of which is controlled by a screw thread, has been opened 8.48 revolutions from its closed position.   Referring to Fig. 15.8 and the accompanying discussion, it is obvious that, when the wheel is prevented from rotating, the torque exerted by the jet upon it will vary within certain limits, depending upon the position of the bucket or buckets upon which the jet is acting.   This variation is shown for the wide-open nozzle only in Fig. 15.11, but it exists for all the other nozzle openings.   When the wheel was permitted to run at a slow speed, the observed fluctuation was less but was still very definite, as shown for $\phi = 0.07$, but when the wheel was run at higher speeds, the brake torque became constant.   It should be made clear that the torque exerted by the fluid on the wheel fluctuates at all speeds, but what is recorded and plotted in Fig. 15.11 is the torque measured by a brake.   The inertia of the rotating parts at the higher speeds produces a uniform torque output.

The difference between the ideal torque shown in Fig. 15.11 and the actual brake torque for the wide-open nozzle is due in part to the effect of k and β_2 in case 2 of Sec. 15.10.   Also, an important factor is the value of the average angle α_1, especially at very low values of ϕ.   As the relative wheel speed increases, the average value of α_1 decreases, but is probably never zero.

It is observed that the torque curves of Fig. 15.11 are very nearly straight lines for the lower speeds, but at higher speeds the torque decreases more rapidly and becomes zero at a maximum peripheral velocity much less than V_1, that is, for ϕ much less than 1.0.   This is due to two factors, one of them being that at speeds above the design value some of the water fails to complete its action upon the buckets or even to overtake them at all, as explained in Sec. 15.8. Another factor is that at these higher speeds the back of the bucket hits the water that has previously been intercepted by it and throws it up around the case. Thus the back of the bucket is doing work upon some of the water. In addition, there is some normal mechanical friction and windage as shown in Fig. 15.12. Hence, for all these reasons, the actual brake-torque curve differs from the purely ideal.

There are some very practical observations to be made from an inspection of these curves. While the value of ϕ for maximum efficiency is not $C_v/2$, as for the ideal case, it is only a very little less than that, usually 0.43 to 0.47. Also, it is seen that ϕ for maximum efficiency decreases slightly for smaller nozzle openings. It is also seen that the torque at zero speed is nearly twice the torque at normal speed, the latter being the speed at which the efficiency is a maximum. But the important feature is that the maximum speed possible, or the runaway speed, is only about 60 per cent more than the normal speed. If the wheel and the generator are designed to withstand a speed only that much above normal, no damage can result if some failure of the governor permits the wheel to run away.

From the torque-speed relations of Fig. 15.11, the power-speed curves can be plotted, but only that for the maximum nozzle opening is shown in Fig. 15.12. Power curves for smaller nozzle openings would have lower values, and their maximum points would be found at lower values of ϕ, as indicated by the dashed line in Fig. 15.11. Because the actual brake-torque curve is not a straight line, the actual power curve is not a parabola, the right-hand side of the curve being steeper than the left-hand side.

The power consumed in mechanical friction in the bearings and in windage was determined by a separate test and is shown in Fig. 15.12. For this particular wheel at normal speed the mechanical friction and windage are 1.5 per cent of the maximum brake horsepower.

For a constant nozzle opening and a constant head, the tangential force or the torque varies as ΔV_u, which is the tangential component of the vector change of absolute velocity. As shown by the photographs in Fig. 15.13 and the velocity diagrams below each, the value of ΔV_u is a maximum when the wheel is at rest and is a minimum at runaway speed. The velocity diagrams show also that the value of V_2 decreases as the wheel speed increases from zero until it reaches some minimum value and then increases again. Hence, at some intermediate speed, the kinetic energy lost at discharge from the buckets is a minimum. There is no

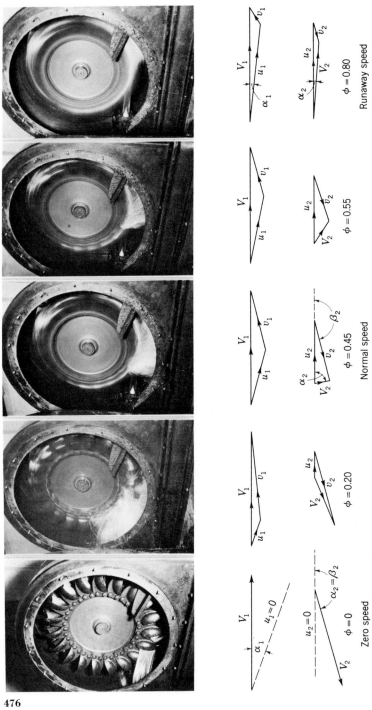

Fig. 15.13. A 42-in. Pelton wheel at different speeds under the same head. (*Photographs at Cornell University by R. L. Daugherty.*)

476

simple or exact theory to determine this point, but as a close approximation, the discharge velocity will be about a minimum when $u = v_2$, and consequently α_2 will then be only a little less than 90°. However, the efficiency is a maximum when the sum of *all* the losses is a minimum. Because the relative velocity of flow over the buckets decreases with increasing wheel speed, the fluid-friction losses in the buckets decrease with speed. But in Fig. 15.12 it is seen that mechanical-friction and windage losses increase with speed. The summation of these three losses reaches a minimum at a speed slightly greater than the one for which the discharge loss is a minimum. Hence the maximum overall efficiency is usually not far from the speed where $\alpha_2 = 90°$, although there is nothing exact about this.

Figure 15.14 is an instantaneous photograph of a Pelton wheel running at somewhere near its speed for maximum efficiency. The discharge seen here is similar to that shown in the middle picture of Fig. 15.13.

15.12. EFFICIENCY VARIATION WITH SIZE AND HEAD

Ideally, the efficiency of homologous impulse wheels is independent of size and head. However, the largest of a series of homologous wheels will have a slightly higher efficiency because mechanical-friction and windage losses do not increase at the same rate as the hydraulic properties. For

Fig. 15.14. Instantaneous photograph of a Pelton wheel at $\phi = 0.5$. (*California Institute of Technology, Mechanical Engineering Laboratory.*)

the same reason a given wheel of any size will generally operate at a slightly higher efficiency at higher heads.

However, there is a factor that may operate to decrease the efficiency with an increase in head. The absolute velocity of the water discharged from the buckets will increase as $\sqrt{h}$, and the rebound velocity from the vertical sides of the setting (Fig. 15.1) will vary in proportion. If this rebound velocity is high enough, some of the water reflected from the walls will hit the wheel. This will result in an increased loss of the windage type. Hence, for high-head installations, the width of the setting for the lower part of the wheel should be made great enough to prevent this.

15.13. OPERATION AT CONSTANT SPEED

A turbine is usually operated at a constant rotative speed, and this is necessarily some synchronous speed if it drives an a-c generator. In the United States, 60-cycle current is most common, and under such conditions the rotative speed of the turbine in revolutions per minute is given by $n = 7,200/N$, where N is the number of poles in the generator and must be an even integer. Most generators have from 12 to 96 poles.

The foregoing discussion shows that there is one speed ratio that is most efficient for any one nozzle opening but that this optimum speed ratio varies slightly with the nozzle opening, as shown in Fig. 15.11. Also, the static, or gross, head varies with changing level in the reservoir at intake, and the net head varies not only because of this but with the flow through the pipe. Thus, at the San Francisquito plant 1 of the City of Los Angeles, the head on the plant varies from 940 ft static to 830 ft at full load. Not only will ϕ vary with wheel speed, but even if the revolutions per minute is constant, it will vary if the head changes. Hence the maximum efficiency of a turbine at some constant speed might not be the maximum efficiency of which the turbine is capable.

In Fig. 15.15 is shown an efficiency curve for an impulse turbine at a constant rotative speed with varying load. If this speed were at some other value, but for the same head, the curve would be different. This figure shows that for an impulse wheel the efficiency curve is relatively flat over a wide load range. Thus this type of turbine is desirable for a variable load, especially if the load is light over long periods of time.

The capacity of a turbine at constant speed under a given head may be stated in several different ways. The *rated* horsepower is the guaranteed brake horsepower, and the turbine is designed to develop this. However, as seen in Fig. 15.15, the maximum efficiency is obtained at a smaller capacity, which is designated as the *normal* horsepower. The

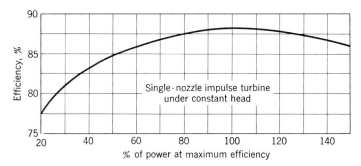

Fig. 15.15. Efficiency at constant speed.

overload, or *maximum* horsepower, is usually somewhat greater than the rated power, but sometimes they may coincide.

15.14. SPECIFIC SPEED

In Sec. 14.7 the expression for specific speed of a turbine was derived and found to be

$$n_s = \frac{n_e \sqrt{\mathrm{bhp}}}{h^{5/4}} \tag{15.6}$$

where n_e is the revolutions per minute for either best efficiency or normal operating speed, while the power may be either the normal power for maximum efficiency or the rated power. The former value would give the *normal specific speed*, and the latter the *rated specific speed*.

It is instructive to see what factors determine the numerical value of the specific speed for the Pelton wheel. Thus

$$n = \frac{60u}{\pi D} = 60\phi \frac{\sqrt{2gh}}{\pi D}$$

$Q = V_1(\pi d^2/4)$, where d is the jet diameter, and $\mathrm{bhp} = \gamma Q h e/550$. Making these various substitutions and reducing,

$$n_s = \frac{60(2g)^{3/4}\phi \sqrt{\gamma C_v e}}{2\sqrt{\pi 550}} \frac{d}{D} \tag{15.7}$$

As the factors ϕ, C_v, and e should vary only slightly, it is seen that the value of the specific speed depends principally upon the ratio of the wheel to the jet diameter. It has been stated that there is no definite physical limit to the maximum value of the ratio D/d, but a large value results in a relatively large and therefore more costly wheel, and the efficiency suffers because of the proportionally large bearing friction and windage loss.

However, if the ratio D/d becomes too small, the size of the buckets becomes unreasonable in relation to the wheel diameter; it is physically impossible to space the buckets close enough together; and some of the water from the nozzle will not act upon the wheel at all, as explained in Sec. 15.8.   But even before this point is reached, the efficiency of the wheel will suffer because of the increased departure from the tangential action, which is the ideal.

Thus, as seen in Fig. 15.16, the impulse wheel attains its best efficiency at a normal specific speed of about 4.5, and the upper limit for a single nozzle wheel is about 6 or 7, for beyond that value the efficiency drops too much.   It should be emphasized that these values are for single-nozzle wheels only.   If two or more nozzles are used on the one wheel, the horsepower is increased and thus the specific-speed values here mentioned are to be multiplied by the square root of the number of nozzles.

The curve shown in Fig. 15.16 should be understood to indicate a trend rather than absolute values in all cases.   Wheels of poor design or

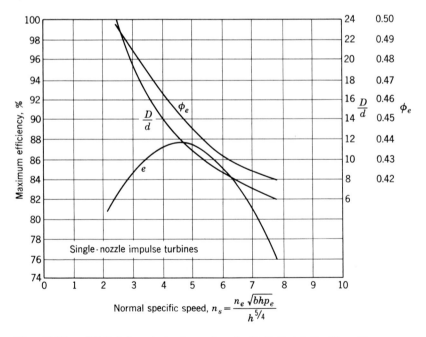

Fig. 15.16.   (*Plotted from test values given by R. S. Quick, Problems Encountered in the Design and Operation of Impulse Turbines, Trans. ASME, vol. 62, no. 1, January, 1940.*)

small size, operating under low head or other unfavorable conditions, will have efficiencies lower than indicated by this single curve.

Illustrative example 15.2: (a) A turbine is to operate at 400 rpm under a net head of 1,320 ft. If a single 6-in.-diameter water jet is used, find the specific speed of this machine assuming $C_v = 0.98$, $\phi = 0.45$, and $e = 0.85$. Find also the required pitch diameter of the wheel.

$$V = C_v \sqrt{2gh} = 0.98 \times 8.02 \times 36.4 = 286 \text{ fps}$$

$$Q = AV = 0.196 \times 286 = 56.0 \text{ cfs}$$

$$\text{bhp} = e \frac{\gamma Qh}{550} = 0.85 \left(\frac{62.4 \times 56 \times 1,320}{550} \right) = 7,130$$

$$n_s = \frac{n_e \sqrt{\text{bhp}}}{h^{5\!/\!4}} = \frac{400 \sqrt{7,130}}{(1,320)^{5\!/\!4}} = 4.22$$

$$u = \phi \sqrt{2gh} = 0.45 \times 8.02 \times 36.4 = 131.5 \text{ fps}$$

$$n = 400 \text{ rpm} = \frac{u(60)}{\pi D} = \frac{131.5 \times 60}{\pi D}$$

$$D = 6.26 \text{ ft} = 75 \text{ in.}$$

(b) In lieu of the single impulse wheel of the preceding example, suppose that three identical single-nozzle wheels are to be used, operating under the same head of 1,320 ft. The total flow rate is to be 56.0 cfs. Determine the required specific speed of these turbines, their pitch diameter, the jet diameter, and the operating speed. Once again, assume $C_v = 0.98$, $\phi = 0.45$, and $e = 0.85$.
As before, $V = 286$ fps and $u = 131.5$ fps.

$$Q = {}^{56.0\!/\!3} = 18.7 \text{ cfs}$$

$$\text{bhp} = \frac{7,130}{3} = 2,377$$

$$n_s = \frac{n_e \sqrt{2,377}}{(1,320^{5\!/\!4})} = n_e \times 0.0062$$

$$n = \frac{131.5(60)}{\pi D} = \frac{2,510}{D}$$

From the two preceding expressions it is apparent that the required n_s depends on the operating speed, as does D. Hence there are a number of possible answers. If we let the operating speed be 400 rpm,

$$n_s = 400 \times 0.0062 = 2.48$$

$$D = \frac{2,510}{n} = 6.26 \text{ ft} = 75 \text{ in.}$$

Thus three $n_s = 2.48$ wheels of pitch diameter 75 in. operating at 400 rpm would suffice. An alternative solution, for example, would be to use an operating speed of 600 rpm (12-pole generator). For this case,

$$n_s = 600 \times 0.0062 = 3.72$$

$$D = \frac{2,510}{n} = 4.18 \text{ ft} = 50.2 \text{ in.}$$

Thus three $n_s = 3.72$ wheels of pitch diameter 50.2 in. operating at 600 rpm would suffice.

Let us now determine the required jet diameter for the 50.2-in.-diameter wheel operating at 600 rpm.

$$Q = AV = \frac{\pi}{4}\left(\frac{d}{12}\right)^2 286 = 18.7 \text{ cfs}$$

$$d = 3.46 \text{ in.}$$

As a check, refer to Fig. 15.16, which shows that $D/d = 14.5$ for $n_s = 3.72$. Since $D = 50.2$ in., $d = 50.2/14.5 = 3.46$ in.

15.15. INSTALLATIONS

The impulse wheel is especially adapted for use under high heads. For heads above 1,500 ft it is the only type that can be considered, and for many years it was the only one ever used for heads above 800 ft. Among some interesting installations are the following.

At Dixence, Switzerland, a double-overhung unit operates under a gross head of 5,735 ft and a net head of 5,330 ft, giving a jet velocity of approximately 587 fps. Each single-nozzle wheel delivers 25,000 hp, or 50,000 hp for the unit, and runs at 500 rpm. The jets are 3.71 in. in diameter, and the pitch diameter of the wheels is 10.89 ft.

At Reisseck, Austria, an impulse wheel delivers 31,000 hp at 750 rpm under a gross head of 5,800 ft.

The Fully plant in Valais, Switzerland, operates under a gross head of 5,410 ft and a net head of 4,830 ft. There are four wheels of 3,000 hp each running at 500 rpm. The jets are 1.5 in. in diameter, and the wheels are 11.67 ft in diameter.

A multiple-nozzle wheel at Pragnières, France, delivers 100,000 hp at 428 rpm under a gross head of 3,920 ft.

The Kitimat plant in British Columbia of the Aluminum Company of Canada has three four-nozzle vertical-shaft units that operate at 327 rpm under a net head of 2,500 ft. Each unit is rated at 140,000 hp.

The highest-head plant in South America is 3,460 ft at Ros Molles, Chile. The wheel develops 11,500 hp at 1,000 rpm.

In North America there are a number of plants operating under heads of between 2,000 and 2,500 ft.

At the Big Creek-2A plant of the Southern California Edison Co. is an Allis-Chalmers double-overhung single-jet impulse turbine 137 in. in diameter with an 8.4-in. jet on each wheel and a similar Pelton Water Wheel Co. impulse turbine 135.25 in. in diameter with an 8.5-in. jet on each wheel. Each unit runs at 300 rpm, and the maximum static head with a full reservoir is 2,418 ft. With both units carrying full load, the net head is 2,200 ft, and the maximum output is 65,100 bhp for the Allis-

Chalmers unit and 67,300 bhp for the Pelton unit. At maximum efficiency under 2,200 ft head, the former delivers 50,000 bhp and the latter 31,000 bhp.

The Bucks Creek plant of the Feather River Power Co. has a gross head of 2,562 ft and a net head of 2,350 ft. The double-overhung unit has a capacity of 35,000 hp and runs at 450 rpm.

At the Balch plant of the former San Joaquin Light and Power Co., now the Pacific Gas and Electric Co., is an Allis-Chalmers double-overhung unit with wheels 115 in. in diameter with a 7.5-in. jet on each wheel. It runs at 360 rpm and develops 49,000 hp under a net head of 2,243 ft.

One of the largest jets in the world is 14 in. in diameter from a nozzle with an orifice diameter of 16.75 in. This is in an Allis-Chalmers double-overhung unit in the San Francisquito plant 1 of the City of Los Angeles. Each wheel is 176 in. in diameter, and the speed is 171.6 rpm. The maximum static head on the plant is 940 ft, but when the entire plant is running, the net head is 830 ft. In a test of this one unit under a net head of 870 ft, each nozzle discharged 250 cfs and the unit delivered 40,100 hp with an efficiency of 81 per cent. The maximum efficiency was obtained at approximately 20,000 hp and was 86 per cent.

PROBLEMS

15.1. A Pelton wheel is 6 ft in diameter and is acted upon by a jet that is 6 in. in diameter. The velocity of the jet is 400 fps. The bucket angle is 165°, and k may be assumed to be 0.21. Assuming ideal case 2, find the torque in foot-pounds for bucket speeds of 0, 100, 200, 300, and 400 fps.

15.2. If the velocity coefficient of the nozzle is 0.98, what are the horsepower and efficiency for the five speeds in Prob. 15.1?

15.3. At the bucket speed of 200 fps in Prob. 15.1, what is the value of the head lost in friction in the buckets, and what is the head lost in the kinetic energy at discharge?

15.4. Using the data of Prob. 15.1, find values of (a) head lost in bucket friction; (b) velocity head lost at discharge; (c) total head lost, for bucket speeds of 180, 185, 191, 195, 200, 205 fps. (This is best solved by tabulation.) At what speed is the discharge loss a minimum? At what speed is the total head loss a minimum?

15.5. Find the approximate hydraulic efficiency of an impulse wheel for which the nozzle velocity coefficient is 0.97 and the bucket angle is 160°, if $\phi = 0.46$ and $k = 0.1$.

15.6. For the Pelton wheel of Fig. 15.11 with the nozzle wide open and $Q = 0.286$ cfs, find the torque for 1 ft head for zero speed ($\phi = 0$) and for $\phi = 0.49$, assuming the ideal case 2 with $C_v = 0.98$, $\beta_2 = 165°$, and $k = 0.7$.

15.7. Solve Prob. 15.6 for a wheel that is 8 ft in diameter and with the jet also four times the diameter of that in Fig. 15.11.

15.8. Find the torque, power, efficiency, and rotative speed of the impulse wheel of Illustrative Example 15.1 if it were to operate under a head of 60 ft.

15.9. Under a net head of 1 ft the Pelton wheel of Fig. 15.12 discharges 0.286 cfs at full nozzle opening and the maximum power is 0.025 bhp for a value of $\phi = 0.465$. The corresponding brake torque is 3.69 ft-lb as shown in Fig. 15.11. Assuming that the similarity laws apply precisely, determine the discharge, torque, power, and rotative speed of this wheel when it operates under a head of 1,600 ft.

15.10. A wheel and nozzle similar to that of Figs. 15.11 and 15.12 with a pitch diameter of 12 ft is used under a net head of 1,600 ft. What is the torque, power, and rpm at point of best efficiency for full nozzle opening?

15.11. A 24-in. laboratory wheel was tested under a head of 65.5 ft. With the nozzle open 6 turns of the needle, the net brake load at 275 rpm was 40 lb at a brake arm of 5.25 ft and the discharge was 1.897 cfs. Find values of brake horsepower and efficiency under operating conditions. What would be values of torque and brake horsepower under 1 ft head?

15.12. At 275 rpm the bearing-friction and windage losses of the Pelton wheel in Prob. 15.11 were found to be 0.2 hp. What percentage is this of the brake horsepower? What is the value of the mechanical efficiency? What is the value of the hydraulic efficiency?

15.13. If the Pelton wheel of Prob. 15.12 were run at double the speed, or 550 rpm, the head should be $4 \times 65.5 = 262$ ft for the same value of ϕ. At this higher head the power input will be $4^{3/2}$, or 8 times the value found in Prob. 15.11; the hydraulic losses will also be in the same proportion, and so the hydraulic efficiency will remain unchanged. A special test showed that at 550 rpm the bearing friction and windage losses were 0.8 hp.

What would then be the power input to the shaft? What will be the brake horsepower? What percentage is 0.8 hp of the brake horsepower? What are the values of the mechanical efficiency and of the total efficiency?

15.14. The discharges under 65.5 ft head for the nozzle openings shown in Fig. 15.11 were 0.397, 0.773, 1.114, 1.414, 1.896, and 2.315 cfs. At a constant speed of 275 rpm, or $\phi = 0.443$, the net brake scale readings at a brake arm of 5.25 ft were 6.8, 14.9, 22.0, 28.9, 40.0, and 48.0 lb, respectively. When there was no load at 275 rpm, the discharge was 0.110 cfs. Compute and plot power input and efficiency vs. brake horsepower.

15.15. If the speed of the wheel in Prob. 15.14 were raised to 300 rpm, the discharge at no load would be 0.125 cfs; for the same head of 65.5 ft the net scale readings were 5.9, 12.9, 19.8, 25.5, 36.0, and 43.8 lb, respectively. Compute and plot power input and efficiency vs. brake horsepower.

15.16. The pressure of the water at the base of a nozzle of a Pelton wheel is 700 psi, and the velocity at that same point is 20 fps. The jet diameter is 8 in., and the velocity coefficient of the nozzle is 0.98. If the efficiency of the wheel is 86 per cent, find the brake horsepower.

15.17. In Prob. 15.16 if the pitch diameter of the wheel is 8 ft, what should be the normal operating speed? What is an approximate value for the runaway speed?

15.18. What is the torque exerted on the wheel in Prob. 15.16, and what is an approximate value of the torque at zero speed?

15.19. Assuming a general case for any type of impulse turbine where $x = r_2/r_1$, prove that the equation for torque is

$$T = \rho Q r_1 \left(V_1 \cos \alpha_1 - x^2 u_1 - \frac{x \cos \beta_2}{\sqrt{1+k}} \sqrt{V_1^2 + x^2 u_1^2 - 2u_1 V_1 \cos \alpha_1} \right)$$

15.20. A nozzle having a velocity coefficient of 0.98 discharges a jet 7 in. in diameter under a net head of 1,600 ft. This jet acts upon a wheel with the following dimensions: $D = 7$ ft, $\alpha_1 = 15°$, $\beta_2 = 160°$, and it is assumed $k = 0.6$. Find the tangential force exerted upon the buckets when $\phi = 0.45$.

15.21. A test of the impulse turbine shown in Fig. 15.2 gave a maximum efficiency of 92 per cent at 35,000 bhp and 89.95 per cent at the rated 62,000 bhp. The net head is 1,118 ft at full load, and the speed is 300 rpm. The static head is 1,226 ft. What is the net head at the load for maximum efficiency? What are the normal and the rated values of specific speed per jet?

15.22. Compute the normal and the rated specific speeds for the two units at Big Creek-2A.

15.23. Compute the normal and the rated specific speeds for the Allis-Chalmers unit at the San Francisquito plant.

15.24. It is desired to develop 15,000 bhp under a head of 1,000 ft. Make any necessary assumptions, and estimate the diameter of the wheel required and the rotative speed.

15.25. A single-nozzle impulse wheel is required to develop 20,000 bhp under a net head of 1,190 ft and is to run at 225 rpm. What should be the probable diameter of the wheel?

15.26. A nozzle having a velocity coefficient of 0.98 discharges a jet 6 in. in diameter under a head of 900 ft. As a simplifying assumption take $\alpha_1 = 0°$. The wheel diameter is 8 ft, $\beta_2 = 165°$, and it may be assumed that $k = 0.5$. The mechanical efficiency of the wheel is 97 per cent. What is the hydraulic efficiency? What is the gross efficiency? (Assume a reasonable value of ϕ.)

15.27. In Prob. 15.26 find the power lost in hydraulic friction in the buckets. Find the value of V_2, and determine the power carried away in the water discharged from the buckets.

15.28. Refer to Illustrative Example 15.2. Suppose a two-nozzle single-wheel installation were designed to operate under a head of 1,320 ft with a total flow (for both nozzles) of 56 cfs. Determine the required specific speed of this turbine, its pitch diameter, and jet diameter for rotative speeds of 300, 400, and 600 rpm.

SIXTEEN

REACTION TURBINES

16.1. DEFINITION

A reaction turbine, whether hydraulic or steam or gas, is one in which the major portion of the pressure drop takes place in the rotating wheel. As a consequence the proportions must be such that the fluid fills all the runner passages completely. This makes it necessary that the fluid be admitted to the rotor around its entire circumference. Since the entire circumference of the reaction turbine is in action, its rotor need not be as large as that of an impulse wheel for the same power.

16.2. EVOLUTION OF THE REACTION TURBINE

The first reaction turbine known is the steam turbine of Hero in Egypt about 120 B.C. It may never even have been built, but the drawings for it are still in existence and show a spherical vessel in which steam was generated and discharged through two small nozzles in a tangential direction.   The reaction of these jets would cause the device to rotate.

In the hydraulic field the rotating lawn sprinkler is an elementary reaction turbine.   As stated in Sec. 6.14, the addition of more arms to permit a greater flow, so as to produce a net power output, developed a power machine known as Barker's mill.   A continuing increase in the number of arms terminated in a complete wheel with passages separated by vanes, but the device was not very efficient, until in 1826, a Frenchman by the name of Fourneyron added stationary guide vanes in the central portion. These guide vanes gave the water a definite tangential component, thereby imparting angular momentum to the fluid entering the rotor. This outward-flow turbine was efficient, but the mechanical construction was not good because the rotating element was on the outside with the fixed guide vanes near the axis.

The inward-flow turbine permits a better mechanical construction since the rotor and shaft form a compact unit in the center, while the stationary guide vanes are on the outside.   Several crude inward-flow turbines were constructed around 1838, but the first to be well designed was built in 1849 by the eminent hydraulic engineer James B. Francis, who made an accurate test of this turbine.[1]   All inward-flow reaction hydraulic turbines are known as *Francis turbines*, both in this country and in Europe, even though they have developed into very different forms from the original.

The design of the original Francis turbine is shown in Fig. 16.1.   It is a purely radial-flow turbine with both entrance and discharge edges of the runner vanes parallel to the axis of rotation, so that the radii at entrance and exit are the same for all streamlines.   The inner diameter of the runner was almost as large as the outer diameter.

[1] J. B. Francis, "Lowell Hydraulic Experiments," 5th ed., D. Van Nostrand Company, Inc., Princeton, N.J., 1909.

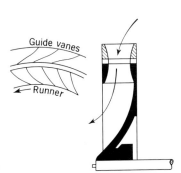

Fig. 16.1.   Francis turbine.

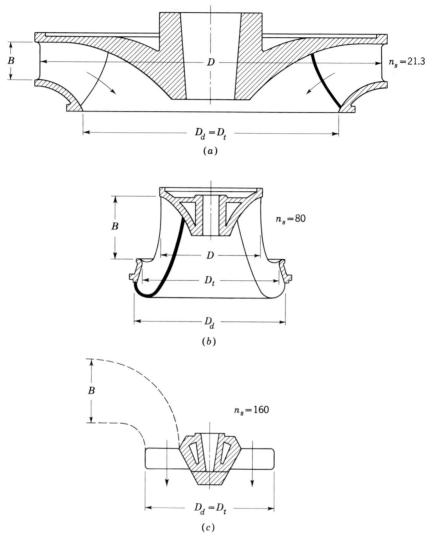

$n_s = 21.3$

$D_d = D_t$

(a)

$n_s = 80$

(b)

$n_s = 160$

$D_d = D_t$

(c)

Fig. 16.2. Relative sizes of different types of runner for the same power under the same head.

To make a more compact runner, the inner diameter was reduced and the water was discharged with a velocity having an axial as well as a radial component, as in Fig. 16.2a. Carrying this a step further, the dimensions of the runner parallel to the shaft were increased, resulting in the *mixed-flow runner* of Fig. 16.2b, also called a *Francis runner*. In this runner all flow lines have both axial and radial components throughout. The velocity at exit near the *band*, or *shroud ring*, may even have a slight outward component at high specific speeds. Inasmuch as the different streamlines vary so much from *crown* to band, it is obvious that the application of any simple theory to this type of runner is impossible.

The range of specific speeds of Francis runners can be from 10 to 110, but the usual practice is from 20 to 80 or 90. In order to obtain both speed and power under very low heads, the axial-flow, or propeller, type of runner shown in Fig. 16.2c is employed. With this design specific speeds can be from 100 to 250, but the general practice is from 100 to 200.

The axial-flow, or propeller, type of runner may have fixed blades, or the pitch of the blades may be adjusted to vary the area between them in proportion to the load. This operation is usually accomplished through the actuation of a governor. This type of axial-flow turbine with adjustable blades is called a *Kaplan turbine*. It has a much higher efficiency on part load than the fixed-blade propeller.

16.3. SIGNIFICANCE OF SPECIFIC SPEED

Figure 16.2 shows the decrease in the size of a Francis runner for the same power under the same head as the specific speed is increased. It also shows that there is a definite relation between the profile of the runner, or the type, and the value of the specific speed. Thus the numerical value of the latter at once fixes the type or design of the runner.

For a small power under a high head a Pelton wheel with its low specific speed is used to keep the rotative speed down to a suitable value, while for a large power under a low head a reaction turbine with its higher specific speed is used to raise the rotative speed to a suitable value. Since $n \sqrt{\text{bhp}} = n_s h^{5/4}$, it is apparent that for a given specific speed and a fixed head any number of combinations of rotative speed and power are possible. If the power is low, the speed can be high, or vice versa. It is also obvious that if both speed and power are high, the specific speed must be high if the head is low.

Illustrative example 16.1: (a) In Sec. 15.15 an impulse wheel is described, running at 500 rpm under a head of 5,330 ft and producing 25,000 hp. The specific speed of this turbine is 1.74. Investigate the possibility of using a reaction turbine at this installation.

Suppose we use the turbine of Fig. 16.2a, for which $n_s = 21.3$. Applying Eq. (14.23), we find $n = 6,130$ rpm, which is impractical. Moreover, it would not be economically feasible to construct a casing designed to withstand such high pressures.

(b) At Keokuk on the Mississippi River are reaction turbines with runners 16 ft in diameter and 12 ft high. They run at 57.7 rpm and develop 10,000 hp under a head of 32 ft and thus have a specific speed of 75.8.   Investigate the possibility of using an impulse wheel at this installation.

Suppose we assume an impulse wheel with $n_s = 5$.   Applying Eq. (14.23), we find $n = 3.8$ rpm, which is impractical.   It should be noted, however, that an impulse wheel is applicable at a 32-ft head if the power to be developed is low.   For example, with a rotative speed of 100 rpm, an impulse wheel with $n_s = 5$ will develop 14.5 hp.

(c) Suppose it is desired to produce 22,500 hp at 600 rpm under a head of 81 ft. Then, applying Eq. (14.23), we find $n_s = 370$, which is impossible.   Either the power may be divided among several units or a single unit may be used if the speed is reduced to a lower value.   One possible solution is to use four units of 5,625 hp, each having a specific speed of 185.   Another solution is to use a single unit operating at 240 rpm with a specific speed of 148.   From a practical viewpoint it is advantageous to have more than one unit at any installation so that power can be developed even when a unit is shut down for repairs.

16.4. CONSTRUCTION OF REACTION TURBINES

A Francis runner is shown in Fig. 16.3, and a Kaplan runner in Fig. 16.4. Francis runners are cast in one piece unless the size is too large for shipment, in which case they are cast in sections and bolted together.   The

Fig. 16.3.   Runner at Niagara Falls. $h = 214$ ft, $n = 107$ rpm, $e = 93.8$ per cent at 72,500 hp, diameter = 176 in., overall diameter at band = $183\frac{3}{8}$ in.   (*Courtesy of Allis-Chalmers Mfg. Co.*)

Fig. 16.4. Kaplan runner 17.5 ft in diameter, $e = 93$ per cent at 30,000 hp under 69 ft head, $n = 120$ rpm. (*Courtesy of Allis-Chalmers Mfg. Co.*)

blades are warped surfaces, and sometimes a die is made and the blades are formed from sheet steel. These blades are then welded to the crown and to the shroud ring.

Axial runners with fixed blades may be cast in one piece, or again the blades may be formed by a die and then welded or bolted to the hub. Of course, Kaplan runners must be made with separate movable blades.

Francis runners are surrounded by pivoted guide vanes,[1] as shown in Figs. 6.11 and 16.5. The water is greatly accelerated in the guide-vane passages and given a definite tangential-velocity component as it enters the runner. The governor regulates the flow rate by rotating these vanes about their pivots so as to vary the area between them. This also has the effect of varying the angle α_1 from practically 0° up to values of 15 to 40° for maximum gate opening, depending upon the specific speed of the turbine. At the load for maximum efficiency the value of α_1 is much less than these. The value of V_1, however, is not much affected by the change in the guide-vane angle.

The water rotates as a free vortex in the space between the ends of

[1] This type of assembly is commonly referred to as *wicket gates*.

the guide vanes and the entrance edges of the turbine runner.   The guide vanes for the propeller turbine are placed in the same way as for a Francis runner, but there is considerable distance between them and the propeller. In the case of the Kaplan turbine, the governor moves the guide vanes about their pivots and at the same time changes the angle of the blades by means of a mechanism in the hub.

For large turbines there is also a stay ring, or *speed ring*, outside of the guide-vane assembly.   This contains stay vanes which are fixed in position and whose primary function is to serve as columns to aid in supporting the weight of the generator above.   The vanes should be so shaped as to conform to the natural streamlines, which are spiral in character.   The water velocity increases in passing through this assembly because of the decreasing cross-sectional area.

The guide-vane assembly, or the stay-vane assembly if there is one, is surrounded in turn by a spiral case, such as shown in Fig. 16.6, which maintains a uniform velocity around the turbine circumference.   For high heads the case is of metal, but for low heads it may be merely formed in the concrete.   It is preferably circular in cross section as in Figs. 16.6 and 16.7, but if formed in concrete, it may be rectangular as in Fig. 16.8.

Fig. 16.5.   Guide-vane assembly.   (*Courtesy of S. Morgan Smith Co.*)

16.5. SETTINGS

Some reaction turbines are set with a horizontal shaft, especially in small sizes or for very high heads.   But the majority of reaction turbines are set with vertical shafts, as shown in Figs. 16.7 and 16.8.   One advantage of the vertical setting is that the draft tube is then more efficient.

16.6. DRAFT TUBES

The draft tube is an integral part of a reaction turbine, and its design should be specified by the turbine manufacturer.   It has two functions. One is to enable the turbine to be set above the tailwater level without losing any head thereby.   A partial vacuum is produced at the upper end of the draft tube, which compensates for the height at which the turbine runner is set.   Within limits the turbine can be set at different elevations without altering the net head.   By its use there is an unbroken stream of fluid from headwater to tailwater.

The second function of the draft tube is to reduce the velocity of discharge from V_2 at exit from the runner to V_3 at exit from the draft tube, thus reducing the final loss of kinetic energy of discharge.

Fig. 16.6.   Scroll case.   (*Courtesy of The James Leffel and Co.*)

Applying the energy equation to the draft tube, as in Figs. 16.9 and 16.10 and letting z_2 signify the elevation of the top of the draft tube above the surface of the water in the tailrace, the absolute pressure head at that section is given by $p_2/\gamma = p_a/\gamma - z_2 - V_2^2/2g + h_L$, where h_L is the fluid friction in the draft tube plus the kinetic energy $V_3^2/2g$ lost at exit.

Equation (8.48) together with Fig. 8.20 will enable a friction factor to be estimated for a diverging draft tube. In the notation of Fig. 16.9, $h_L = k'[1 - (A_2/A_3)]^2(V_2^2/2g) + (V_3^2/2g)$, and as V_3 can be replaced by V_2 from the continuity equation, this entire expression can be reduced to $h_L = kV_2^2/2g$. The absolute pressure head is

$$\frac{p_2}{\gamma} = \frac{p_a}{\gamma} - z_2 - (1 - k)\frac{V_2^2}{2g}$$

If the draft-tube efficiency were 100 per cent, there would be no energy losses and k would then be zero. Hence it follows that the efficiency of the draft tube is

$$e_d = 1 - k \qquad (16.1)$$

If there were a nondiverging draft tube, the energy equation would give

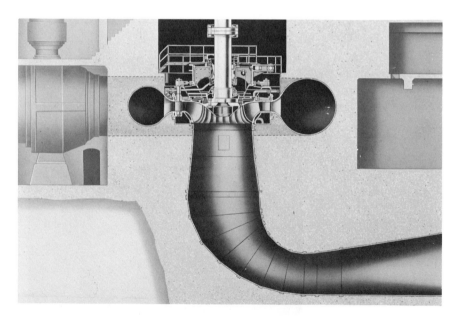

Fig. 16.7. Turbine at Hoover Dam on the Colorado River. Rated at 115,000 hp at 180 rpm under a head of 480 ft. Runner diameter = 171 in. (*Courtesy of Allis-Chalmers Mfg. Co.*)

Fig. 16.8. Kaplan turbine at Watts Bar Dam, 42,000 hp at 94.7 rpm under a head of 52 ft. (*Courtesy of Baldwin-Lima-Hamilton Corp.*)

$p_2/\gamma = (p_a/\gamma) - z + f(L/D)(V_2{}^2/2g)$, where L is the length of the tube. For the diverging draft tube the absolute pressure head is

$$\frac{p_2}{\gamma} = \frac{p_a}{\gamma} - z_2 - e_d \frac{V_2{}^2}{2g} \qquad (16.2)$$

Many different designs of draft tube have been developed to turn the water through 90° with the least loss of energy. Among them is the Moody spreading draft tube shown in Fig. 16.9. In some cases the central cone is extended up to meet the runner so as to form a solid core in the entire central portion of the tube. If the water leaves the turbine with any whirl, there will be a free vortex in the tube, and it has been shown that, as the radius of a free vortex approaches zero, the whirl component approaches infinity. Since this is physically impossible, the central core of a free vortex cannot follow the free-vortex law, and this is conducive to eddy losses, which are avoided by the solid core. In some cases, as at Hoover Dam, a little air is bled into the central section of the draft tube to provide smoother operation with less vibration, but not enough air is admitted to impair the vacuum materially.

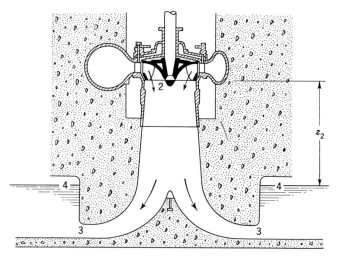

Fig. 16.9. Moody spreading draft tube.

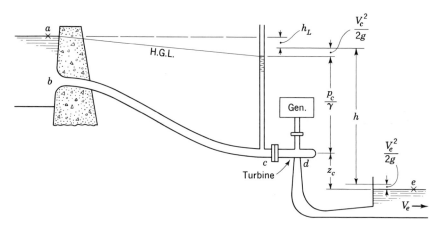

Fig. 16.10. Net head on reaction turbine.

Figure 16.7 shows a draft tube where the principal reduction in velocity is in the vertical conical portion and the 90° turn at the bottom has been made with a flattened cross section, but one of increasing cross-sectional area. This design has been found to give good efficiency and is extensively used. There are still other forms, which space does not permit us to describe.

16.7. NET HEAD

For a reaction turbine the net, or effective, head is the total difference in elevation between headwater and tailwater minus the pipe friction losses and the velocity head in the tailrace at the point of discharge from the draft tube. Referring to Fig. 16.10, the net head on the turbine is $h = H_c - H_e$, or

$$h = \frac{p_c}{\gamma} + z_c + \frac{V_c^2}{2g} - \frac{V_e^2}{2g} \tag{16.3}$$

where c is located at the intake flange to the turbine case. It is apparent that, for the same installation, the head on a reaction turbine is greater than that on a Pelton wheel. The difference is of small importance in a high-head plant, but is important for a low-head plant.

16.8. OPERATION AT VARIABLE SPEED

The characteristics of a reaction turbine at various speeds under a constant head and a constant gate opening are shown in Fig. 16.11.[1] These

[1] Figures 16.11 and 16.12 are from a test made by R. L. Daugherty, Investigation of the Performance of a Reaction Turbine, *Trans. ASCE*, vol. 78, p. 1270, 1915.

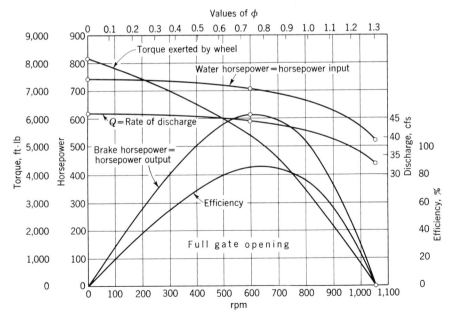

Fig. 16.11. Operation at variable speed under constant head with constant gate opening. Runner diameter = 27 in., head = 140.5 ft.

are similar to those for the impulse turbine in Figs. 15.11 and 15.12, with certain exceptions.   The flow is no longer independent of the runner speed because of the unbroken flow from headwater to tailwater, and any change within the runner will affect the flow.   In Sec. 6.14 it was seen that, for the rotating lawn sprinkler, the rate of flow increased with the rotative speed.   This would also be true for any outward-flow reaction turbine.

For the inward-flow Francis turbine the centrifugal action decreases the flow with increasing wheel speed, as shown in Fig. 16.11.   The next important difference is that the value of ϕ for maximum efficiency is not less than 0.5, as in the Pelton wheel, but greater.   In this specific case it is 0.8, but in general it ranges between 0.7 and 0.85 for Francis turbines. The runaway speed is still only about 60 per cent more than the normal speed, but the maximum value of ϕ is greater than 1 instead of less. Inasmuch as the power input is not a constant, the maximum efficiency occurs at a slightly higher speed than the maximum power output; so these two curves cannot be made to coincide.

16.9. OPERATION AT CONSTANT SPEED

The practical condition of operation is usually at constant speed with a gate opening which varies with the load.   It will here be assumed that

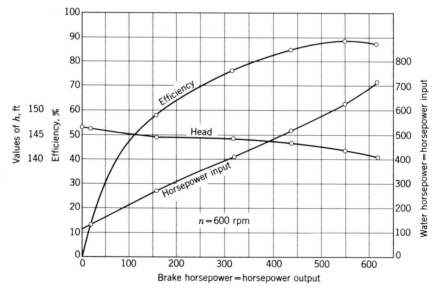

Fig. 16.12.   Operation at constant speed and variable gate opening.   Runner diameter = 27 in.

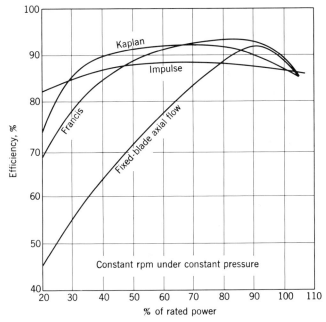

Fig. 16.13. Typical efficiency curves at constant speed under constant head.

the head is constant, although generally it decreases slightly with increased load because the pipe friction varies approximately as Q^2.   Also, the static head may change from time to time, for the level of both headwater and tailwater may vary.   This is important for low-head plants, where in time of flood the tailwater level rises more than the headwater level. This decrease in head may cause a serious reduction in the power that can then be generated.

Figure 16.12 shows the performance of a certain reaction turbine at constant speed.   The efficiency curve is not as flat as that for the impulse wheel in Fig. 15.15.   For the impulse turbine the velocity triangles are independent of the quantity of flow, and so theoretically the hydraulic efficiency should be constant at all loads at constant speed.   Practically this is not so, but the variation is small except for extremes of very light load or very large overload.

Figure 16.13 shows typical efficiency curves for various types of turbines.   The Pelton wheel and the Kaplan turbine both have very flat efficiency curves.   The power at maximum efficiency for both is much lower than the rated power.   As in Sec. 15.13, there are three powers that may be used for a turbine: the rated power, which is that guaranteed by the manufacturer; the maximum power, which usually would be a little more than the rated power; and the normal power, which is that for maximum efficiency.

The Francis turbine has a high maximum efficiency but a poorer part-load efficiency than either the impulse wheel or the Kaplan turbine. The fixed-blade propeller turbine has a high efficiency at the maximum point but a very low part-load efficiency. The normal power of the Francis turbine is nearer to the rated power than it is with either the impulse turbine or the Kaplan turbine. The normal power of the fixed-blade propeller turbine is very near to the rated power.

For the reaction turbine operating at constant speed the requirement that the runner passages be completely filled means that the relative velocity through the fixed areas must decrease as the load is decreased. That is, the continuity equation $Q = A_1 V_1 = a_1 v_1 = a_2 v_2$ must be satisfied. At part load the area A_1 is decreased by the movement of the guide vanes about their pivots. This also decreases the angle α_1, and Q is reduced substantially. The net result is that the velocity diagrams at entrance and exit are changed. At entrance with reduced load, the flow does not enter the runner tangentially to the blades, resulting in a *shock loss*, and at exit, V_2 may increase, resulting in an increase in kinetic energy lost at discharge from the runner. Also, an increased whirl at discharge causes the water to flow through the draft tube with spiral streamlines, which decreases the draft-tube efficiency. In addition, the quantity of water leaking past the seal rings will not be diminished, thus reducing the volumetric efficiency. For these reasons the efficiency of a reaction turbine tends to be less on light load than that of a Pelton wheel, although it may be more efficient at normal load.

16.10. EFFICIENCY

The trend of maximum efficiency as a function of specific speed is shown in Fig. 16.14. These are optimum values and apply to large turbines. Small turbines, no matter how well designed or constructed, should not be expected to yield values as high as these.

One reason for the difference between large and small turbines is that of relative leakage. For a large turbine the leakage loss is very small, being of the order of 1 per cent. For a small runner the clearance distances in the seal rings cannot be reduced in proportion to other dimensions, and thus the leakage loss becomes a larger percentage value. Also, for the same velocity, the fluid friction in flow through the small passages is greater than that through the much larger passages, largely because of greater relative roughness.

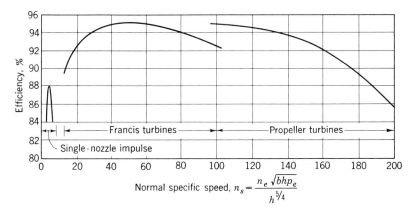

Fig. 16.14. Optimum values of efficiency.

The effect of size on turbine efficiency is of importance in transferring test results on small models to their prototypes. For both Francis turbines and propeller turbines this can be done by the Moody *step-up* formula, which is

$$\frac{1 - e_1}{1 - e} = \left(\frac{D}{D_1}\right)^{\frac{1}{5}} \tag{16.4}$$

This applies, of course, only to homologous machines. It has some theoretical basis and has been found in practice to give satisfactory results.

Equation (16.4) does not apply to Pelton wheels since it is assumed that their efficiencies are nearly independent of size. This is logical because they have no leakage losses to make a difference. Thus, although a large reaction turbine may be more efficient than a Pelton wheel, a small one may be less efficient. It is impossible to give an absolute value of size below which a reaction turbine would be less efficient than an impulse turbine, but a rough approximation would be that if the diameter of the reaction runner is less than about 20 in., its efficiency may be less than that of a Pelton wheel.

It will be observed in Fig. 16.14 that the most favorable specific speed for a Francis turbine is around 50 and that the efficiency is lower at both extremes. A Francis runner of low specific speed will have a large diameter D and a narrow width B for a given power. Disk friction loss due to the drag exerted by the water in the spaces between the runner and the case varies as D^5, and so this loss is proportionally large. Also, there is increased fluid friction in the long and narrow runner passages characteristic of the low-specific-speed Francis runner.

At a higher specific speed these effects diminish in importance and the efficiency increases.   But at very high specific speed the fluid friction is greater because of the higher relative velocity through the runner.   Also, the kinetic energy lost at discharge is greater.   Therefore the efficiency decreases, and the propeller turbine then becomes more desirable.

16.11. THEORY

The primary object of the presentation of theory in this chapter is to explain the operating characteristics of reaction turbines and to point out some features in their design.   An understanding of these is of value to many engineers.   The theory and certain values used in practice as given here will enable one to compute fundamental values for any turbine. Very few engineers will ever have occasion to design the detail of a runner vane, and that topic will not be discussed here.

 · The energy losses in a reaction turbine may be very simply described as the so-called *shock* loss at entrance to the runner if the relative velocity of the water leaving the guide vanes is abruptly changed in either magnitude or direction or both when it enters the runner; fluid friction in the casing, through the guide-vane passages and through the runner passages; kinetic energy due to the absolute velocity of the water at discharge from the runner, of which up to 80 per cent might be regained in the most efficient draft tube; and mechanical friction of the bearings and stuffing boxes, as well as disk friction.   All these losses vary in different ways, and it is not possible to have all of them a minimum at the same point.   The turbine efficiency will be a maximum when the sum of all the losses is a minimum.

In order to avoid shock loss at entrance, it is necessary that the runner-vane angle, which will be designated by β_1' and which is fixed by construction, should be the same as β_1, determined by the velocity triangle. The latter will vary with the operating conditions.   The relations as determined by the velocity triangle (Fig. 6.11) are

$$V_1 \sin \alpha_1 = v_1 \sin \beta_1$$

$$V_1 \cos \alpha_1 = u_1 + v_1 \cos \beta_1$$

Eliminating v_1 between these two equations,

$$u_1 = \frac{\sin (\beta_1 - \alpha_1)}{\sin \beta_1} V_1$$

and if β_1 be assigned a fixed value of β_1', this is the relation between u_1 and V_1 for which there is no shock loss.   If, on the other hand, u_1 and V_1 are given, the equation may be put into a more convenient form as

$$\cot \beta_1 = \frac{V_1 \cos \alpha_1 - u_1}{V_1 \sin \alpha_1}$$

which determines the value of the vane angle β_1' for no shock loss. Both equations in dimensionless terms are

$$\phi = \frac{\sin (\beta_1 - \alpha_1)}{\sin \beta_1} C_1 \tag{16.5}$$

$$\cot \beta_1 = \frac{C_1 \cos \alpha_1 - \phi}{C_1 \sin \alpha_1} \tag{16.6}$$

Values of the runner vane angle β_1' smaller than 90° have been found to cause cavitation at the inlet and to give poor efficiency; so the angle is generally made 90° or more.

A deviation from the point of operation at which the runner-vane angle and the velocity vector angle β_1 are the same will result in a shock loss. An expression for this loss is not given in this text, since the treatment here is confined to the relations for maximum efficiency. No attempt is made to present any theory for operation under other conditions, since for the modern mixed-flow turbine such theory is complicated and of doubtful practical value. The hydraulic efficiency for turbines was given by Eq. (14.22) as

$$e_h = 2\phi \left(C_1 \cos \alpha_1 - \frac{r_2}{r_1} C_2 \cos \alpha_2 \right) \tag{16.7}$$

For maximum efficiency α_2 will be close to 90°, for then the value of V_2, and hence the loss of kinetic energy at discharge from the runner, will be a minimum. Experimental evidence indicates that α_2 for maximum efficiency varies from 85° for low-specific-speed Francis turbines to about 75° for high-specific-speed ones. As a simplifying assumption for this discussion let us assume $\alpha_2 = 90°$. Equation (16.7) then becomes

$$e_h = 2\phi_e C_1 \cos \alpha_1 \tag{16.8}$$

From this equation it is seen that ϕ_e and C_1 are inversely proportional to each other. Thus, for the Pelton wheel, where ϕ is a little less than 0.5, $C_1 = C_v$, the nozzle velocity coefficient, which is nearly 1. For the reaction turbine, where less than half of the net head is converted into the kinetic energy leaving the guide vanes and entering the runner, the value of C_1 must be of the order of 0.6, and therefore ϕ_e is correspondingly high. As the specific speed increases, values of C_1 decrease and ϕ_e

becomes higher.   Typical values of ϕ_e for axial-flow turbines range from 1.4 to 2.0.

16.12 TURBINE PROPORTIONS AND FACTORS

Figures 16.2 and 16.15 show the nomenclature used.   In a high-specific-speed runner the diameter at the entrance varies from crown to band and the nominal diameter D is taken at the mid-height of the guide vanes. For our purpose much use will be made of this dimension.   For the designer, however, an important dimension is the *throat* diameter D_t, which is less than D for low-specific-speed runners and greater than D for high-specific-speed runners.   The diameter D_d of the upper end of the draft tube is slightly less than D_t for low-specific-speed runners and slightly greater than D_t for high-specific-speed runners.

Values of certain runner proportions and factors are shown in Fig. 16.16.   All quantities which may vary with either load or speed are here shown as the values for the point of maximum efficiency.   The exact form of a runner profile and the values of these factors will vary from one manufacturer to the next and are developed as a result of experience. However, the values shown are representative and do show the trend of each as a function of specific speed.

The theory as presented in this chapter represents the capacity of a runner as a function of D, but the quantity which determines capacity is the discharge area of the runner.   This area is determined on the drafting board and is carefully checked in manufacture.

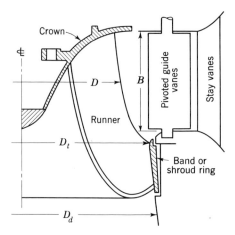

Fig. 16.15

The circumferential area of the runner is

$$A_c = 0.95\pi BD = 0.95\pi \left(\frac{B}{D}\right) D^2$$

where 0.95 is a factor arbitrarily inserted to correct for the area occupied by the runner vanes. In a specific design the precise value could be obtained. The ratio B/D is a function of specific speed.

The radial component of the velocity at entrance is $V_r = C_r \sqrt{2gh}$ and $Q = V_r A_c$. Since bhp $= e\gamma Qh/550$ and also bhp $= n_s^2 h^{5/2}/n^2$, where $n = 153.2\phi \sqrt{h}/D$ from Eq. (14.20), it is possible to employ all these relations to obtain

$$C_r = \frac{n_s^2}{63,740\phi_e^2(B/D)e} \tag{16.9}$$

if γ is assumed as 62.4 pcf. (For any other specific weight γ', multiply 63,740 by γ'/γ.) Then, by employing values of ϕ_e and B/D from Fig. 16.16, a value of eC_r may be obtained for any specific speed. It is seen that in any given case the value of C_r depends upon the turbine efficiency,

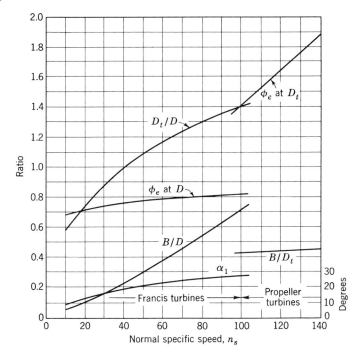

Fig. 16.16

which is proper, because, for a given power for a given specific speed, the quantity Q required will depend upon the turbine efficiency. The value of the latter is not necessarily that shown in Fig. 16.14, for those in the figure are merely typical values.

Also, $V_r = V_1 \sin \alpha_1$, and it is therefore clear that, as C_r and V_r depend upon the turbine efficiency, so also must α_1 depend upon turbine efficiency. That is, in order to provide a greater flow for a turbine of lower efficiency, the gates must be opened to a larger angle to provide a larger area for the flow. Hence the values of α_1 shown in Fig. 16.16 are only approximations.

The foregoing discussion and equations apply to the Francis turbine. For the axial-flow turbine, D is replaced by D_t and the value of ϕ_e becomes that for D_t, the maximum diameter. If the diameter of the guide-vane-tip circle is D_o, Eq. (16.9) is replaced by

$$C_r = \frac{n_s^2 D_t^2}{63{,}740 \phi_e^2 B D_o e} \tag{16.10}$$

Often D_o is slightly greater than D_t, but in many cases the two are practically identical. If the latter is the case, then Eq. (16.10) reduces to the same form as Eq. (16.9).

Illustrative example 16.2: (a) Find typical values for the blade angles α_1 and β_1' of a Francis turbine having a specific speed $n_s = 20$.

From Figs. 16.14 and 16.16, $e = 0.925$, $B/D = 0.095$, and $\phi_e = 0.72$. Assume $e_h = 0.94$ and $\alpha_2 = 90°$. Then

$$C_r = \frac{400}{(0.72)^2 \times 0.095 \times 63{,}740 \times 0.925} = 0.138$$

From Eq. (16.8), $C_1 \cos \alpha_1 = e_h / 2\phi_e$. Thus

$$C_1 \cos \alpha_1 = \frac{0.94}{2 \times 0.72} = 0.653$$

$$\tan \alpha_1 = \frac{C_1 \sin \alpha_1}{C_1 \cos \alpha_1} = \frac{C_r}{C_1 \cos \alpha_1} = \frac{0.138}{0.653} = 0.211$$

from which $\alpha_1 = 12°$. Hence $C_1 = C_r/\sin \alpha_1 = 0.138/0.208 = 0.665$. Applying Eq. (16.6),

$$\cot \beta_1 = \frac{0.653 - 0.72}{0.138} = -0.503$$

and $\beta_1 = 116.5°$, which should also be the blade angle β_1'.

(b) If the turbine of (a) above is to be used to develop 3,600 bhp under a head of 402 ft at 600 rpm, determine its dimensions B and D; find V_r and Q.

$$n_s = \frac{600 \sqrt{3{,}600}}{(402)^{5/4}} = 20 \qquad \text{as in } (a)$$

Then

$$D = \frac{153.2\phi \sqrt{h}}{n} = \frac{153.2 \times 0.72 \times 20.05}{600} = 3.69 \text{ ft}$$

From Fig. 16.16, $B = 0.095 \times 3.69 = 0.351$ ft, and $D_t = 0.735 \times 3.69 = 2.71$ ft. Thus $A_C = 0.95\pi DB = 3.87$ ft². $V_r = 0.138 \times 8.02 \times 20.05 = 22.15$ fps, and $Q = 3.87 \times 22.15 = 85.7$ cfs.

16.13. CAVITATION

Whenever the magnitude or direction of the velocity of a fluid is changed by a guiding surface over which the flow passes, there will be a change in pressure. At some point on the surface the pressure will have a minimum value, and this is usually at a point not only near where the local velocity is high, but also where the flow tends to depart from the surface. If this minimum pressure is denoted by p_m, while p_0 is the pressure in the undisturbed flow where v_0 is the relative velocity with respect to the surface, it is convenient to define a dimensionless pressure coefficient

$$K_i = \frac{p_0 - p_m}{\rho v_0^2/2}$$

This pressure coefficient is a function of the vane design only and for a given vane is a constant at a given angle of attack. In some special cases its value can be computed, but in general it must be determined experimentally.

For a given flow, i.e., for a constant value of v_0, if the pressure p_0 is lowered, the value of p_m will be reduced the same amount, since K_i is a constant. If p_m is reduced to the vapor pressure p_v either by reducing p_0 or by raising v_0, cavitation will ensue, as explained in Sec. 4.8. An expression that denotes the cavitation tendency of the flow is

$$K = \frac{p_0 - p_v}{\rho v_0^2/2}$$

where K is a variable and depends on the base pressure and the vapor pressure. If K is greater than K_i, then p_m is greater than p_v, and cavitation will not ensue. But if $K = K_i$, then cavitation is incipient. Thus the lower the value of K_i, the better the vane is from the cavitation standpoint. If either p_0 or v_0 is such as to make K less than K_i, cavitation will be severe and will increase as K continues to decrease.

The coefficients K_i and K refer to a uniform pressure field. As this does not exist in the rotating elements of a turbine, the values p_0 and v_0 must be the average values in the passage where p_m is determined. Inasmuch as p_0 and p_m are not easily measured and cannot be computed, K may be replaced by a cavitation number σ'. This parameter σ' is also a pressure coefficient, but it has only a slight relationship to K. It is defined as

$$\sigma' = \frac{p_2/\gamma + V_2^2/2g - p_v/\gamma}{h}$$

where the subscript 2 refers to values at the top of the draft tube or, preferably, to the highest point in the runner where cavitation might occur, and where h is the net head on the turbine. However, even this is not a practical expression because it is impossible to measure either p_2 or V_2 at the top of the draft tube with any degree of precision, because of the whirl and general turbulence that usually exist at this section. And if the point is taken within the runner, the determination is even more difficult.

Writing an energy equation between this section and the surface of the water in the tailrace and employing absolute pressures, we have

$$\frac{p_2}{\gamma} + \frac{V_2^2}{2g} + z_2 = \frac{p_a}{\gamma} + h_L$$

where p_a is the atmospheric or barometer pressure, and h_L is the head loss between the two points. However, the draft tube is considered an integral part of the turbine. Hence the term for head loss is omitted, and the resulting parameter then covers the combination of runner and its draft tube.

The resulting cavitation parameter, as proposed by Thoma, is then

$$\sigma = \frac{p_a/\gamma - p_v/\gamma - z_2}{h}$$

If either z_2 or h is increased, the value of σ will be decreased, and the local pressure on the vane will also decrease. When the latter is reduced to the vapor pressure, cavitation will ensue. The value of σ at which cavitation is detected is called the critical value and is denoted by σ_c. Its value may be determined experimentally by noting the value of σ at which the power or the efficiency or some other property is observed to start to change. The exact value of σ_c may be slightly different according to which criterion is used.

The practical utility of the preceding equation is to determine the maximum elevation above the tailwater surface at which a turbine can be set without resultant cavitation. This limiting height is given as

$$z_2 = \frac{p_a}{\gamma} - \frac{p_v}{\gamma} - \sigma_c h \tag{16.11}$$

This limiting height depends upon the barometric pressure, which is a

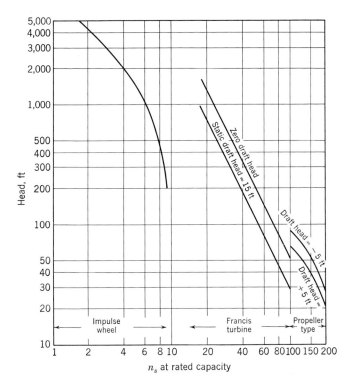

Fig. 16.17. Recommended limits of specific speed for turbines under various effective heads at sea level with water temperature at 80°F. (*After Moody, in Davis (ed.), "Handbook of Applied Hydraulics," McGraw-Hill Book Company,* 1952.)

function of the elevation above sea level, and upon the net head under which the turbine operates. Thus the higher the net head upon a given turbine, the lower it must be set relative to the tailwater level. Equation (16.11) gives a limiting value. The safe value of z_2 is slightly less. Figure 16.17 shows recommended limits of safe specific speed for various heads based on experience with existing units.

Unlike K_i, the numerical value of σ_c varies with the specific speed, as well as with the pressure characteristic of the vanes and other guide surfaces, including the draft tube, and thus is not a direct measure of the excellence of the design. However, it is widely used and is valuable for the comparison of machines of the same specific speed. It is impossible to compute the value of σ_c by theory, and the only certain way to ensure freedom from cavitation is to make model tests in a suitable laboratory.

Limiting safe values of σ_c given by Moody[1] for rated specific speeds are:

	Francis turbines					Propeller turbines		
n_s	20	40	60	80	100	100	150	200
σ_c	0.025	0.10	0.23	0.40	0.64	0.43	0.73	1.5

Inspection of these values and those of Fig. 16.17 shows that a turbine of high specific speed must be set much lower than one of low specific speed. In fact, for a high net head h, it might be necessary to set the turbine even below the level of the tailwater surface. This is a factor which restricts the use of propeller turbines to the low head range, which is fortunately the condition for which they are best suited in other ways also.

Illustrative example 16.3:   Find the maximum permissible head under which a Francis turbine ($n_s = 70$) can operate if it is set 10 ft above tailwater at an elevation of 5,000 ft with water temperature at 60°F.

At 5,000 ft elevation, $\dfrac{p_a}{\gamma} = \dfrac{12.2 \times 144}{62.4} = 28.2$ ft

At 60°F, $\dfrac{p_v}{\gamma} = \dfrac{0.26 \times 144}{62.4} = 0.5$ ft

From the above table, $\sigma_c = 0.31$

From Eq. (16.11),

$$10 = 28.2 - 0.5 - 0.31(h)$$
$$h = 57 \text{ ft}   \text{(maximum permissible head to assure against cavitation)}$$

16.14. INSTALLATIONS

The reaction turbine is especially adapted for use under moderately low heads and even for high heads up to a possible maximum of 1,500 ft for large powers, if the water does not carry silt that would cut the clearance rings and produce excessive leakage loss. The propeller type of reaction turbine is particularly suitable for the combination of low head with extremely large power. Its cavitation characteristics limit it to relatively low head use.

Among some interesting installations of reaction turbines are the following. At Fionnay, Switzerland, a Francis turbine operates under a head of 1,490 ft and delivers 63,200 hp at 750 rpm. In Austria a head of

---

[1] L. F. Moody, in C. V. Davis (ed.), "Handbook of Applied Hydraulics," p. 591, McGraw-Hill Book Company, New York, 1952.

1,430 ft is used for a 77,700-hp turbine at 500 rpm.   In Norway a head of 1,360 ft is used to develop 69,000 hp at 500 rpm.   In Italy a reaction turbine running at 1,000 rpm develops 20,140 hp under a head of 1,320 ft.   At Oak Grove, Ore., a Francis turbine under a head of 850 ft delivers 35,000 hp at 514 rpm.   These are all low-specific-speed reaction turbines.

Examples of higher specific speeds are a Francis turbine in France, which delivers 154,000 hp at 187.5 rpm under a head of 336 ft and another one, also in France, which runs under a head of 233 ft and develops 135,000 hp at 150 rpm.   At Conowingo on the Susquehanna River 54,000-hp units run at 81.8 rpm under a head of 89 ft.   The Conowingo runners are 18 ft in maximum diameter.

Kaplan turbines are represented by one in Sweden which develops 105,600 hp at 127 rpm under a head of 130 ft and one in Italy which runs at 600 rpm under a head of 141 ft and delivers 7,500 hp.   At Bonneville, on the Columbia River, are units which have runners 280 in. in diameter and with only five blades.   They deliver 66,000 hp at 75 rpm at 50 ft head.   At Safe Harbor on the Susquehanna River are six units with runners 220 in. in diameter running at 109.1 rpm under a head of 53 ft and delivering 42,500 hp each.   At Wheeler Dam in Alabama a fixed-blade propeller unit delivers 45,000 hp at 85.7 rpm under a head of 48 ft. At Rock River in Illinois a Kaplan turbine runs under a head of only 7 ft.   It has a runner 138 in. in diameter and develops 800 hp at 80 rpm.

PROBLEMS

16.1. Refer to Illustrative Example 16.1c.   Suppose two units are to be used. Select several different specific-speed–operating-speed combinations that would satisfy the requirements.

16.2. (a) At a plant of the Utah Power and Light Co. is a turbine runner 76 in. in diameter which develops 8,500 hp at 300 rpm under a head of 440 ft. (b) At Niagara Falls a turbine runner 176 in. in diameter develops 72,500 hp at 107 rpm under a head of 214 ft.   (c) At Cedar Rapids a turbine runner 143 in. in diameter develops 10,800 hp at 55.6 rpm under a head of 32 ft.   (d) At Rock River in Illinois a turbine runner 138 in. in maximum diameter develops 800 hp at 80 rpm under a head of 7 ft.   For each case compute the specific speed and the value of ϕ.   (For a propeller turbine ϕ_t is the value at the tip, not that of the mean entrance radius.)

16.3. It is desired to develop 300,000 hp under a head of 49 ft and to operate at 60 rpm.   (a) If turbines with a specific speed of approximately 150 are to be used, how many units will be required?   (b) If Francis turbines with a specific speed of 80 were to be used, how many units would be required?

16.4. The Cornell University turbine for which the test curves are shown in Figs. 16.11 and 16.12 has a runner 27 in. in diameter and a maximum efficiency of 88 per cent when discharging 38.8 cfs and developing 550 bhp at 600 rpm under a net head of 141.8 ft.   Compute n_s, ϕ_e, and C_r, assuming $B/D = 0.15$.

16.5. In addition to the data of Prob. 16.4, the mechanical-friction losses in the Cornell University turbine were measured and found to be 2.7 hp. Assuming that the leakage is 1 per cent of the measured discharge and that $\alpha_2 = 90°$, find values of e_h, α_1, and β_1.

16.6. If a turbine homologous to that in Prob. 16.4 were made with a runner diameter of 135 in., what would be its probable efficiency under the same head?

16.7. The turbine of Prob. 16.4 has a horizontal shaft, and at the time of the test the center line of the shaft was 12.67 ft above the surface of the water in the tailrace.   The discharge edge of the runner at its highest point is 0.83 ft above the center line of the shaft.   If the temperature of the water were as high as 80°F (vapor pressure = 0.5 psia) and the barometer pressure were 14.6 psia, what would be the value of the cavitation factor σ?

16.8. If it is assumed that the critical value of the cavitation factor for the turbine in Prob. 16.4 is 0.06 and if the other data of Prob. 16.7 are used, what would be the maximum allowable height of the center line of the shaft above the tailwater surface?

16.9. In Prob. 16.8, assume all values the same except that the net head on the turbine is 400 ft.   What would then be the maximum allowable height of the center line of the shaft above the tailwater level?

16.10. The top of the draft tube for the turbine in Prob. 16.4 is 24.5 in. in diameter, where it joins the flange of the elbow discharge from the runner, the latter being on a horizontal shaft.   The top of the draft tube at this flange connection is 11.0 ft above the surface of the water in the tailrace. The discharge end of the draft tube is 42 in. in diameter, and the velocity in the tailrace may be considered negligible.   The total loss in the draft tube is $0.15V_2^2/2g$ plus the discharge loss of $V_3^2/2g$, where subscripts 2 and 3 refer to the top and bottom ends of the draft tube, respectively. When the flow is 38.8 cfs, what is the pressure at the top of the draft tube?

16.11. Suppose the draft tube in Prob. 16.10 were of uniform diameter, what would then be the pressure at the top of the tube?   How much head is saved by the diverging tube?

16.12. What is the efficiency of the draft tube for the data as given in Prob. 16.10?

16.13. Compute the specific speeds for the various turbines for which data are given in Sec. 16.14.

16.14. A Kaplan turbine is to run at 75 rpm and develop 66,000 hp at a head of 50 ft.   Assume that for this particular design $\phi_e = 1.61$ at D_t and that $B/D_t = 0.403$.   (These values are not identical with those in Fig. 16.16 merely because of a difference in the practice of different companies.) Compute the maximum diameter of the runner and the height of the guide vanes.

16.15. In the test of the Cornell University turbine the pressure at the flange at the entrance to the spiral-turbine case where the diameter is 30 in. was read by a mercury manometer.   At a flow of 44.5 cfs the manometer differential reading in the U tube was 9.541 ft Hg, the top of the lower mercury column being 9.730 ft above the surface of the water in the tail-

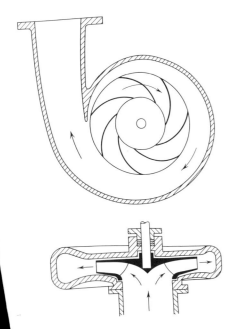

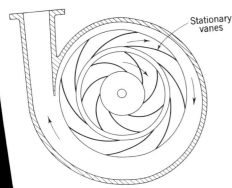

17.8. NORMAL CAPACITY

The discharge from any type of impeller may be found by multiplying the outlet area by the velocity. The area that is most readily computed is the circumferential area for radial-flow impellers and corresponding areas for other types. It is $f\pi BD$, where f is a factor to allow for the space taken up by the vanes. This area is to be multiplied by the component of velocity that is normal to it, which is the radial component for the pure centrifugal impeller, or the axial component for the propeller type, or in general for all types the meridional component, which we shall designate at discharge by V_m. Then the discharge is $f\pi BDV_m$. This meridional component is proportional to u_2 or to $\sqrt{2gh}$, but the exact relationship must be determined by experience.

The ratio of V_m to u_2 depends primarily upon the specific speed but is also affected by the vane angle at exit, the number of vanes, and the casing design. Thus the same impeller might be used in different sizes of case and give a different normal rate of discharge in each.

Illustrative example 17.3: (a) The pump whose characteristics when operating at 2,133.5 rpm are shown in Fig. 17.12 delivers 7.8 cfs against a head of 310 ft when operating at peak efficiency. Determine its specific speed.

$$N_s = \frac{n\sqrt{\text{gpm}}}{h^{3/4}} = \frac{2,133.5\sqrt{7.8 \times 449}}{(310)^{3/4}} = 1,700$$

(b) Determine the specific speed of the prototype of the pump mentioned in (a). The operating characteristics of the prototype are given in the text near the end of Sec. 17.6.

$$N_s = \frac{400\sqrt{213 \times 449}}{(310)^{3/4}} = 1,670$$

The answers to (a) and (b) should be identical because the impellers are homologous. However, since the efficiency curve is flat, it is difficult to ascertain precisely the capacity at maximum efficiency.

17.9. ENERGY LOSSES IN PUMPS

The design of a pump is a specialized field which is of interest to comparatively few and is beyond the scope of this text. The discussion presented here is to enable one to understand the characteristics of pumps, which should be of value to the large number who are users of pumps.[1] In Fig. 17.13 is shown an analysis of the losses in a centrifugal pump as determined by test. Deducting the measured mechanical losses and the computed leakage losses from the measured brake horsepower gives the

---

[1] For detailed methods of design see A. J. Stepanoff, "Centrifugal and Axial Flow Pumps," 2d ed., John Wiley & Sons, Inc., New York, 1957.

race. Neglecting the small velocity head in the tailrace, find the net head on the turbine.

16.16. Francis gave the following dimensions for the turbine (Fig. 16.1) designed and tested by him: $D = 9.338$ ft, $D_2 = 7.987$ ft, $B = 0.9990$ ft, $B_2 = 1.2300$ ft, minimum distance between runner vanes at exit $= 0.1384$ ft, minimum distance between guide vanes at exit $= 0.1467$ ft, 40 runner vanes made of $\frac{1}{4}$-in. iron plate, 40 guide vanes made of $\frac{3}{16}$-in. iron plate. (To avoid pulsating flow, the number of runner vanes should not be the same as the number of guide vanes or any multiple of them.) From these data and scaling the drawings, it is estimated that approximately $\alpha_1 = 13°$, $\beta_2 = 168°$, $\beta_1' = 115°$, and $a_2 = 6.65$ ft².

At the most efficient speed Francis reported the test data as $h = 13.378$ ft, $Q = 113$ cfs, $n = 40.3$ rpm, bhp $= 136.6$, and $e = 0.797$, from which $\phi = 0.672$, $u_1 = 19.7$, $u_2 = 16.85$, and $\sqrt{2gh} = 29.3$.

Compute (a) specific speed, (b) C_r, (c) C_1, (d) β_1, and compare with the vane angle β_1', as measured.

16.17. From the data given in Prob. 16.16, compute (a) v_2; (b) $v_2 \cos \beta_2$; (c) α_2; (d) V_2; (e) per cent of the head lost in the kinetic energy at discharge from the runner. (This turbine was submerged below tailwater level and had no draft tube.)

16.18. In the test of the turbine of Prob. 16.16 at zero speed, $h = 13.565$ ft and $Q = 110.3$ cfs. (a) What were the magnitude and direction of the absolute velocity at discharge from the runner? (b) What percentage of the head was the unit kinetic energy at discharge from the runner? (c) How was the rest of the head expended?

16.19. In the test of the turbine of Prob. 16.16 at runaway speed, $h = 13.596$ ft, $Q = 99.8$ cfs, $u_1 = 37.7$ fps, $u_2 = 32.3$ fps. (a) What were the magnitude and direction of the absolute velocity at discharge from the runner? (b) What percentage of the head was the unit kinetic energy at discharge from the runner? (c) How was the rest of the head expended? (d) What was the maximum value of ϕ?

16.20. The Grand Coulee turbines have runner diameters of 197 in. The height of the guide vanes is 34.375 in. The diameter of the throat of the runner and also the diameter of the draft tube adjacent to the runner are 172 in. They are rated at 150,000 hp under a head of 330 ft at 120 rpm. At this power the efficiency is 89 per cent and the absolute velocity of the water entering the runner is 77.2 fps. Compute (a) rated specific speed; (b) ϕ; (c) C_1; (d) C_r; (e) α_1 and β_1 for this full gate opening.

16.21. The turbines of Prob. 16.20 have a maximum efficiency of 93 per cent at 125,000 hp under a head of 330 ft at 120 rpm. The axial component of velocity at the top of the draft tube is 23 fps, and if it is assumed that at this normal load the angle of whirl in the draft tube is 7°, which is good practice, some assumptions will lead to an estimate of $(r_2/r_1)C_2 \cos \alpha_2 = 0.013$. Compute (a) normal specific speed; (b) C_r; (c) $C_1 \cos \alpha_1$, assuming hydraulic efficiency $= 94$ per cent; (d) α_1 and β_1 for normal power; (e) C_1.

16.22. A radial-flow reaction turbine has the following characteristics: $A_c = a_1 = 40$ in.², $a_2 = 28$ in.², $Q = 1,600$ gpm, $e = 0.82$, $r_1 = 10$ in., $r_2 = 5$ in., $\beta_1' = 140°$, $\beta_2 = 155°$. Assume shockless entrance and assume $\alpha_2 = 90°$. Find the rotative speed under these conditions. Find also the torque, the brake horsepower, the net head, and the value of C_1. Assume $\phi_e = 0.75$.

16.23. A turbine is to be installed where the net available head is 185 ft, and the available flow will average 900 cfs. What type of turbine would you recommend? Specify the operating speed and number of generator poles for 60-cycle electricity if a turbine with the highest tolerable specific speed that will safeguard against cavitation is selected. Assume the turbine is set 5 ft above tailwater. Assume turbine efficiency is 90 per cent. Approximately what size of runner is required?

16.24. Find the maximum permissible head under which an axial-flow turbine ($n_s = 160$) can operate if it is set 5 ft below tailwater. The installation is at elevation 3,150 ft, and the water temperature is 65°F.

SEVENTEEN

CENTRIFUGAL
AND AXIAL-FLOW PUMPS

17.1. DEFINITIONS

The centrifugal pump is so called because the pressure increase within its rotor due to centrifugal action is an important factor in its operation. In brief, it consists of an impeller rotating within a case, as in Fig. 17.1. Fluid enters the impeller in the central portion, called the *eye*, flows radially outward, and is discharged around the entire circumference into a casing. During flow through the rotating impeller the fluid receives energy from the vanes, resulting in an increase in both pressure and absolute velocity. Since a large part of the energy of the fluid leaving the impeller is kinetic, it is necessary to reduce the absolute velocity and transform the larger portion of this velocity head into pressure head. This is accomplished in the volute casing surrounding the impeller (Fig. 17.1) or in flow through diffuser vanes (Fig. 17.2).

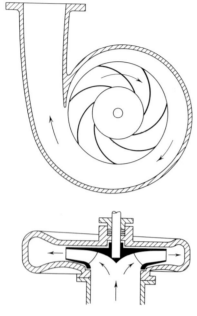

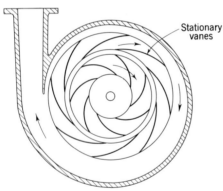

Fig. 17.1.   Volute centrifugal pump.

Stationary
vanes

Fig. 17.2.   Diffuser (or turbine) pump. This illustration is not typical of modern practice and would be found only in large pumps where the diffuser vanes are needed for structural reasons. In modern turbine pumps the diffuser vanes are three-dimensional, as in Fig. 17.5, and cannot readily be shown in a drawing.

As with the reaction turbine, the demand for greater capacity, without increasing the diameter to obtain it, resulted in an increase in the dimensions parallel to the shaft. This in turn required an increase in the eye diameter to accommodate the larger flow and a corresponding change in the vanes at entrance, resulting in the mixed-flow impeller.

A still further increase in specific speed is obtained with the propeller, or axial-flow, pump in Fig. 6.15. In this type there is no change in radius of a given streamline, and hence centrifugal action plays no part. However, the theorem of angular momentum applies alike to all types.

The principles of this chapter apply equally to fans and blowers as well as to pumps handling liquids so long as there is only a small change in density of the air or other gas.

17.2. CLASSIFICATION

Centrifugal pumps are divided into two general classes: (1) volute pumps and (2) diffuser, or turbine, pumps. In the former the impeller is surrounded by a spiral case, as in Fig. 17.1, the outer boundary of which may be a curve called a *volute*. The absolute velocity of the fluid leaving the impeller is reduced in the volute casing, with a resultant increase in pressure. In the latter, shown in Fig. 17.2, the impeller is surrounded by diffuser vanes which provide gradually enlarging passages to effect a gradual reduction in velocity. Because of the superficial resemblance to a reaction turbine, this type is often called a *turbine pump*. However, it is still a centrifugal pump. These diffusion vanes are usually fixed or immovable, but in a very few instances they have been pivoted like the guide vanes in a turbine in order that the angle might be changed to conform to conditions with different rates of flow.

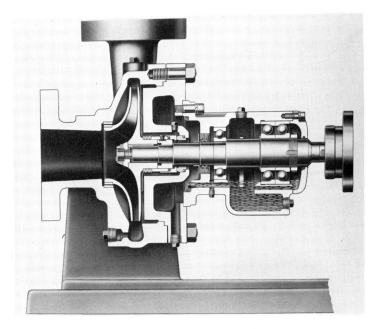

Fig. 17.3. Single-suction pump. (*Courtesy of Ingersoll-Rand.*)

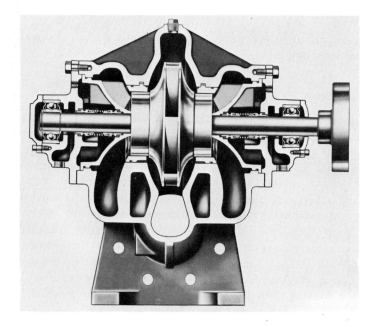

Fig. 17.4.   Double-suction pump.   (*Courtesy of Ingersoll-Rand.*)

Centrifugal pumps are also divided into single-suction pumps, as in Fig. 17.3, and double-suction pumps, as in Fig. 17.4.   The latter have the advantage of symmetry, which ideally should eliminate end thrust. They also provide a larger inlet area with lower intake velocities than would be possible with a single-suction pump of the same outside diameter of the impeller.

All types of pumps may be single-stage or multistage.   With the latter, two or more impellers are arranged in series.   The quantity of flow is the same as for one alone, but the total head developed by the unit is the product of the head of one stage times the number of stages.

A very special type is the deep-well pump of Fig. 17.5.   Since this must be installed in a well casing of limited size, the total diameter of the pump assembly must be relatively small, and thus the impellers are even smaller in diameter.   Because of the small diameter of the impeller, the head developed is not very great in one stage, and so for a deep well it is necessary to have a number of stages in order to lift the water to the desired height.

Since the casings, or *bowls*, of the deep-well pump are usually concentric and are not volutes and the water must be led from the discharge from one impeller into the eye of the next, it is customary to employ diffusion vanes in the intervening passages.

Figure 17.6 shows the impeller for Fig. 17.5.   It is of the mixed-flow type and is also an open, or unshrouded, impeller.   The stationary casing forms one boundary wall for the rotor passage, which necessitates the vanes having a small clearance with the casing.   By contrast Fig. 17.7 shows a shrouded impeller for another deep-well pump, and in this the rotor passages are completely enclosed as in Figs. 17.3 and 17.4.   These latter could also have open impellers, in which event the edges of the vanes would have to make a close fit against the casing so that there could not be the space that is now seen in the figures.

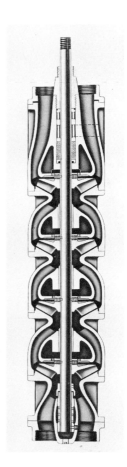

Fig. 17.5. Deep-well multistage mixed-flow turbine pump. (*Courtesy of Byron Jackson Company.*)

Fig. 17.6.   Open, or unshrouded, impeller for pump of
Fig. 17.5.   (*Courtesy of Byron Jackson Company.*)

Fig. 17.7.   Shrouded mixed-flow impeller for deep-well
pump.   (*Courtesy of Byron Jackson Company.*)

17.3. SIZE AND RATING OF PUMPS

It is customary to express the size of a pump by the internal diameter of
the flange at discharge, probably because this indicates the size of the
discharge pipe that might be used.   This gives no indication as to the
size of the impeller, which is in contrast with turbine practice, where the
impeller diameter is usually given.

A pump is rated by its capacity and head at the point of maximum efficiency for a given rotative speed. Of course, both these values depend upon the speed that is specified. These values will be referred to as the *normal* capacity and the *normal* head for that speed.

17.4. HEAD DELIVERED

The head which a pump delivers must equal the static lift plus all friction in both suction and discharge piping. If Fig. 17.8 shows the relation between the head developed by a given pump as a function of its rate of discharge and if this pump is required to deliver fluid through a piping system with a static lift h_s and pipe friction h_L proportional to Q^2, the actual operating head and flow rate are determined by the intersection of the two curves.

The particular values of h and Q determined by this intersection may or may not be those for the maximum efficiency of the particular pump. If they are not the normal values, this means that the pump is not exactly suited to the specific conditions.

In a test of a pump the head is determined by measuring the pressures on both the intake and the discharge sides, as indicated in Fig. 17.9, and the total head is then

$$h = \frac{p_d}{\gamma} - \frac{p_s}{\gamma} + z_d - z_s + \frac{V_d{}^2}{2g} - \frac{V_s{}^2}{2g} \qquad (17.1)$$

where V_d and V_s are the velocities at the sections where the pressures are measured and must be computed from the measured discharge. If the two pipes are of the same size, these cancel, but frequently the intake pipe is larger than the discharge pipe. It should be noted that in Eq. (17.1), h, the head put into the fluid by the pump, was previously referred to as h_p, in Sec. 4.6.

The official test code provides that the head on a pump be the differ-

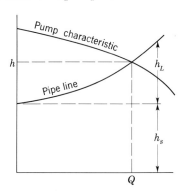

Fig. 17.8.   Pump and pipeline.

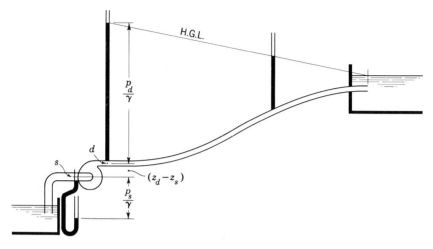

Fig. 17.9.   Head developed by pump.

ence between the heads at the intake and the discharge flanges.   However, flow conditions at the discharge flange are usually too irregular for accurate pressure measurement, and it is more reliable to measure the pressure at 10 or more pipe diameters away from the pump and to add an estimated pipe friction head for that length of pipe.   On the intake side, prerotation sometimes exists in the pipe near the pump, and this will cause the pressure reading on a gage to be higher than the true average pressure at that section.

For a deep-well pump it is physically impossible to take pressure readings at such points, and the pressure is measured in the pipe at the top of the well.   To this pressure head is added the velocity head at that section and the elevation above the level of the water in the well outside of the casing.   Hence, for such installations, the pump head includes the friction losses in the foot valve and strainer below the pump, the friction in the vertical column of pipe, and also that in an elbow at the top of the well.

17.5. SPECIFIC SPEED

For pumps there are two commonly used definitions of specific speed given in Eqs. (14.24) and (14.25).   They are

$$n_s = \frac{n \sqrt{Q}}{h^{3/4}} \quad \text{and} \quad N_s = \frac{n \sqrt{\text{gpm}}}{h^{3/4}}$$

where $N_s = 21.2 n_s$.   Pumps are customarily rated in gallons per minute; hence N_s is the more commonly used specific speed and will be the one referred to in this text. Computed values of specific speed for a given pump throughout its entire operating range from zero discharge to zero head (and maximum discharge) would give values from zero to infinity, but the only value that has any real significance is that corresponding to the values of head, discharge, and speed at the point of maximum efficiency.

As in the case of the reaction turbine, the numerical value of the specific speed indicates the type of pump. On the gallons-per-minute basis specific speeds for volute centrifugal pumps range from 500 to 5,000, for mixed-flow pumps from 4,000 to 10,000, and for axial-flow pumps from 10,000 to 15,000 as approximate limits.

For fans it is customary to express capacity in cubic feet of air per minute. With these units specific speeds for fans range from 140 to 8,000.

For a double-suction pump it is customary to base the specific speed on one-half of the total capacity of the pump, on the assumption that a double-suction impeller is the equivalent of two single-suction impellers placed back to back.

Illustrative example 17.1: (a) It is desired to deliver 1,600 gpm at a head of 900 ft with a single-stage pump. What would be the minimum speed that could be used?

Assuming that the minimum practical specific speed is 500, we get

$$n = \frac{N_s h^{3/4}}{\sqrt{\text{gpm}}} = \frac{500(900)^{3/4}}{\sqrt{1,600}} = 2,060 \text{ rpm}$$

(b) For the conditions of (a), how many stages must the pump ($N_s = 500$) have if a rotative speed of 600 rpm is to be used?

$$h^{3/4} = \frac{n \sqrt{\text{gpm}}}{N_s} = \frac{600 \sqrt{1,600}}{500} = 48$$

or $h = 175$ ft per stage

Hence $900/175 = 5.14$ (6 stages are required)

To meet the exact specifications of head and capacity, either the rotative speed or the specific speed or both could be changed slightly.

Illustrative example 17.2: (a) Determine the specific speed of a pump that is to deliver 2,000 gpm against a head of 150 ft with a rotative speed of 600 rpm.

$$N_s = \frac{n \sqrt{\text{gpm}}}{h^{3/4}} = \frac{600 \sqrt{2,000}}{(150)^{3/4}} = 625$$

(b) If the rotative speed were doubled, what would be the flow rate and the head developed by the pump? Assume no change in efficiency.

Eq. (14.14): $Q \propto n$, so $Q = 2 \times 2,000 = 4,000$ gpm.

Eq. (14.13): $h \propto n^2$, so $h = 2^2 \times 150 = 600$ ft.

(c) Check the specific speed for the conditions given in (b).

$$N_s = \frac{1,200 \sqrt{4,000}}{(600)^{3/4}} = 625$$

This result was expected, for the same impeller was involved in (a) and (b).

(d) Find the required operating speed of a two-stage pump ($N_s = 625$) to satisfy the requirements in (a).

$$N_s = 625 = \frac{n \sqrt{2,000}}{(75)^{3/4}}$$

$$n = 365 \text{ rpm}$$

17.6. CHARACTERISTICS AT CONSTANT SPEED

The usual mode of operation of a pump is at constant speed, and typical characteristics of a centrifugal pump for such operation are shown in Fig. 17.10. These curves may be transformed into those for some other speed by means of the similarity laws (Illustrative Example 17.3). It will be observed that the power required to run the pump with the discharge

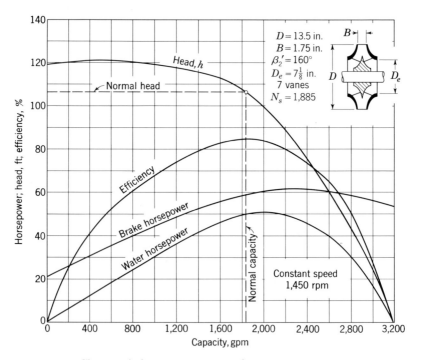

Fig. 17.10.   Characteristics at constant speed.

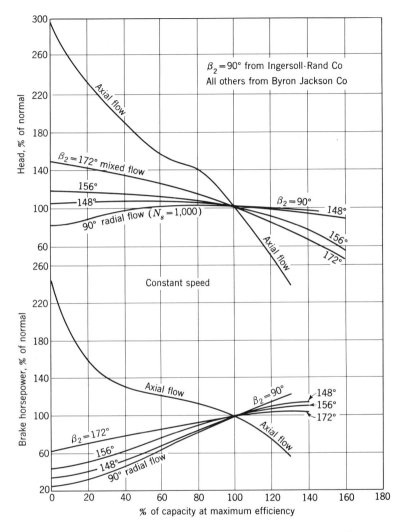

Fig. 17.11. Head-capacity characteristics for different types of pumps.

valve closed, so that there is no flow, is much less than the normal power at the point of maximum efficiency. Also, the maximum power is very little more than the normal power. Hence, if a motor is selected for the normal power, there is no danger of an appreciable overload at this speed no matter what operating conditions may be encountered.

By different impeller and casing designs it is possible to vary the characteristics, as shown by Fig. 17.11, and each one has special advantages for particular conditions.   Thus a *flat characteristic* permits a considerable variation in the rate of discharge with but very little change in head, while a *steep characteristic* gives only a small variation in the flow for a relatively large change in head.

The axial-flow pump has a much steeper head-capacity curve than does any centrifugal pump, and instead of the power at shutoff being a minimum, as for the centrifugal pump, it not only is a maximum but is very much larger than the power required at the point of maximum efficiency.   This is a disadvantage both in starting up and in continued operation at low capacity.   The characteristics of the axial-flow pump shown in Fig. 17.11 are for the fixed-blade type.   In a few instances this type of pump is made with adjustable blades similar to the runner of the Kaplan turbine, and the blades can be adjusted during operation to suit conditions.

Discontinuities will frequently be found in the head or power curves or both and also in the efficiency curve.   They are caused by a shift in the flow pattern, probably due to a separation.   Such discontinuities occur

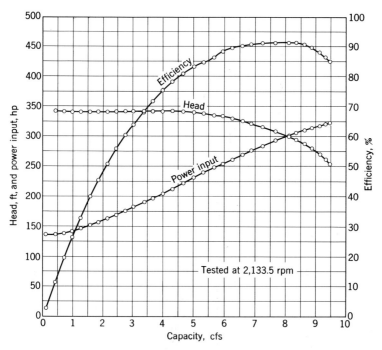

Fig. 17.12.   Test of Byron Jackson model pump at California Institute of Technology.

in most pumps of high efficiency, but are not always detected unless accurate tests are made and the points closely spaced as in Fig. 17.12. They exist in many low-specific-speed centrifugal pumps, as well as in the high-specific-speed axial-flow pumps. Discontinuity may arise in the impeller or the case or both, and the point at which it occurs can be shifted by an alteration in design but generally cannot be altogether eliminated. In any event the discontinuity should be made to occur outside of the operating range, because the flow is unstable at this point and gives rise to vibration.

Figure 17.12 shows the results of a test of a model pump for one of the plants on the Colorado River Aqueduct. It was operated at such a speed as to give the same fluid velocities and the same head as those of the prototype. As the scale ratio is 1:5.334, the speed of the prototype is 400 rpm and the normal capacity is 213 cfs at a head of 310 ft, with a power requirement of 8,150 bhp. The efficiency of the model pump with an impeller diameter of 14.62 in. was 91.7 per cent.

17.7 SHUTOFF HEAD

When a pump filled with the fluid to be pumped is operated at normal speed with the discharge valve closed, the head developed is called the *shutoff head*. Ideally, this would appear to be a case of a forced vortex with a pressure-head difference between the eye and the periphery of the impeller of $(u_2{}^2 - u_1{}^2)/2g$. However, the case is not so simple. Although there is no fluid delivered, it is not a case of zero flow so far as the impeller is concerned since fluid flows from the case through the clearance spaces back into the intake side so that there is really some impeller discharge.

Furthermore, it has been well established by observation that for this condition of operation there is a great deal of internal circulation within the impeller, an actual flow back into the intake pipe around the outer circumference of the eye, and an equal flow back into the impeller in the central portion. The result of this is that there is a rotation of the fluid in the eye of the impeller and even for a distance of several pipe diameters in the intake pipe. The result of this prerotation is that the actual shutoff head is approximately given by $u_2{}^2/2g$. However, the flow conditions are so complex that any precise theoretical analysis is out of the question. It is known that the actual shutoff head is affected by the value of the impeller-vane angle at exit, by the design of the case, and even by the nature of the intake, since the latter has some influence on the prerotation. Thus, in one instance, where the same impeller was tested at the same speed but with several different types of intakes, the shutoff head ranged from 240 to 282 ft.

17.8. NORMAL CAPACITY

The discharge from any type of impeller may be found by multiplying the outlet area by the velocity. The area that is most readily computed is the circumferential area for radial-flow impellers and corresponding areas for other types. It is $f\pi BD$, where f is a factor to allow for the space taken up by the vanes. This area is to be multiplied by the component of velocity that is normal to it, which is the radial component for the pure centrifugal impeller, or the axial component for the propeller type, or in general for all types the meridional component, which we shall designate at discharge by V_m. Then the discharge is $f\pi BDV_m$. This meridional component is proportional to u_2 or to $\sqrt{2gh}$, but the exact relationship must be determined by experience.

The ratio of V_m to u_2 depends primarily upon the specific speed but is also affected by the vane angle at exit, the number of vanes, and the casing design. Thus the same impeller might be used in different sizes of case and give a different normal rate of discharge in each.

Illustrative example 17.3: (a) The pump whose characteristics when operating at 2,133.5 rpm are shown in Fig. 17.12 delivers 7.8 cfs against a head of 310 ft when operating at peak efficiency. Determine its specific speed.

$$N_s = \frac{n\sqrt{\mathrm{gpm}}}{h^{3/4}} = \frac{2{,}133.5\sqrt{7.8\times449}}{(310)^{3/4}} = 1{,}700$$

(b) Determine the specific speed of the prototype of the pump mentioned in (a). The operating characteristics of the prototype are given in the text near the end of Sec. 17.6.

$$N_s = \frac{400\sqrt{213\times449}}{(310)^{3/4}} = 1{,}670$$

The answers to (a) and (b) should be identical because the impellers are homologous. However, since the efficiency curve is flat, it is difficult to ascertain precisely the capacity at maximum efficiency.

17.9. ENERGY LOSSES IN PUMPS

The design of a pump is a specialized field which is of interest to comparatively few and is beyond the scope of this text. The discussion presented here is to enable one to understand the characteristics of pumps, which should be of value to the large number who are users of pumps.[1] In Fig. 17.13 is shown an analysis of the losses in a centrifugal pump as determined by test. Deducting the measured mechanical losses and the computed leakage losses from the measured brake horsepower gives the

---

[1] For detailed methods of design see A. J. Stepanoff, "Centrifugal and Axial Flow Pumps," 2d ed., John Wiley & Sons, Inc., New York, 1957.

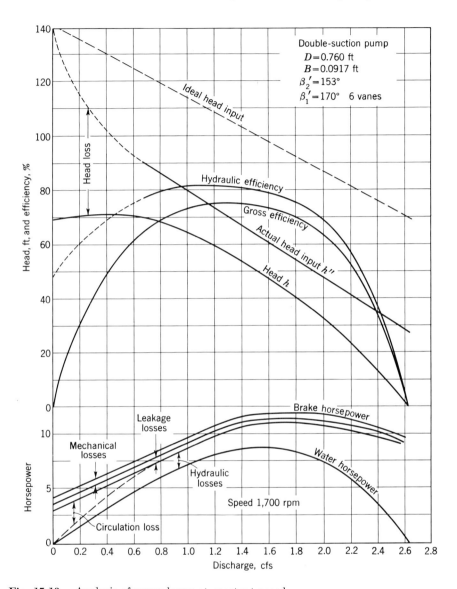

Fig. 17.13.   Analysis of pump losses at constant speed.

actual power delivered to the water by the vanes.   The difference
between this power and the measured water horsepower is the total of the
hydraulic losses.   The hydraulic losses are of two kinds: (1) skin friction,
which should vary as Q^2, and (2) shock losses at impeller entrance and at
discharge into the volute.   The shock losses should be high for both zero

flow and for the maximum flow and will be a minimum at some intermediate flow.   The total losses may be seen to be a minimum at a flow somewhat smaller than that at which the shock losses are a minimum, and since the head is not a constant, the maximum hydraulic efficiency will be found at a still different flow, usually slightly smaller than the others.

High efficiencies have been obtained with pumps having volute cases. Diffuser (or turbine) pumps are not superior in efficiency to volute pumps. They are largely used for multistage high-head low-capacity pumps only.

It has been found that at flows different from the normal there is an irregular discharge around the impeller circumference and at very low flows the fluid may flow back into the impeller near the *tongue*, or *cut-water*, which is the start of the volute.   This variation in flow is accompanied by a variation in the static pressure in the case around the impeller. This produces a radial thrust on the impeller which is a maximum at shutoff, decreases to zero at normal flow, and then increases with larger flow than normal.   This radial thrust may produce a shaft deflection sufficient to cause contact of the wearing rings.   The resulting wear will increase the leakage loss.   Pumps require a stiff shaft to avoid this if only the usual volute case is used.

In order to minimize this radial thrust in large-size high-head pumps, cases have been made in various forms, one of which is the double volute. In this type there are two tongues 180° apart, and a partition in the case extends from this second tongue as far as the discharge flange.

17.10. CAVITATION

An important factor in satisfactory operation of a pump is the avoidance of cavitation, both for the sake of good efficiency and for the prevention of impeller damage (Secs. 4.8 and 16.13).   For pumps a cavitation parameter is

$$\sigma = \frac{p_s/\gamma + V_s^2/2g - p_v/\gamma}{h} \tag{17.2}$$

where subscript s refers to values at the pump intake, h is the head developed by the pump, and p_v is the vapor pressure.   As the latter is normally given in absolute units, it follows that p_s must also be absolute pressure.

With a long straight inlet pipe it may be possible to measure p_s with precision and to compute an accurate value of the mean V_s from the continuity equation.   But where prerotation exists or a fitting, such as an elbow, precedes this section by a short distance, neither of these values can be accurately determined.   It is then preferable to write the energy equation between the pump intake and the surface of the liquid source. Thus, using absolute pressures,

$$\frac{p_s}{\gamma} + \frac{V_s^{\,2}}{2g} + z_s = \frac{p_0}{\gamma} - h_L$$

where z_s is the elevation of the pump intake above the surface of the liquid, as in Fig. 17.9, and p_0 is the pressure upon that surface.   If the liquid is drawn from a closed tank, this pressure could be either greater or less than the atmospheric pressure.   Making this substitution in Eq. (17.2),

$$\sigma = \frac{p_0/\gamma - p_v/\gamma - z_s - h_L}{h} \qquad (17.3)$$

The critical value σ_c is that at which there is an observed change in efficiency or head or some other property.   The value will depend not only upon what criterion is used, but also upon the conditions of operation.   In Fig. 17.14 is shown an experimental curve where the total head and capacity were kept constant while the intake pressure p_s was decreased, resulting in a decrease in σ.   The critical value is fixed by the point where the efficiency was found to drop.   A different value of σ_c would be found for a different capacity.   For safe operation it is desirable to operate at values above the critical for the capacity involved.   The critical value for any specified operating condition depends upon the design of the particular pump, and in any important installation it should be determined experimentally upon a model.

Since cavitation is determined by conditions at entrance to the impeller and not by those at discharge, an expression has been devised known as *suction specific speed*, which is analogous to the usual specific speed except that the total head is replaced by the suction head above the vapor pressure.   This is the numerator of either Eq. (17.2) or (17.3) and

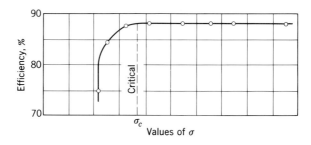

Fig. 17.14.   Effect of varying the cavitation parameter.

is designated as NPSH, which stands for *net positive suction head*. The suction specific speed is then

$$S = \frac{n \sqrt{\text{gpm}}}{\text{NPSH}^{3/4}}$$

For a double-suction pump the total capacity should be divided by 2 for the determination of S.

Inasmuch as the critical value σ_c has been found to depend upon both the usual specific speed and the suction specific speed, there has been devised the relation

$$\sigma_c = \left(\frac{N_s}{S}\right)^{4/3} \tag{17.4}$$

which is obtained by eliminating $n \sqrt{\text{gpm}}$ between the expressions for N_s and S. In order to obtain σ_c, it is necessary to use the critical value of NPSH in evaluating S.

Critical values of the cavitation parameter vary with the design of the pump, but typical approximate values for σ_c are 0.05 for a specific speed of $N_s = 1,000$, 0.10 for $N_s = 2,000$, and 0.30 for $N_s = 4,000$. For values of N_s greater than 4,000 the Hydraulic Institute recommends that the value of S should be less than 8,140.

Introducing the critical value of σ into Eq. (17.3), we obtain

$$z_s = \frac{p_0}{\gamma} - \frac{p_v}{\gamma} - \sigma_c h - h_L \tag{17.5}$$

which will give the maximum allowable elevation of the pump intake above the surface of the liquid. It is apparent that, to ensure freedom from cavitation, the intake pressure should be increased or the pump should be set lower, as (*a*) the total head developed is increased, (*b*) the specific speed for a given head is increased, and (*c*) the vapor pressure of the liquid is increased.[1]

If the value of z_s determined by this equation is negative, it indicates that the pump must be placed below the surface of the liquid.

Illustrative example 17.4: In the accompanying figure is shown the effect of suction pressure on the operating characteristics of a centrifugal pump as determined by experimental test. At the point of maximum efficiency the critical value of NPSH is 10.4 ft. Determine the value of σ_c for this pump, and find where the

---

[1] G. F. Wislicenus, R. M. Watson, and I. J. Karassik, Cavitation Characteristics of Centrifugal Pumps Described by Similarity Considerations, *Trans. ASME*, vol. 61, p. 17, 1939. C. A. Gongwer, A Theory of Cavitation Flow in Centrifugal Pump Impellers, *Trans. ASME*, vol. 63, p. 29, 1941.

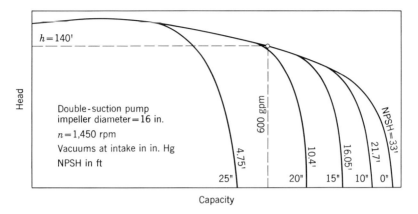

Illustrative Example 17.4

pump should be set to assure against cavitation for this operating condition.   Assume
that the friction loss in the intake pipe is 3 ft.

$$N_s = \frac{1,450 \sqrt{600/2}}{(140)^{3/4}} = 617$$

$$S = \frac{1,450 \sqrt{600/2}}{(10.4)^{3/4}} = 4,330$$

From this, $\sigma_c = (617/4,330)^{4/3} = 0.0745$.   By direct computation, using Eq. (17.2),

$$\sigma_c = \frac{10.4}{140} = 0.0743$$

which is a close check.   The fact that this critical value is larger than the typical
value indicated in the text for such a low specific speed merely emphasizes the fact
that variation in design will give values which differ from the norm.

As this particular pump was tested at sea level and with cold water, it may be
assumed that $p_a/\gamma = 34$ ft and $p_v/\gamma = 1$ ft.   Assuming the friction losses in the
intake piping to be 3 ft, $z = 34 - 3 - 1 - 10.4 = 19.6$ ft, which would be the maximum allowable elevation above the surface to avoid cavitation at this one operating
point.   If it is desired to avoid cavitation at any point, even for maximum discharge,
it would appear that NPSH should be about 33 ft.   In this case $z = 34 - 3 - 1 - 33$
$= -3$ ft, which means the pump should be submerged that amount.

17.11.   VISCOSITY EFFECT

Centrifugal pumps are also used to pump liquids with viscosities different
from that of water.   Figure 17.15 shows actual test curves of performance
for the very extreme range, from water to an oil with a kinematic viscosity
3,200 times that of water.   It is seen that, as the viscosity is increased,
the head-capacity curve becomes steeper and the power required increases.
The dashed line indicates the maximum efficiency points for each viscosity

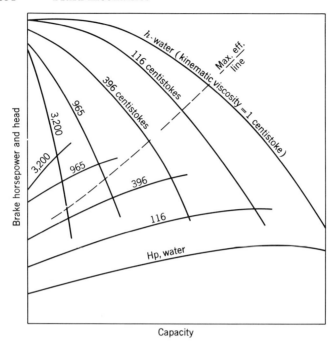

Fig. 17.15. Centrifugal pump with viscous oils. (*R. L. Daugherty, A Further Investigation of the Performance of Centrifugal Pumps when Pumping Oils, Goulds Pumps, Inc., Bull.* 130, *Seneca Falls, N.Y.,* 1926.)

curve. It is seen that both the head and the capacity at the point of maximum efficiency decrease with increasing viscosity. As these are accompanied by an increase in the brake horsepower, there is a marked decrease in efficiency.

17.12. EFFICIENCY

Figure 17.16 presents what are believed to be optimum efficiencies of modern pumps of large capacity. The figure also shows typical runner profiles for a few specific speeds. It is seen that in each type there is presumed to be an optimum efficiency that decreases for either extreme. However, there is a gradual merging of one type into another, and so the dashed line indicates the probable maximum values in these border zones. The difference between one type and another is not so much in the impellers, since these change only gradually with the increase in specific speed, but rather that the volute case is replaced by a completely different arrangement at the higher specific speeds.

It is not to be expected that these curves represent absolute maximum values, because special cases with very favorable conditions may show efficiencies slightly higher, especially in the very low specific-speed range.   Neither is it to be expected that all pumps should attain values as high as shown, since these efficiencies can be attained only by pumps of large size and only where great care is taken in both the design and the construction.

The efficiency of a pump not only is determined by its specific speed but also is affected much more by its physical size, which is represented by its capacity.   In Fig. 17.17 are shown typical efficiency curves for normal commercial pumps as functions of capacity.

For most purposes the specific speed of a double-suction pump is computed by using one-half of the total capacity, and this is especially neces-

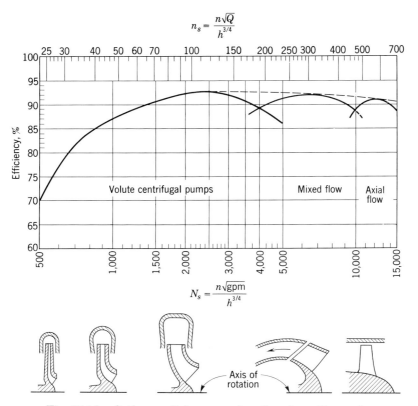

$$n_s = \frac{n\sqrt{Q}}{h^{3/4}}$$

$$N_s = \frac{n\sqrt{\text{gpm}}}{h^{3/4}}$$

Fig. 17.16.   Optimum efficiency as a function of specific speed.

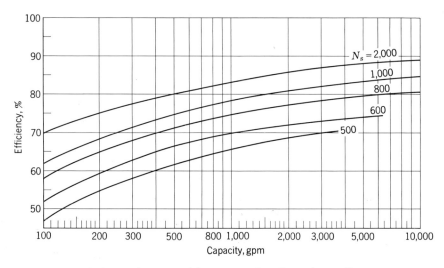

Fig. 17.17. Efficiency of commercial pumps as functions of capacity.

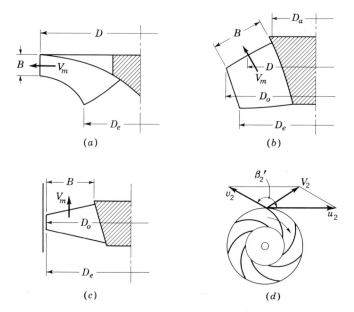

Fig. 17.18. Nomenclature for pump factors and proportions. (*a*) Centrifugal. (*b*) Mixed flow. (*c*) Axial flow. (*d*) Definition of β_2'. (*Note:* In the centrifugal, or radial-flow, pump the extreme diameter D_o is the same as the mean exit diameter D. In the axial-flow pump $D = D_o - B$.)

sary in considering conditions at entrance to the impeller and with regard to cavitation. But the efficiency of a pump is largely determined by the conditions at exit from the impeller and in the casing and is practically unaffected by subdividing the inlet. Hence, for efficiency diagrams such as Figs. 17.16 and 17.17, the specific speed for double-suction pumps is based on the total capacity.

The relation between the efficiency of a model pump and its prototype may be estimated by the Moody formula for turbines [Eq. (16.4)], which is $(1 - e_1)/(1 - e) = (D/D_1)^{1/5}$. Wislicenus has proposed the following formula for pumps:

$$\frac{0.95 - e_1}{0.95 - e} = \left(\frac{\log \text{gpm}}{\log \text{gpm}_1}\right)^2 \qquad (17.6)$$

based on a statistical study of commercial pumps.

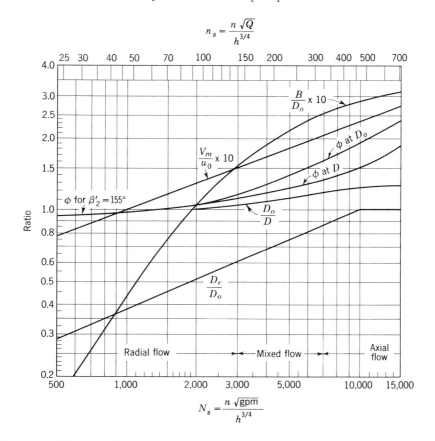

Fig. 17.19. Factors and proportions for pumps. (*Note:* u_o is the peripheral velocity at the extreme diameter D_o.)

17.13. PROPORTIONS AND FACTORS

Figure 17.18 shows the nomenclature to be used, and Fig. 17.19 shows some basic ratios and factors for pumps with a specific speed range of 500 to 15,000. These particular values are not the only ones which may be used, for each manufacturer will have values based upon experience that apply to the particular designs employed. However, the values shown in Fig. 17.19 are typical; data from various sources will lie either on these curves or reasonably close to them, and they do show the trend as a function of specific speed.

Illustrative example 17.5: A pump that will deliver 84,500 gpm against a head of 225 ft when operating at 600 rpm is desired. Determine the specific speed of this pump and its approximate dimensions.

$$N_s = \frac{600 \sqrt{84,500}}{(225)^{3/4}} = 3,000$$

Assume $\beta_2' = 155°$, so that Fig. 17.19 is applicable. From Fig. 17.19, $\phi = 1.1$ at diameter D. Hence $u_2 = 1.1\sqrt{2gh} = 132.5$ fps. From Eq. (14.20),

$$D = 153.2 \times 1.1 \times \frac{\sqrt{225}}{600} = 4.22 \text{ ft} = 50.7 \text{ in.}$$

From Fig. 17.19,

$$\frac{D_o}{D} = 1.07 \qquad \frac{B}{D_o} = 0.155$$

$$\frac{D_e}{D_o} = 0.6 \qquad \frac{V_m}{u_o} = 0.15$$

Hence

$$D_o = 1.07 \times 50.7 = 54.3 \text{ in.}$$
$$B = 0.155 \times 54.3 = 8.42 \text{ in.}$$

The eye diameter is

$$D_e = 0.6 \times 54.3 = 32.6 \text{ in.}$$

The peripheral velocity at D_o is

$$D_o = 1.07 \times 132.5 = 142 \text{ fps}$$
$$(V_m)_2 = 0.15 \times 142 = 21.3 \text{ fps}$$

$$\text{Circumferential area} = 0.95\pi \times 8.42 \times \frac{50.7}{144} = 8.85 \text{ ft}^2$$

$$Q = A_{\text{circum}}(V_m)_2 = 8.85 \times 21.3 = 188.5 \text{ cfs} = 84,500 \text{ gpm}$$

which checks the initial value.

17.14. INSTALLATIONS

A few examples of pump construction and installation will be presented as illustrations of modern practice.

The Byron Jackson Company has built pumps with as many as 54 stages. Water has been lifted to heights of several thousand feet by multistage pumps. Ingersoll-Rand produced a 6-in. 10-stage pump operating at 3,750 rpm which delivers 1,600 gpm at a head of 6,000 ft, the shutoff head being 7,000 ft. The Worthington Corporation installed a pump at Rocky River to deliver 279.5 cfs at a head of 238.84 ft and running at 327 rpm. The brake horsepower was 8,259, giving an efficiency of 91.7 per cent. The impeller diameter was approximately 7.54 ft, and the width at outlet approximately 0.72 ft, with an eye diameter of 4.24 ft.

On the Colorado River Aqueduct the Worthington Corporation built three pumps for the Hayfield plant to deliver 200 cfs each at a head of 444 ft when running at 450 rpm and three similar pumps for Eagle Mountain with a head of 440 ft. The impeller diameters are approximately 81.6 in., and the eye diameters 34 in. The Byron Jackson Company built three pumps for the Gene plant to deliver 200 cfs each at a head of 310 ft when running at 400 rpm. The impeller diameters are 78 in. At the Intake plant, where the head is 294 ft, the impeller diameters are 76 in. The Allis-Chalmers Company built three pumps for the Iron Mountain plant to deliver 200 cfs each at a head of 146 ft when running at 300 rpm. The Byron Jackson model-pump test is shown in Fig. 17.12.

A noteworthy pumping project is that at Grand Coulee on the Columbia River, for which pumps have been built by the Byron Jackson Company and the Pelton Water Wheel Company jointly. The head and capacity for the point of maximum efficiency have been given in Prob. 17.4, but the pumps may also operate at a head as low as 270 ft and discharge 1,650 cfs, at which point they require approximately 60,000 bhp.

The Allis-Chalmers Company has built a combination reversible pump-turbine for the Hiwasee plant of the TVA, which as a pump will deliver 3,900 cfs at a head of 205 ft at the point of maximum efficiency while requiring approximately 100,000 bhp. The impeller diameter is 266 in., and it runs at 105.9 rpm. The maximum capacity is 5,200 cfs at 135 ft head.

In Italy is a pump built in Switzerland which discharges 250,000 gpm, or 558 cfs, at a head of 787 ft at 450 rpm. It requires 62,000 bhp.

A hot-oil pump to deliver 875 gpm at a head of 8,600 ft with 19 stages has been built by the Byron Jackson Company; this is believed to be the highest-head pump in existence.

PROBLEMS

17.1. Suppose 10 stages were to be used for a total head of 900 ft, a capacity of 1,600 gpm, and a pump speed of 600 rpm. What would be the specific speed in both gallons-per-minute and cubic-feet-per-second units?

17.2. A pump is to discharge 160,000 gpm at a head of 16 ft when running at 300 rpm. What type of pump will be required? Suppose the required speed is 450 rpm. What could then be done?

17.3. Assuming $\phi = 1$ in Eq. (14.20), compute the diameter for the impeller in Illustrative Example 17.1a.

17.4. The Grand Coulee pumps on the Columbia River have impellers with a diameter of $167\frac{3}{8}$ in. and width at exit 19.5 in. The speed is 200 rpm, and the maximum efficiency 90.8 per cent. At the point of maximum efficiency the discharge is 1,250 cfs at a head of 344 ft. The shutoff head is 422 ft. Compute ϕ for maximum efficiency, V_m, and V_m/u_2. Assume that the fractional part of area which is free space is 0.95.

17.5. A 54-in. pump at Rocky River has an impeller 90 in. in diameter, and B is 0.75 ft. It runs at 327 rpm. If $\phi = 1.034$ and $V_m/u_2 = 0.128$, compute the head and capacity.

17.6. A 2.5-in. two-stage pump had impellers 12 in. in diameter with widths at outlet of 0.25 in. At a speed of 2,000 rpm the head was 320 ft and the discharge 0.47 cfs. Compute ϕ, K, V_m, and V_m/u_2.

17.7. Using Eqs. (14.13) and (14.14), transform the head-capacity curve for the pump of Fig. 17.10 to a new curve applicable to operation at 1,750 rpm. Assume there is no change in efficiency.

17.8. Plot the head-capacity curve for a pump homologous to the one whose operating characteristics are shown in Fig. 17.10. Plot the head-capacity curve for a pump that is one-third as large as the pump of Fig. 17.10 if it is to operate at 600 rpm. Assume both pumps have the same efficiency.

17.9. The pump of Fig. 17.13 is used to increase the flow from reservoir A to reservoir B. When the water level in A is 10 ft above B, the flow rate is 1.6 cfs. What will the flow rate be when the water surface in A is 40 ft above that in B? Assume turbulent flow at high Reynolds numbers. Pump speed is 1,700 rpm.

17.10. Repeat Prob. 17.9 for a pump speed of 2,250 rpm.

17.11. Select the specific speed of the pump or pumps required to lift 15 cfs of water 375 ft through 10,000 ft of 3-ft-diameter pipe ($f = 0.020$). The pump rotative speed is to be 1,750 rpm. Consider the following cases: single pump, two pumps in series, three pumps in series, two pumps in parallel, three pumps in parallel.

17.12. A very long pipeline connects two reservoirs whose water levels are the same. Identical pumps A and B are connected to the pipe in parallel. The operating characteristics of these pumps are shown in Fig. 17.13. The pumps operate at 1,700 rpm. When one pump was operating, the flow rate was found to be 800 gpm. How much flow will there be when both pumps operate? Assume the flow occurs at high Reynolds number so that friction factor f remains constant. Find also the rates of delivery for one pump and two pumps if the rotative speed is increased to 2,250 rpm.

17.13. Suppose the pump of Illustrative Example 17.4 were to be operated at its maximum efficiency point at a speed of 3,600 rpm, what would be the minimum allowable value of NPSH and what would be the maximum allowable elevation above the water surface, assuming a barometric pressure of 32 ft of water, a vapor pressure of 1 ft of water, and intake-pipe friction of 3 ft? (*Note:* σ_c is constant at the value found in the illustrative example.)

17.14. Suppose the pump in Illustrative Example 17.4 were to pump gasoline with a temperature of 70°F and having the vapor pressure given in Table 1.2. Assume the specific gravity of the gasoline to be 0.72. When $h = 140$ ft, $V_s = 10$ fps. Using the same value of σ_c as for water, what is the minimum allowable intake pressure in feet of gasoline and in pounds per square inch? (For gasoline the head-capacity curve is practically the same as that for water, if the head is expressed in feet of gasoline.)

17.15. Suppose a pump were to pump water at a head of 130 ft, the water temperature being 100°F and the barometric pressure being 14.3 psia. At intake the pressure is a vacuum of 17 in. Hg and the velocity is 12 fps. What are the values of NPSH and σ?

17.16. The pump of Illustrative Example 17.4 when pumping gasoline delivered 600 gpm at a head of 140 ft of gasoline with an intake pressure of 0 gage. With a vacuum-gage reading of 10 in. Hg at the intake, the pump delivered 600 gpm with $h = 94$ ft of gasoline; with a vacuum-gage reading of 15 in. Hg, it delivered 250 gpm with $h = 88$ ft of gasoline. These points are neither the points of maximum efficiency nor the points of incipient cavitation. Assume the vapor pressure of the gasoline to be 4.42 psia and the specific weight to be 45 pcf. If the barometric pressure is 14.7 psia, compute the values of NPSH and of σ for these points, assuming the velocity head to be negligible.

17.17. A pump with a critical value of σ of 0.10 is to pump against a head of 500 ft. The barometric pressure is 14.3 psia, and the vapor pressure of the water is 0.5 psia. Assume the friction losses in the intake piping are 5 ft. Find maximum allowable height of the pump relative to the water surface at intake.

17.18. Consider a pump to deliver 84,500 gpm at a head of 225 ft, as in Illustrative Example 17.5. Determine the rotative speeds and maximum impeller diameters for specific speeds of 500, 1,000, 2,000, 5,000, 8,000, 10,000, and 15,000.

17.19. For a constant maximum or outside diameter $D_o = 4$ ft and a constant head of 81 ft, compute the rotative speeds and capacities for specific speeds (N_s) of 500, 1,000, 2,000, 5,000, 10,000, and 15,000.

17.20. A centrifugal pump with an impeller diameter of 2.84 in. ran at 20,000 rpm and delivered 250 gpm at a head of 700 ft with an efficiency of 60 per cent. Compute the peripheral velocity, the specific speed, and ϕ.

17.21. A centrifugal pump with an impeller 3.15 in. in diameter ran at 18,000 rpm and delivered 189 gpm at a head of 863 ft with an efficiency of 60 per cent. Compute the peripheral velocity, the specific speed, and ϕ.

17.22. Compute the specific speed of the pumps at Grand Coulee and of those on the Colorado River Aqueduct at Hayfield, Gene, and Iron Mountain plants.

17.23. The diameter of the discharge pipe of a pump is 6 in., and that of the intake pipe is 8 in. The pressure gage reads 30 psi, and the vacuum gage at intake reads 10 in. Hg. If $Q = 3.0$ cfs of water and the brake horsepower is 35.0, find the efficiency. $\Delta z = 0$.

17.24. Water leaves the impeller of a centrifugal pump with a velocity of 70 fps at an angle $\alpha_2 = 10°$. It flows through a *whirlpool chamber* consisting of parallel sides before it reaches the volute case. The inner and outer radii of this chamber are 6 and 10 in., respectively. What will be the values of $V \cos \alpha$, V_m, and V for the water as it leaves the chamber and enters the volute?   If there were no loss of energy, what would be the gain in pressure head?

17.25. A boiler feed pump delivers water at 212°F which it draws from an open hot well with a friction loss of 2 ft in the intake pipe between it and the hot well.   The barometer pressure is 29 in. Hg, and the value of σ_c for the pump is 0.10.   What must be the elevation of the water surface in the hot well relative to that of the pump intake?   The total pumping head is 240 ft.

17.26. In a model pump delivering 5.14 cfs with a total head of 400 ft the efficiency started to drop when the gage pressure head plus velocity head at inlet was reduced to 10 ft.   What was the value of σ_c if the barometric pressure was 14.3 psia and the water temperature 80°F?

17.27. A pump is required to deliver 2,420 gpm at a head of 150 ft when running at 1,750 rpm.   Determine the principal impeller dimensions.

17.28. A pump is required to deliver 9,580 gpm at a head of 36 ft when running at 1,200 rpm.   Determine the principal impeller dimensions.

EIGHTEEN

FLUID COUPLINGS
AND TORQUE CONVERTERS

18.1. FLUID COUPLING

The fluid coupling (Fig. 18.1) consists of a centrifugal-pump impeller and a turbine runner, both within the same case. Each rotating element is shaped as one-half of a hollow ring and contains thin, straight radial blades. Such radial vanes not only are less expensive than curved blades, but have the advantage of being adapted for rotation in either direction.

The casing is partially filled with oil, and on starting up the driving shaft, this oil is thrown outward through the pump impeller, enters the turbine runner, through which it flows inwardly, and reenters the pump impeller, thus following a closed circuit. When the turbine also rotates, the path of the fluid is that of a helix wound around a circle concentric with the axis of rotation.

If the pump and the turbine were entirely separate machines, the efficiency of the combination would be the product of their separate efficiencies and the maximum efficiency could hardly be above 80 per cent at best and would usually be much lower. By having the pump impeller discharge directly into the turbine runner and the discharge from the latter go directly into the impeller intake, the usual transformation losses are eliminated, with the result that the fluid-coupling efficiency can be as high as 98 per cent.

The fluid coupling has three valuable characteristics. One is that it damps out any torsional vibrations which otherwise would be transmitted between the driving and the driven shafts. The second is that it is a slipping clutch, but one without any wear. This permits the driven shaft to operate at a slower speed than the driving shaft. While such operation results in a loss of efficiency, it is useful for the sake of flexibility. The third is that the torque imposed by it varies with the speed of the driving shaft, and thus there is very little starting torque for such devices as internal-combustion engines or electric motors when a fluid coupling is interposed between them and the load.

The pump imparts angular momentum to the fluid, and since the velocities leaving and entering the impeller are the same as those entering and leaving the turbine, respectively, the torque must be the same for each element. Another, more general approach is that there are no other members in the flow, and considering the combination as a free body, it follows that for steady flow the summation of the torques acting upon it must be zero. Hence a feature of the fluid coupling is that the input torque and the output torque are equal. That is, the torque ratio is always 1:1.

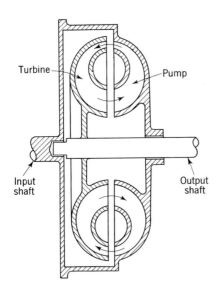

Fig. 18.1. Fluid coupling.

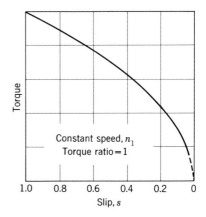

Fig. 18.2.   Fluid-coupling torque.

When the impeller is rotated, centrifugal action causes fluid to flow outward and into the turbine.   But centrifugal action in the latter opposes the flow of fluid, and hence the circulation decreases as the two speeds approach each other.   If they were equal, there could be no flow. Since there can be a flow of fluid only if the turbine speed is less than the pump speed, there must be what is known as *slip*.   If there is no slip, there is no flow and consequently no torque.

Figure 18.2 shows the general nature of the relation between torque and slip for a *constant* speed of the *driving* shaft.   The torque is a maximum at 100 per cent slip and decreases to zero at zero slip.   However, before that point is reached it must terminate at a finite value of the torque that is required to drive the load on the output shaft.

If n_1 refers to the drive speed and n_2 to the speed of the driven shaft, then slip is defined as $s = (n_1 - n_2)/n_1 = 1 - n_2/n_1$.   Since the torques for both shafts are the same, the power for each is proportional to the rotative speed for each.   Hence the coupling efficiency is

$$e = \frac{n_2}{n_1} = 1 - s \tag{18.1}$$

This relation is shown in Fig. 18.3, which indicates that the slip should be small if high efficiency is to be attained, though, as explained before, it cannot be reduced to zero.   A reason for the high efficiency at small values of the slip is that the opposing centrifugal force of the turbine, as the two speeds approach each other, causes the velocity of the circulation to be very low.

The dashed line in Fig. 18.3 shows that the efficiency drops to zero as the slip is reduced to zero.   The meaning of this dashed line is that in this range the driving torque is no longer adequate and the driven shaft is

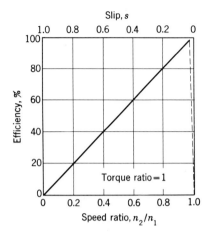

Fig. 18.3. Fluid-coupling efficiency.

receiving energy from some other source, as in the case of an automobile going downhill. In the latter case the ratio n_2/n_1 can become greater than 1, which means that the former driven shaft has become the driving shaft and Fig. 18.3 is reproduced in the opposite quadrant.

18.2. TORQUE AND POWER OF FLUID COUPLINGS

Equation (6.18) shows that, for rotation, torque is a function of ρQ, r, and V. Equation (14.14) shows that ρQ is proportional to $\rho D^3 n_1$. Since V is proportional to Dn_1 and r may be replaced by D, it follows that torque is proportional to $(\rho D^3 n_1)D(Dn_1)$, or

$$T = C_M \rho D^5 n_1{}^2 \tag{18.2}$$

where C_M is a coefficient to be determined experimentally for any given design of fluid coupling. It is a function of slip, as shown by Fig. 18.2, and it must also depend upon the volume of the fluid in proportion to the volume of the coupling. It is only slightly affected by a change in Reynolds number.

From Eq. (18.2), the power input to a fluid coupling can be expressed as

$$P = C_P \rho D^5 n_1{}^3 \tag{18.3}$$

where C_P is a coefficient which is determined from the value of C_M in Eq. (18.2) or which may be determined directly by experiment.

From the fact that C_M and C_P are functions of the volume of fluid in a given coupling, it follows that the torque and power can be varied by changing the amount of fluid in the coupling. For this purpose some couplings are provided with means for withdrawing or adding fluid during operation.

18.3. FLUID COUPLING WITH ENGINE

Figure 18.3 conveys the impression that the average operating efficiency might be low, but Fig. 18.4 will lead to a different conclusion. The latter shows the combination of a fluid coupling with an internal-combustion engine operated at constant throttle from zero speed up to the maximum engine speed. (At constant throttle the torque delivered by such an engine varies only slightly with the speed.)

It is seen that the coupling torque is very small at low engine speed, and thus the engine is easily started. As the engine speed increases, the coupling-torque capacity increases indefinitely as the square of the speed for 100 per cent slip, but it terminates when the coupling torque equals the engine torque, at which point the driven shaft starts to turn, and then the slip starts to decrease. From this point on, as the engine speed continues to increase, power is delivered to the output shaft in increasing amounts and with an increasing efficiency as the slip decreases.

From Fig. 18.4 it is possible to construct Fig. 18.5, which shows the coupling efficiency as a function of the speed of the *driven* shaft. This efficiency curve is much flatter than that of Fig. 18.3. Since both Figs. 18.4 and 18.5 are dimensionless, they apply at any throttle position. For the usual automobile operation the average speed is probably above 50 per

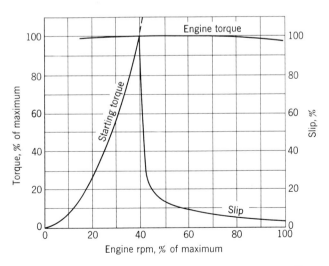

Fig. 18.4. Internal-combustion engine with fluid coupling.

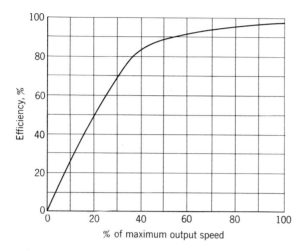

Fig. 18.5. Fluid-coupling performance.

cent of the maximum for any particular throttle position; so the average operating efficiency is 90 to 95 per cent.

Illustrative example 18.1: From Fig. 18.4 it is seen that the slip is 2 per cent at the maximum engine speed and 10 per cent at 60 per cent of the maximum speed. Thus, at this reduced speed, the coupling efficiency is 90 per cent. But $e = n_2/n_1$, and hence $n_2 = 0.9n_1$; but n_1 is 0.6 times the maximum engine speed. Thus $n_2 = 0.9 \times 0.6 = 0.54$ times the maximum engine speed. The maximum speed of the driven shaft is 0.98 times that of the engine shaft. Hence, for Fig. 18.5, the efficiency of 90 per cent is obtained for an output speed of

$$\frac{0.54}{0.98} = 0.551$$

times the maximum output speed.

18.4. TORQUE CONVERTER

The torque output of a fluid coupling is always equal to the torque input. If it is desired to multiply the torque, a torque converter is used. A one-stage torque converter is shown in Fig. 18.6, so called because there is only one turbine stage. More complicated arrangements are used with two and even three turbine stages, but rarely more than three, for the efficiency diminishes rapidly with an increase in the number.

The additional feature in Fig. 18.6 compared with the plain coupling is the *reactor*, or *stator*, which consists of a series of fixed blades receiving the flow from the turbine and delivering it to the pump. The reactor is so shaped as to change the direction of flow over it and thus increase the angular momentum. The pump impeller adds to this angular momentum, and the fluid flowing through the turbine gives up angular momentum equal to the sum of that from the stator plus that in the pump. Thus the torque of the turbine, which is that delivered to the output shaft, is the sum of the reactor torque plus the pump torque, the latter being the torque of the input shaft.

By this means the torque ratio may be made much greater than 1, as shown in Fig. 18.7, but there is a decrease in the maximum efficiency due to the more complicated flow conditions. It is also seen that the maximum efficiency is found at a much lower speed ratio. With more than one turbine stage the maximum efficiency is still lower and found at a still lower speed ratio, but the torque multiplication is greater.

18.5. CONVERTER COUPLING

It is seen that the maximum efficiency of the torque converter is lower than the maximum efficiency of the plain coupling, but it is found at a lower speed ratio, where the coupling efficiency is very poor. On the other hand, the converter efficiency is very low at the high speed range, where the coupling is at its best. In order to have a high torque ratio at low speed ratios and also to combine the efficiency features of these two devices, the reactor in Fig. 18.6 is provided with a one-way clutch.

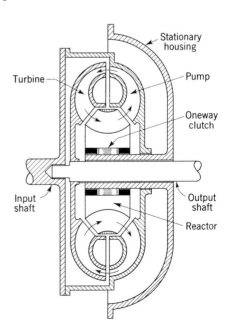

Fig. 18.6. Torque converter.

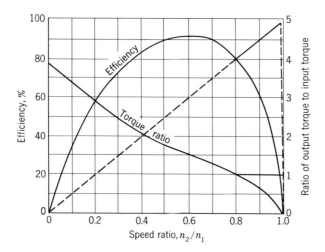

Fig. 18.7.   Single-stage torque-converter characteristics.

It was shown in Fig. 15.13 that α_2, the angle of the water leaving the buckets, varies from approximately 165 to 5° as the speed of the wheel increases from standstill to runaway.   A similar change takes place in the reaction turbine and also in the turbine element of a torque converter. The blades, or vanes, in a torque converter are usually curved and provided with rounded entrance edges to improve efficiency.   The stator, or reactor, blade is similarly shaped.   The reactor blade is placed at such an angle that at low speed ratios the direction of the fluid leaving the turbine runner is such as to hold it in place in its fixed position.   But at high speed ratios the fluid from the turbine approaches the reactor from a different direction; so the torque on it is just the opposite from the former case.   The one-way clutch then permits the stator to rotate freely, and the device behaves as a plain fluid coupling.

In Fig. 18.7 the transition from a torque converter to a plain coupling is shown as occurring at a speed ratio of 0.8, which is where the efficiency curves for the two separate devices intersect.   This transition point is called the *clutch point* and is fixed by the entrance angle of the reactor blade, which determines when the torque on the vane changes in sign.

Figure 18.7 shows that this combination gives a high torque ratio and good efficiency at medium speed ratios, while above a speed ratio of 0.8 the high efficiency of the plain coupling is obtained, but with a torque ratio of only 1.

There are many arrangements of both fluid couplings and torque converters and combinations of the two which differ from those described here, but the principles are the same for all.

PROBLEMS

18.1. In Fig. 18.4 the slip is 20 per cent at 45 per cent of the maximum engine speed. Determine the coordinates of the corresponding point in Fig. 18.5.

18.2. A power chart of the American Blower Co. shows that for small slips the input horsepower to its fluid couplings may be expressed as $(6.3 \times 10^{-13})sd^5n_1^3$, where d is the coupling diameter in inches and n_1 is the revolutions per minute of the input shaft. For one of this company's fluid couplings 20 in. in diameter determine the horsepower input at a speed of 1,000 rpm if the slip is 0.02.

18.3. In Prob. 18.2, how much heat will be dissipated in Btu per hour when equilibrium is attained?

18.4. A fluid coupling with impeller diameter of 20 in. has a torque characteristic curve as given in Fig. 18.2. If the coupling is filled with oil of specific gravity 0.85 and delivers 50 hp at an output shaft speed of 800 rpm with an efficiency of 95 per cent, evaluate C_M and C_P.

18.5. Suppose the oil in the coupling of Prob. 18.4 is drained and replaced only by air ($\gamma = 0.0765$ pcf). What power can be supplied at the output shaft speed of 800 rpm? What is the maximum torque that can be developed if the output shaft is stalled?

18.6. What power can be supplied by the fluid coupling of Prob. 18.4 if the output shaft is braked down to 400 rpm, assuming the input shaft speed to remain unchanged? What is then the coupling efficiency, power input, and torque?

18.7. Problem 18.6 is for constant input shaft speed and variation in torque. For constant torque and variation in input shaft speed, assume a fluid coupling driven by an internal-combustion engine for which the torque is assumed constant. If the coupling delivers 60 hp at a maximum output speed of 1,000 rpm when $n_2/n_1 = 0.98$, as in Fig. 18.5, what will be the power output, coupling efficiency, and input shaft speed if the output shaft is braked down to 500 rpm?

18.8. If the fluid coupling of Prob. 18.4 were combined with a torque converter having the characteristics of Fig. 18.7, what would be the power supplied with the output shaft braked to half the normal speed? What would be the efficiency? Compare results with those of Prob. 18.6.

DIMENSIONS AND UNITS, CONVERSION FACTORS

The systems of dimensions and units used in mechanics are based upon Newton's second law of motion, which is force equals mass times acceleration, or $F = ma$, if suitable units are chosen. There are four systems generally recognized, two in the metric system and two in the English system. Of the two, one is known as the absolute, or physicists', system and the other as the gravitational, or engineers', system. The following table illustrates all four, the units being defined so that 1 unit of force equals 1 unit of mass times 1 unit of acceleration.

Systems ·	Metric	English
Absolute, or physicists'	$1 \text{ dyne} = 1 \text{ g} \times 1 \dfrac{\text{cm}}{\text{sec}^2}$	$1 \text{ poundal} = 1 \text{ lb} \times 1 \dfrac{\text{ft}}{\text{sec}^2}$
Gravitational, or engineers'	$1 \text{ kg} = 1 \text{ metric slug} \times 1 \dfrac{\text{m}}{\text{sec}^2}$	$1 \text{ lb} = 1 \text{ slug} \times 1 \dfrac{\text{ft}}{\text{sec}^2}$

Physicists use the metric absolute system, often called the cm-g-sec system, or *cgs* system, while engineers in the United States use the English gravitational system, sometimes called the ft-lb-sec system, or *fps* system. The two other systems in the table are rarely used.[1]

The difference between the absolute and gravitational systems is that in the former the standard is the unit of mass; i.e., the kilogram and the pound are defined by comparison with certain standard masses which exist physically in Paris and in London. The unit of force is then derived by Newton's law. In the gravitational system the standard is the unit of force; i.e., the force units, such as the kilogram or the pound, are taken as the gravitational pulls on the standard masses. The unit of mass is then derived by Newton's law.

Unfortunately, engineers are not consistent in following these systems. In Continental Europe and in many other parts of the world engineers use the kilogram for both force and mass units, while in Great Britain and the United States it is common practice to use the pound for both force and mass, though sometimes the distinction

---

[1] In the English system 1 slug = 32.174 lb (mass).

is made between "pound force" and "pound mass." But if such inconsistent units are used, it is necessary to introduce g into Newton's equation so that $Fg = Wa$, where F and W are *both* in pounds.

The value of g varies with altitude and latitude, and thus the value of W for a certain mass will also vary with its location. This variation is not considered in this text.

The following table, where L denotes length and T denotes time, may be useful for dimensional analysis:

Symbol	Quantity	Mass-Length-Time	Force-Length-Time
A	Area	L^2	L^2
a	Linear acceleration	LT^{-2}	LT^{-2}
E	Modulus of elasticity	$ML^{-1}T^{-2}$	FL^{-2}
F	Force	MLT^{-2}	F
G	Rate of weight flow	MLT^{-3}	FT^{-1}
g	Acceleration of gravity	LT^{-2}	LT^{-2}
M	Mass	M	$FL^{-1}T^2$
n	Revolutions per unit time	T^{-1}	T^{-1}
P	Power	ML^2T^{-3}	FLT^{-1}
p	Pressure	$ML^{-1}T^{-2}$	FL^{-2}
Q	Rate of volume flow	L^3T^{-1}	L^3T^{-1}
V	Linear velocity	LT^{-1}	LT^{-1}
W	Weight	MLT^{-2}	F
Γ	Circulation	L^2T^{-1}	L^2T^{-1}
γ	Specific weight	$ML^{-2}T^{-2}$	FL^{-3}
μ	Dynamic viscosity	$ML^{-1}T^{-1}$	$FL^{-2}T$
ν	Kinematic viscosity	L^2T^{-1}	L^2T^{-1}
ρ	Density	ML^{-3}	$FL^{-4}T^2$
σ	Surface tension	MT^{-2}	FL^{-1}
τ	Shearing stress	$ML^{-1}T^{-2}$	FL^{-2}
ω	Angular velocity	T^{-1}	T^{-1}

CONVERSION FACTORS

Discharge

   1 cfs = 448.83 gpm

Energy

   1 Btu = 778 ft-lb
   1 kwhr = 2.66×10^6 ft-lb

Force

   1 lb (force) = 32.2 poundals = 4.45×10^5 dynes = 454 g

Length

   1 ft = 30.48 cm
   1 mile = 5,280 ft

Mass

1 slug = 32.2 lb (mass)

Power

1 hp = 550 ft-lb/sec = 0.746 kw = 0.708 Btu/sec

Pressure

1 psi = 2.309 ft of water at 60°F
     = 0.0703 kg/cm^2
1 in. Hg = 1.13 ft of water = 0.49 psi

Velocity

1 mph = 1.467 fps
1 knot = 1.69 fps

Viscosity

1 poise = 100 centipoises = 1 dyne-sec/cm^2
     = 0.00209 lb-sec/ft^2
1 lb-sec/ft^2 = 478.7 poises
1 stoke = 100 centistokes = 1 cm^2/sec
     = 0.001076 ft^2/sec
1 ft^2/sec = 929 stokes

Volume

1 ft^3 = 7.48 U.S. gal = 28.315 liters
1 U.S. gal = 231 in.^{3} = 0.13368 ft^3
        = 8.3376 lb of water at 60°F
1 British Imperial gal = 1.2003 U.S. gal

APPENDIX TWO

VELOCITY OF PRESSURE WAVE

Consider an elastic fluid at rest in a rigid pipe of cross-sectional area A. Suppose a piston at one end is suddenly moved with a velocity V for a time dt. This will produce an increase in pressure which will travel through the fluid with a velocity c. While the piston moves the distance $V\,dt$, the wave front will move the distance $c\,dt$. During this time the piston will displace a mass of fluid $\rho\,AV\,dt$, and during this same time the increase in pressure dp will increase the density of the portion between (1) and (2) by $d\rho$. Equating the mass displaced by the piston to the gain in mass between (1) and (2) due to increased density, $\rho AV\,dt = Ac\,dt\,d\rho$, from which (Fig. A.1)

$$c = \frac{V\rho}{d\rho} \tag{A.1}$$

From mechanics the impulse of a force equals the resulting increase in momentum. The impulse of the force produced by the piston is $A\,dp\,dt$. The mass $\rho\,Ac\,dt$

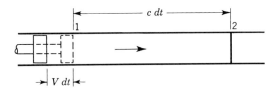

Fig. A.1

is initially at rest, but as the pressure wave travels through it, each element of it will have its velocity increased to V, so that at the end of the time dt the entire mass will have the velocity V. Hence the increase in momentum is $\rho AcV\,dt$. Thus $A\,dp\,dt = \rho AcV\,dt$, and

$$c = \frac{dp}{V\rho} \tag{A.2}$$

Multiplying Eqs. (A.1) and (A.2), we have

$$c^2 = \frac{dp}{d\rho} \tag{A.3}$$

In Sec. 1.6 the volume modulus of elasticity is defined as $E_v = -(v/dv)\,d\rho$.

555

Since $\rho = \gamma/g = 1/vg$, $\rho v = 1/g$ = constant, and thus $\rho\, dv + v\, d\rho = 0$, and $-v/dv = +\rho/d\rho$. Hence $E_v = \rho\, dp/d\rho$. Substituting this value of $dp/d\rho$ in Eq. (A.3), we have

$$c = \sqrt{\frac{E_v}{\rho}} = \sqrt{\frac{g}{\gamma}\, E_v} \qquad\qquad (A.4)$$

This is also known as the velocity of a sound wave, or the acoustic velocity.

An acoustic, or pressure, wave travels through a fluid with such a high velocity that there is no time for any appreciable heat transfer from any heat of compression, and thus the process is adiabatic. In Sec. 1.8 it is shown that the adiabatic modulus of elasticity for a perfect gas is $E_v = kp$. Inserting this value in Eq. (A.4) gives for a gas $c = \sqrt{gkp/\gamma} = \sqrt{gkpv} = \sqrt{gkRT}$, thus showing that for a gas the acoustic velocity is a function of its absolute temperature.

The foregoing analysis has considered the pipe to be rigid. In reality the pipe is elastic, and the stretching of the pipe walls due to the pressure wave makes the modulus of the combination less than that of the fluid alone.

This new modulus will be expressed by K, and we shall let $dv = dv' + dv''$, where dv' is due to compression of the fluid and dv'' is due to stretching of the pipe wall. Thus $K = -v\, dp/(dv' + dv'')$, from which

$$\frac{1}{K} = -\frac{dv'}{v\, dp} - \frac{dv''}{v\, dp}$$

The first term on the right is seen to be $1/E_v$. In mechanics E = increment of stress/increment of unit deformation. The increment of stress is $r\, dp/t$. If the circumference is stretched an amount dl, the increment of unit deformation is $dl/2\pi r$. Since $dl = 2\pi\, dr$, this last expression becomes dr/r. From these relations we obtain $dp = Et\, dr/r^2$. Per unit length of pipe $v = \pi r^2$, and the increase in volume is equal to the increase in area, so that $dv'' = 2\pi r\, dr$. Substituting these quantities for the three items in the second term of the equation for $1/K$, it reduces to $2r/Et = D/Et$. Therefore $1/K = 1/E_v + D/Et$, from which

$$K = \frac{E_v}{1 + (D/t)(E_v/E)} \qquad\qquad (A.5)$$

The velocity of a pressure wave in an elastic fluid in an elastic pipe is then

$$c_P = \sqrt{\left(\frac{g}{\gamma}\right) K}$$

but the value of c_P for water can be more readily evaluated by the form given in Eq. (12.5).

In every case c is the velocity of the pressure wave relative to the fluid. If the fluid is moving with a velocity V, the absolute velocity of the pressure wave is

$$c_{\text{abs}} = c \pm V \qquad\qquad (A.6)$$

from which it is seen that, if the fluid velocity is equal to or greater than c, no effect of a pressure wave can then appear upstream. As the velocity of a pressure wave is not a velocity of physical matter, it is often called *celerity*.

APPENDIX THREE

USEFUL TABLES

Table A.1 *Physical properties of water*

Temp, °F	Specific weight γ, pcf	Density ρ, slugs/ft^3	Viscosity $\mu \times 10^5$, lb-sec/ft^2	Kine-matic viscosity $\nu \times 10^5$, ft^2/sec	Surface tension $\sigma \times 10^2$, lb/ft	Vapor pressure head p_v/γ, ft	Bulk modulus of elasticity $K \times 10^{-3}$, psi
32	62.42	1.940	3.746	1.931	0.518	0.20	293
40	62.43	1.940	3.229	1.664	0.514	0.28	294
50	62.41	1.940	2.735	1.410	0.509	0.41	305
60	62.37	1.938	2.359	1.217	0.504	0.59	311
70	62.30	1.936	2.050	1.059	0.500	0.84	320
80	62.22	1.934	1.799	0.930	0.492	1.17	322
90	62.11	1.931	1.595	0.826	0.486	1.61	323
100	62.00	1.927	1.424	0.739	0.480	2.19	327
110	61.86	1.923	1.284	0.667	0.473	2.95	331
120	61.71	1.918	1.168	0.609	0.465	3.91	333
130	61.55	1.913	1.069	0.558	0.460	5.13	334
140	61.38	1.908	0.981	0.514	0.454	6.67	330
150	61.20	1.902	0.905	0.476	0.447	8.58	328
160	61.00	1.896	0.838	0.442	0.441	10.95	326
170	60.80	1.890	0.780	0.413	0.433	13.83	322
180	60.58	1.883	0.726	0.385	0.426	17.33	318
190	60.36	1.876	0.678	0.362	0.419	21.55	313
200	60.12	1.868	0.637	0.341	0.412	26.59	308
212	59.83	1.860	0.593	0.319	0.404	33.90	300

Table A.2.   Physical properties of air at standard atmospheric pressure

Temperature T, °F	Density $\rho \times 10^3$, slugs/ft^3	Specific weight $\gamma \times 10^2$, pcf	Dynamic viscosity $\mu \times 10^7$, lb-sec/ft^2	Kinematic viscosity $\nu \times 10^4$, ft^2/sec
−40	2.94	9.46	3.12	1.06
−20	2.80	9.03	3.25	1.16
0	2.68	8.62	3.38	1.26
10	2.63	8.46	3.45	1.31
20	2.57	8.27	3.50	1.36
30	2.52	8.11	3.58	1.42
40	2.47	7.94	3.62	1.46
50	2.42	7.79	3.68	1.52
60	2.37	7.63	3.74	1.58
70	2.33	7.50	3.82	1.64
80	2.28	7.35	3.85	1.69
90	2.24	7.23	3.90	1.74
100	2.20	7.09	3.96	1.80
120	2.15	6.84	4.07	1.89
140	2.06	6.63	4.14	2.01
160	1.99	6.41	4.22	2.12
180	1.93	6.21	4.34	2.25
200	1.87	6.02	4.49	2.40
250	1.74	5.60	4.87	2.80

Table A.3.   *The ICAO Standard Atmosphere*

Altitude, ft	Temp, °F	Pressure, psia	Specific weight γ, pcf	Density ρ, slugs/ft^3	Viscosity $\mu \times 10^7$, lb-sec/ft^2
0	59.0	14.70	0.07648	0.002377	3.737
5,000	41.2	12.24	0.06587	0.002048	3.637
10,000	23.4	10.11	0.05643	0.001756	3.534
15,000	5.6	8.30	0.04807	0.001496	3.430
20,000	−12.3	6.76	0.04070	0.001267	3.325
25,000	−30.1	5.46	0.03422	0.001066	3.217
30,000	−47.8	4.37	0.02858	0.000891	3.107
35,000	−65.6	3.47	0.02367	0.000738	2.995
40,000	−69.7	2.73	0.01882	0.000587	2.969
45,000	−69.7	2.15	0.01481	0.000462	2.969
50,000	−69.7	1.69	0.01165	0.000364	2.969
55,000	−69.7	1.33	0.00917	0.000287	2.969
60,000	−69.7	1.05	0.00722	0.000226	2.969
65,000	−69.7	0.83	0.00568	0.000178	2.969
70,000	−69.7	0.65	0.00447	0.000140	2.969
75,000	−69.7	0.51	0.00352	0.000110	2.969
80,000	−69.7	0.40	0.00277	0.000087	2.969
85,000	−65.4	0.32	0.00216	0.000068	2.997
90,000	−57.2	0.25	0.00168	0.000053	3.048
95,000	−49.0	0.20	0.00131	0.000041	3.099
100,000	−40.9	0.16	0.00102	0.000032	3.150

*Table A.4.   Physical properties of common gases**

Gas	Specific weight γ, pcf	Dynamic viscosity μ, lb-sec/ft^2	Gas constant R, ft/°F	Molecular weight m	Adiabatic exponent k	Specific heat at constant pressure c_p, ft-lb/ (lb)(°R)
Air	0.0753	3.72×10^{-7}	53.3	29	1.40	186.5
Carbon dioxide	0.114	3.34×10^{-7}	34.1	44	1.29	159.5
Helium	0.0104	4.11×10^{-7}	386	4	1.66	945
Hydrogen	0.00522	1.89×10^{-7}	767	2	1.40	2,685
Methane	0.0416	2.51×10^{-7}	96.4	16	1.26	407
Nitrogen	0.0728	3.68×10^{-7}	55.1	28	1.40	193
Oxygen	0.0830	4.42×10^{-7}	48.3	32	1.40	169

* Approximate values at standard atmospheric pressure and 68°F. R, m, and k do not change with variations in pressure and temperature.

*Table A.5.   Physical properties of common liquids**

Liquid	Specific gravity, sp gr	Dynamic viscosity μ, lb-sec/ft^2	Surface energy† σ, lb/ft	Vapor pressure p_v, psia	Volume modulus E_v, psi
Benzene	0.90	1.4×10^{-5}	2.0×10^{-3}	1.50	150,000
Gasoline	0.68	6.2×10^{-6}			
Glycerin	1.26	3.1×10^{-2}	4.3×10^{-3}	2×10^{-6}	630,000
Kerosene	0.81	4.0×10^{-5}	1.7×10^{-3}		
Mercury	13.55	3.3×10^{-5}	3.2×10^{-2}	2.33×10^{-5}	3,800,000
SAE 10 oil	0.92	1.7×10^{-3}	2.5×10^{-3}		
SAE 30 oil	0.92	9.2×10^{-3}	2.4×10^{-3}		
Water	1.00	2.1×10^{-5}	5.0×10^{-3}	0.34	300,000

* Approximate values at standard atmospheric pressure and 68°F.
† In contact with air.

Table A.6. **Areas of circles**

Diameter, in.	Area		Diameter, in.	Area	
	in.^{2}	ft^2		in.^{2}	ft^2
0.25	0.049	0.00034	4.00	12.57	0.0873
0.50	0.196	0.00136	6.00	28.27	0.196
1.00	0.785	0.00545	8.00	50.27	0.349
2.00	3.142	0.0218	10.00	78.54	0.545
3.00	7.069	0.0491	12.00	113.10	0.785

Table A.7. **Properties of areas**

	Sketch	Area or volume	Location of centroid	I or I_c
Rectangle		bh	$y_c = \dfrac{h}{2}$	$I_c = \dfrac{bh^3}{12}$
Triangle		$\dfrac{bh}{2}$	$y_c = \dfrac{h}{3}$	$I_c = \dfrac{bh^3}{36}$
Circle		$\dfrac{\pi D^2}{4}$	$y_c = \dfrac{D}{2}$	$I_c = \dfrac{\pi D^4}{64}$
Semicircle		$\dfrac{\pi D^2}{8}$	$y_c = \dfrac{4r}{3\pi}$	$I = \dfrac{\pi D^4}{128}$
Ellipse		$\dfrac{\pi bh}{4}$	$y_c = \dfrac{h}{2}$	$I_c = \dfrac{\pi bh^3}{64}$
Semiellipse		$\dfrac{\pi bh}{4}$	$y_c = \dfrac{4h}{3\pi}$	$I = \dfrac{\pi bh^3}{16}$

REFERENCES

There is a great volume of literature available on the various aspects of fluid mechanics. The results of original research may be found in papers published in technical journals. A list of books covering various topics of fluid mechanics is presented here for the convenience of the student. This list by no means includes all the important books that have been written; the intent here is merely to provide a representative list of books. The student is encouraged to "probe deeper" and to widen his horizons by further reading.

Bird, R. B., W. E. Stewart, and E. N. Lightfoot: "Transport Phenomena," John Wiley & Sons, Inc., New York, 1960.

Brenkert, Karl: "Elementary Fluid Mechanics, " John Wiley & Sons, Inc., New York, 1960.

Bridgman, P. W.: "Dimensional Analysis," Yale University Press, New Haven, Conn., 1922.

Cambel, A. B., and B. H. Jennings: "Gas Dynamics," McGraw-Hill Book Company, New York, 1958.

Chow, Ven Te: "Open-channel Hydraulics," McGraw-Hill Book Company, New York, 1959.

Csanady, G. T.: "Theory of Turbomachines," McGraw-Hill Book Company, New York, 1964.

Daugherty, R. L.: "Centrifugal Pumps," McGraw-Hill Book Company, New York, 1915.

Daugherty, R. L.: "Hydraulic Turbines," McGraw-Hill Book Company, New York, 1920.

Dryden, H. L., F. P. Murnaghan, and H. Bateman: "Hydrodynamics," Dover Publications, Inc., New York, 1956.

"Flow Meters: Their Theory and Application," 5th ed., American Society of Mechanical Engineers, New York, 1959.

Goldstein, S.: "Modern Developments in Fluid Dynamics," 2 vols., Oxford University Press, Fair Lawn, N.J., 1938.

Hinze, J. O.: "Turbulence," McGraw-Hill Book Company, New York, 1959.

Hydraulic Models, *ASCE Manual Eng. Practice* 25, 1942.

Jaeger, Charles: "Engineering Fluid Mechanics," Blackie & Son, Ltd., Glasgow, 1956.

King, H. W., and E. F. Brater: "Handbook of Hydraulics," 5th ed., McGraw-Hill Book Company, New York, 1963.

Knudsen, J. G., and D. L. Katz: "Fluid Dynamics and Heat Transfer," McGraw-Hill Book Company, New York, 1958.

Kuethe, A. M., and J. D. Schetzer: "Foundations of Aerodynamics," John Wiley & Sons, Inc., New York, 1950.

Lamb, H.: "Hydrodynamics," 6th ed., Dover Publications, Inc., New York, 1945.
Langhaar, H. L.: "Dimensional Analysis and Theory of Models," John Wiley & Sons, Inc., New York, 1951.
Levich, V. G.: "Physicochemical Hydrodynamics," Prentice-Hall, Inc., Englewood Cliffs, N.J., 1962.
Linsley, R. K., and J. B. Franzini: "Water-resources Engineering," McGraw-Hill Book Company, New York, 1964.
Pai, S. I.: "Viscous Flow Theory," 2 vols., D. Van Nostrand Company, Princeton, N.J., 1958.
Parmakian, John: "Waterhammer Analysis," Prentice-Hall, Inc., Englewood Cliffs, N.J., 1955.
Prandtl, L., and O. G. Tietjens: "Fundamentals of Hydro- and Aeromechanics," McGraw-Hill Book Company, New York, 1934.
Rouse, H. (ed.): "Engineering Hydraulics," John Wiley & Sons, Inc., New York, 1950.
Rouse, H., and S. Ince: "History of Hydraulics," Iowa Institute of Hydraulic Research, 1957.
Schlichting, H.: "Boundary Layer Theory," Pergamon Press, New York, 1955.
Shapiro, A. H.: "The Dynamics and Thermodynamics of Compressible Fluid Flow," 2 vols., The Ronald Press Company, New York, 1953.
Shepherd, D. G.: "Principles of Turbomachinery," The Macmillan Company, New York, 1956.
Stepanoff, A. J.: "Centrifugal and Axial Flow Pumps," 2d ed., John Wiley & Sons, Inc., New York, 1957.
Stoker, J. J.: "Water Waves," Interscience Publishers, Inc., New York, 1957.
Streeter, V. L. (ed.): "Handbook of Fluid Dynamics," McGraw-Hill Book Company, New York, 1961.
Sutton, G. P.: "Rocket Propulsion Elements," 2d ed., John Wiley & Sons, Inc., New York, 1956.
Vallentine, H. R.: "Applied Hydrodynamics," Butterworth & Co. (Publishers), Ltd., London, 1959.
Van Wylen, G. J.: "Thermodynamics," John Wiley & Sons, Inc., New York, 1959.
Vennard, J. K.: "Elementary Fluid Mechanics," 4th ed., John Wiley & Sons, Inc., New York, 1961.
von Kármán, T.: "Aerodynamics," Cornell University Press, Ithaca, N.Y., 1954.
von Mises, R.: "Theory of Flight," McGraw-Hill Book Company, New York, 1945.

INDEX

ANSWERS TO SELECTED ODD-NUMBERED PROBLEMS

1.1   1.40 scf, 0.022 cfp
1.3   2.45 scf, 1.26
1.5   0.000548 cfp, 0.015077 cfp, 66.33 pcf
1.7   3.58 ft lb/lb
1.9   6,700 cu ft
1.11 0.00153 pcf
1.13 0.34 pcf, 2.94 cfp
1.15 3.33, 300, 1.896
1.17 4.8 centipoises, 375°F
1.19 1:55.5, 15.7:1
1.21 150 Btu/hr
1.23 0.422 lb, 0.477 lb
1.25 48, 36, 24, 12, 0 sec^{-1}; 0.40, 0.30, 0.20, 0.10, 0 psf
1.27 4.44 in.
1.29 0.0823 in.
1.33 13.75 psi below 14.7 psia

2.1   6,670 psi
2.3   55.5 pcf, 1.73 slugs/cu ft, 0.89
2.5   9,050 ft
2.7   27,900 ft
2.9   52.3 psi
2.11 59.5 psia, 55.1 psi
2.13 36.4 in.
2.15 9.2 ft of water, 4.0 psi, 86 in.
2.17 26.7 psi
2.19 46.1 ft, 5.6 ft
2.21 $\frac{3}{4}d$, $\frac{3}{4}d$
2.23 $\frac{1}{2}d$
2.25 .591r
2.27 5616, 7490, 193000 lb; 4, 4.75, 103.03 ft
2.29 7480 lb; 0.75, 0.66, 0.375, 0 ft
2.31 2,350 lb, 3.33 ft
2.35 17,280 lb, 15,985 lb
2.37 392 lb, 147 lb, 20.8 psi, 7.8 psi
2.39 3,930 lb, 19,650 ft lb
2.41 5.35 ft; yes
2.43 12,480 lb/ft, 13.33 ft, 2,265 lb/ft, 18.32 ft
2.45 13,480, 10,980, 17,380 lb; 39.2°
2.47 2.24 ft to left of AB
2.49 8060 lb/ft, 4600 lb/ft
2.53 $5\gamma y^2$, $\frac{2}{3}\gamma y^3$, $\frac{5}{3}\gamma y^3 + 0.04y^5$
2.55 722 lb
2.57 2.4 ft, 549 tons
2.59 1.15 ft submerged, 1.25 ft submerged, 0.56 ft
2.65 3.4 in.
2.67 2.08 psi

3.5   6.25 fps, 3.85 fps
3.13 3.39 fps/sec
3.15 72 fps/sec
3.17 8.33 fps/ft, 0
3.19 −0.0198, −0.00885, −0.0037 fps/sec
3.21 16.2 fps, 5.4 fps/sec
3.23 22.6 fps/sec radially outward, 14.2 fps/sec tangentially downward to the right

4.1   2.0
4.3 $1\frac{0}{9}$
4.5   10 fps, 40 fps, 39.3 ft
4.7   62.3 ft for downflow, 78.3 ft for upflow
4.9   155.7 ft, 155.7 ft
4.11 6,550 hp, 418 hp
4.13 5,880 hp
4.15 4,820 ft lb/sec = 8.77 hp
4.17 24.6 hp
4.19 $D_c = 0.58D$
4.21 33,000 Btu/hr
4.23 1,071.3 Btu/lb, 0.913
4.25 417 in., 31.4 in.
4.27 6.30 cfs, −20 ft
4.29 28 ft
4.31 100, −11.6, 28.4, 67.4 ft
4.33 0.240 cfs, 0.107 cfs
4.35 81.4 lb, 61.1 lb
4.37 −3.64 ft
4.39 18.31, 24.46 psi
4.43 45°, 310 ft
4.45 5.90 fps
4.47 102 rpm, 102 rpm
4.49 45 fps, 24.5 ft
4.51 13.80 and 10.80 fps at 37.5° at entrance; 18.40 and 17.00 fps at 42.7° at exit

5.1   Continuity is satisfied; Vorticity = 0
5.3   Yes, yes
5.5 $\frac{1}{3}$; 14.1, 71.0; 2.04 fps upwards at angle of 2°18′ from vertical
5.11 23.7 fps, 32.5°

6.1 $\frac{4}{3}$
6.3 $\frac{2}{3}$, $5\frac{4}{3}5$, $\frac{6}{5}$
6.5 $(G/g)V_1(1.64 − 1.6 \cos \theta)^{\frac{1}{2}}$
6.7   590, 292, 658 lb; −26.3°
6.9   67.4 psi, 6.73 psi

6.11 392 lb
6.13 50 lb plate cannot be held in position; for 5 lb plate, $h_2 = 6.15$ ft
6.15 1,249 lb
6.17 3160 lb at 32.8°
6.19 58 lb to right, 5.5 lb downwards
6.21 15.6 lb
6.23 2 lb assuming streamlines are parallel until 1.0 ft from cone
6.29 54.6° for $u = 50$ fps, 108° for $u = 80$ fps
6.31 49°40′, 96°
6.33 515 lb to right, 179 lb down
6.35 47 lbs
6.37 5,000 lb, 5,410 lb
6.39 28,870 ft lb, 1,650 hp, 85.6 ft
6.41 148 fps, 218.5 fps
6.43 $F_u = (\gamma A_1/g)(1 - \cos \beta_2)(V_1 - u)^2$
6.45 493 hp, 135.3 lb
6.47 1,880 ft lb
6.49 $\Delta p/\gamma = -131$ ft; 916 ft lb, 210 hp
6.51 0.077 cfs, zero, zero
6.53 1200 rpm
6.55 59.5 psf = 0.413 psi, 1080
6.57 0.96 lb, 0.44 psf
6.59 33.2 lb, 117 cfs
6.61 267.8 lb to right

7.1 230,000
7.3 8,000 mph
7.5 0.55 cfs, 0.14 lb/sec
7.9 4.73 fps, 0.264
7.11 2.70×10^{-8} ft²/sec, no
7.13 32.8 fps
7.15 1532 fps
7.19 3.61 psia
7.21 6.38 psia = 16.9 in. Hg Vac.
7.27 $\phi(N_F, N_R)\rho L^2 V^2$
7.29 $\phi(H/P, N_W, N_R)(g)^{1/2}H^{3/2}$

8.1 <0.6 fps
8.3 0.0155 lb/sec
8.5 0.155 psf
8.7 7.25 ft
8.9 0.0253 ft per ft
8.11 $(\tfrac{1}{2})(u_{max})$
8.13 0.364 psf
8.15 0.0705 ft
8.17 0.00328 ft
8.19 0.0000704 ft
8.21 $(14.12D)/N_R f^{1/2}$
8.23 0.398 ft, 0.90 fps, 5.3×10^{-4} ft
8.25 67.6 cfs
8.27 $0.78 r_0$

8.29 0.00322 ft per ft, 0.0232 cfs
8.33 0.146 ft per ft
8.37 3.56 cfs
8.39 0.00070 ft
8.41 91
8.43 2.05, 3.49, 1.40, 0.443 ft
8.45 7.79 ft
8.47 11.1 ft steam, 0.0557 psi
8.49 10.99 ft
8.51 0.159, 2.58, 8.98 ft; 27.5, 445, 1555 ft
8.53 7.1 in.
8.55 2.12 cfs, 66.5 psi
8.57 93%, 43,400 hp
8.59 4.8 fps, 28.4 psi, 696 ft
8.61 4.01 ft, -1.11 ft
8.63 1.59 cfs, 9.28 cfs; 4.08:1, 5.84:1
8.65 45.7 psi
8.67 9.5 in.
8.69 2010 hp
8.71 240 bhp
8.73 -19.47 ft, 322.75 ft, 25 ft
8.75 25.2 bhp
8.77 114.6 ft, 141.6 ft
8.79 31.2 ft, 8.38 cfs, 29.7 hp
8.81 112.2 ft, 76.3 hp
8.83 8.05 cfs, 112.1 ft
8.85 1.77 cfs, 1.96 cfs
8.87 181.1 ft
8.89 11.0, 12.5, 23.5 cfs
8.91 0.0225, 2.15 fps, 0.111 cfs
8.93 0.0575, 0.233, 0.310, 0.60 cfs
8.95 7.08 cfs
8.97 16.5 cfs
8.99 226.9 ft
8.101 18.8%
8.103 0.677, 0.073, 0.750 cfs; 15.8, 5.6 psi
8.105 0.08 ft per ft, 0.0145 HP per ft
8.107 $4.32Q^{1.946}$

9.1 At 100 ft: 78.8 psia, 257 fps, 80.64 ft; At 300 ft: 72.5 psia, 275 fps, 75.52 ft
9.3 Add 57.5 Btu/sec
9.5 15,500 Btu/hr
9.7 1,800 fps
9.9 665 fps, 665 fps
9.11 1076 fps, 12.51 psia, 12.47 psia
9.19 At 30 psia: 3.21 lb/sec, 49°F; At 50 psia: 3.19 lb/sec, 64°F; At 70 psia: 2.49 lb/sec, 117°F; At 85 psia: 0 lb/sec, 150°F
9.21 14.2 psia, 58.5°F, 641 fps
9.23 1680 fps, 7.2 lb/sec, -156°F

9.25   6.4 lb/sec, 2.2 in.

9.27   3.2 lb/sec; attaching a diverging nozzle will not change the flow rate

9.29   47.4 psia, 790 fps, 370°F

9.31   1,352 fps, 1,300 fps, 3.9%

10.1 25.4×10^5, 0.0163 ft

10.3 $96/N_R$

10.5   108 cfs

10.7 1.32×10^{-4} cfs/ft

10.9   0.00015, 0.792 ft per mile

10.11   7.1 ft

10.13   0.000646; 3.41 ft per mile

10.15   0.001644

10.17 $0.63y$, 4.83 fps

10.21   92.2 cfs, 79.5 cfs

10.23   6.56 ft; 10.3 ft compared to 12 ft

10.25   19.4 ft, 2.4 ft

10.27 $3.54A^{1/2}$, $2.51A^{1/2}$, $2.64A^{1/2}$, $2.83A^{1/2}$; 3 on 4

10.29   2.33 ft, 8.67 fps, 0.007

10.31   3.735 ft, 9.19 fps

10.33   Flow is subcritical, $y = 0.841$ ft

10.35   2.93 ft, 28.5 cfs/ft

10.37   0.01492

10.39   834 cfs

10.41   2.11 ft, 4.22 ft

10.43   0.00474, 0.0162

10.45   0.792 ft, 0.874 ft

10.47   0.08 ft drop

10.49   Depth changes from 2.80 to 2.59 ft; minimum width is 2.49 ft

10.51   0.22 ft

10.53 -0.000405, adverse

10.55   0.01165

10.59   5.10 ft

10.61 M_2 profile

10.63   Increase

10.65 M_1 profile

10.67   20 ft, 68,600 ft

10.69   230 cfs, 785 ft

10.71   738 ft

10.73   4.52 ft, 2.40 ft

10.75   6.8 ft, 6.1 hp

10.77   Jump from 1.0 ft to 2.7 ft; 2.93 hp

10.79   No jump because flow is subcritical; 1.46 ft, M_1 profile upstream

10.81   1,405 cfs

10.83   Normal depth of 4.8 ft upstream, then M_2 profile, critical depth of 3.68 ft at break in slope, S_2 profile to normal depth of 2.17 ft downstream

10.85   1260 ft

10.87 M_1 profile upstream tending toward normal depth of 5.16 ft

10.89   0.436 ft

11.1   1.55 slugs per cu ft

11.3   Approximately 0.6 in.

11.5   0.081 lb sec/ft²

11.7 2.45×10^{-4} lb sec/ft²

11.9   0.064

11.13   27.8 in.

11.15   14.08 fps

11.17   3.84 cfs

11.19   2.15 ft

11.21   0.601, 0.620, 0.970

11.23   35.2 fps, 2.14 in., 0.872 cfs, 0.79 ft

11.25   45.5 ft, 0.969, 2.96 ft, 1.733 in.

11.27   35.9 fps, -15 ft

11.29   25.14 fps, 5.01 ft

11.31   0.95, 0.642

11.33   0.399, 0.435

11.37   0.977, 0.764, 13.5% decrease

11.39   1.312 ft

11.41   2.43 cfs

11.43   37.2 ft, 26.4 ft; 14.4 ft, 8.8 ft; 14.15 ft

11.45   35.4 lb/sec

11.47   69.0 lb/sec

11.49   5.33 lb/sec, 5.40 lb/sec

11.51   17.8% increase

11.53   0.551, 0.487

11.55   0.138 lb/sec

11.57   58.0 psia, 1,456 fps

11.59   35.0 cfs; 35.9 cfs, 2.55% over (a)

11.61   3.08 ft

11.63   0.186 cfs; 0.446 cfs, 140% increase over (a); 1.145 ft

11.67   10%, 27.3%

11.69   2.716 ft

11.71   20.9 cfs, 0.580

12.3   269.5 sq ft

12.5   2.335 ft, 10,430 sec

12.7 $\gamma A_s h^2/2$

12.9   490 sec

12.11   57.6 sec

12.13 -0.0045 ft

12.15   At times 0, 100, 300 sec; 3.56, 3.84, 4.05 cfs

12.17   0.050 cfs, 0.052 cfs

12.19   3340 fps

12.21   3200 fps, 3000 fps

12.23   317 ft

12.27   138 ft

12.29   At times 2, 6, 10, ∞ sec; 0.18, 0.40, 0.49, 0.52 cfs

12.31   At times 5, 10, 25, ∞ sec; 1.60, 2.62, 3.80, 3.92 cfs

12.33   At times 2, 5, 10, ∞ sec; 0.0050, 0.0083, 0.0097, 0.0102 cfs

13.7   0.1628 in.; 0.230 in., 0.00402 psf; 0.241 lb

13.9   2,900

13.11   0.1565 lb

13.13   0.000469 ft, 85.6 lb

13.15   0.00294, 0.0030

13.17   Through 60°F water 0.29, 2.29, 5.70 lb at 10, 30, 50 fps

13.19   0.314 sec/ft²

13.21   0.24, 2.60, 7.10 lb at 20, 60, 100 fps

13.23   18.9 fps

13.25   130 lb

13.27   0.815 fps, 25.5 fps

13.29   0.75, 14.5, 72.1 cm/sec

13.31   0.0275 lb, 0.9770 ft/sec²; 12.7% increase

13.33   0.94 lb, 2.92% of thrust; 0.0054 lb or 0.017% of thrust

13.35   1,677 cycles/sec

13.39   1,962 lb

13.41 $-18.57°$, 11,630 lb

13.43   0.0481 lb, 2.02 ft²/sec, 13.12 ft²/sec

13.45   0.267, 3.4 fps, 51.0 lb

13.47   0.907

13.49   2.72°, 42,000 ft, 96.3 fps, 4.57 fps

14.1   85.2%, 96.3%, 4015 hp, 3915 hp, 97.5%, 0.800

14.3   75 rpm, 800 cfs, 6400 bhp

14.5   6.62 ft, 0.508, 0.0382, 110.2, 0.000803

14.7   0.0000308, 0.00617, $(2.54 \times 10^{-8})/\gamma$, 190, 4020

14.9   360 rpm, 300 cfs, 47.3 bhp, 4680 bhp

15.1   At 0, 200, 400 fps; 342800, 171400, 0 ft lb

15.3   108 ft, 43.8 ft

15.5   88.8%

15.7   486.4 ft lb for $\phi = 0$; 243.2 ft lb for $\phi = 0.49$

15.9   11.4 cfs, 5900 ft lb, 1420 rpm, 1600

15.11   11.0 bhp, 78.1%, 3.21 ft lb, 0.0208 bhp

15.13   112.6 hp, 89.5 hp, 88.7 bhp; 0.9, 99.1, 78.8, 78.8%

15.17   348 rpm, 618 rpm

15.21   3.26, 4.71

15.23   3.64, 5.15

15.25   10.6 ft

15.27   423 hp, 69.2 hp

16.1   For $n = 150$ rpm, $n_s = 66$, Francis turbine
For $n = 300$ rpm, $n_s = 132$, Propeller turbine

16.3   3 units, 10 units

16.5   0.894, $\alpha_1 = 16.6°$, $\beta_1 = 127.2°$

16.7   0.135

16.9   7.81 ft

16.11   1.927 ft

16.15   140.5 ft

16.17   17 fps; 16.62 fps; 3.54 fps, 1.45%

16.19   10°, 36.8%, 1.275

16.21   30.2; 0.1765; 0.6778; 14.6°, 99.36°; 0.700

16.23   6.35 ft

17.1   821, 38.7

17.3   2.23 ft

17.5   240 ft, 276 cfs

17.9   1.85 cfs

17.11   1670, 2820, 3770, 1180, 965

17.13   64.2 ft; Pump must be submerged 36.2 ft

17.15   13.97 ft, 0.1073

17.17 -23.15 ft

17.19   For N_s of 1000, 5000, 15000; 341, 485, 830 rpm; 6200, 76500, 235000 gpm

17.21   236.4 fps, 1,540, 1.005

17.23   0.807

17.25   Surface of water must be 27.2 ft above pump suction

17.27   13.38, 1.39, 6.72 in.

18.1 $0.367 n_{0max}$

18.3   2056 Btu per hour

18.5   0.0723 hp, 2.375 ft lb

18.7   89%, 564 rpm, 30 hp